PUBLICATION No. 6
of the Mathematics Research Center
United States Army
The University of Wisconsin

ELECTROMAGNETIC WAVES

Electromagnetic Waves

Proceedings of a Symposium Conducted by the Mathematics Research Center, United States Army, at the University of Wisconsin, Madison, April 10-12, 1961

edited by

RUDOLPH E. LANGER

Madison, 1962

THE UNIVERSITY OF WISCONSIN PRESS

Published by
THE UNIVERSITY OF WISCONSIN PRESS
430 Sterling Court, Madison 6, Wisconsin

Prepared for the camera by Phyllis J. Kern
Printed in the United States of America by
Cushing-Malloy, Inc., Ann Arbor, Michigan

Library of Congress Catalog Card Number 62-60005

FOREWORD

This volume is put forth as the record of a symposium that was conducted by the Mathematics Research Center, United States Army, at the University of Wisconsin, April 10-12, 1961. It includes in full the papers that were presented—all by invited speakers—and includes in addition one paper, that by J. Wait, which was invited but not presented because of the author's inability to fulfill his symposium commitment.

The motivation of the symposium hardly seems to be in need of extended comment. With electromagnetic waves functioning centrally and indispensably in the advance of the frontiers of terrestrial as well as spatial communications, the urge to ferret out an optimum comprehension of the characteristics of wave behavior in transit or in interaction with obstacles is eminently timely. A symposium affords not only a forum for the proclamation of the latest deductions and discoveries, but also an occasion for personal associations of researchers and direct conversational exchanges of conjectures and ideas.

This symposium was opened by a message of welcome by Kurt F. Wendt, Dean of the College of Engineering of the University of Wisconsin. The papers—fifteen in number—were all delivered in the auditorium of the Wisconsin Center Building. They were from thirty-five to forty-five minutes in length, with three scheduled for each morning and afternoon session. The ensuing discussions were, without exception, lively and pertinent.

For early arrivals at the symposium an informal gathering was held in the common room of the Mathematics Research Center in the evening of April 9. A general reception for symposium attendants, as well as for members of the University's Mathematics Department and members of the Mathematics Research Center was held in the parlor of the Wisconsin Center Building in the evening of April 10.

Our thanks are extended to the lecturers for their readiness to participate, and indeed to all who helped make this symposium a success. The program committee consisted of:

Dr. Philip M. Anselone,
Dr. Jean G. von Bladel,
Dr. Hans F. Bueckner,
Dr. L. M. Milne-Thomson.

PREFACE

The fact that a number of important symposiums on electromagnetic theory have been held during the last decade is convincing evidence of the vitality and enterprise of current research in this field. This is not surprising, for a spur to it is not lacking. Technology is manifestly poised to seize upon, and to seek a utilization of, almost any research finding.

Even the casual newspaper reader—if he is at all alert—cannot fail to be impressed by the ubiquity of electromagnetic waves as instruments of communication and remote control, and of exploration and detection at fabulous distances. The capabilities of the waves are apt to seem miraculous, and their potentialities boundless. With the advent of rockets and the prospects of systems of satellites, the realization of global communication ranges, and the telemetric exploration of new worlds, have assumed the aspect of promises certain to be soon fulfilled.

This symposium, however, was not designed to deal with, and did not deal with, such implementations of electromagnetic waves. Its objective was at once humbler and more profound; namely, the analysis of the fundamental facts of the wave's behavior, their propagation, their diffraction, their scattering, etc. It is upon the fullest understanding of these facts that ultimate technological developments wait. Recent findings in this domain were announced in the papers presented, and are now set forth in this volume. They are herewith thrown into the cauldron of contemporary knowledge, which will, in its time, boil down its ingredients to crystalize their essences, in greater or less measure, into the residue which will persist as comprehensive and dependable theory.

R. E. Langer

CONTENTS

ELECTROMAGNETIC WAVES

MORRIS KLINE

Electromagnetic Theory and Geometrical Optics

I. INTRODUCTION. It may seem unnecessary at this late date to discuss the relationship of electromagnetic theory to geometrical optics. The content of both fields is well known and everyone knows also that geometrical optics is the limit for vanishing wave length of electromagnetic theory. Moreover, since Maxwell's theory supersedes the older geometrical optics, presumably, then, geometrical optics could be discarded. The optical industry continues to use it but perhaps that is because it is behind the times.

There are, however, at least three major reasons for pursuing and clarifying the relationship in question. The first is the purely theoretical or academic problem of building a mathematical bridge between the two domains, electromagnetic theory and geometrical optics. The older bases for asserting that geometrical optics is a limiting case of electromagnetic theory are vague and from a mathematical standpoint highly unsatisfactory.

The second major reason for the investigation is a practical one. To solve problems of electromagnetic theory, whether in the range of radio frequencies or visible light frequencies, one should solve Maxwell's equations with the appropriate initial and boundary conditions. However, as is well known, Maxwell's equations can be solved exactly in only a few problems. Hence physicists and engineers, especially those concerned with ultra-high frequency problems, have resorted to the simpler methods of geometrical optics. Although these methods have proved remarkably efficacious in the optical domain, they are intrinsically limited; they do not furnish information about some of the most important phenomena such as diffraction, polarization, and interference, to say nothing about the numerical accuracy of what geometrical optics does yield. Hence the practical question becomes whether the establishment of a better link between Maxwell's theory and geometrical optics will provide more accurate approximate methods of solving electromagnetic problems. Insofar as ultra-high frequency problems are concerned, the answer, based on work of the last ten years, can already be given affirmatively. It is also a fact that optical people are now looking more and more into diffraction effects and one might venture that the practice of optics is on the verge of entering into an electromagnetic treatment of optical problems.

The investigation serves a third purpose. In principal it is concerned with the relationship between a wave theory and a non-periodic phenomenon with the latter in some sense a limiting case of the wave theory as a parameter, the wave length in the case of electromagnetic phenomena, goes to zero. However there are many branches of physics, acoustics, hydrodynamics, magnetohydrodynamics and quantum mechanics, which also treat wave theories. Hence in each case there should be a corresponding "optical" theory or if one exists, as in the case of quantum mechanics, the present theory should shed light on the two complementary domains. We shall in fact see that the electromagnetic investigations to be surveyed here do indeed lead to new creations or new insights into other branches of physics.

2. SOME RELEVANT HISTORY. To appreciate just what the problem of reconciling geometrical optics and electromagnetic theory amounts to we shall examine briefly the historical background.

The science of geometrical optics was founded in the seventeenth century. To the law of relection, known since Euclid's day, René Descartes and Willebrord Snell added the law of refraction; Robert Boyle and Robert Hooke discovered interference; Olaf Römer established the finiteness of the velocity of light; F. M. Grimaldi and Hooke discovered diffraction; Erasmus Bartholinus discovered double refraction in Iceland spar; and Newton discovered dispersion.

Two physical theories of light were created in the seventeenth century. Christiaan Huygens formulated the "wave" theory of light[1] and Newton formulated a theory of propagation of particles[2]. Huygens thought of light as a longitudinal motion of ether and as spreading out at a finite velocity from a point source. The farthermost position reached by the light in space filled out a surface which he called the front of the wave. In homogeneous media this surface is a sphere. To explain further how light propagates, Huygens supposed that when the disturbance reached any point in the ether this point imparted its motion to all neighboring points. Thus if the wave front at time t_1 should be the surface S_1 and if P is a typical point on S_1, the point P communicated its motion to all points in its neighborhood and from P the light spread out in all directions. Its velocity in these various directions depended upon the nature of the medium. Thus in some small interval of time (and in an isotropic medium) the front of the light emanating from a point would be a sphere with P as a center. The same would be true at any other point of the surface S_1, except that the radii of the spheres might differ as the medium differs along S_1. The new position of the front at some time t_2 greater than t_1 is the envelope in the mathematical sense of the family of spheres attached one to each point of S_1. (There is according to this theory also a backward wave. This backward wave troubled scientists until

Kirchhoff showed under his formulation that it does not exist. We shall not pursue this historical point.) To explain reflection and refraction Huygens supposed that the same phenomenon takes place at each point on the reflecting or refracting interface when the front reaches it, except, of course, that no waves penetrate the reflecting surface.

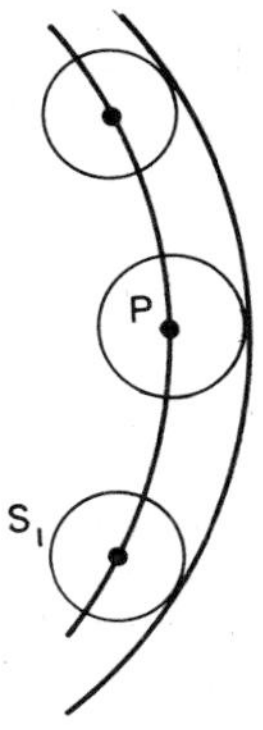

Figure 1

There are many more details to Huygens' theory which explain the phenomena of geometrical optics including double refraction. However, more relevant for us is the fact that Huygens considered light as a series of successive impulses each travelling as already described and he did not explain the relationship of the impulses to each other. Thus the periodicity of light is not contained in Huygens' theory. Also, though the phenomenon of diffraction had already been observed by Hooke and Grimaldi, Huygens apparently did not know it and he did not consider it though his theory could have covered at least a crude theory of diffraction.

The second major theory of light was Newton's. He suggested in opposition to Huygens' "wave" theory, that a source of light emits a stream of particles in all directions in which the light propagates. These particles are distinct from the ether in which the particles move. In homogeneous space these particles travel in straight lines unless deflected by foreign bodies such as reflecting and refracting bodies. Newton did introduce a kind of periodicity, "fits", which he used to explain bright and dark rings appearing in certain phenomena of refraction. However, the nature of the periodicity was vague. His theory was on the whole crude for the variety of phenomena he tried to embrace and he made many ad hoc assumptions. Nevertheless, Newton developed this mechanical theory so thoroughly that its completeness—it included diffraction—and Newton's own great reputation caused others, aside from Euler, to accept it for 100 years. Huygens' work was, on the whole, ignored. Both men, incidentally, obtained some inkling of polarization through reasoning about double refraction in Iceland spar.

Despite the recognition in the seventeenth century of phenomena such as diffraction, a limited theory of light called geometrical optics was erected on the basis of four principles. In homogeneous media light travels in straight lines. The light rays from a source travel out independently of one another. That light rays obey the law of reflection was the third principle, and that they obey the law of refraction for abrupt or continuous changes in the medium was the fourth. (The phenomenon of double refraction in crystals was embraced by supposing that the medium has two indices of refraction which depend upon position and the direction of the propagation.)

All of these laws follow from Fermat's Principle of Least Time. This principle presupposes that any medium is characterized by a function $n(x, y, z)$ called the index of refraction (the absolute index or index to a vacuum). The optical distance between two points P_1 with coordinates (x_1, y_1, z_1) and P_2 with coordinates (x_2, y_2, z_2) over any given path is defined to be the line integral

$$\int_{P_1}^{P_2} n(x, y, z)\, ds$$

taken over that path. Fermat's principle as stated by him and others following him, says that the optical path, the path which light actually takes, between P_1 and P_2, is that curve of all those joining P_1 and P_2 which makes the value of the integral least. This formulation is physically incorrect, as can be shown by examples, and the correct statement is that the first variation of this integral, in the sense of the calculus of variations, must be zero. This principle could be and was applied to the design of numerous optical instruments. It is to be noted that this principle or any other formulation of geometrical optics says nothing about the nature of light.

The mathematical theory of geometrical optics received its definitive formulation in the work of William R. Hamilton during the years 1824 to 1844.[3] Though Hamilton was aware of Fresnel's work, which we shall mention shortly, he was indifferent to the physical interpretation, that is Huygens' or Newtons's, and to a possible extension to include interference. He was concerned to build a deductive, mathematical science of optics. Though his work is described as geometrical optics, he did include doubly refracting media (which are sometimes regarded as outside the pale of strict geometrical optics) and dispersion.

Hamilton's chief idea was a characteristic function, of which he gave several types. The basic one of these expressed the optical length of the ray which joined a point in the object space to a point in the image space as a function of the positions of these two points. The partial derivatives of this function give the direction of the light ray at the point in question. Hamilton also introduced three other types of characteristic functions. He shows that from a knowledge of any one of these, all problems in optics involving, for example, lenses, mirrors, crystals, and propagation in the atmosphere, can be solved. From Hamilton's work the equivalence of Fermat's principle and Huygens' principle is clear.

As we have already observed, geometrical optics cannot be regarded as an adequate theory of light because it does not take into account interference, diffraction, polarization, or even a measure of the intensity of light. In the early part of the nineteenth century new experimental work by Thomas Young, Augustin Fresnel, E. L. Malnus, D. F. J. Arago, J. B. Biot, D. Brewster, W. H. Wollaston and others made it clear that a wave theory of light was needed to account for all these phenomena. Fresnel extended Huygens' theory by adding periodicity in space and time to Huygens' wave fronts. Thereby interference was incorporated and Fresnel used the extended theory to explain diffraction as the mutual interference of the secondary waves emitted by those portions of the original wave front which have not been obstructed by the diffracting obstacle.

Up to this time (1818) thinking on the wave theory of light (and for that matter even the corpuscular theory) had been guided by the analogy with sound. Young in 1817 suggested transverse rather than longitudinal wave motion. Young's suggestion caused Fresnel to think about waves in solids and to suggest that rigidity should give rise to transverse waves. This idea was important for the yet to be developed theory of waves in elastic solids and also for the ether. He sought then to base the theory of light on the dynamical properties of ether.

However, Fresnel's theoretical foundations were incomplete and even inconsistent. He tried to explain the physical nature of light propagating through isotropic and anisotropic media by regarding the ether as a quasi-elastic medium and the light as a displacement of the ether particles. When an ether particle was displaced, the other particles exerted a restoring force proportional to displacement. But the phenomena of interference, the intensity in reflection and refraction, and particularly polarization, led to the conclusion that the vibrations of the ether particles must be transverse, whereas an elastic medium can support transverse and longitudinal waves. Nor could the ether be a rare gas because there only longitudinal waves are transmitted and there is no elastic resistance. Hence Fresnel assumed his ether was infinitely compressible. It was like a gas but with elasticity in place of viscosity. The theory of waves in elastic media was not well developed in Fresnel's time so that his approach was over-simple, and he could not readily eliminate the longitudinal waves which an elastic medium can support.

A number of great mathematical physicists, C. L. Navier, S. D. Poisson, A. L. Cauchy, G. Green, F. Neumann, G. Lamé and J. W. Strutt (Lord Rayleigh) worked on the theory of waves in elastic media and the application of this theory to light[4]. In all this work the ether was an elastic medium which existed in isotropic and anisotropic media. Some of the theories supposed that the ether particles interacted with the particles of ponderable matter through which the light passed. This approach to light was pursued even after Maxwell's time but was never quite satisfactory. One of the principal difficulties was to explain away longitudinal waves. Another was the lack of a consistent explanation of the phenomena of reflection and refraction at the boundaries of isotropic and anisotropic media. A third was that dispersion was not explained.

Of additional efforts preceding Maxwell's work, we shall mention the work of James MacCullagh. MacCullagh in 1839 (published 1848) changed the nature of the elastic solid which represented ether. Instead of a solid which resists compression and distortion, he introduced one whose potential energy depends only on the rotation of the volume elements. Waves in MacCullagh's ether could be only transverse and the vector $\underline{e}$ which represented a wave motion satisfied the equation

$$\mu \Delta \underline{e} = \rho \frac{\partial^2 \underline{e}}{\partial t^2} .$$

Moreover, div $\underline{e} = 0$. MacCullagh did have to introduce independent boundary conditions. (Whittaker, following Heaviside, points out that this $\underline{e}$ amounts to the magnetic field intensity of Maxwell.)

This solid ether of MacCullagh placed difficulties in the way of representing the relationship between ether and ordinary matter (when light travels through matter) and obliged him to postulate a particular force (later called Kirchhoff's force) in order to explain the differing elasticity of the ether on the two sides of a surface which separates diversely refracting media. What is significant about MacCullagh's work is that his differential equations are closely related to Maxwell's though physically the former's theory bore no relation to electromagnetism.

The most satisfactory theory of light which we have today came about not through the study of light per se but through the development of electricity and magnetism by Clerk Maxwell. We shall not pursue here the history of the researches in electricity and magnetism of Gauss, Oersted, Ampère, Faraday, Riemann and others because their contributions are still taught as a basis for Maxwell's electromagnetic theory and so are largely familiar. It is well known that one of Maxwell's great discoveries was the realization that light must be an electromagnetic phenomenon. Maxwell wrote to a friend in January of 1865 "I have a paper afloat, with an electromagnetic theory of light, which 'till I am convinced to the contrary, I hold to be great guns."

Though Maxwell did try unsuccessfully to obtain a mechanical theory of electromagnetic phenomena in terms of pressures and tensions in an elastic medium and after Maxwell, H. Hertz, W. Thomson, C. A. Bjerknes and H. Poincaré tried to improve mechanical models but equally unsuccessfully, the acceptance of Maxwell's theory marked the end of elastic theories of light. The adoption of Maxwell's theory means also the adoption of a purely mathematical view, for the knowledge that light consists of a conjoined electric and magnetic field travelling through space hardly explains the physical nature of light. It merely reduces the number of mysteries in science by compounding one of them.

We might mention that the possibility of linking light and electromagnetism was considered by several predecessors of Maxwell. Euler, Young and Faraday had suggested this possibility on different grounds. Riemann had observed the identity of the velocity of light with the ratio of the electrostatic to the electromagnetic units of charge and so produced an ad hoc theory by extending the electrostatic potential equation

$$\Delta \phi = 4\pi\rho$$

to

$$\Delta\phi - \frac{1}{c^2}\frac{\partial^2\phi}{\partial t^2} = 4\pi\rho \ .$$

Thus he had a wave motion which for the proper value of c moved with the velocity of light. However light was still a scalar in this theory nor was there any physical justification for adding $\partial^2\phi/\partial t^2$.

Maxwell's assertion that light is an electromagnetic wave had other arguments to recommend it than the wave equation to which his equations reduce and the fact that the ratio of the electrostatic to the electromagnetic unit of charge is the velocity of light. It is well known that from the first two equations when expressed in rectangular coordinates, for example, and in a non-conducting medium one can obtain for any component of E or H precisely the same mathematical equation which Navier and Poisson had derived for waves in an elastic medium[5] and these latter waves did explain many of the phenomena of light. Moreover, Maxwell's equations possessed a superior feature. Navier, Poisson and other workers in the elastic theory of light had to make the arbitrary assumption that the dilatation (divergence) of the medium is 0 to eliminate longitudinal waves. In Maxwell's equations this condition is automatically present, that is, $\text{div}\ \underline{D} = 0$ and $\text{div}\ \underline{B} = 0$. One could also derive from his equations, as Helmholtz did, the proper boundary conditions at an interface between two media without additional assumptions. Of course Hertz's experimental confirmations, principally the existence of travelling electromagnetic fields, at least showed that radio waves behave like light waves. One must remember, however, that Maxwell's assertion about light was bold and even questionable in his day. The sources of light available then and even up to the present day are not monochromatic and so no fine experimental confirmation could be expected. We are just at the point today, in the development of lasers, of producing coherent monochromatic light.

Though there are unresolved difficulties in Maxwell's theory, chiefly in connection with the interaction of electromagnetic waves with matter (these problems are, of course, being investigated in quantum electrodynamics), we must accept as our best theory that light is an electromagnetic phenomenon subject to Maxwell's equations. Geometrical optics then can be only an approximate representation in several respects. First, wave length considerations do not enter, and so interference is not taken into account. The vector character of the field, that is, polarization, and diffraction, that is, the penetration of the field behind obstacles, are not incorporated. Finally, since wave length considerations do not enter, neither does dispersion.

3. EARLY EFFORTS TO LINK ELECTROMAGNETIC THEORY AND GEOMETRICAL OPTICS. The first significant effort to derive geometrical optics from the electromagnetic theory of light is due to Kirchhoff. Kirchhoff sought a strong mathematical foundation for light and

introduced a modification of Huygen's principle which incorporated the interference in space and time. (The physical interpretation was for him irrelevant.) Since light was represented as a scalar function, in this respect Kirchhoff's representation of light is not directly relevant. Moreover, as is well known, there are difficulties in the use of the Kirchhoff-Huygens principle which he tried to overcome by the assumption of rather arbitrary boundary conditions on the diffracting obstacle and these lead to mathematical inconsistencies.

Nevertheless, in 1882 Kirchhoff did show[6] that when the wave length of the source approaches 0 the wave field given by the Kirchhoff integral approaches the field given by geometrical optics; specifically the diffracted field vanishes and there is sharp transition between the illuminated field and the dark region. That is, the waves behave like straight lines. Hence the idea was generally accepted by the end of the nineteenth century that geometrical optics must be some sort of limit of electromagnetic theory as the wave length goes to 0 .

The most widely accepted argument for the connection between electromagnetic theory and geometrical optics is that given by Sommerfeld and Runge who followed a suggestion of P. Debye.[7] In this argument a function u , which may represent some component of $\underline{E}$ or a component of a Hertz vector, is assumed to satisfy the scalar reduced wave equation

$$\Delta u + k^2 u = 0 , \tag{1}$$

wherein $k = \sqrt{\epsilon\mu}\,\omega = 2\pi/\lambda$. Here ϵ and μ may be functions of position and λ is the variable wave length in the inhomogeneous medium. The field is generated by a source, whose frequency is ω and whose wave length in a constant medium ϵ_0 , μ_0 is λ_0 so that $k_0 = \sqrt{\epsilon_0 \mu_0}\,\omega = 2\pi/\lambda_0$

Sommerfeld and Runge now make the assumption that

$$u(x, y, z) = A(x, y, z) e^{ik_0 S(x, y, z)} , \tag{2}$$

that is, that u is determined by an amplitude function A and a phase function S . The latter, incidentally, is called the eiconal function (because, as we shall see in a moment, it satisfies the eiconal differential equation). While u will vary rapidly as λ_0 approaches 0 or k_0 approaches ∞ , it is assumed that A and S do not vary rapidly in x, y and z (relative to the wave length) and that they remain bounded as k_0 approaches ∞ . The form of (2) is a generalization of the form of plane waves which exhibit some of the properties of geometrical optics.

By direct differentiation of (2) and substitution in equation (1), one obtains

$$-k_0^2 u\left[\left(\frac{\partial S}{\partial x}\right)^2 + \left(\frac{\partial S}{\partial y}\right)^2 + \left(\frac{\partial S}{\partial z}\right)^2 - \frac{k^2}{k_0^2}\right]$$

$$+ 2ik_0 u[\tfrac{1}{2}\Delta S + \text{grad} \log A \cdot \text{grad } S] + e^{ik_0 S}\Delta A = 0 \ .$$

If we now divide through by $k_0^2 u$ and assume that the resulting last term on the left side, namely $\Delta A/k_0^2 A$, remains small as k_0 becomes infinite, then we may satisfy the last equation by requiring that

$$(\text{grad})^2 = n^2 \ , \tag{3}$$

where $n = k/k_0$, and

$$\text{grad} \log A \cdot \text{grad } S + \tfrac{1}{2}\Delta S = 0 \ . \tag{4}$$

Equation (3) is called the eiconal differential equation and its solutions $S = \text{const.}$ are the wave surfaces or wave fronts of geometrical optics. The second equation can be written in terms of the directional derivative of $\log A$ in the direction of grad S. Since, by (3), $|\text{grad } S| = n$, we may write

$$n\frac{\text{grad } S}{n} \cdot \text{grad} \log A + \tfrac{1}{2}\Delta S = 0$$

and denoting the directional derivative in the direction of grad S by d/ds, we have

$$n\frac{d(\log A)}{ds} + \tfrac{1}{2}\Delta S = 0 \ . \tag{5}$$

The direction of grad S is normal to the surface $S = \text{const.}$ and so equation (5) gives us the behavior of $\log A$ along any normal (orthogonal trajectory) to the family of surfaces $S = \text{const.}$ or along a ray.

The fact that equation (3) is derived from the scalar wave equation by letting λ_0 approach 0 and the fact that the equation so obtained is the eiconal equation already known in geometrical optics and from which all of geometrical optics can be derived, provides the argument for concluding that geometrical optics can be derived from Maxwell's equations. Also the fact that the amplitude A travels along the rays is in accord with geometrical optics, though of course A may vary in other directions not revealed by the above derivation.

The Sommerfeld-Runge derivation of geometrical optics is open to many objections. The derivation from the scalar wave equation is not sufficiently general in that not all electromagnetic problems can be reduced to the scalar wave equation. However this criticism has been met in that the same kind of argument has been made for Maxwell's equations. That is, one assumes

$$
\begin{aligned}
\underline{E}(x, y, z) &= \underline{u}(x, y, z)\, e^{ik_0 S(x, y, z)} \\
\underline{H}(x, y, z) &= \underline{v}(x, y, z)\, e^{ikS_0 (x, y, z)}
\end{aligned}
\qquad (6)
$$

and one obtains the eiconal equation for S and vector equations for $\underline{u}$ and $\underline{v}$ which are the analogues of (5) above.[8]

Though the Sommerfeld-Runge procedure can be applied to Maxwell's equations as well as the scalar wave equation, it is not a satisfactory derivation of geometrical optics from electromagnetic theory. The assumption (2) represents a very restricted class of fields because it assumes that the function A is independent of k_0. This assumption is fulfilled for plane waves but is not true of the fields encountered even in relatively simple problems of propagation in unbounded media. Hence the argument shows only that a very restricted class of fields gives rise to a geometrical optics field. Secondly, the argument that the A and S determined as solutions of (3) and (4) are limits of the A and S in $u = Ae^{ik_0 S}$ when k_0 is infinite is incomplete. The differential equations (3) and (4) are a limit of the differential equation (1), but this fact must be brought to bear on the solutions. Thirdly, since initial and boundary conditions play no role in the entire derivation the limiting field determined by A and S serves no purpose in representing a geometric optics approximation to some desired field. Finally, the derivation seems to offer no insight into the relationship between wave theory and geometrical optics which might be used to make some gradual transition from one to the other.

Another procedure commonly used to link geometrical optics and Maxwell's theory is to take time harmonic plane wave solutions of Maxwell's equations and to apply the electromagnetic boundary conditions at a plane interface between two homogeneous media. As a consequence one deduces the law of reflection and Snell's law of refraction. Thus the basic laws of geometrical optics are derived. The same procedure is used in homogeneous anisotropic media. As a matter of fact, even the Fresnel formulas for the amplitudes of the reflected and refracted waves are also derivable in this way.

There are several objections to this procedure. Plane waves and plane boundaries are especially simple. There is no indication from such a derivation as to what may happen for curved wave fronts and curved boundaries. The argument is commonly given that the laws of plane waves in homogeneous media suffice for the approximate electromagnetic treatment of such phenomena in which the wave fronts are no longer plane but where the curvature of the wave front can be neglected over domains whose linear dimensions are large compared to the wave length of light. The analogous remark is often made about curved boundaries. But in geometrical optics the laws of reflection and refraction do hold for curved fronts and curved boundaries and even in inhomogeneous media. These facts are not obtained by the argument based on plane waves.

Secondly, in order to use the results obtained from this argument in geometrical optical problems, the practice is to assume that any normal to the wave front is a ray and that each ray behaves at any one point of an interface as though it were independent of all the other rays. But the plane wave argument treats the infinitely extended plane wave and the infinite plane boundary and the argument does not isolate what may happen for any individual ray at a single boundary point. Yet the laws are used thus even at a point on a curved boundary such as the surface of a lens.

Thirdly plane waves have infinite energy and are a highly ideal concept. No physical source sends out plane waves. Finally plane waves have a wave length. Since this fact does not show up in the laws derived, it is ignored.[9]

All one can really say from the study of plane waves is that they obey some of the laws of geometrical optics but they do not suffice to derive geometrical optics from Maxwell's equations.

4. THE RELATIONSHIP OF GEOMETRICAL OPTICS TO ELECTROMAGNETIC THEORY. I should now like to present two new views of geometrical optics from the standpoint of electromagnetic theory. The new viewpoints are valid in both isotropic and anisotropic media, but I shall treat isotropic media. We have Maxwell's equations, which, for simplicity, I shall treat in non-conducting media, namely

$$\text{curl}\, \underline{H} - \frac{\epsilon}{c}\underline{E}_t = \frac{1}{c}\underline{F}_t \tag{7}$$
$$\text{curl}\, \underline{E} + \frac{\mu}{c}\underline{H}_t = 0 \,.$$

The term containing $\underline{F}_t$, or strictly the real part of $(1/4\pi)\underline{F}_t$, represents a source current density. In the present discussion its role is irrelevant and one can suppose instead that initial values of $\underline{E}$ and $\underline{H}$, which are functions of x, y, z and t, are specified instead. There may also be boundary conditions.

The first view of geometrical optics is that the geometrical optics field corresponding to any electromagnetic field at any point (x, y, z) of space consists of the singularities of $\underline{E}$ and $\underline{H}$ as functions of time t. By the singularities we mean, of course, the discontinuities of $\underline{E}$ and $\underline{H}$ or of any of their successive time derivatives as functions of t. This definition is, in a sense, too general. If we wish to obtain classical geometrical optics we should restrict ourselves to singularities which are finite discontinuities with respect to time in $\underline{E}$, $\underline{H}$ and their successive time derivatives. There may very well be singularities at which $\underline{E}$ and $\underline{H}$ are continuous, but some time derivative is discontinuous or where the discontinuities of $\underline{E}$ and $\underline{H}$ are finite but those of some time derivative are not.

Before pursuing this concept analytically, let us examine it geometrically. We shall consider two space dimensions. If we suppose that some source located in the plane $t = 0$ begins to act at time $t = 0$, then we know that a field spreads out into space which at a particular time t_0 covers only a bounded region of (x, y, t)-space, the shaded region in Fig. 2. That is, during the time $0 \leq t \leq t_0$ the field will traverse the interior of a cone which lies between $t = 0$ and $t = t_0$. At a point such as P or (x_0, y_0, t_0) the field will be 0 for $t < t_0$ and at $t = t_0$ there will be a jump in the value of $\underline{E}$ and $\underline{H}$ from 0 to a finite value. This finite value of E and $\underline{H}$ is the geometrical optics field at P. Alternatively, the geometrical optics $\underline{E}$ and $\underline{H}$ are the limits approached by $\underline{E}(x_0, y_0, t)$ and $\underline{H}(x_0, y_0, t)$ as t approaches t_0 through values greater than t_0. At times $t > t_0$ the field may continue to be non-zero at the points (x_0, y_0, t) but this field is not a part of the geometrical optics field; it is part of the wave field $\underline{E}(x, y, t)$, $\underline{H}(x, y, t)$ which satisfies Maxwell's equations. Thus the geometrical optics field for all t values is the set of $\underline{E}$ and $\underline{H}$ values which exist only on the surface of the cone.

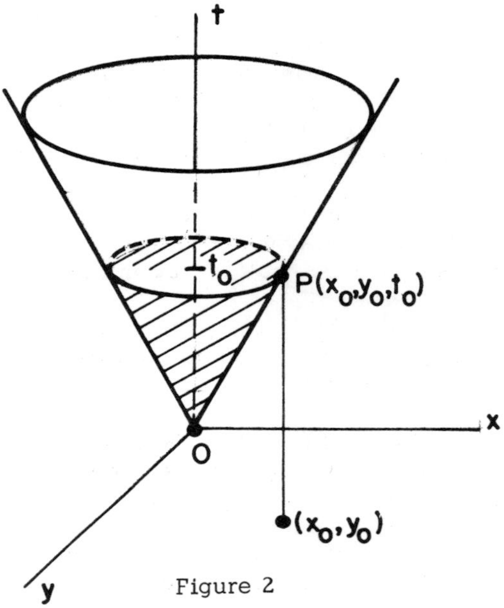

Figure 2

The cone itself is given by some equation $\phi(x, y, t) = 0$ in (x, y, t)-space. One can introduce rays in this space-time picture as the generators of this cone and follow the geometrical optics field along such a ray. (Mathematically these rays have a precise definition as the bicharacteristics of Maxwell's equations.)

There is a second geometrical picture which may be more useful in physical thinking. At each time t the locus of $\phi(x, y, t) = 0$ is a curve. We may plot these curves as a family of curves in (x, y)-space (Fig. 3). These curves are the wave fronts of geometrical optics. Analytically, we suppose that $\phi(x, y, t) = 0$ can be written as $t = \psi(x, y)/c$ and for each value of t there is one curve of this family of wave fronts. The usual rays of geometrical optics are (in isotropic media) the orthogonal trajectories of this family of wave fronts. Insofar as the geometrical optics field is concerned, at each point on a wave front and at the time t_0 given by the equation $\psi/c = t_0$ of this front the values of $\underline{E}$ and $\underline{H}$ change from 0 for $t < t_0$ to some non-zero value. This jump in $\underline{E}$ and $\underline{H}$ is the geometrical optics field at that point. At the same point and at later times $t > t_0$, there may indeed be values of $\underline{E}$ and $\underline{H}$ but these belong to the wave solution of Maxwell's equation and not to the geometrical optics field.

To study the propagation of the geometrical optics field in (x, y)-space one follows it along the rays. Now the wave function $\underline{E}$ is a function of x, y and t. However, for the geometrical optics value of $\underline{E}$, $t = \psi/c$. Hence denoting the geometrical optics $\underline{E}$ by $\underline{E}^*$ we may write

$$\underline{E}^*(x, y) = \underline{E}(x, y, \psi/c) .$$

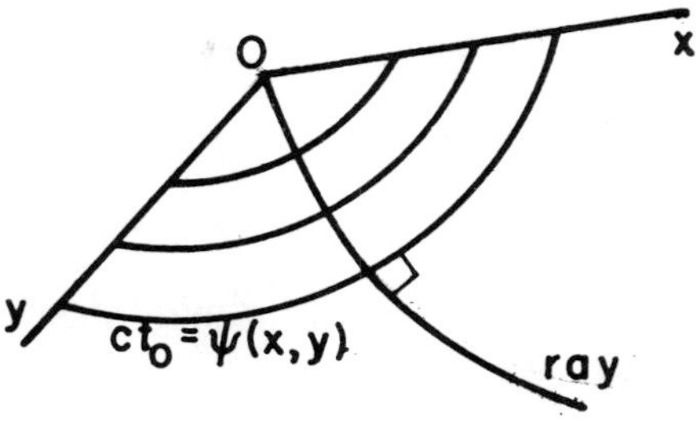

Figure 3

As a function of x and y only, E^* varies continuously.

Now we can show by precise mathematical arguments[10] that

$$\psi_x^2 + \psi_y^2 = n^2(x, y) ,$$

that is, that the wave fronts do indeed satisfy the eiconal equation and that the values of $\underline{E}^*$ and $\underline{H}^*$ along a ray satisfy the vector transport equations

$$\begin{aligned} 2\frac{d\underline{E}^*}{d\tau} + \underline{E}^*\Delta_\mu \psi + \frac{2}{n}(\text{grad } n \cdot \underline{E}^*)\,\text{grad } \psi &= 0 \\ 2\frac{d\underline{H}^*}{d\tau} + \underline{H}^*\Delta_\epsilon \psi \quad \frac{2}{n}(\text{grad } n \cdot \underline{H}^*)\,\text{grad } \psi &= 0 \end{aligned} \qquad (8)$$

where τ is any convenient parameter along the rays $x(\tau)$, $y(\tau)$ and

$$\Delta_\mu \psi = \mu\left(\left(\frac{\psi_x}{\mu}\right)_x + \left(\frac{\psi_y}{\mu}\right)_y\right) = -\text{grad } \psi \cdot \text{grad } \log \mu + \Delta\psi .$$

These transport equations are the vector analogue of (5) above. However the present ones are derived by a precise mathematical argument.

When a front strikes a discontinuity in the medium, then reflected and refracted fronts arise and the discontinuities of $\underline{E}$ and $\underline{H}$, that is $\underline{E}^*$ and $\underline{H}^*$, propagate with the reflected and refracted fronts and satisfy the Fresnel laws at the discontinuity in the medium. The transport equations again describe the propagation of the discontinuities of $\underline{E}$ and $\underline{H}$ along the reflected and refracted rays.

Thus far the approach to geometrical optics is no more than a new mathematical formulation of classical geometrical optics, but indeed one which relates geometrical optics to Maxwell's equations. Classical geometrical optics becomes the behavior of special values of the electromagnetic field. Actually this approach gives more than classical optics, because it gives the vector amplitudes of the geometrical optic fields and the Fresnel laws.

The above-described point of view yields a new insight at once. Let us return to space-time[11]. Consider the field (Fig. 2) at (x_0, y_0, t_0). As t increases beyond t_0 the field $\underline{E}(x_0, y_0, t)$, $\underline{H}(x_0, y_0, t)$ is non-zero. Hence, if $\underline{E}$ and $\underline{H}$ are analytic within the cone, both $\underline{E}$ and $\underline{H}$ should be expressible in power series whose variable is $t-t_0$ which represents the true field for $t > t_0$ [12]. The coefficients of the power series for $\underline{E}$, for example, should be $\underline{E}_t(x_0, y_0, t_0)$, $\underline{E}_{tt}$, $\cdots$, where we mean by these derivatives the values assumed by the functions for $t = t_{0+}$ or alternatively the limits approached, for example, by $\underline{E}_t(x_0, y_0, t)$ as t approaches t_0 through values larger than t_0. The values of $\underline{E}$, $\underline{H}$ and their successive time derivatives at $t = t_{0-}$ are 0 because for values of $t < t_0$ the field has not reached (x_0, y_0). The quantities $\underline{E}_t(x_0, y_0, t_0)$, $\underline{E}_{tt}$, $\cdots$ are then discontinuities of the successive time derivatives of $\underline{E}(x, y, t)$ on the surface $\phi = 0$. Since $t_0 = \psi(x_0, y_0)/c$ each of these discontinuities may be expressed as a function of x_0 and y_0 only.

We may express the thought of the preceding paragraph in terms of the pure space picture (Fig. 3). At any point (x, y) on the wave front $t_0 = \psi(x, y)/c$ and at the time t_0, $\underline{E}$, $\underline{H}$, $\underline{E}_t$, $\underline{H}_t$, $\cdots$ are discontinuous as functions of t. However, for $t > t_0$ and for points (x, y) on this wave front $\underline{E}$ and $\underline{H}$ are not zero and may be expressed as Taylor's series in powers of $t-t_0$.

Thus under either interpretation we have the expansions

$$\underline{E}(x, y, t) = \underline{E}(x, y, t_0) + \underline{E}_t(x, y, t_0)(t-t_0) + \underline{E}_{tt}(x, y, t_0)\frac{(t-t_0)^2}{2!} + \cdots \quad \text{for } t > t_0 \ ;$$

$$\underline{E}(x, y, t) = 0 \qquad \text{for } t < t_0 \ ,$$

and the analogous expansions for $\underline{H}$. Since $t_0 = \psi(x, y,)/c$,

$$\underline{E}(x, y, t) = \underline{E}(x, y, \tfrac{\psi}{c}) + \underline{E}_t(x, y, \tfrac{\psi}{c})(t - \tfrac{\psi}{c}) + \underline{E}_{tt}(x, y, \tfrac{\psi}{c})\frac{(t-\psi/c)^2}{2!} + \cdots \quad \text{for } t > \frac{\psi}{c} \ ;$$

$$\underline{E}(x, y, t) = 0 \qquad \text{for } t < \frac{\psi}{c} \ . \tag{9}$$

To obtain these power series we must be able to calculate the coefficients. We have already indicated how we can calculate $\underline{E}(x, y, \psi/c) = \underline{E}^*(x, y)$. The method which leads to information about the discontinuities of $\underline{E}$ and $\underline{H}$ themselves, that is, which leads to the transport equations, can be utilized[13] to obtain linear, first order, ordinary differential equations for the discontinuities in $\underline{E}_t$, $\underline{E}_{tt}, \ldots$, $\underline{H}_t$, $\underline{H}_{tt}, \ldots$ as these propagate along the generators of the cone in the space-time picture or with the wave front or along the rays in the space picture. These differential equations, which we call the higher transport equations, can be solved and so we can obtain the values of these discontinuities at any point (x, y) at the time $t_0 = \psi/c$.

We can then obtain the power series in question and learn something about the time-dependent fields $\underline{E}(x, y, t)$, $\underline{H}(x, y, t)$ in the neighborhood of a wave front, that is, for times t near the time t_0 at which $\underline{E}$ and $\underline{H}$ first become non-zero at (x, y). Stated otherwise, we can obtain the series expansions (9) for $\underline{E}$ and $\underline{H}$ in which the geometrical optics field is the first term.

The second view of geometrical optics to be presented derives from considering time harmonic solutions of Maxwell's equations. The fields we are dealing with then have the form (we now use three space variables)

$$\underline{E}(x, y, z, t) = \underline{u}(x, y, z) e^{-i\omega t}, \quad \underline{H}(x, y, z, t) = \underline{v}(x, y, z) e^{-i\omega t} \tag{10}$$

wherein $\underline{u}$ and $\underline{v}$ are complex vectors. The key result, phrased for simplicity on the assumption that only one family of wave fronts exists, is that

$$\underline{u}(x, y, z) \sim e^{ik\psi(x, y, z)} \left\{ \underline{A}_0(x, y, z) + \frac{\underline{A}_1(x, y, z)}{i\omega} + \frac{\underline{A}_2(x, y, z)}{(i\omega)^2} + \cdots \right\} \tag{11}$$

$$\underline{v}(x, y, z) \sim e^{ik\psi(x, y, z)} \left\{ \underline{B}_0(x, y, z) + \frac{\underline{B}_1(x, y, z)}{i\omega} + \frac{\underline{B}_2(x, y, z)}{(i\omega)^2} + \cdots \right\} \tag{12}$$

wherein the series are asymptotic for large ω and ψ satisfies the eiconal differential equation. The quantity k is ω/c. Thus the functions $\underline{u}$ and $\underline{v}$, which are the amplitudes of the time-harmonic field vectors $\underline{E}$ and $\underline{H}$, may be represented asymptotically by series asymptotic in $1/\omega$ for large ω.

Loosely one can now define the geometrical optics field as the limit for large ω of the field amplitudes $\underline{u}$ and $\underline{v}$. Then the first terms of these two series are the geometrical optics field. The definition as a limit for infinite ω is not quite proper because the first terms of the two series contain the factor $e^{ik\psi}$ and these have no limit as ω becomes infinite. One can however say that the geometrical optics field consists of the first terms of series which are asymptotic for large ω provided we now include in geometrical optics the phase factor $e^{ik\omega}$. This field then is not strictly the classical geometrical optics field but contains an additional and by no means undesirable feature. We also see clearly how this geometrical optics field is related to the full wave solution of Maxwell's equations.

The introduction of this second definition of the geometrical optics field raises the question of whether it is identical, except for the phase factor, with the geometrical optical field previously introduced as the discontinuities of $\underline{E}(x, y, z, t)$ and $\underline{H}(x, y, z, t)$. The answer is that the very derivation of the series (11) and (12) shows that[14]

$$
\begin{aligned}
\underline{A}_0(x, y, z) &= \underline{E}(x, y, z, \psi/c) = \underline{E}^*(x, y, z) \\
\underline{B}_0(x, y, z) &= \underline{H}(x, y, z, \psi/c) = \underline{H}^*(x, y, z) \\
\underline{A}_1(x, y, z) &= \underline{E}_t(x, y, z, \psi/c) \\
\underline{B}_1(x, y, z) &= \underline{H}_t(x, y, z, \psi/c) \qquad (13) \\
&\ldots\ldots\ldots\ldots
\end{aligned}
$$

Moreover since we know that the above $\underline{E}$, $\underline{H}$, $\underline{E}_t$, $\underline{H}_t \ldots$ satisfy linear, first order differential equations, we know that the same is true for the coefficients of the asymptotic series and so these coefficients can be readily determined. To obtain the geometrical optics field we have but to solve the eiconal equation

$$\psi_x^2 + \psi_y^2 + \psi_z^2 = n^2 \quad ,$$

as must be done in any case, and then solve just the first transport equations, one for $\underline{A}_0$ or $\underline{E}^*$ and the other for $\underline{B}_0$ or $\underline{H}^*$.

The larger mathematical point of interest here is that if one is satisfied to obtain an asymptotic series solution of a time harmonic problem in place of the exact solution, he can replace the solution of Maxwell's partial differential equations by the solution of a series of first order ordinary differential equations. This method must be distinguished from obtaining an exact solution of Maxwell's equations in the form of an integral, say, and then evaluating the integral asymptotically by a method appropriate to the asymptotic evaluation of integrals.

Both views of geometrical optics not only relate this theory directly to Maxwell's equations by precise mathematical connections but accomplish even more. Since one can calculate terms beyond the first ones in the series (11) and (12) this view of the relationship between optics and electromagnetics permits us to improve on geometrical optics approximations to electromagnetic problems. Likewise the Taylor series expansion of the time-dependent $\underline{E}$ and $\underline{H}$ in the neighborhood of $t_0 = \psi(x, y, z)/c$ improves on the geometrical optics field in the direction of the full time-dependent solution. Thus our new views of geometrical optics permit us to make better approximations to wave solutions than geometrical optics itself. We see, incidentally, that we have supplied the mathematical foundation for what Sommerfeld and Runge did.

The theory discussed thus far applies to the direct transmission, reflection and refraction in homogeneous and inhomogeneous isotropic media, and, insofar as geometrical optics as a study of discontinuities is concerned, it has also been carried out for homogeneous and inhomogeneous anisotropic media. Stated otherwise, wherever the rays of classical geometrical optics had been defined, the new theory applies also. For this class of problems one can obtain asymptotic series solutions corresponding to given sources, initial conditions, and boundary conditions.

5. SOME APPLICATIONS OF THE THEORY. The more careful study of the relationship of geometrical optics to electromagnetic theory has stimulated a number of investigations and has thrown new light on older ones within the domain of electromagnetics and outside. We see more clearly that the propagation of discontinuities is the first approximation to aperiodic or time dependent solutions of various equations of mathematical physics and the approximations obtained by letting some parameter approach ∞ are the first terms in asymptotic series developments of time harmonic fields or of solutions of the time free elliptic partial differential equations. I should like to give some indication of the scope of the problems encompassed by the theory presented in article 4.

Since many electromagnetic problems can be treated as scalar problems and since other branches of mathematical physics involve either scalar quantities or different systems of partial differential equations, I should like to point out first that the theory I have sketched for Maxwell's equations has been extended first of all to the general linear second order hyperbolic partial differential equation[15]

$$\sum_{i,j=1}^{n} a^{ij} u_{ij} + \sum_{k=1}^{n} b^{k} u_{k} + cu = f_{tt} \tag{14}$$

wherein u is a function of $(x_1, x_2, \ldots, x_n)$ and the coefficients a^{ij}, b^k, and c are functions of $x_1, x_2, \ldots, x_{n-1}$, and $u_{ij} = \partial^2 u/\partial x^i \partial x^j$. Thus treating x_n as t, one may study the behavior of the discontinuities $[u]$, $[u_t]$, $[u_{tt}]$, ... of u and obtain transport equations for their propagation along what are called the bicharacteristics of (1) or, in the $(x_1, \ldots, x_{n-1})$-space, along the rays. One may also discuss the asymptotic series representation of solutions $u(x_1, \ldots, x_{n-1}) e^{-i\omega t}$, that is, of time-harmonic solutions of (1), and all of the relations between the time-dependent solution and the time-independent solution which hold for Maxwell's equations apply here too.

The theory has been further extended[16] to symmetric linear hyperbolic systems of partial differential equations and thus can be applied to more complicated systems of first order partial differential equations than Maxwell's equations.

Insofar as applications to electromagnetic theory are concerned, the applications made in the last ten years have been numerous. A large number of scalar problems involving scattering from the exterior of smooth bodies has been treated by Keller, Seckler and Lewis[17]. Since the method of geometrical optics proper had been available the progress in this work is to obtain improvements over the geometrical optics field by calculating more terms of the asymptotic series solution of steady state problems. Still in the domain of electromagnetic problems I should also like to call attention to the surprising result obtained by Schensted[18]. Schensted calculated the asymptotic series for the vector field diffracted by the exterior of a paraboloid of revolution when a plane wave is incident along the axis (the normal is directed along the axis) and found that the asymptotic series consists only of the first term. In this case, then, the geometrical optics field is also the exact electromagnetic solution.

Our theory has an important bearing on quantum mechanics. In erecting the system of wave mechanics Schrödinger in 1926 gave the following construction[19]. He considered a particle of mass m with momentum p and total energy E in a field of force with potential $V(x, y, z)$. Then Hamilton's partial differential equation for the motion is

$$\frac{\partial W}{\partial t} + H\left(x, y, z, \frac{\partial W}{\partial x}, \frac{\partial W}{\partial y}, \frac{\partial W}{\partial z}\right) = 0$$

where H is the Hamiltonian function for the particle, namely,

$$H = \frac{1}{2m}(p_x^2 + p_y^2 + p_z^2) + V(x, y, z)$$

and W is Hamilton's principal function. Thus the partial differential equation in this case is

$$\frac{\partial W}{\partial t} + \frac{1}{2m}\left\{\left(\frac{\partial W}{\partial x}\right)^2 + \left(\frac{\partial W}{\partial y}\right)^2 + \left(\frac{\partial W}{\partial z}\right)^2\right\} + V(x, y, z) = 0 .$$

In accordance with Hamilton's theory the principal function can be written as

$$W = -Et + S(x, y, z)$$

where S is Hamilton's characteristic function. The equation for S now is

$$\left(\frac{\partial S}{\partial x}\right)^2 + \left(\frac{\partial S}{\partial y}\right)^2 + \left(\frac{\partial S}{\partial z}\right)^2 + 2m(V-E) = 0 .$$

On the basis of heuristic considerations, Schrödinger now introduced a wave function ψ and was led to the time-independent (reduced) Schrödinger equation

$$\nabla^2\psi + \frac{8\pi^2 m}{h^2}(E-V)\psi = 0 \tag{15}$$

wherein ψ is a function of x, y and z . This derivation of the Schrödinger equation indicated that wave mechanics is in some sense a generalization of classical mechanics in the same vague way that electromagnetic theory appeared in 1926 to be a generalization of geometrical optics. In fact Schrödinger was guided by that analogy and spoke of "working from the Hamiltonian analogy on the lines of undulatory optics."

In 1933[20] Birkhoff suggested that asymptotic series solutions for the function ψ in (15) might be obtained by assuming a series

$$\psi(x, y, z) \sim e^{kS}\left(v_0 + \frac{v_1}{k} + \frac{v_2}{k^2} + \dots\right), \quad k = \frac{2\pi i}{h}, \qquad (16)$$

where S and the v_i are functions of x, y and z . By substitution for ψ in the partial differential equation (15) Birkhoff obtained a first order non-linear partial differential equation for S (which corresponds to our eiconal equation) and showed that the v_n satisfy a system of recursive ordinary differential equations

$$\frac{dv_n}{d\tau} + \Phi v_n = A_{n-1}, \qquad (17)$$

where A_{n-1} is a known linear differential expression in $v_0, v_1, \dots, v_{n-1}$.

The first order partial differential equation (eiconal equation) which Birkhoff obtains is the Hamilton-Jacobi equation from which Schrödinger started. Thus on a purely formal basis Birkhoff showed that classical mechanics is derived from wave mechanics by the introduction of an asymptotic series in practically the same formal way that Sommerfeld and Runge derived the eiconal equation of optics from the scalar wave equation except that Birkhoff assumed a full asymptotic series where Sommerfeld and Runge assumed only the first term. However, the precise mathematical relationship of the Schrödinger equation to the original Hamilton-Jacobi first order partial differential equation remained unclear.

It is now apparent from our theory of asymptotic series solution of partial differential equations that the series (16) adopted purely formally by Birkhoff does indeed provide an asymptotic series solution of the Schrödinger equation (15) and that the corresponding eiconal equation is the Hamilton-Jacobi equation

$$\left(\frac{\partial S}{\partial x}\right)^2 + \left(\frac{\partial S}{\partial y}\right)^2 + \left(\frac{\partial S}{\partial z}\right)^2 = 2m(E-V).$$

Here S is Hamilton's characteristic function. We now know too that this last equation holds precisely in the limit for small h . In other words classical mechanics is indeed the limiting case of quantum mechanics.

But our theory goes farther in the domain of quantum mechanics.

To solve the reduced Schrödinger equation for its eigenfunctions and eigenvalues, physicists used separation of variables and obtained the one-dimensional ordinary differential equation

$$\psi''(x) + \frac{8\pi^2 m}{h^2}(E-V(x))\psi = 0 , \quad -\infty < x < \infty \tag{18}$$

wherein m is a mass, $V(x)$ is the potential energy and E is the total energy (and the eigenvalue parameter) and then (1926) applied the approximation method now known as the WKB method after its innovators Wentzel, Kramers and Brillouin to approximate the eigenvalues. At this time (1926) the precise nature of this approximation remained unclear.

In 1908 Birkhoff had given[21] a theory of asymptotic solution of the n-th order ordinary differential equation

$$\frac{d^n z}{dx^n} + \rho\, a_{n-1}(x,\rho)\frac{d^{n-1}z}{dx^{n-1}} + \cdots + \rho^n a_0(x,\rho)z = 0 \tag{19}$$

and had shown that each solution z_i can be expressed in the asymptotic form

$$z_i(x,\rho) \sim e^{\rho\int_a^x w_i(t)\,dt} \sum_{j=0}^{\infty} z_{ij}(x)\rho^{-j} \tag{20}$$

where the $w_i(t)$ are the solutions of the indicial equation

$$w_n + a_{n-1}(x,0)w^{n-1} + \cdots + a_0(x,0) = 0$$

and the z_{ij} can be successively determined by solving a recursive system of rather simple ordinary differential equations. Birkhoff showed in the second of his 1933 papers that his 1908 paper readily covers the one-dimensional Schrödinger equation and the first term of (20) yields the WKB solution of this reduced or time free Schrödinger equation.

Our theory now permits us to say that the first term in the series (16), namely $e^{ks}v_0$, wherein all three variables x, y and z are present, is the direct generalization to partial differential equations of the WKB approximation used in one-dimensional problems.

This latter point may need and warrant elaboration. Let us consider the second order wave equation

$$\Delta u - \frac{n^2}{c^2}u_{tt} = 0 \tag{21}$$

Our theory for the asymptotic series solution of time harmonic solutions of this equation tells us that the time harmonic solution $u = v(x,y,z)e^{-i\omega t}$ can be represented in the form

$$v = e^{ik\psi}\left(v_0 + \frac{v_1}{ik} + \frac{v_2}{(ik)^2} + \cdots\right) \tag{22}$$

wherein k is ω/c, ψ is a solution of the eiconal equation

$$\psi_x^2 + \psi_y^2 + \psi_z^2 = n^2 , \tag{23}$$

and the v_i satisfy the recursive system of first order linear ordinary differential equations

$$n \frac{d}{ds} v_n + \frac{1}{2} \Delta\psi\, v_n = -\Delta v_{n-1} \tag{24}$$

where d/ds is the derivative along the rays in (x, y, z)-space[22].

Now in the case of one space dimension, the equation (21) becomes for $u = v(x)e^{-i\omega t}$

$$v''(x) + \frac{\omega^2}{c^2} n^2 v(x) = 0 . \tag{25}$$

The eiconal equation is

$$(\psi'(x))^2 = n^2 \tag{26}$$

and the equation for v_0 becomes (v_{n-1} is 0 for $n = 0$)

$$n \frac{dv_0}{ds} + \frac{1}{2} \psi''(x) v_0 = 0 . \tag{27}$$

In view of (26)

$$\psi'(x) \frac{dv_0}{ds} + \frac{1}{2}\psi''(x) v_0 = 0 .$$

This equation is readily solvable and gives

$$v_0 = c \frac{1}{\sqrt{\psi'(x)}} .$$

Then by (22) the first term in the asymptotic approximation to v is

$$v \sim C\frac{1}{\sqrt{\psi'(x)}} e^{ik\psi} = C \frac{1}{\sqrt{n}} e^{ik\int_0^x n\, dx} .$$

This result for v obtained from the first term of our asymptotic series agrees precisely with the WKB solution of equation (25)[23].

In view of the fact that the first term of our asymptotic series is a generalization to partial differential equations of the WKB method for one-dimensional equations, we can now go a step further in quantum mechanical and related problems. The asymptotic theory of partial differential equations can be used for the three-dimensional Schrödinger equation and other equations when separation of variables is not possible. Thus Keller[24] has derived the half integer quantum numbers for the three-dimensional Schrödinger equation by using the first term of the asymptotic series solution for ψ , that is, by assuming that ψ is represented approximately (for large k or small h) by

$$\psi_0 = \sum_{n=1}^{M} A_n(x, y, z) e^{ikS_n(x, y, z, t)}$$

and the condition that ψ_0 must be single-valued. The summation of terms merely takes care of the fact that there may be many series if S is multiple-valued or in optical terms, if many families of wave fronts pass a given point.

The work described in the preceding paragraph was applied to the Schrödinger equation in unbounded domains. However the same method has been used to find asymptotic values of the large eigenvalues and the corresponding eigenfunctions in bounded domains and indeed for the reduced wave equation[25]. That is, the method is applied to

$$(\Delta + k^2)u = 0 ,$$

where k is the eigenvalue parameter, the equation is valid in some domain D , and a boundary condition, for example, $\partial u/\partial u = 0$, is imposed on the boundary B of D . The method was also applied to the (reduced Schrödinger equation with a spherically symmetric potential $V(r)$, namely,

$$\Delta^2 u + (-k^2 - V(r))u = 0 ,$$

where $-k^2$ is the eigenvalue parameter. Here the domain B is all of space.

Whereas the application of the theory of article 4 to quantum mechanics utilizes the time-harmonic high frequency point of view other applications recently have made utilized the study of discontinuities. Acoustics had been developed from the wave theory point of view almost from the start of this science. One can however introduce a geometrical acoustics, as Keller[26] and Friedlander[27] have and find that the point of view of discontinuities permits one to study weak shock waves in gases. If one assumes for a fluid motion that the shock waves in the medium are weak and so can ignore the interaction of the shock and the medium behind the shock (the side into which the shock is proceeding) and if one neglects viscosity and heat conduction in the fluid then the shock waves are the discontinuities in the (excess) pressure and the change or discontinuity in pressure at the front is the shock strength. One obtains as in geometrical optics an eiconal equation for the wave or shock front. The rays are orthogonal to the fronts and one derives a transport equation for the variation of the shock strength along a ray. One can also treat the reflection and transmission of the shocks across boundaries as in geometrical optics.

It is also possible to obtain asymptotic series solutions of the linearized acoustic equations for periodic waves of high frequency by using the theory presented earlier for periodic solutions of Maxwell's equations or the general second order scalar equation[28]. Then the theory for weak shocks provides an approximation to the periodic solutions in the same way that geometrical optics is an approximation to wave solutions of Maxwell's equations.

The usefulness of a "geometrical optics" of water wave theory as well as of asymptotic approximation for high frequency periodic water waves has also been favorably considered[29]. For water waves in shallow water the wave amplitude $u(x, y, t)$ satisfies the partial differential equation

$$(ghu_x)_x + (ghu_y)_y = u_{tt}$$

wherein g is the acceleration due to gravity and $h(x, y)$ is the variable depth measured from the equilibrium water surface. In this domain of application the treatment of breakers and surf near a beach can be handled effectively by either the study of the discontinuities of the time dependent equation or by examing the high frequency approximation to periodic waves. We know of course that the first term of either approximation is the same except that the phase factor $e^{ik\psi}$ is present in the latter case[30].

Another class of applications deals with the linearized equations of motion in elastic isotropic media[31]. Here for small amplitude shear and compressional waves one can obtain the propagation of pulses or the asymptotic form of periodic waves of high frequency in both homogeneous and inhomogeneous media. For homogeneous isotropic media the linearized equation of elastic wave motion is

$$\rho \frac{\partial^2 \underline{u}}{\partial t^2} = (\lambda+\mu) \nabla(\nabla \cdot \underline{u}) + \mu \nabla^2 \underline{u} \quad .$$

Here $\underline{u}$ is the displacement vector (in rectangular coordinates), ρ is the density of the medium and λ and μ are Lamé's constants. A more complicated equation holds for inhomogeneous media.

One starts with an asymptotic series solution of the form

$$\underline{u} = \sum_0^{\infty} \frac{\underline{A}_n}{(i\omega)^n} e^{i\omega(S-t)}$$

where $\underline{A}_n$ and S are functions if x, y and z and ω is the angular frequency of the solutions sought. In this case, one gets two different eiconal equations and two different sets of transport equations, one for compressional and one for transverse waves (because the original differential equation is different from Maxwell's), but the method of obtaining the asymptotic series solutions is that sketched above for Maxwell's equations. The "rays" are the orthogonal trajectories to the solutions of the eiconal equations.

Geometrical optics as the study of discontinuities has application to current problems of magnetohydrodynamics. Here we are definitely in the realm of anisotropic media. For electromagnetic theory proper the geometrical optics of anisotropic media is, as in the case of isotropic media, the transport of the discontinuities of $\underline{E}$ and $\underline{H}$. From this viewpoint we derive first the eiconal equation or the Hamiltonian as it is more commonly called in the case of anisotropic media. In such media the energy of the electromagnetic field does not propagate along the normals to the wave fronts but along distinct curves called rays. The variation of these discontinuities along the rays also satisfy transport equations which prove to be first order ordinary differential equations.

The method of electromagnetics has been applied to plasmas. If one approaches a plasma as a perfect (non-viscous), compressible, infinitely conducting fluid, one applies the equations of fluid dynamics and electromagnetics. For weak shocks the equations may be linearized and one obtains four vector partial differential equations in the velocity vector $\underline{u}$, the magnetic field intensity $\underline{H}$, the density ρ, and the entropy S per unit mass. A discontinuity surface is one across which $\underline{u}$, $\underline{H}$ or ρ is discontinuous. For these equations the study of the propagation of the discontinuities leads to three families of fronts (each with its own speed called Alfvén, slow and fast) in any one normal direction and accordingly three families of rays. The surface of wave normals is accordingly more complicated than the Fresnel surface for crystals. It is then possible to obtain transport equations for each of the discontinuities along each family of rays. The results are extremely useful, for such shock waves can be generated[32].

It is also possible to apply the asymptotic theory to periodic waves of high frequency in plasmas but this has not been carried out as yet.

6. SOME OPEN PROBLEMS. The theory developed for Maxwell's equations permits us to obtain useful approximate solutions for time dependent and for time harmonic problems provided that the corresponding geometrical optics approximation exists, that is, in problems where the wave fronts and rays of classical geometric optics are defined. Physically this limitation means a restriction to propagation, reflection and refraction in homogeneous and inhomogeneous isotropic and anisotropic media. Even in these phenomena, no caustics must be present. In view of the importance of diffraction phenomena and in view of the difficulties encountered in solving diffraction problems it would of course be highly desirable to extend the theory of article 4 to cover

such problems.

The first difficulty one faces in attempting such an extension is that the theory already developed presupposes the existence of geometrical optics; that is, we must be able to obtain the wave fronts as solutions of the eiconal equation and their orthogonal trajectories, the rays. In fact the transport equations describe the behavior of the coefficients of the asymptotic series along the rays. Certainly then when there are no wave fronts and rays, the theory thus far developed has no meaning. Also where the rays form an envelope or come together at a focus, the transport equations break down because the phase function $\psi(x, y, z)$ becomes singular. The first major step in the extension of our theory is to extend geometrical optics itself. This idea has already been tackled by a number of men. It has been developed and systematically handled by J. B. Keller[33] who also suggests the unifying principle that diffracted rays can be obtained from an extension of Fermat's principle. Now Fermat's principle for classical geometrical optics is deducible from Maxwell's equations by the process sketched in article 4 (for the very reason that geometrical optics is deducible.) However, the problem remains as to whether the extended Fermat principle, which encompasses rays and wave fronts not in classical geometrical optics, can be deduced from Maxwell's equations. The deduction already carried out presupposes $\underline{E}(x, y, z, t)$, $\underline{H}(x, y, z, t)$ and their successive time derivatives have finite discontinuities on the wave fronts. This condition limits the wave fronts and rays to those of geometrical optics.

Granted the extension of geometrical optics, the next step in diffraction problems is to derive the form of the asymptotic series solution which is valid in diffraction regions. The theory already available proves that in the case of pure propagation, reflection and refraction the form of the asymptotic series is that of a power series in $1/\omega$ and that the series is truly asymptotic to the time harmonic solutions of Maxwell's equations. The corresponding step is missing for series valid in diffraction regions[34]. At the present writing all that we have been able to do is to assume a form recommended by the asymptotic expansion of solutions obtained in an entirely different manner. Thus the problem of diffraction by a circular cylinder can be solved and its solution expanded asymptotically. The form of this asymptotic series or some generalization of it has been used to solve problems involving other shapes.

The third step would be to learn how to determine the coefficients of the asymptotic series. If it should prove to be the case that these coefficients also satisfy transport equations, then the initial values of the solutions of these transport equations would also have to be determined.

In view of the applicability of the theory already developed for electromagnetics to many other branches of physics, the problems just sketched merit attention. Though some progress has been made beyond what was described in the earlier parts of this paper, the accomplishments are not broad enough to warrant attention in this survey.

FOOTNOTES

1. Huygens, C., Traité de la Luminere (1690). An English translation is available from the University of Chicago Press, Chicago, 1945.

2. Newton, I., Optiks (1704, 1706). An English edition is available from Dover Publications, Inc., N.Y., 1952.

3. Synge, J. L., and Conway, W., The Mathematical Papers of Wm. R. Hamilton, I, Cambridge University Press, London, 1931.

4. A full account of the very long series of efforts to develop an elastic theory of light is given by Whittaker, E. T., History of the Theories of Aether and Electricity, V. I, Rev. Ed., Thomas Nelson and Sons, Ltd., London, 1951.

5. König, W., Electromagnetische Lichttheorie, Handbuch der Physik, Old Ed., XX, p. 147, J. Springer, Berlin, 1928.

6. Kirchhoff's proof is in Ann. der Physik (2), 18, 1883, p. 663, and in his Vorlesungen über Mathematische Physik, Teubner, Leipzig, 1891, V. 2, p. 35. An account of it is given by König, W., Electromagnetische Lichttheorie, Handbuch der Physik, Old. Ed., XX, p. 167 ff., J. Springer, Berlin, 1928. An alternative proof which utilizes the transformation of the Kirchhoff double integral into the incident field plus a line integral is given by Baker, B., and Copson, E. T., The Mathematical Theory of Huygens' Principle, Oxford U. Press, London, 1939, p. 79, and Rubinowicz, A., Die Beugungswelle in der Kirchhoffschen Theorie der Beugung, Warsaw, 1957, p. 166 ff.

7. Sommerfeld, A., and Runge, J., Anwendung der Vektorrechnung auf die Grundlagen der geometrischen Optik, Ann. der Phys. 35, 1911, pp. 277-298. Also in Sommerfeld, A., Optik, 2nd ed., Akademische Verlagsgesellschaft, Leipzig, 1959, p. 187 ff.

8. For isotropic media the derivation is carried out in Born, Max, and Wolf, E., Principles of Optics, Pergamon Press, London, 1959, p. 109. References are given there to original papers and to papers in which the analogous procedure can be employed in anisotropic media.

9. Actually Clemens Schaefer in his Einführung in die Theoretische Physik, III, 1, p. 386 ff., W. De Gruyter, Berlin, 1950, avoids the frequency dependence at least in non-dispersive homogeneous media by using functions such as $F(t - \frac{x \cos\alpha + y \cos\beta + z \cos\gamma}{v})$.

10. This result is due to R. K. Luneberg and can be found in Kline, M., An Asymptotic Solution of Maxwell's Equations, Comm. on Pure

and Appl. Math., 4, 1951, 225-262. Also in Theory of Electromagnetic Waves, A Symposium, Interscience Pub., Inc. N.Y., 1951.

11. We continue to use two space variables in order to illustrate geometrically. However all statements apply when three space variables are present.

12. The series exist and converge for values of $t < t_0$ but do not represent the field.

13. Kline, M., loc. cit.

14. Strictly the identification of the coefficients of the asymptotic series with the discontinuities of the time dependent field presupposes that the same source, say $\underline{g}(x, y, z)$ creates both fields but that the time behavior of the source is $e^{-i\omega t}$ in one case and is $\eta(t)$, the Heaviside unit function, in the other. This fact can be ignored in some applications and is helpful in others.
The existence of the asymptotic series (11) and (12) and the relations (13) are due to R.K. Luneberg. An exposition can be found in Kline, M., loc. cit., 1951.

15. Kline, M., Asymptotic Solution of Linear Hyperbolic Partial Differential Equations, Jour. of Rat. Mech. & Anal., 3, 1954, 315-342.

16. Lewis, Robert M., Asymptotic Expansion of Steady-State Solutions of Symmetric Hyperbolic Linear Differential Equations, Jour. of Math. & Mech., 7, 1958, 593-628.

17. Keller, J.B., Lewis, R.M., and Seckler, B.D., Asymptotic Solution of Some Diffraction Problems, Comm. on Pure and Appl. Math., 9, 1956, 207.

18. Schensted, Craig E., Electromagnetic and Acoustic Scattering by a Semi-Infinite Body of Revolution, Jour. Appl. Phys. 26, 1955, 306-8.

19. Whittaker, E.T., History of the Theories of Aether and Electricity, II, p. 270, Thomas Nelson and Sons, Ltd., London, 1953.

20. Birkhoff, George D., Some remarks concerning Schrödinger's Wave Equation, Proc. Nat'l. Acad. of Sciences, 19, 1933, 339-344, p. 475; Quantum Mechanics and Asymptotic Series, Bull. A.M.S., 39, 1933, 681-700; The Foundations of Quantum Mechanics, Comptes Rendus du Congrès Internat. des Math., Oslo, 1936, 207-225. All of these papers are in Birkhoff's Collected Papers, V. II, American Math. Soc., Providence, 1950.

21. Birkhoff, George D., On the Asymptotic Character of the Solutions of Certain Differential Equations Containing a Parameter, Trans. Amer. Math. Soc., 9, 1908, 219-231.

22. These equations will be found in Kline, M., loc. cit., 1954.

23. For a good description of the WKB method, see Kamke, E., Differential-Gleichungen, Lösungsmethoden und Lösungen, 3rd. ed., Chelsea Pub. Co., N.Y., 1948, p. 138. See also p. 276.

24. Keller, Joseph B., Corrected Bohr-Sommerfeld Quantum Conditions for Nonseparable Systems, Annals of Physics, 4, 1958, 180-188.

25. Keller, J.B., and Rubinow, S.I., Asymptotic Solution of Eigenvalue Problems, Annals of Physics, 9, 1960, pp. 24-75, and 10, 1960, 303-305.

26. Keller, J.B., Geometrical Acoustics I. The Theory of Weak Shock Waves, J. Appl. Phys., 25, 1954, 938-947. Also Friedrichs, K., and Keller, J.B., Geometrical Acoustics II, J. Appl. Phys., 26, 1955, 961-966. Whitham, G.B., On the Propagation of Weak Shock Waves, J. Fluid Mech., 1, 1956, 290-318.

27. Friedlander, F.G., Sound Pulses, Cambridge Univ. Press, London, 1958.

28. See Friedrichs and Keller, loc. cit.

29. Lowell, Sherman C., The Propagation of Waves in Shallow Water, Comm. on Pure and Appl. Math., 2, 1949, pp. 275-291.

30. To handle the time periodic case, Lowell reduced to an ordinary differential equation and applied the WKB method. We now know that the approximate solution obtained by this method is the first term of our asymptotic series.

31. Karal, Frank C., Jr., and Keller, Joseph B., Elastic Wave Propagation in Homogeneous and Inhomogeneous Media, J. Acous. Soc. Amer., 31, 1959, 694-705.

32. Bazer, J., and Fleischman, O., Propagation of Weak Hydromagnetic Discontinuities, Physics of Fluids, 2, 1959, 366-378.

33. Keller's work and the best single discussion of diffracted rays will be found in Keller, J.B., A Geometrical Theory of Diffraction. This paper is in Graves, L.M., ed., Calculus of Variations and its Applications, Proc. of Symposia in Appl. Math., VIII, McGraw-Hill Book Co., N.Y., 1958, pp. 27-52. This paper also contains references to other work on diffracted rays and gives applications.

34. In a number of applications already made of the asymptotic series valid for propagation, reflection and refraction, the authors have assumed the existence of a series $\Sigma_{n=0}^{\infty} v_n(x, y, z)/k^n$ or some more general form and have substituted in Maxwell's equations or the reduced scalar wave equation. This procedure is justified only as a convenience in papers which seek to avoid matters of theory and wish

to get on with applications. It is however no more than a heuristic device and logically is inadequate.

The research reported in this paper has been sponsored by the Electronics Research Directorate of the Air Force Cambridge Research Laboratories, Office of Aerospace Research, under Contract No. AF 19(604) 5238, (USAF), Bedford, Mass.

F. J. TISCHER

Fields Excited in a Receiving-type Antenna

SUMMARY: The paper deals with the fields excited in a primary radiator which is a part of an antenna structure. The diffraction field of the structure, with the aperture closed by a conducting surface, is assumed to be known. The received field is computed from the interaction of aperture fields of the primary radiator with the diffraction field.

The following considerations deal with the fields in an antenna operating under receiving conditions. Considerations of this type are necessary if the reciprocity theorem is not applicable.

The operational conditions are as follows: A primary radiator in the form of a horn antenna is a part of a more complicated antenna structure. The primary radiator, if considered separately, consists of the horn and a waveguide which connects the oscillator to the horn as indicated in Fig. 1a. A cross-section of the waveguide is ΔS, the aperture of the horn is denoted by ΔA. If the primary radiator operates as a receiving device, the waveguide is terminated by a receiver which acts as a perfectly matched termination as indicated in Fig. 1b.

The primary radiator is incorporated in a more complicated antenna structure as shown in Fig. 2. Let us now assume that the diffracted field of the antenna structure which, as an example, may be a cone, but can have an arbitrary shape, is known in the absence of the primary radiator. The question arises, what is the field excited in the inside of the primary radiator if waves travel toward the antenna structure.

Preparatory Computations

We assume two types of fields $\bar{E}^{(1)}$, $\bar{H}^{(1)}$ and $\bar{E}^{(2)}$ and $\bar{H}^{(2)}$ which satisfy Maxwell's equations. The first type of field is derived from a Hertz vector $\bar{\pi}^{(1)}$, similarly as in the case of current sources. The following set of equations shows the relations between these magnitudes in the region under consideration for harmonically varying fields:

$$\nabla \times \bar{E}^{(1),(2)} = -j\omega\mu \bar{H}^{(1),(2)} , \tag{1}$$

$$\nabla \times \bar{H}^{(1),(2)} = j\omega\varepsilon \bar{E}^{(1),(2)} , \tag{2}$$

$$\nabla \cdot \bar{E}^{(1),(2)} = 0 , \tag{3}$$

$$\nabla \cdot \bar{H}^{(1),(2)} = 0 , \tag{4}$$

$$\bar{H}^{(1)} = j\omega\,\varepsilon \nabla \times \bar{\pi}^{(1)} , \tag{5}$$

$$\bar{E}^{(1)} = \beta^2 \bar{\pi}^{(1)} - \nabla\phi^{(1)} . \tag{6}$$

We find the wave equations

$$\nabla \times \nabla \times \bar{E}^{(2)} - \beta^2 \bar{E}^{(2)} = 0 , \tag{7}$$

and

$$\nabla \times \nabla \times \bar{\pi}^{(1)} - \beta^2 \bar{\pi}^{(1)} + \nabla\phi^{(1)} = 0 . \tag{8}$$

Applying Green's theorem in vector form [1] to the wave equations,

$$\int_V [\bar{A} \cdot (\nabla \times \nabla \times \bar{B}) - \bar{B} \cdot (\nabla \times \nabla \times \bar{A})]\,dV = \int_S (\bar{B} \times \nabla \times \bar{A} - \bar{A} \times \nabla \times \bar{B}) \cdot \bar{n}\,dS . \tag{9}$$

where $\bar{A} = \bar{\pi}^{(1)}$ and $\bar{B} = \bar{E}^{(2)}$, we find

$$\int_S (\bar{E}^{(2)} \times \nabla \times \bar{\pi}^{(1)} - \bar{\pi}^{(1)} \times \nabla \times \bar{E}^{(2)}) \cdot \bar{n}\,dS = \int_V \bar{E}^{(2)} \cdot \nabla\phi^{(1)}\,dV . \tag{10}$$

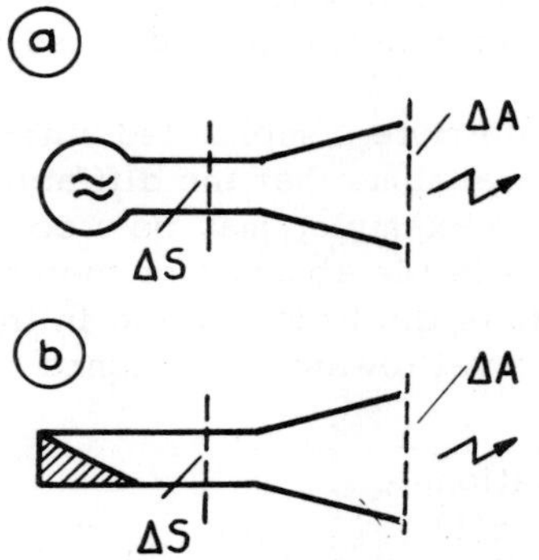

Fig. 1. Horn antenna as primary radiator
a) Transmitting case
b) Receiving operation

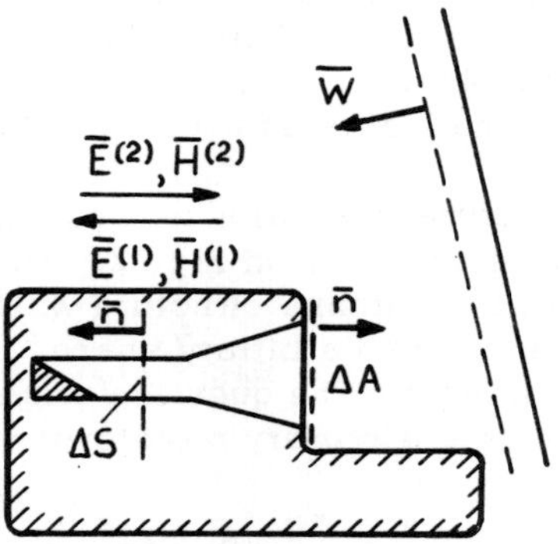

Fig. 2. Antenna structure with primary radiator

Application to the Problem

Let us apply the above equation for the computation of the excited fields in the antenna structure of Fig. 2. We consider, for this purpose, a region inside the primary radiator which is bounded on the left side by ΔS, the cross-section of the waveguide, and on the right side by the aperture ΔA, slightly outside the contour of the antenna structure A. The outside-normals to these boundaries are $\bar{n}$.

We assume that one of the two types of fields considered above, $\bar{E}^{(2)}$ and $\bar{H}^{(2)}$, is that of waves traveling from left to right, as if the primary horn would be excited by an oscillator. The field $\bar{E}^{(1)}$, $\bar{H}^{(1)}$ derived from $\bar{\pi}^{(1)}$ is that excited in the primary radiator by waves W traveling toward the antenna and passing through the aperture into the waveguide. These latter fields can be expressed in the cross-section ΔS by waves traveling from right to left toward the receiver terminating the waveguide.

Applying equation (10) to the region bounded by ΔS and ΔA, we separate the left-hand integral into the contributions by the various bounding surfaces. The conducting walls do not yield any contribution since the tangential components of the E-fields are zero. Hence,

$$\int_{\Delta S} (\ ) \cdot \bar{n}\, dS + \int_{\Delta A} (\ ) \cdot \bar{n}\, dS = \int_{V} \bar{E}^{(2)} \cdot \nabla\phi^{(1)}\, dV \ . \tag{11}$$

Let us consider next the integral over the waveguide cross-section ΔS, the first integral of (11). We can express the transverse components of the complex field amplitude by the following equations,

$$\bar{E}^{(1)} = E_0^{(1)}\, \bar{f}(x_1, x_2) = Z_T(-\bar{n} \times \bar{H}^{(1)}) \ , \tag{12}$$

$$\bar{H}^{(1)} = \frac{E_0^{(1)}}{Z_T} [\bar{n} \times \bar{f}(x_1, x_2)] \ , \tag{13}$$

$$\bar{E}^{(2)} = E_0^{(2)}\, \bar{f}(x_1, x_2) = Z_T(\bar{n} \times \bar{H}^{(1)}) \ , \tag{14}$$

$$\bar{H}^{(2)} = -\frac{E_0^{(2)}}{Z_T} [\bar{n} \times \bar{f}(x_1, x_2)] \ , \tag{15}$$

where $E_0^{(1)}$ and $E_0^{(2)}$ are representative field amplitudes, where $f(x_1, x_2)$ is a cross-sectional distribution function, and where Z_T is the transverse impedance.

Substitution of equations (12) and (14) in the first integral of Eq. (11) yields

$$\int_{\Delta S} (\ ) \cdot \bar{n}\, dS = \frac{2}{j\omega\varepsilon} \int_{\Delta S} \frac{\bar{E}^{(1)} \cdot \bar{E}^{(2)}}{Z_T}\, dS \ . \tag{16}$$

Considering that the power carried by the waves represented by $\bar{E}^{(2)}$ and $\bar{H}^{(2)}$ through the cross-section ΔS is

$$P^{(2)} = \frac{1}{2} \int_{\Delta S} \frac{E_0^{(2)} E_0^{(2)*}}{Z_T} |f(x_1, x_2)|^2 dS \ , \tag{17}$$

we find

$$\int_{\Delta S} (\ ) \cdot \bar{n}\, dS = \frac{1}{j\omega\varepsilon} \frac{E_0^{(1)}}{E_0^{(2)}} 4P^{(2)} \ , \tag{18}$$

where the reference plane for ΔS is chosen such that $E_0^{(2)}$ is a real quantity. We obtain evaluating Eq. (11)

$$E_0^{(1)} = -(E_0^{(2)}/4P^{(2)}) \Big[\int_{\Delta A} (\bar{E}^{(2)} \times \bar{H}^{(1)} - \bar{E}^{(1)} \times \bar{H}^{(2)}) \cdot \bar{n}\, dS + j\omega\varepsilon \int_V \bar{E}^{(2)} \cdot \nabla\phi\, dV \Big] \ . \tag{19}$$

The result shows that we can express the received wave amplitude $E_0^{(1)}$ in the waveguide in terms of the hypothetical wave amplitudes traveling in the waveguide to the right, which carry the power $P_1^{(2)}$, and the corresponding two types of fields on the aperture of the primary radiator.

Diffraction Fields on the Antenna Structure

As indicated in the introduction, we assume that the diffraction fields of the antenna structure are known with the aperture closed by a conductor surface. We can express these fields by the incident and the scattered fields and write,

$$\bar{E}^{(1)'} = \bar{E}_i + \bar{E}_s \ , \tag{20}$$

$$\bar{H}^{(1)'} = \bar{H}_i + \bar{H}_s \ . \tag{21}$$

If the aperture is open, we have to add complementary fields $\Delta\bar{E}^{(1)}$ and $\Delta\bar{H}^{(1)}$, so that the total field becomes,

$$\bar{E}^{(1)} = \bar{E}_i + \bar{E}_s + \Delta\bar{E}^{(1)} \ , \tag{22}$$

$$\bar{H}^{(1)} = \bar{H}_i + \bar{H}_s + \Delta\bar{H}^{(1)} \ . \tag{23}$$

We observe that the fields $\Delta\bar{E}^{(1)}$ and $\Delta\bar{H}^{(1)}$ are those of waves radiated through the aperture into the outside region.

Continuation of the Field Problem

Evaluation of the integral over the aperture ΔA in Eq. (19) shows that the contribution by $\Delta\bar{E}^{(1)}$ and $\Delta\bar{H}^{(1)}$ cancel each other since these waves have the same direction and aperture distribution as those expressed by $\bar{E}^{(2)}$ and $\bar{H}^{(2)}$. We find consequently, considering that $\bar{E}_i + \bar{E}_s = 0$ on the close aperture,

$$\int_{\Delta A} (\ ) \cdot \bar{n}\, dS = \int_{\Delta A} \bar{E}^{(2)} \times (\bar{H}_i + \bar{H}_s) \cdot \bar{n}\, dA\,, \qquad (24)$$

where $\bar{E}^{(2)}$ is the aperture field of the primary radiator related to a transmitted power $P^{(2)}$ inside the waveguide.

The volume integral of Eq. (19) can be written as a difference according to

$$\int_V \bar{E}^{(2)} \cdot \nabla\phi\, dV - \int_V [\nabla\cdot(\bar{E}^{(2)}\phi^{(1)}) - \phi\nabla\cdot\bar{E}^{(2)}]\, dV\,, \qquad (25)$$

where $\nabla\cdot\bar{E}^{(2)} = 0$, so that, finally

$$E_0^{(1)} = -(E_0^{(2)}/4P^{(2)}) \int_{\Delta A} \left\{[\bar{E}^{(2)} \times (\bar{H}_i + \bar{H}_s)] \cdot \bar{n} + \bar{n} \cdot \bar{E}^{(2)}\phi^{(1)}\right\} dA\,. \qquad (26)$$

This result opens a way to compute the fields excited in primary radiators which are incorporated in complicated antenna structures if the diffraction field of the structure is known. Receiving slot and horn antennas in cylindrical, spherical and conical bodies are simple examples where the outlined principle can be applied.

REFERENCE

[1] J.A. Stratton, Electromagnetic Theory, McGraw-Hill Book Co., Inc. New York, 1941, pp. 250.

HENDRICUS BREMMER

The Pulse Solution Connected with the Sommerfeld Problem for a Dipole in the Interface between Two Dielectrics

SUMMARY. The field of a vertical dipole above the horizontal interface between two homogeneous dielectrics is investigated when the transmitter current suddenly jumps at $t = 0$ from zero to a constant value. This field is determined straightforwardly, without using the corresponding time-harmonic solution which constitutes the starting point in other publications, but the same results are obtained as in the latter. It is also shown that the expression found by de Hoop and Frankena for the upper medium (of lower dielectric constant) can be transformed into that derived by Van der Pol and Levelt by a proper deformation of an integration path. All final integrals can be considered as continuous sets of elementary axially symmetric modes which satisfy the general scalar wave equation for arbitrary non-harmonic time dependence. The Fresnel reflection coefficient for plane waves also determines the reflection amplitudes for these time dependent modes, and is useful for a physical interpretation of the results. A part of the field can be ascribed to an analogue of the Zenneck wave.

1. INTRODUCTION. Sommerfeld's classical problem concerning the time-harmonic field of a transmitting dipole near the plane interface between two infinite homogeneous half spaces leads to a transcendental expression described by an integral involving a Bessel function. The rigorous solution cannot be reduced to an elementary function, even in the simplest case of a transmitter and receiver both situated in the interface itself. However, it was first noticed by Van der Pol [1] that the corresponding pulse solution, describing the field produced when the transmitter current jumps suddenly from zero to a constant value at $t = 0$, does degenerate to a very simple algebraic function when the transmitter and receiver are situated in the interface and the media are assumed to be lossless. All complications connected with dispersion are then avoided.

The more difficult evaluation of the field for the pulse solution in the case of a transmitter and/or receiver raised above the plane interface has stimulated much interest since then. The assumption of lossless media has been maintained. The discussion usually refers to a transmitting dipole still assumed in the interface, but concerns the effect of the finite distance of the receiver from the interface. We mention in particular an investigation by Pekeris and Alterman [2] which leads to expressions involving elliptic integrals. The possibility of reducing the pulse solution to elliptic integrals has been worked out explicitly by Van der Pol and Levelt [3] in a publication which constitutes the last, posthumous work of Van der Pol. The same problem has been treated in a different way by de Hoop and Frankena [4], who take an arbitrary time function for the transmitter current and discuss the field in the upper medium (having the lower dielectric constant). The specialization of their results to the pulse solution gives rather simple elliptic integrals which prove to be equivalent to those derived by Van der Pol and Levelt.

All these authors start from the well known time-harmonic solution derived by Sommerfeld. The pulse solution can be derived from the latter with the aid of the inversion of a Laplace transform. The method developed by Van der Pol and Levelt requires a rather complicated analysis depending on contour integrals over multi-valued integrands. These complications are partly overcome by de Hoop and Frankena by the introduction of a two-dimensional Fourier transform with respect to two space variables. In this paper we show how the final solution of the pulse problem may also be obtained directly, without knowing the solution for the time-harmonic case.

2. FORMULATION OF THE PROBLEM CONCERNING THE PULSE SOLUTION. Our problem concerns two homogeneous non-magnetic half spaces $z > 0$ and $z < 0$ characterized by real refractive indices n_1 and n_2 respectively. We assume $n_2 > n_1$, in accordance with the practical application in which the upper medium $z > 0$ is to be identified with the air, and the lower medium $z < 0$ with the lossless dielectric earth. We further restrict ourselves to the field generated by a vertical infinitesimal dipole at $x = 0$, $y = 0$, $z = h_1$; its current jumps at $t = 0$ from zero to a constant value which is normalized so as to correspond to a unit value of the product of current and antenna length. Maxwell's equations read as follows for the upper medium (in Gaussian units):

$$\operatorname{curl} \vec{E} + \frac{1}{c}\frac{\partial \vec{H}}{\partial t} = 0 ,$$

$$\operatorname{curl} \vec{H} - \frac{n_1^2}{c}\frac{\partial \vec{E}}{\partial t} = \frac{4\pi}{c}\,\delta(x)\,\delta(y)\,\delta(z-h_1)\,U(t)\,\vec{u}_z ,$$

where $\vec{u}_z$ is a unit vector in the vertical direction, and $U(t)$ Heaviside's unit function (zero for negative, and unity for positive argument), and for the lower medium:

$$\operatorname{curl} \vec{E} + \frac{1}{c}\frac{\partial \vec{H}}{\partial t} = 0 \ ,$$

$$\operatorname{curl} \vec{H} - \frac{n_2^2}{c}\frac{\partial \vec{E}}{\partial t} = 0 \ .$$

In either medium the solution can be put in the following form:

$$\vec{E} = -\frac{n^2}{c}\frac{\partial \Pi}{\partial t}\vec{u}_z + c\int_{-\infty}^{t} d\tau \operatorname{grad}\operatorname{div}\{\Pi(x, y, z, \tau)\vec{u}_z\} \ ,$$

$$\vec{H} = n^2 \operatorname{curl}(\Pi \vec{u}_z) \ ,$$

where the Hertzian scalar Π satisfies the wave equations:

$$\left.\begin{aligned} \left(\Delta - \frac{n_1^2}{c^2}\frac{\partial^2}{\partial t^2}\right)\Pi &= -\frac{4\pi}{cn_1^2}\,\delta(x)\,\delta(y)\,\delta(z-h_1)\,U(t) \quad &\text{for } z > 0 \\ \left(\Delta - \frac{n_2^2}{c^2}\frac{\partial^2}{\partial t^2}\right)\Pi &= 0 \quad &\text{for } z < 0 \end{aligned}\right\} \qquad (1)$$

The expressions for the primary field are obtained by setting $n_1 = n_2$. Solution of equations (1) then gives

$$\Pi_{pr} = \frac{U(t - \frac{n_1}{c}R)}{c\,n_1^2\,R} \ , \qquad (2)$$

in which

$$R = \{x^2 + y^2 + (z-h_1)^2\}^{\frac{1}{2}} = \{\rho^2 + (z-h_1)^2\}^{\frac{1}{2}}$$

represents the distance from the source dipole to the point of observation. The general solution to our problem must satisfy, apart from (1), the radiation condition at infinity, and the condition that the horizontal components of $\vec{E}$ and $\vec{H}$ shall be continuous along the interface $z=0$. This involves:

$$n_2\Pi \text{ and } \frac{\partial \Pi}{\partial z} \text{ continuous at } z = 0 \ . \qquad (3)$$

3. THE BASIC REPRESENTATION OF THE PRIMARY FIELD OF THE PULSE SOLUTION. The following expression for Π_{pr} will be the starting point for the subsequent analysis.

$$\Pi_{pr} = -\frac{i}{2\pi c^2 n_1}\int_L \frac{d\cos\gamma}{\sqrt{\{t - \frac{n_1}{c}|z-h_1|\cos\gamma\}^2 - \frac{n_1^2}{c^2}\rho^2\sin^2\gamma}} \ , \qquad (4)$$

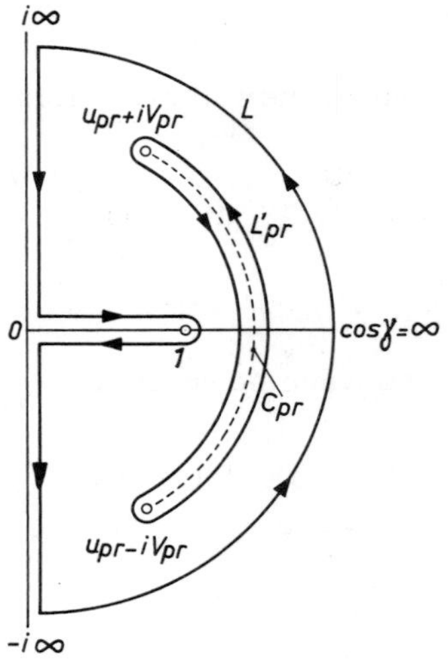

Figure 1. Contours used in the representation of the primary field.

where the path of integration is the contour shown in Fig. 1, consisting of the infinite semicircle of the right-hand half of the cos γ-plane, of lines parallel to the imaginary axis at an infinitesimal distance from it, and of a loop enclosing the positive axis up to the point +1, again an infinitesimal distance from this axis. The square root is defined as having the value $+\infty$ at $\cos\gamma = \infty$, and with the aid of a cross-cut connecting its zeros and not intersecting L.

We must first show that the expression (4) is indeed equivalent to (2). For $t^2 < n_1^2 R^2/c^2$ the zeros of the radicand prove to be on the real axis at:

$$\cos\gamma_{\substack{max,\,pr\\ min,\,pr}} = \frac{ct|z-h_1| \pm \rho\sqrt{n_1^2R^2 - c^2t^2}}{n_1 R^2} \cdot \qquad (5)$$

The maximum value of $\cos\gamma_{max,pr}$ as a function of t is found at $t = (n_1/c)|z - h_1|$ and is equal to $+1$, so both zeros are always outside L. Hence the right-hand side of (4) vanishes for $t^2 < n_1^2R^2/c^2$, the integrand then having no singularities whatever inside L.

We next consider $t^2 > n_1^2R^2/c^2$. The zeros of the radicand now are situated at $\cos\gamma = u_{pr} \pm iv_{pr}$, with

$$u_{pr} = \frac{ct|z-h_1|}{n_1R^2}, \qquad v_{pr} = \frac{\rho\sqrt{c^2t^2 - n_1^2R^2}}{n_1R^2} \qquad (6)$$

If $t < 0$ both zeros are in the left part of the cos γ-plane and thus once again outside L. Hence (4) vanishes if $t^2 < n_1^2R^2/c^2$ and if $t < 0$, i.e. for $t < n_1R/c$, as it should.

We next pass to the remaining case $t > n_1R/c$. Here, both zeros $\cos\gamma = u_{pr} \pm iv_{pr}$ are inside L, and the contour of integration can be contracted to a loop L' enclosing, at an infinitesimal distance, a cross-cut C_{pr} (see Fig. 1) which connects the zeros. The radicand can now be represented by

$$\frac{n_1^2}{c^2} R^2 \{(\cos\gamma - u_{pr})^2 + v_{pr}^2\} \quad ,$$

which involves the following expression for the right-hand side of (4):

$$-\frac{i}{2\pi c n_1^2 R} \int_{L'} \frac{d\cos\gamma}{\sqrt{(\cos\gamma - u_{pr})^2 + v_{pr}^2}} \quad .$$

The evaluation of the elementary integral leads to expression (2). This concludes our verification of the validity of (4) for all values of t.

4. THE RESOLUTION OF THE EXPRESSION FOR THE PRIMARY FIELD. The expression $\sqrt{(\cos\gamma - u_{pr})^2 + v_{pr}^2}$ occurring in (4) may be considered, in view of (6), as a special case of a term of the general form

$$\frac{1}{\sqrt{\{t - t_0 \mp \frac{n_1}{c}\cos\gamma(z - z_0)\}^2 - \frac{n_1^2}{c^2}\sin^2\gamma\,\rho^2}} \quad . \tag{7}$$

Each such contribution satisfies the scalar wave equation

$$\left(\Delta - \frac{n_1^2}{c^2}\frac{\partial^2}{\partial t^2}\right)\Pi = 0 \ ,$$

as may easily be verified.

The propagation properties of the wave functions (7) are illustrated by the locus of their infinities. For real $\cos\gamma$ between -1 and 1 these infinities are situated along the moving cones:

$$\sin\gamma\rho \mp \cos\gamma(z - z_0) = -\frac{c}{n_1}(t - t_0)$$

and

$$\sin\gamma\rho \pm \cos\gamma(z - z_0) = \frac{c}{n_1}(t - t_0) \ ,$$

the tops of which move either upward toward $z \to \infty$ (upper signs), or downward toward $z \to -\infty$ (lower signs), if $\cos\gamma > 0$.

In the case of (4), however, all contributions depend on complex values of $\cos\gamma$. A wave function of the type (7) then becomes infinite, at a given moment, only for a special set (z, ρ), that is along a special circle around the z-axis. The propagation direction of the latter with respect to z corresponds, for $\mathrm{Re}\cos\gamma > 0$, to that of the top of the above cone. In fact, a somewhat tedious, though elementary, evaluation of the zeros of the denominator of (7) shows that the circle in question constitutes the intersection of the moving plane

$$z - z_0 = \pm\frac{c(t - t_0)}{n_1}\,\frac{\mathrm{Re}\cos\gamma}{(\mathrm{Re}\cos\gamma)^2 + (\mathrm{Re}\sin\gamma)^2} \tag{8}$$

with the fixed cone

$$\frac{\rho}{z} = \pm \frac{|\mathrm{Re}\,\sin\gamma|}{\mathrm{Re}\,\cos\gamma} \quad . \tag{9}$$

Hence, the circle moves upward (upper sign) or downward (lower sign) as the case may be. For $\mathrm{Re}\cos\gamma > 0$ all wave functions (7) must accordingly be interpreted as rising or descending waves respectively.

In view of these remarks the expression (4) for the primary field is composed of rising waves above the level of the transmitter ($|z - h_1| = z - h_1$), and of descending waves in the slab $0 < z < h_1$ ($|z - h_1| = h_1 - z$), in complete agreement with the geometrical situation.

5. THE REFLECTED AND REFRACTED FIELD GENERATED BY THE PRIMARY PULSE. The descending primary waves arriving at the interface $z = 0$ are split there in reflected waves traveling upward in the space $z > 0$ with $n = n_1$, and refracted waves traveling downward by penetrating in the space $z < 0$ with $n = n_2$. The former are the elements of the secondary or reflected field Π_{sec} in the upper space, the latter those of the total diffracted field Π in the lower space. The above considerations suggest the following representations for these fields

$$\Pi_{sec} = -\frac{i}{2\pi c^2 n_1} \int_L \frac{\mathscr{R}(\gamma)\, d\cos\gamma}{\sqrt{\{t - \frac{n_1}{c}(h_1 + z)\cos\gamma\}^2 - \frac{n_1^2}{c^2}\rho^2 \sin^2\gamma}}, \quad (z > 0) \tag{10a}$$

$$\Pi = -\frac{i n_1}{2\pi c^2 n_2^2} \int_L \frac{\{1 + \mathscr{R}(\gamma)\}\, d\cos\gamma}{\sqrt{\{t - \frac{n_1}{c} h_1 \cos\gamma + \frac{n_2}{c} z\cos\gamma'\}^2 - \frac{n_2^2}{c^2}\sin^2\gamma' \rho^2}} \quad (z < 0) \tag{10b}$$

in which γ' is defined by

$$n_1 \sin\gamma = n_2 \sin\gamma' \tag{11}$$

The additional condition $\mathrm{Re}\cos\gamma' > 0$ along L fixes $\cos\gamma'$ completely, and guarantees that (10b) is composed of descending waves (see the preceding section), just as (10a) is composed of rising waves. The sign of $\cos\gamma'$ thus defined along L is in accordance with the following general definition to be used henceforth. With a view to the further calculations it is more convenient to express the above condition as:

$$\cos\gamma' = \sqrt{1 - \frac{n_1^2}{n_2^2} + \frac{n_1^2}{n_2^2}\cos^2\gamma} \quad , \tag{12}$$

where the sign of the square root is defined by a cross cut along the part of the imaginary $\cos\gamma$-axis between $-i\sqrt{(n_2^2/n_1^2)-1}$ and $i\sqrt{(n_2^2/n_1^2)-1}$, together with the assumption that $\cos\gamma'$ and $\cos\gamma$ are identical at infinity.

The correctness of (10), for a proper choice of the function $\mathscr{R}(\gamma)$, is demonstrated as follows. First of all both (10a) and (10b) satisfy the relevant homogeneous wave equations since they are composed of contributions of the type (7). Next, if we add the primary field (4) for $z = 0$ to the corresponding value of the secondary field given by (10a) we obtain the following expression for the total field immediately above the interface:

$$\Pi = -\frac{i}{2\pi c^2 n_1}\int_L \frac{\{1+\mathscr{R}(\gamma)\}\, d\cos\gamma}{\sqrt{(t-\frac{n_1}{c}h_1\cos\gamma)^2-\frac{n_1^2}{c^2}\rho^2\sin^2\gamma}}\,, \quad z=+0\,.$$

On the other hand, if we substitute $z = 0$ in (10b) and apply Snell's relation (11), we obtain an expression for the field immediately beneath the interface $(z = -0)$ which differs from the former only by an additional factor n_1^2/n_2^2. Hence, the first boundary condition (3), viz. the continuity of $n^2\Pi$ at $z = 0$, is satisfied automatically. In order to take the remaining boundary condition, the continuity of $\partial\Pi/\partial z$, into account, we must differentiate (a) the total field in the upper space described by the sum of (4) and (10a), and (b) the total field in the lower space described by (10b) at $z = 0$:

$$\left(\frac{\partial\Pi}{\partial z}\right)_{z=+0} = \frac{i}{2\pi c^3}\int_L \frac{(t-\frac{n_1}{c}h_1\cos\gamma)\cos\gamma\{1-\mathscr{R}(\gamma)\}}{\{(t-\frac{n_1}{c}h_1\cos\gamma)^2-\frac{n_1^2}{c^2}\rho^2\sin^2\gamma\}^{\frac{3}{2}}}\, d\cos\gamma\,,$$

$$\left(\frac{\partial\Pi}{\partial z}\right)_{z=-0} = \frac{i n_1}{2\pi c^3 n_2}\int_L \frac{(t-\frac{n_1}{c}h_1\cos\gamma)\cos\gamma'\{1+\mathscr{R}(\gamma)\}}{\{(t-\frac{n_1}{c}h_1\cos\gamma)^2-\frac{n_2^2}{c^2}\rho^2\sin^2\gamma'\}^{\frac{3}{2}}}\, d\cos\gamma\,.$$

Obviously, the continuity of $\partial\Pi/\partial z$ is then guaranteed, if we assume, apart from (11), the relation:

$$\cos\gamma\,\{1-\mathscr{R}(\gamma)\} = \frac{n_1}{n_2}\cos\gamma'\,\{1+\mathscr{R}(\gamma)\}\,.$$

This leads to the familiar expression

$$\mathscr{R}(\gamma) = \frac{n_2\cos\gamma - n_1\cos\gamma'}{n_2\cos\gamma + n_1\cos\gamma'} = \frac{n_2^2\cos\gamma - n_1\sqrt{n_2^2-n_1^2+n_1^2\cos^2\gamma}}{n_2^2\cos\gamma + n_1\sqrt{n_2^2-n_1^2+n_1^2\cos^2\gamma}} \tag{13}$$

for the reflection coefficient for a plane or cylindrical wave incident at an angle γ with the normal to the interface. This reflection coefficient thus maintains its significance for wave functions of the form (7). Substituting this coefficient in (10a) we obtain elliptic integrals for the complete field of the pulse solution. The latter then satisfies all the necessary boundary conditions, that at infinity (radiation condition) being in accordance with the fact that (10a) is composed of rising waves.

6. DERIVATION OF DE HOOP AND FRANKENA'S EXPRESSION FOR THE SECONDARY FIELD. The contours of (10) can be contracted so as to obtain simpler results. We then have to know the singularities of the integrand inside L. For the secondary field represented by (10a), they can be classified as follows:

(a) Zeros of the radicand entering explicitly into (10a). These are of the same type as the corresponding quantities $\cos\gamma = u_{pr} \pm i v_{pr}$ (compare (5) and (6)) connected with the primary field. We accordingly discriminate between $t^2 < (n_1^2/c^2)R^2_{sec}$ leading to the real zeros given by

$$\cos\gamma_{\substack{max, sec\\ min, sec}} = \frac{ct(z + h_1) \pm \rho\sqrt{n_1^2 R^2_{sec} - c^2t^2}}{n_1 R^2_{sec}}, \tag{14}$$

and $t^2 > (n_1^2/c^2)R^2_{sec}$ giving two complex zeroes $\cos\gamma = u_{sec} \pm i v_{sec}$, where

$$u_{sec} = \frac{ct(z + h_1)}{n_1 R^2_{sec}}, \qquad v_{sec} = \frac{\rho\sqrt{c^2t^2 - n_1^2 R^2_{sec}}}{n_1 R^2_{sec}}. \tag{15}$$

The new parameter $R_{sec} = \{\rho^2 + (z + h_1)^2\}^{\frac{1}{2}}$ is the distance from the image of the transmitter with respect to the interface, to the point of observation.

(b) Singularities of $\mathscr{R}(\gamma)$, i.e. the branch points $\cos\gamma = \pm i\sqrt{(n_2^2/n_1^2) - 1}$ connected with the definition (12) of $\cos\gamma'$, and possible zeros γ_0 of the denominator of (13). A necessary condition for such zeros is obtained from the relationship

$$n_2^2 \cos\gamma_0 = -n_1\sqrt{n_2^2 - n_1^2 + n_1^2\cos^2\gamma_0},$$

whence:

$$\cos\gamma_0 = \pm\frac{n_1}{\sqrt{n_1^2 + n_2^2}}.$$

However, in view of the cross-cut for $\cos\gamma'$ introduced above, the corresponding values of γ' are given by

$$\cos\gamma_0' = \pm\frac{n_2}{\sqrt{n_1^2 + n_2^2}},$$

so that the denominator $n_2 \cos\gamma_0 + n_1 \cos\gamma_0'$ of $\mathscr{R}(\gamma_0)$ becomes different from zero for both signs. Hence the denominator of the reflection coefficient has no zeros. This is a consequence of our special choice of the cross-cut of $\cos\gamma'$. If, for example, we had taken the latter along the parts of the imaginary $\cos\gamma$-axis outside the interval between $i\sqrt{(n_2^2/n_1^2) - 1}$ and $-i\sqrt{(n_2^2/n_1^2) - 1}$, with $\cos\gamma = \cos\gamma'$ along the right part of the semi-infinite circle, a zero would exist at $\cos\gamma_0 = -n_1/(n_1^2 + n_2^2)^{\frac{1}{2}}$. This zero corresponds to the propagation direction of the well-known surface wave connected with lossy media.

The following singularities of the integrand of (10a) thus remain:

(1) the branchpoints $\cos\gamma = \pm i\sqrt{(n_2^2/n_1^2) - 1}$ of $\cos\gamma'$ which are just outside L.

(2) the real zeros $\cos\gamma_{\substack{\max,\,\mathrm{sec}\\ \min,\,\mathrm{sec}}}$ for $t^2 < (n_1^2/c^2)R^2_{\mathrm{sec}}$. As with $\cos\gamma_{\substack{\max,\,\mathrm{pr}\\ \min,\,\mathrm{pr}}}$ these zeros are always situated on the real axis to the left of $\cos\gamma = +1$ (cf. section 3) and are thus also outside L.

(3) the complex zeros $\cos\gamma = u_{\mathrm{sec}} \pm i v_{\mathrm{sec}}$ for $t^2 > (n_1^2/c^2)R^2_{\mathrm{sec}}$. Since $z + h_1$ is positive the real part u_{sec} has the same sign as t. Therefore, these zeros are to the left of the imaginary axis, once again outside L, if $t < 0$. For $t > 0$ they are inside L.

Singularities inside L thus only exist if both $t^2 > (n_1^2/c^2)R^2_{\mathrm{sec}}$ and $t > 0$, i.e. if $t > (n_1/c)R_{\mathrm{sec}}$. This is the only case in which (10a) does not vanish, in accordance with the finite propagation velocity of the disturbance. The contour L can then be contracted to L'_{sec} (see Fig. 2) which encloses, at an infinitesimal distance, a

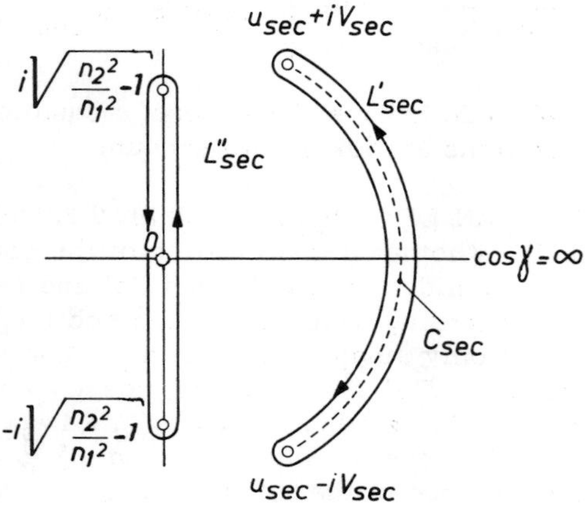

Figure 2. Contours used in the representation of the secondary field.

line C_{sec} connecting the only two singularities $u_{sec} - iv_{sec}$ and $u_{sec} + iv_{sec}$. The latter contour integral can be reduced to twice the line integral along C_{sec}. Replacing the radicand of (10a) by

$$(n_1^2/c^2)R_{sec}^2\{(\cos\gamma - u_{sec})^2 + v_{sec}^2\} ,$$

we thus find:

$$\Pi_{sec} = \frac{U(t-\frac{n_1}{c}R_{sec})}{2\pi i c n_1^2 R_{sec}} \int_{L'_{sec}} \frac{\mathscr{R}(\gamma)\, d\cos\gamma}{\sqrt{(\cos\gamma - u_{sec})^2 + v_{sec}^2}} \tag{16a}$$

$$= \frac{U(t-\frac{n_1}{c}R_{sec})}{\pi i c n_1^2 R_{sec}} \int_{u_{sec}-iv_{sec}}^{u_{sec}+iv_{sec}} \frac{\mathscr{R}(\gamma)\, d\cos\gamma}{\sqrt{(\cos\gamma - u_{sec})^2 + v_{sec}^2}} . \tag{16b}$$

The sign of the square root in (16b) corresponds to that of its value along the right-hand side of the path of integration.

A final substitution $\cos\gamma = u_{sec} - iv_{sec}\cos\psi$ transforms (16) into

$$\Pi_{sec} = \frac{U(t-\frac{n_1}{c}R_{sec})}{\pi c n_1^2 R_{sec}} \int_0^{\pi} \mathscr{R}\{\cos^{-1}(u_{sec} - iv_{sec}\cos\psi)\}\, d\psi ,$$

which is equivalent to:

$$\Pi_{sec} = \frac{2U(t-\frac{n_1}{c}R_{sec})}{\pi c n_1^2 R_{sec}} \cdot \mathrm{Re} \int_0^{\pi/2} \mathscr{R}\{\cos^{-1}(u_{sec} - iv_{sec}\cos\psi)\}\, d\psi , \tag{17}$$

which is identical to de Hoop and Frankena's equation (3.14) if the different normalizations are taken into account.

7. DERIVATION OF VAN DER POL AND LEVELT'S EXPRESSION FOR THE SECONDARY FIELD. Another transformation of the contour L in (10a) leads to the expression derived by Van der Pol and Levelt for the secondary field. According to the preceding section, when $t > (n_1/c)R_{sec}$, the only singularities of the integrand of (10a) are the branch points of $\cos\gamma'$, situated at $\cos\gamma = \pm i\sqrt{(n_2^2/n_1^2) - 1}$, together with the complex zeros $\cos\gamma = u_{sec} \pm iv_{sec}$ which are situated inside L'_{sec}. The contour integral along L'_{sec} can therefore be replaced by the difference of the integral round the complete circle at infinity (taken in the positive direction), and the integral taken along a new contour L''_{sec} enclosing, at an infinitesimal distance, the cut

of $\cos\gamma'$ along the part of the imaginary axis between the mentioned branch points (see Fig. 2).

The first integral, at infinity, depends on the asymptotic value of the integrand of (16a), viz. $\mathscr{R}(\gamma)/\cos\gamma$. In its turn $\mathscr{R}(\gamma)$ tends to the limiting value $(n_2^2 - n_1^2)/(n_2^2 + n_1^2)$. The integral at infinity thus gives:

$$\frac{U(t - \frac{n_1}{c} R_{sec})}{c\, n_1^2} \frac{(n_2^2 - n_1^2)}{(n_2^2 + n_1^2)} \frac{1}{R_{sec}} . \tag{18}$$

The integral along L''_{sec} can be reduced to a line integral along the cut of $\cos\gamma'$. The positive value of $\cos\gamma'$ at the right-hand side of this cut, and its negative value at the left-hand side mean that the value $\mathscr{R}(\gamma)$ of the reflection coefficient at the right-hand side transforms into $1/\mathscr{R}(\gamma)$ at the other side. The corresponding reduction from the contour integral to the line integral along the cut results, after subtraction from (18), in the following expression for the secondary field:

$$\Pi_{sec} = \tag{19}$$

$$\frac{U(t - \frac{n_1}{c} R_{sec})}{c\, n_1^2 R_{sec}} \left[\frac{n_2^2 - n_1^2}{n_2^2 + n_1^2} + \frac{i}{2\pi} \int_{-i\sqrt{\frac{n_2^2}{n_1^2} - 1}}^{i\sqrt{\frac{n_2^2}{n_1^2} - 1}} \frac{\mathscr{R}(\gamma) - \frac{1}{\mathscr{R}(\gamma)}}{\sqrt{(\cos\gamma - u_{sec})^2 + v_{sec}^2}} \, d\cos\gamma \right].$$

If we substitute equation (11) into this expression, write the denominator of the integrand as in (10a), and change the variable to $s = i n_1 \cos\gamma$, we obtain:

$$\Pi_{sec} = \frac{U(t - \frac{n_1}{c} R_{sec})}{c\, n_1^2} \left[\frac{(n_2^2 - n_1^2)}{(n_2^2 + n_1^2)} \frac{1}{R_{sec}} + \right. \tag{20}$$

$$\left. + \frac{2i}{\pi} \frac{n_1^2 n_2^2}{(n_2^2 - n_1^2)} \int_{-\sqrt{n_2^2 - n_1^2}}^{\sqrt{n_2^2 - n_1^2}} \frac{s\sqrt{n_2^2 - n_1^2 - s^2}\, ds}{\{(n_1^2 + n_2^2)s^2 + n_1^4\} \sqrt{-R_{sec}^2 s^2 + 2ict(z+h_1)s + c^2t^2 - n_1^2\rho^2}} \right]$$

Adding equation (2) we obtain an expression for the total field in $z > 0$ which proves to be identical with the equation (4.2) derived by Van der Pol and Levelt, at least in the special case $h_1 = 0$ considered by these authors.

8. A SIMPLIFICATION OF THE EXPRESSION FOR THE PULSE SOLUTION IN THE LOWER MEDIUM. This solution is much more complicated than that for the upper half space, because the transmitter source had been assumed to be in the latter so that the energy must suffer a refraction before penetrating into the lower halfspace. However, as shown in Van der Pol and Levelt's article, the final results can still be described by elliptic integrals in the limiting case of a transmitter in the interface $(h_1 \to 0)$.

The integral (10b) depends explicitly on the variables $\cos\gamma$ and $\cos\gamma'$ which are connected by Snell's relation (11). It proves to be useful to introduce $\cos\gamma'$ as a new integration variable, using the transformation formula

$$\cos\gamma = \sqrt{\frac{n_2^2}{n_1^2}\cos^2\gamma' - \frac{n_2^2}{n_1^2} + 1} \quad . \tag{21}$$

The sign of $\cos\gamma$ will be fixed, for any given value of $\cos\gamma'$, if we agree that $\cos\gamma$ and $\cos\gamma'$ coincide at infinity while $\cos\gamma$ should have a cross-cut along the part

$$-\sqrt{1-\frac{n_1^2}{n_2^2}} < \cos\gamma' < \sqrt{1-\frac{n_1^2}{n_2^2}}$$

of the real axis in the $\cos\gamma'$-plane. It is easily verified that the contour L in the $\cos\gamma$-plane does transform to an identical curve in the $\cos\gamma'$-plane, though the individual points on L in the former plane are shifted to other points in the $\cos\gamma'$-plane. For instance, the original branch points of $\cos\gamma'$ at $\cos\gamma = \pm i\sqrt{(n_2^2/n_1^2)-1}$ are at $\cos\gamma' = 0$, whereas the former origin $\cos\gamma = 0$ is split into the two branch points of $\cos\gamma$ at $\cos\gamma' = \pm\sqrt{1-n_1^2/n_2^2}$.

The final transformation of (10b) into a new integral in terms of $\cos\gamma'$ can be conveniently performed with the aid of the following two relations resulting from (21) and (13):

$$d(\cos\gamma) = \frac{n_2^2}{n_1^2}\,\frac{\cos\gamma'}{\cos\gamma}\,d(\cos\gamma') \;,$$

$$\frac{1+\mathscr{R}(\gamma)}{\cos\gamma} = \frac{2n_2}{n_2\cos\gamma + n_1\cos\gamma'}$$

$$= \frac{2n_1 n_2}{(n_2^2-n_1^2)}\;\frac{n_2\sqrt{n_2^2\cos^2\gamma' - n_2^2 + n_1^2} - n_1^2\cos\gamma'}{(n_1^2+n_2^2)\cos^2\gamma' - n_2^2} \quad .$$

We thus obtain:

$$\Pi = -\frac{i n_2}{\pi c(n_2^2-n_1^2)}\int_L \frac{\{n_2\sqrt{n_2^2\cos^2\gamma' - n_2^2+n_1^2} - n_1^2\cos\gamma'\}\cos\gamma'\,d(\cos\gamma')}{\{(n_1^2+n_2^2)\cos^2\gamma' - n_2^2\}\sqrt{\{ct - h_1\sqrt{n_2^2\cos^2\gamma' - n_2^2+n_1^2} + n_2 z\cos\gamma'\}^2 - n_2^2\rho^2\sin^2\gamma'}} \tag{22}$$

for $z < 0$.

As before, the position of the singularities of the integrand is critical. The singularities formed by the zeros of the radicand in the denominator are now determined by an equation of the fourth degree in $\cos \gamma'$ which only reduces to an equation of the second degree when $h_1 = 0$. In the following analysis we shall therefore restrict ourselves to a transmitting dipole in the interface, that is to the special case also considered by Van der Pol and Levelt. The general case $h_1 \neq 0$ cannot be described by elliptic integrals. Even the simplified case $h_1 = 0$ involves complications not occurring in the upper medium. In particular we shall have to discriminate between the periods before and after the arrival of the "main wave" at $t = (n_2/c)r = (n_2/c)(\rho^2 + z^2)^{\frac{1}{2}}$. By the latter we understand a wave that propagates directly towards the point of observation at a distance r with the phase velocity c/n_2 which is characteristic for the lower medium.

9. A FIRST REPRESENTATION OF THE PULSE SOLUTION IN THE LOWER MEDIUM, AFTER THE ARRIVAL OF THE MAIN WAVE. The singularities of the integrand of (22) that remain for $h_1 = 0$ are the following:

(a) the branchpoints

$$\cos \gamma' = \pm \sqrt{1 - \frac{n_1^2}{n_2^2}}$$

which form the ends of the cross-cut of the radicand in the numerator;

(b) the zeros of the radicand in the denominator; for $h_1 = 0$ these are given by

$$\cos \gamma' = \frac{-ctz \pm i\rho\sqrt{c^2t^2 - n_2^2 r^2}}{n_2 r^2} \qquad (23)$$

$$= u' + iv', \text{ say.}$$

We observe that the other factor in the denominator does involve no pole, its zero being connected with a simultaneous zero of the numerator (compare the corresponding remark concerning (10a) in section 6).

Obviously, both zeros (23) are complex for $t > n_2 r/c$, that is after the arrival of the main wave, the period to be investigated in this section. Since $z < 0$ we further have $u' > 0$ and $v' \neq 0$. Hence both zeros (23) are inside L, and form the only singularities enclosed by this contour. Therefore, the latter can be contracted to a loop L' surrounding a cross-cut C' which connects, inside L, $u' - iv'$ with $u' + iv'$ (see Fig. 3). As in section 6 the integration round L' can be further reduced to twice the line integral along C' itself. Replacing the radicand in the denominator of (22) by the alternative form

$$n_2^2 r^2 \{(\cos \gamma' - u')^2 + v'^2\} ,$$

we obtain

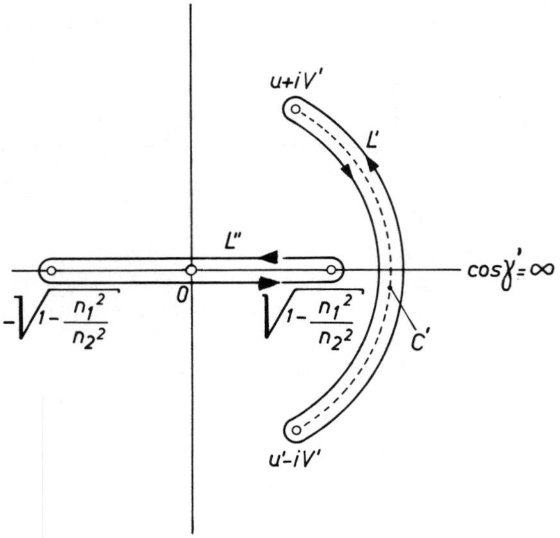

Figure 3. Contours used for the representation of the field in the lower medium, after the arrival of the main wave.

$$\Pi = -\frac{2i}{\pi c(n_2^2 - n_1^2)r} \int_{u'-iv'}^{u'+iv'} \frac{\{n_2\sqrt{n_2^2\cos^2\gamma' - n_2^2 + n_1^2} - n_1^2\cos\gamma'\}\cos\gamma'}{\{(n_1^2 + n_2^2)\cos^2\gamma' - n_2^2\}\sqrt{(\cos\gamma' - u')^2 + v'^2}}\, d\cos\gamma' \quad , (24)$$

for $z < 0,\ t > n_2 r/c,\ h_1 = 0$,

which may be written

$$\Pi = -\frac{i}{\pi c n_1^2 r} \int_{u'-iv'}^{u'+iv'} \frac{1 - \mathscr{R}(\gamma')}{\sqrt{(\cos\gamma' - u')^2 + v'^2}}\, d\cos\gamma'$$

$$= \frac{1}{c n_1^2 r}\left\{1 + \frac{i}{\pi} \int_{u'-iv'}^{u'+iv'} \frac{\mathscr{R}(\gamma')}{\sqrt{(\cos\gamma' - u')^2 + v'^2}}\, d\cos\gamma'\right\}$$

for $z < 0,\ t > n_2 r/c,\ h_1 =$

where

$$\mathscr{R}(\gamma') = \frac{n_2\sqrt{n_2^2\cos^2\gamma' - n_2^2 + n_1^2} - n_1^2\cos\gamma'}{n_2\sqrt{n_2^2\cos^2\gamma' - n_2^2 + n_1^2} + n_1^2\cos\gamma'} .$$

Substituting $\cos\gamma' = u' - iv'\cos\psi$ we obtain

$$\Pi = \frac{1}{c\,n_1^2 r}\left[1 - \frac{1}{\pi}\int_0^{\pi} \mathscr{R}\{\cos^{-1}(u' - iv'\cos\psi)\}\,d\psi\right] =$$

$$= \frac{1}{c\,n_1^2 r}\left[1 - \frac{2}{\pi}\cdot \mathrm{Re}\int_0^{\pi/2} \mathscr{R}\{\cos^{-1}(u' - iv'\cos\psi)\}\,d\psi\right] \qquad (25)$$

$$(z < 0,\ t > n_2 r/c,\ h_1 = 0)$$

which corresponds to the equation (17) for the secondary field in the upper medium.

10. ANOTHER REPRESENTATION OF THE PULSE SOLUTION IN THE LOWER MEDIUM, AFTER THE ARRIVAL OF THE MAIN WAVE. The connection existing in the upper medium between de Hoop and Frankena's expression and that derived by Van der Pol and Levelt occurs in the corresponding version for the lower medium. In fact, for $t > n_2 r/c$, the only singularities of the integrand of (22) that are outside L consist of the branchpoints $\pm\sqrt{1 - n_1^2/n_2^2}$ on the real $\cos\gamma'$-axis. The contour integral along L' can therefore be considered as the difference of: (a) the corresponding integral along the complete circle at infinity (in the positive direction) and (b) the integral along the contour L'' (see Fig. 3) enclosing, at an infinitesimal distance, the cut of $\cos\gamma$ (which connects the mentioned branchpoints along the real $\cos\gamma'$-axis). The further reduction of the latter integral to a line integral along this cut results in the following expression if, moreover, we return to the original denominator of (22), and substitute $s = n_2\cos\gamma'$:

$$\Pi = \frac{2}{c}\left[\frac{1}{(n_1^2+n_2^2)r} - \frac{n_2^2}{\pi(n_2^2-n_1^2)}\int_{-\sqrt{n_2^2-n_1^2}}^{\sqrt{n_2^2-n_1^2}} \frac{\sqrt{n_2^2-n_1^2-s^2}\,s\,ds}{\{(n_1^2+n_2^2)s^2 - n_2^4\}\sqrt{r^2s^2+2ctzs+c^2t^2-n_2^2\rho^2}}\right] \quad (26)$$

$$\text{for } z < 0,\ t > n_2 r/c,\ h_1 = 0 .$$

This equation, corresponding to Van der Pol and Levelt's expression (4.5), is particularly useful for checking the boundary condition of the continuity of $n^2\Pi$ at the interface. For $z = 0$ the integrand becomes odd, leading to a vanishing integral. Hence we obtain:

$$\Pi = \frac{2}{c(n_1^2 + n_2^2)\rho} \qquad \text{for } z = -0,\ t > n_2\rho/c,\ h_1 = 0 .$$

On the other hand, the integral in (20) vanishes for the same reason when the observation point in the upper space tends to the interface ($z = +0$; $h_1 = 0$). Therefore:

$$\Pi_{sec} = \frac{1}{c n_1^2} \frac{(n_2^2 - n_1^2)}{(n_2^2 + n_1^2)\rho} \quad \text{for } z=+0,\ t > n_2\rho/c,\ h_1 = 0.$$

When adding the primary field $1/(c n_1^2 \rho)$ we thus find:

$$n_1^2 \Pi_{z=+0,\ h_1=0,\ t>n_2\rho/c} = n_2^2 \Pi_{z=-0,\ h_1=0,\ t>n_2\rho/c}$$

as it should.

11. THE SINGULARITIES DETERMINING THE PULSE SOLUTION IN THE LOWER MEDIUM BEFORE THE ARRIVAL OF THE MAIN WAVE. The situation is now characterized by $t < n_2 r/c$. Hence (at least for $t > -n_2 r/c$) the zeros $\cos\gamma'$ constituting branchpoints of the denominator of (22) become, instead of (23), two real quantities:

$$\cos\gamma'_{1,0} = \frac{-ctz + \rho\sqrt{n_2^2 r^2 - c^2t^2}}{n_2 r^2} \quad \text{and}$$

$$\cos\gamma'_{2,0} = \frac{-ctz - \rho\sqrt{n_2^2 r^2 - c^2t^2}}{n_2 r^2} \quad . \tag{27}$$

Both parameters are smaller than unity. This might suggest the field vanishes since L then encloses no singularities whatever, the zeros of the denominator and the branchpoints $\pm\sqrt{1 - n_1^2/n_2^2}$ being on a part of the real axis outside L. However, a part of the contour L approaches to within an infinitesimal distance the real axis. Hence L might possibly enclose singularities which (being complex for any finite value of h_1) approach the real axis for $h_1 \to 0$. It is therefore necessary to investigate the situation in which a finite value of h_1 tends to zero. This can be performed as follows.

We start from the equation of the fourth degree which determines the zeros of the denominator for a finite value of h_1. The expansion with respect to h_1 of the relation obtained by equating this denominator to zero starts with:

$$f_0^2(\cos\gamma') - 2h_1^2\{f_0(\cos\gamma') + 2\rho^2\sin^2\gamma'\}(\cos^2\gamma' - 1 + \frac{n_1^2}{n_2^2}) + \ldots = 0\ , \tag{28}$$

where

$$f_0(\cos\gamma') \equiv r^2\cos^2\gamma' + \frac{2ctz}{n_2}\cos\gamma' + \frac{c^2t^2}{n_2^2} - \rho^2\ .$$

The equation $f_0 = 0$ is satisfied by the above limiting zeros (27). The corresponding four zeros of the general equation (28) can be written:

$$\cos\gamma'_1 = \cos\gamma'_{1,0} + \frac{2h_1\rho\sin\gamma'_{1,0}}{f_0'(\cos\gamma'_{1,0})}\sqrt{\cos^2\gamma'_1 - 1 + \frac{n_1^2}{n_2^2}} + \ldots\ ,$$

$$\cos\gamma_2' = \cos\gamma_{2,0}' + \frac{2h_1\rho\sin\gamma_{2,0}'}{f_0'(\cos\gamma_{2,0}'}\sqrt{\cos^2\gamma_2' - 1 + \frac{n_1^2}{n_2^2}} + \cdots ,$$

$$\cos\gamma_3' = \cos\gamma_{1,0}' - \frac{2h_1\rho\sin\gamma_{1,0}'}{f_0'(\cos\gamma_{1,0}')}\sqrt{\cos^2\gamma_1' - 1 + \frac{n_1^2}{n_2^2}} + \cdots ,$$

$$\cos\gamma_4' = \cos\gamma_{2,0}' - \frac{2h_1\rho\sin\gamma_{2,0}'}{f_0'(\cos\gamma_{2,0}')}\sqrt{\cos^2\gamma_2' - 1 + \frac{n_1^2}{n_2^2}} + \cdots .$$

We have to check whether these roots actually make the denominator radicand of (22) zero, since the condition of being a zero of (28) is only necessary, not sufficient. First of all the two quantities $\cos\gamma_2'$ and $\cos\gamma_3'$ may be excluded at once for the following reason. Without loss of generality we assume the real quantities $\sin\gamma_{1,0}'$ and $\sin\gamma_{2,0}'$ to be positive. Further, it can easily be shown that $f'(\cos\gamma_{1,0}') > 0$ and $f'(\cos\gamma_{2,0}') < 0$. The expansions for $\cos\gamma_2'$ and $\cos\gamma_3'$ are therefore of the type

$$\begin{aligned}\cos\gamma_2' &= \cos\gamma_{2,0}' - \alpha h_1\sqrt{\cos^2\gamma_2' - 1 + \frac{n_1^2}{n_2^2}} + \cdots ,\\ \cos\gamma_3' &= \cos\gamma_{1,0}' - \beta h_1\sqrt{\cos^2\gamma_2' - 1 + \frac{n_1^2}{n_2^2}} + \cdots ,\end{aligned} \tag{30}$$

with positive coefficients α and β. A possible singularity of $\cos\gamma_2'$ e.g., just above (below) the real $\cos\gamma'$-axis could only exist if $\cos^2\gamma_2' < 1-n_1^2/n_2^2$. In view of the definition of the sign of $\cos\gamma$ the square root in (30) would then be positive imaginary (negative imaginary) which is inconsistent with the position just assumed for $\cos\gamma_2'$. The impossibility of a singularity of the type $\cos\gamma_3'$ is shown in the same way.

On the other hand the signs occurring in the expressions (29) for $\cos\gamma_1'$ and $\cos\gamma_4'$ prove to be consistent with a position immediately above as well as immediately below the real axis. We still have to investigate whether these latter quantities actually make the radicand in the denominator of (22) zero. We therefore expand this denominator with respect to h_1, while substituting the expressions (29) for $\cos\gamma_1'$ and $\cos\gamma_4'$ respectively. The zero-order term vanishes indeed, but, taking into account (27), the linear term in h_1 proves to be proportional to

$$-ct\rho + \left\{2\rho r^2\frac{\sin\gamma_{1,0}'}{f_0'(\cos\gamma_{1,0}')} - z\right\}\sqrt{n_2^2r^2 - c^2t^2} \quad \text{for } \gamma_1' , \tag{31a}$$

and to

$$-ct\rho + \left\{ 2\rho r^2 \frac{\sin \gamma'_{2,0}}{f'_0(\cos \gamma'_{2,0})} + z \right\} \sqrt{n_2^2 r^2 - c^2 t^2} \quad \text{for } \gamma'_4 \; . \tag{31b}$$

The condition (31b) for $\cos \gamma'_4$ can be put in the form

$$-ct\rho - |z| \sqrt{n_2^2 r^2 - c^2 t^2} = -2\rho r^2 \frac{\sin \gamma'_{2,0}}{f'_0(\cos \gamma'_{2,0})} \sqrt{n_2^2 r^2 - c^2 t^2} \; ,$$

which can never be satisfied, the left-hand side being negative and the right-hand side positive. The only possibility remaining for a singularity that is complex as soon as h_1 becomes finite thus concerns a zero of the type $\cos \gamma'_1$. According to (31a) it has to satisfy the relation:

$$ct\rho - |z| \sqrt{n_2^2 r^2 - c^2 t^2} = 2\rho r^2 \frac{\sin \gamma'_{1,0}}{f'_0(\cos \gamma'_{1,0})} \sqrt{n_2^2 r^2 - c^2 t^2} \; . \tag{32}$$

The right-hand side being positive, we obtain a first necessary condition, viz.

$$ct\rho > |z| \sqrt{n_2^2 r^2 - c^2 t^2} \; ,$$

which is equivalent to:

$$|z| < ct/n_2 \; .$$

If this condition is satisfied we still require the moduli of both sides of (32) to be equal, which can be checked by squaring both sides.

We have thus shown that the only possibility of having a singularity of the denominator of (22) for which $\cos \gamma'_1$ becomes complex as soon as h_1 differs from zero is realized by a set of two zeros near $\cos \gamma'_{1,0}$, the one just above and the other just below the real $\cos \gamma'$-axis. The necessary and sufficient conditions for the existence of such a pair of singularities are:

$$\text{(a)} \quad |z| < ct/n_2 \; ,$$

$$\text{(b)} \quad \cos^2 \gamma'_{1,0} < 1 - \frac{n_1^2}{n_2^2} \; .$$

In order to arrive at more convenient form for these combined conditions we consider the function

$$G(t) \equiv n_2 r^2 \left\{ \sqrt{1 - \frac{n_1^2}{n_2^2}} - \cos \gamma'_{1,0}(t) \right\} \; .$$

Since the quantity $\cos \gamma'_{1,0}$ is positive throughout the lower medium, a positive value of $G(t)$ guarantees the realization of condition (b). In view of (a) we are only interested in the interval

$$\frac{n_2|z|}{c} < t < \frac{n_2 r}{c} \quad .$$

The function G assumes the following values at the ends of this interval

$$G\left(\frac{n_2|z|}{c}\right) = r^2(\sqrt{n_2^2 - n_1^2} - n_2) \quad ,$$

$$G\left(\frac{n_2 r}{c}\right) = r(\sqrt{n_2^2 - n_1^2}\,r - n_2|z|) \quad .$$

The first quantity is negative. The second one is also negative if and only if $r/|z| < n_2/\sqrt{n_2^2 - n_1^2}$, i.e. if $n_1 r > n_2 \rho$. Further, $G'(t)$ is not zero within the interval under consideration. Hence $G(t)$ is negative throughout this interval if $n_1 r > n_2 \rho$, which makes complex $\cos\gamma_1'$ -singularities impossible for $h_1 \to 0$. If $n_1 r < n_2 \rho$, the sign of $G(t)$ is different at the ends of the interval; $G(t)$ is then positive between the zero of $G(t)$, at $t = t_{arr}$ say, and $t = n_2 r/c$. We find:

$$t_{arr} = \frac{n_1 \rho + \sqrt{n_2^2 - n_1^2}\,|z|}{c} \tag{33}$$

The final result can now be put in the following form. Singularities of the denominator radicand in (22) which are complex for $h_1 \to 0$ occur in the interval $n_2|z|/c < t < n_2 r/c$ only if simultaneously

$$\left.\begin{array}{l} n_1 r < n_2 \rho \;, \\ t_{arr} < t < \dfrac{n_2 r}{c} \end{array}\right\} \tag{34}$$

12. A REPRESENTATION OF THE PULSE SOLUTION IN THE LOWER MEDIUM BEFORE THE ARRIVAL OF THE MAIN WAVE.

According to the preceding section complex singularities $\cos\gamma_1'$ for the denominator radicand in (22) only exist if $t < n_2 r/c$ and $h_1 \to 0$, under the condition (34). If not, all singularities of the integrand of (22), both those originating from the radicand just mentioned and those from that in the numerator, are real and smaller than unity. The contour L encloses no singularity whatever, so the field Π is zero.

In the domain characterized by (34), on the other hand, we have two complex singularities S_1 and S_2 near $\cos\gamma' = \cos\gamma_{1,0}'$. The path of integration here passes between the latter and the real axis, leading to the contour L of Fig. 4. Since we are dealing with the limiting case $h_1 \to 0$, involving infinitesimal distances of S_1 and

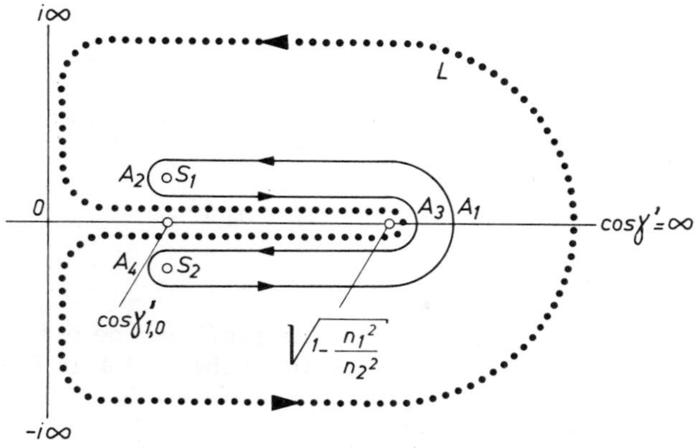

Figure 4. CONTOURS USED FOR THE REPRESENTATION OF THE FIELD IN THE LOWER MEDIUM, BEFORE THE ARRIVAL OF THE MAIN WAVE.

S_2 from the real axis, this contour can be contracted to the double-folded loop $A_1 \to A_2 \to A_3 \to A_4 \to A_1$ (see Fig. 4), which surrounds the three branch points S_1, S_2 and $(1 - n_1^2/n_2^2)^{\frac{1}{2}}$ at an infinitesimal distance. The signs of the square roots D of the denominator, and N of the numerator, are defined with the aid of these branch points and the condition that either radicand tends (apart from a positive factor) to $\cos\gamma'$ along the infinite circle. These definitions are taken into account when choosing the following phases ϕ for D, N and D/N respectively along the four branches composing the loop $A_1A_2A_3A_4A_1$:

A_1A_2	$\phi(D) = 0$	$\phi(N) = \pi/2$	$\phi(N/D) = \pi/2$
A_2A_3	π	$\pi/2$	$-\pi/2$
A_3A_4	π	$-\pi/2$	$-3\pi/2$
A_4A_1	2π	$-\pi/2$	$-5\pi/2$

We first discuss the contribution due to the second term in brackets in the numerator of (22). This contribution is proportional to 1/D, and independent of N . According to (35) it has equal signs along A_2A_3 and A_3A_4 ; the integrations along these branches, which are covered in opposite directions, therefore cancel each other. For the same reason the contribution from A_4A_1 cancels that from A_1A_2 .

Hence, no final contribution whatever remains from the term in question after the complete contraction of L to the four-folded loop $A_1 \to A_2 \to A_3 \to A_4 \to A_1$.

The remaining part of (22) results from a contribution proportional to N/D . It has opposite signs along A_1A_2 and A_2A_3 . In view of the direction of integration the corresponding contributions add up to twice the contribution originating from A_2A_3 alone (with a phase $-\pi/2$ for N/D). In the same way, the contributions from A_3A_4 and A_4A_1 also add up to twice that of A_4A_1 alone (with a phase $-5\pi/2$ for N/D). Finally the joint contribution from $A_1A_2A_3$ equals that of $A_3A_4A_1$, the phases of N/D differing by 2π . The total contribution from the second term in (22) thus equals four times the contribution along A_2A_3 which, in its turn, can be represented in the limit $h_1 = 0$ by a line integral along the real axis from $\cos\gamma'_{1,0}$ to $(1 - n_1^2/n_2^2)^{\frac{1}{2}}$. In this way the expression (22) reduces to the following equation, if we substitute $S = \cos\gamma'$:

$$\Pi = -\frac{4n_2^2}{\pi c(n_2^2-n_1^2)} \int_{\frac{-ctz+\rho\sqrt{n_2^2r^2-c^2t^2}}{r^2}}^{\sqrt{n_2^2-n_1^2}} \frac{\sqrt{n_2^2-n_1^2-s^2}\, s\, ds}{\{(n_1^2+n_2^2)s^2-n_2^4\}\sqrt{(ct+zs)^2+\rho^2s^2-n_2^2\rho^2}}$$

$$\text{for } z<0\,,\ h_1=0\,,\ n_1r<n_2\rho\,,\ t_{arr}<t<n_2r/c\,. \qquad (36)$$

This is equivalent to formula (4.4) derived by Van der Pol and Levelt.

As in Section 10, we may derive as a check the limiting value for $z=0$, i.e., $\rho = r$. Substituting $w = s^2$ we get an elementary integral the evaluation of which yields

$$\Pi = \frac{2n_2^2}{c(n_2^4-n_1^4)} \left\{ \frac{1}{\rho} - \frac{n_1 n_{12}}{n_2\sqrt{c^2t^2 - n_{12}^2\rho^2}} \right\},$$

$$\text{for } z=-0\,,\ n_1\rho/c<t<n_2\rho/c\,,\ h_1=0\,, \qquad (37)$$

where n_{12} is defined by $1/n_{12}^2 = 1/n_1^2 + 1/n_2^2$; c/n_{12} represents the propagation velocity of a surface wave propagating along the interface.

The result (37) has to be compared with the corresponding limit, according to (20), for the secondary field in the upper medium. For the domain under consideration the radicand $-\rho^2s^2 + c^2t^2 - n_1^2\rho^2$ occurring in (20) has two branch points, at $s = \pm\sqrt{c^2t^2/\rho^2 - n_1^2}$, within the integration interval. The phase of the square root has to be taken in accordance with the definitions in terms of the original variable $\cos\gamma = s/(in_1)$. We infer that the square root has to be considered as positive imaginary, positive real and negative imaginary in the three successive intervals:

$$-\sqrt{n_2^2 - n_1^2} < s < -\sqrt{c^2t^2/\rho^2 - n_1^2} \ ,$$

$$-\sqrt{c^2t^2/\rho^2 - n_1^2} < s < \sqrt{c^2t^2/\rho^2 - n_1^2}$$

$$\sqrt{c^2t^2/\rho^2 - n_1^2} < s < \sqrt{n_2^2 - n_1^2} \ .$$

Taking into account the corresponding values of the integrand, we finally arrive at

$$\Pi_{sec} = \frac{2n_2^4}{cn_1^2(n_2^4 - n_1^4)} \left\{ \frac{1}{\rho} - \frac{n_1 n_{12}}{n_2\sqrt{c^2t^2 - n_{12}^2\rho^2}} \right\}$$

$$\text{for } z = +0 \ , \quad n_1\rho/c < t < n_2\rho/c \ , \quad h_1 = 0 \ .$$

Comparing this result with (37) we see that $n^2\Pi$ is indeed continuous at $z = 0$.

13. GENERAL CONSIDERATIONS CONCERNING THE PULSE SOLUTION IN THE LOWER MEDIUM

This solution cannot be described by a single expression holding throughout the complete medium. The separation into two regions $n_1r < n_2\rho$ and $n_1r > n_2\rho$ is particularly striking, though quite understandable: only the former region can be reached by rays which, after leaving the transmitter and traveling just above the interface with the propagation velocity c/n_1 of the upper medium, are refracted somewhere at grazing incidence into the lower medium. Such refracted rays propagate through the latter in a direction making the critical angle arc $\sin(n_1/n_2)$ with the normal to the interface. Such refracted rays never penetrate into the other region $n_1r > n_2\rho$.

These two regions are separated by the line OC of Fig. 5. On the other hand, the main waves propagating away from O with a propagation velocity c/n_2 cover a region limited by the circle $ct = n_2r$. Further, the utmost points reached at the time of observation by the above-mentioned refracted rays prove to be situated on the line $t = t_{arr}$, if t_{arr} is defined by (33). We thus arrive at the following classification of domains with non-vanishing field, which we have labelled by the same roman figures as used in Pekeris and Alterman's paper:

(a) region IV, fixed by the inequalities $ct > n_2r$ and $n_1r > n_2\rho$. Points in this region have been passed by the main wave, but can never be reached by refracted rays. Pulse solution described by (24) and (26).

(b) region III, fixed by $ct > n_2 r$, $n_1 r < n_2 \rho$ and $t > t_{arr}$, containing points which have been reached by both a main wave (along OP) and by a refracted ray (along OP'P). The expressions (24) and (26) also apply here.

(c) region II, fixed by $ct_{arr} < ct < n_2 r$, and $n_1 r < n_2 \rho$, containing points which have already been passed by a refracted ray OP'P, but not yet by a main wave. The solution is represented by (36).

As observed by Pekeris and Alterman, the wave front $n_2 r = ct$ limiting the region passed by the main waves is associated with a logarithmic field singularity. This follows from the fact that, for $n_2 r = ct$, the radicand in the denominator of (24), (26) and (36) has a double zero which is either within the integration interval or at one or both of its ends.

Another interesting point concerns the recognizability of a Zenneck wave. Such a wave propagates in the lower medium in a direction making an angle arc $\tan(n_1/n_2)$, the so-called Brewster angle, with the normal to the interface. It is a refracted wave which emerges from an incident wave (arriving from the upper medium) without an accompanying reflected wave. The contribution of such a wave is recognized from the part of (24) that is independent of the square root in the numerator. This contribution is given by an elementary non-elliptic integral. Its evaluation leads to the second term of the following formula in which the other, elliptical, contribution (represented by the first term) is expressed with the aid of a quantity $\mathscr{R} - 1/\mathscr{R}$ also entering in the representation (19) for the secondary field in the upper medium:

$$\Pi = \frac{1}{2\pi c\, n_1^2 r} \int_0^{\pi} \left(\mathscr{R} - \frac{1}{\mathscr{R}}\right)_{\gamma' = \cos^{-1}(u' - iv' \cos\psi')} d\psi' -$$

$$- \frac{2n_1^2}{c(n_2^4 - n_1^4)} \left[\frac{1}{r} - \frac{n_2 n_{12}}{2cn_1} \left\{ \frac{1}{\sqrt{(t+t_{Br})(t+t'_{Br})}} - \frac{1}{\sqrt{(t-t_{Br})(t-t'_{Br})}} \right\} \right]$$

$$\text{for } z < 0 \ , \quad t > n_2 r/c \ , \quad h_1 = 0 \ , \qquad (37)$$

where

$$t_{Br} = \frac{n_{12}(n_1 \rho + n_2 |z|)}{c\, n_1} \ , \quad t'_{Br} = \frac{n_{12}(-n_1 \rho + n_2 |z|)}{c\, n_1} \ .$$

The second elementary part of (37) becomes infinite, in the region $ct > n_2 r$ of its validity, only along the circle(represented by B in the meridional section of Fig. 5) of contact of the sphere $ct = n_2 r$ with the conical surface $t = t_{Br}$. This constitutes the locus of rays through 0 that make an angle equal to the Brewster angle with the normal to the interface. The elementary non-elliptic contribution to the field may therefore be ascribed to the analogue of a Zenneck wave.

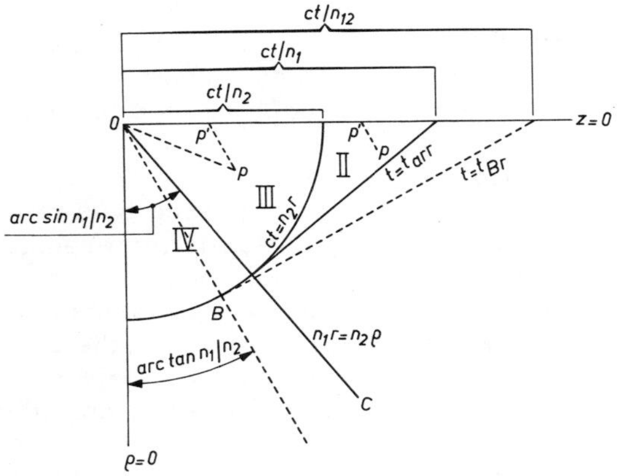

Figure 5. DIVISION OF THE HALF SPACE OF THE LOWER MEDIUM

14. A GENERAL INTERPRETATION OF THE RESULTS, AND THEIR CONNECTION WITH THE TIME-HARMONIC SOLUTION

All results arrived at depend on contour integration of elementary solutions of the type (7) satisfying the scalar wave equation. The propagating character of these solutions is evident from the locus of their infinities, the movement of this locus being described by (8) and (9). These latter relations can also be interpreted as follows. For a given situation (ρ, z, t) of the observation point they determine a complex direction γ which is of dominating numerical importance since its contribution becomes infinite at the point in question. Thus, the zeros $\cos\gamma = u_{sec} \pm i v_{sec}$ determining the secondary field according to (16b), fix two complex directions with the following property—a disturbance leaving the image source at $\rho = 0$, $z = -h_1$, $t = 0$ along these directions, and propagating in accordance with (8) and (9), reaches the mentioned observation point at the right time.

The question arises how the pulse solution is connected with the well-known classical time-harmonic solution of the Sommerfeld problem. In the quoted literature the pulse solution had been derived as an inverse Laplace transform of this latter solution. It must therefore be possible to obtain the time-harmonic solution from our present pulse solution by applying a direct Laplace transform. This may be performed as follows. The pulse solution in any region, $\Pi_{\Sigma}(t)$ say, constitutes the response to an exciting dipole moment of the transmitter given, as a function of the time, by Heaviside's unit function $U(t)$. A periodically varying dipole moment $\exp(-i\omega t)$ can be expressed in terms of $U(t)$ as:

$$e^{-i\omega t} = -i\omega \int_{-\infty}^{\infty} d\tau \, U(t-\tau) e^{-i\omega\tau}$$

for real ω . The integral is to be considered as a Cesaro limit. The response to this harmonically varying dipole moment is:

$$\Pi_\omega = -i\omega \int_{-\infty}^{\infty} d\tau \, \Pi_\zeta(t-\tau) e^{-i\omega\tau} .$$

An individual contribution of the type (7), for instance

$$\frac{1}{\sqrt{\left(t - \frac{n}{c}\cos\gamma z\right)^2 - \frac{n^2}{c^2}\sin^2\gamma \rho^2}} ,$$

then corresponds to a contribution to the time-harmonic solution that is given, if not vanishing, by

$$-i\omega \int_{-\infty}^{\infty} d\tau \frac{e^{-i\omega\tau}}{\sqrt{(t-\tau-\frac{n}{c}\cos\gamma z)^2 - \frac{n^2}{c^2}\sin^2\gamma\rho^2}} =$$

$$= -2\pi\omega e^{-i\omega(t-\frac{n}{c}\cos\gamma z)} J_0(\frac{n}{c}\omega \sin\gamma\rho) . \qquad (38)$$

This identity holds provided that $\mathrm{Im}\cos\gamma > 0$, $\mathrm{Im}\sin\gamma \to 0$, $\omega > 0$, whereas the right-hand side vanishes for $\mathrm{Im}\cos\gamma < 0$ and $\omega > 0$. The correctness of (38) can be shown with the aid of the following relation taken from the theory of Bessel functions:

$$\int_{-k}^{k} d\tau \frac{e^{-i\omega\tau}}{\sqrt{k^2-\tau^2}} = \pi J_0(k\omega) .$$

This expression (38) enables us to transform our results concerning the pulse solution into corresponding expressions for the time-harmonic solution, insofar as the integration path of the former happens to be independent of the observation point. For instance, we obtain from (10a) the following representation for the secondary field if L' represents the part of L above the real axis:

$$\Pi_{\omega,\,sec} = \frac{i\omega e^{-i\omega t}}{c^2 n_1} \int_L \mathscr{R}(\gamma) J_0\left(\frac{n_1}{c}\omega\rho\sin\gamma\right) e^{i\frac{\omega}{c}n_1(h_1+z)\cos\gamma} d\cos\gamma . \qquad (39)$$

Passing to the new variable $\lambda = (n_1/c)\omega\sin\gamma$ the integration path transforms simply into the real axis of the λ-plane. We then arrive at a well-known representation of the classical Sommerfeld theory, in particular since the integration could be reduced to the positive axis.

As another example we mention that the last term of (37) corresponds to a contribution

$$- \frac{\pi n_1 n_2 n_{12}}{c^2 (n_2^4 - n_1^4)} \omega e^{-i\omega(t + \frac{n_2 n_{12}}{c n_1} z)} H_0^{(1)} \left(\frac{n_{12}}{c} |\omega| \rho \right) ,$$

which we recognize at once as a cylindrical Zenneck wave.

It proves to be impossible to represent the solution in waves which are either only attenuated in the ρ-direction, or only in the z-direction. The former would be contained in a line integral along the real axis of the cos γ-plane, the latter along the imaginary axis and a part of the real axis; the latter situation is approximated by the contour L . On the other hand, an integration along the contour L'_{sec} of Fig. 2, entering in the time-harmonic solution corresponding to (16a), clearly involves waves which are attenuated in both directions. The various equivalent expressions occurring in our analysis for one and the same field show that such a field can be composed of contributions with an exponential attentuation in very different ways.

REFERENCES

1. Balth. Van der Pol, Trans. I. R. E. AP 4 (1956), 288.
2. C. L. Pekeris and Z. Alterman, J. Appl. Phys. 28(1957), 1317.
3. Balth. Van der Pol and A. H. M. Levelt, Ned. Akad. Wetensch. Proc. Ser. A 63 = Indag. Math. 22(1960), 254.
4. A. T. DeHoop and H. J. Frankena, Appl. Sc. Res. B 8(1960), 369.

CALVIN H. WILCOX

The Mathematical Foundations of Diffraction Theory

Contents

§1. INTRODUCTION. It is a basic problem of electromagnetic theory to determine the diffracted electromagnetic wave which is produced when a prescribed wave, propagating in a homogeneous isotropic dielectric medium, strikes a prescribed metallic obstacle. The purpose of this paper is to provide the foundations for a mathematical theory of this problem, comprising its precise formulation as a mathematical problem, together with theorems guaranteeing the existence and uniqueness of the solution and theorems describing its functional properties (integrability, domains of dependence on data, existence of derivatives, etc.).

The following notation and terminology is used throughout the paper. The region in which the electromagnetic waves propagate is represented by a domain (= open connected set)

$$\Omega \subset R^3 \;=\; \text{Three dimensional Euclidean space.}$$

The time interval in which the electromagnetic field to be determined is denoted by

$$I = \{t : 0 < t < T\}$$

and

$$Q = \Omega \times I$$

is used to denote the cylindrical domain in R^4 (= space-time) in which the diffracted electromagnetic field is to be determined. The letters E and H are used to represent the electric and magnetic fields, respectively. The usual Gibbs' notation of vector analysis is used.

The electromagnetic fields are required to satisfy the

Condition of Locally Finite Energy:

$$\int_0^T \int_{\Omega \cap K} (|E(x,t)|^2 + |H(x,t)|^2)\,dxdt < \infty \quad \text{for each cube } K \subset R^3 , \tag{1. 1}$$

where x represents a point, and dx a volume element, in R^3.

In the usual formulation of the diffraction problem E and H are required to be continuous, or piece-wise continuous, in Q so that (1. 1) is automatically satisfied unless K intersects $\partial\Omega$, the boundary of Ω. For this reason (1. 1) is sometimes called the "edge condition". It has been used to ensure the uniqueness of the solution when the surface $\partial\Omega$ has a sharp edge [1], and is usually omitted when $\partial\Omega$ is smooth.

The existence theorem presented here makes use of a limiting procedure involving a sequence of approximate solutions to the diffraction problem. In discussing the existence of the limit it is essential to have a class of solutions that form a complete function space. The energy norm (1. 1) suggests consideration of the Lebesgue space

$$L_2(Q) = \{\Phi : \Phi(x,t) \text{ Lebesgue measurable in } Q, \int_Q |\Phi(x,t)|^2 dxdt < \infty\},$$

which is complete by the Riesz-Fischer theorem [8, p. 59]. For this reason, electromagnetic fields with

$$E \in L_2(Q) \ , \quad H \in L_2(Q) \ ,$$

are defined and studied here.

It may be objected that such fields do not provide a suitable model for an electromagnetic field, since they are defined only almost everywhere in Q. However, the quantity of energy in a given (measurable) set $S \subset Q$ is well-defined for fields in $L_2(Q)$ by

$$\int_S (|E|^2 + |H|^2)\,dxdt \ .$$

Moreover, from the point of view of physics $E(x,t)$ and $H(x,t)$ may always be replaced by their averages over a small set containing (x, t) and these quantities are also well-defined for fields in $L_2(Q)$.

The following conditions, in addition to (1. 1), are imposed on the electromagnetic field in the usual formulation of the diffraction problem.

Maxwell's Equation:

$$\left.\begin{aligned} \nabla\times H - \frac{\partial E}{\partial t} &= F \\ \nabla\times E + \frac{\partial H}{\partial t} &= G \end{aligned}\right\} \text{ in } Q , \tag{1. 2}$$

The Initial Conditions:

$$E(x, 0) = E_0(x) , \quad H(x, 0) = H_0(x) \text{ in } \Omega , \tag{1. 3}$$

The Boundary Condition:

$$N(x) \times E(x, t) = 0 \quad \text{for } (x, t) \in \partial\Omega \times I . \tag{1. 4}$$

The functions F and G represent the prescribed sources of the electromagnetic field, and E_0 and H_0 represent its prescribed initial values. Hence the four fields (F, G, E_0, H_0) represent the "data" of the diffraction problem. $N(x)$ represents a vector normal to the boundary $\partial\Omega$ at the point x. The boundary condition (1. 4) is appropriate for a boundary that is a perfect electrical conductor (a metal in most applications).

It is necessary to reformulate conditions (1. 2), (1. 3) and (1. 4), which are not meaningful for fields E and H in $L_2(Q)$. This is done by extending the domains of definition of the operators $\nabla\times$ and $\partial/\partial t$ to certain complete subspaces of $L_2(Q)$. The precise statement of the diffraction problem and the fundamental theorems concerning it are given in §3 and §4, after a discussion of the appropriate function spaces and their properties in §2.

In the final formulation of the diffraction problem Ω is an arbitrary domain, and the sources F, G and initial values E_0, H_0 are subjected to the single requirement of being locally square-integrable. This degree of generality is of interest both for the theory and for the applications, where one frequently has to deal with irregular boundaries (obstacles with sharp edges or vertices, etc.) and with incident fields bearing discontinuities or other singularities.

The theory presented here makes essential use of concepts from abstract functional analysis, both in its formulation and in its development. Expositions of the relevant concepts and theorems may be found in Riesz-Nagy [8] and Hille-Phillips [3].

The electromagnetic diffraction problem belongs to the class of initial-boundary value (or mixed) problems in the theory of partial differential equations. The beginnings of a general theory of such problems have been developed during the last decade. The principal contributors are O. A. Ladyzhenskaya and M. I. Vishik in the U. S. S. R. J.-L. Lions in France, and R. S. Phillips in the U. S. A. Expositions of their work, and references to the original literature, may be found in [4], [5], [6], [7], and [10]. The present work provides an application to the electromagnetic diffraction problem of ideas and techniques pioneered by these authors. An application of Ladyzhenskaya's work to the diffraction problem has been announced by I. I. Rohkind [9]. Unfortunately, this paper has not been accessible to me for comparison with the present work.

§2. PRELIMINARY THEOREMS ON FUNCTION SPACES. Several function spaces are considered in this section, including functions with domain of definition Ω and range in R^1 or R^3 and functions with domain of definition I and range in $L_2(\Omega)$ or some other Hilbert space. In order to give a concise and unified discussion of these spaces the following notations are used in this section only.

R^n = n-dimensional Euclidean space,

$x = (x_1, \ldots, x_n)$ = a point in R^n,

$dx = dx_1 \cdots dx_n$ = element of Lebesgue measure in R^n,

D = an arbitrary domain (open connected set) in R^n,

H = a separable Hilbert space over the real number field,

$(f, g)_H$ = the scalar product in H,

$\|f\|_H = (f, f)_H^{\frac{1}{2}}$ = the norm in H.

All the function spaces that are used here consist of classes of functions $u : D \to H$, defined on D, with values in H. In subsequent sections D is Ω, Q, or I and H is one of a number of Hilbert spaces that are defined below.

To begin, let

$$C^m(D, H) = \{u: u \text{ has continuous derivatives of order } k \text{ in } D \text{ for } 0 \le k \le m\},$$

$$C_0^m(D, H) = \{u : u \in C^m(D, H) \text{ and has compact support } \subset D\},$$

and

$$C^m(\bar{D}, H) = \{u : u \in C^m(\Sigma, H) \text{ for some open set } \Sigma \supset \bar{D}\}.$$

The definitions of continuity and derivative for functions with values in H are the same as for real-valued functions [3, Ch. III]. Thus

$$v(x) = \frac{\partial u(x)}{\partial x_i} \text{ means } \lim_{h\to 0} \left\| \frac{u(x_1, \ldots, x_i+h, \ldots, x_n) - u(x)}{h} - v(x) \right\|_H = 0$$

and

$$u(x) \text{ is continuous at } x_0 \Leftrightarrow \lim_{x\to x_0} \| u(x) - u(x_0) \|_H = 0 \ .$$

The space

$$H = R^3 \quad \text{with} \quad (x, y)_H = x \cdot y = x_1 y_1 + x_2 y_2 + x_3 y_3$$

is a separable Hilbert space, and the corresponding function classes occur so frequently below that the special notations

$$C^m(D) = C^m(D, R^3) \ , \quad C_0^m(D) = C_0^m(D, R^3) \ , \text{ etc.}$$

are used.

Some concepts and facts from the theory of Lebesgue integration for functions with values in H are needed below. The theory parallels closely the standard theory for real-valued functions; see [3, Ch. III] for a systematic exposition. The discussion here is limited to a statement of the basic definitions and theorems.

Definition. A function $u: D \to H$ is measurable if and only if $(u(x), h)_H$ is Lebesgue measurable on D for every $h \in H$, [3, pp. 72-73].

Definition (Bochner integral). A function $u: D \to H$ is (Bochner) integrable if and only if it is measurable and [3, p. 80]

$$\int_D \| u(x) \|_H dx < \infty \ .$$

The Bochner integral of u is then defined by [3, p. 77 and p. 80].

$$\left(\int_D u(x)\, dx, h \right)_H = \int_D (u(x), h)_H dx \ ,$$

and satisfies

$$\left\| \int_D u(x)\, dx \right\|_H \leq \int_D \| u(x) \|_H dx \ .$$

The function spaces

$$L_2(D, H) = \{u : u \text{ is measurable}, \int_D \| u(x) \|_H^2 dx < \infty \}$$

occur frequently below. They are Hilbert spaces with respect to the scalar product [3, pp. 88-89]

$$(u, v)_{L_2(D, H)} = \int_D (u(x), v(x))_H dx .$$

In particular, $L_2(D, R)$ is the usual Lebesgue space of square-integrable real-valued functions on D, and

$$L_2(D) = L_2(D, R^3)$$

with scalar product

$$(u, v)_{L_2(D)} = \int_D \{u_1(x) v_1(x) + u_2(x) v_2(x) + u_3(x) v_3(x)\} dx ,$$

is the space of square-integrable vector fields on D. The spaces of locally square-integrable functions, defined by

$$L_2^{loc}(D, H) = \{u: u \text{ is defined on } D,\ u \in L_2(K \cap D, H) \text{ for every bounded measurable } K \subset R^n\}$$

are also used below.

Several subspaces of $L_2^{loc}(D, H)$, consisting of functions that admit a differential operator, are needed below. To define this concept let Λ be a linear partial differential operator of order m, with constant coefficients, and let Λ^+ denote its formal adjoint.

<u>Definition.</u> Let $u \in L_2^{loc}(D, H)$. Then Λu is said to exist in $L_2^{loc}(D, H) \Leftrightarrow$ there exists a function $v \in L_2^{loc}(D, H)$ such that

$$\int_D (u(x), \Lambda^+ \phi(x))_H dx = \int_D (v(x), \phi(x))_H dx$$

for all $\phi \in C_0^m(D, H)$. In this case Λu is defined to be v.

Note that Λu is uniquely determined, because the spaces $C_0^m(D, H)$ are dense in $L_2(D \cap K, H)$. (Cf. [3, p. 86]).

Now consider the linear subspace of $L_2(D, H)$ defined by

$$L_2(\Lambda, D, H) = \{u: u \in L_2(D, H) \text{ and } \Lambda u \in L_2(D, H)\} .$$

If a scalar product is defined by

$$(u, v)_{L_2(\Lambda, D, H)} = \int_D \{(u(x), v(x))_H + (\Lambda u(x), \Lambda v(x))_H\} dx$$

it becomes a Hilbert space. (This is easily verified.)

The notation

$$L_2(\Lambda, D) = L_2(\Lambda, D, R^3)$$

is used. In particular, $L_2(\nabla\times, \Omega)$ is the space of square-integrable vector fields having a square-integrable curl. It plays an important part in the formulation of the diffraction problem.

The familiar vector identity

$$\int_\Omega (A \cdot \nabla\times B - B \cdot \nabla\times A)\, dx = \int_{\partial\Omega} N \times A \cdot B\, dS \tag{2.1}$$

shows that $\nabla\times$ is its own formal adjoint. Thus

$$\int_\Omega A \cdot \nabla\times \Phi\, dx = \int_\Omega \nabla\times A \cdot \Phi\, dx \tag{2.2}$$

for all $A \in L_2(\nabla\times, \Omega)$ and all $\Phi \in C_0^1(\Omega)$.

If A satisfies the boundary condition (1.4), $N \times A = 0$ on $\partial\Omega$, then (2.1) implies (2.2) for all B. This suggests that the space

$$L_2^0(\nabla\times, \Omega) = \{A: A \in L_2(\nabla\times, \Omega), \int_\Omega A \cdot \nabla\times B\, dx = \int_\Omega B \cdot \nabla\times A\, dx \text{ for all } B \in L_2(\nabla\times, \Omega)\}$$

is an appropriate generalization of the class of fields that satisfy the boundary condition (1.4). $L_2^0(\nabla\times, \Omega)$ is obviously a closed linear subspace of $L_2(\nabla\times, \Omega)$.

The space

$$L_2(\frac{d}{dt}, I, H) ,$$

where

$$I = \{t: 0 < t < T\} \subset R^1$$

and H is one of the function spaces defined above, occurs in the discussion of the diffraction problem. Several of its properties that are needed in the discussion are derived in the remainder of this section.

A basic property of the Bochner integral is described by

<u>Theorem 2.1.</u> If $v \in L_2(I, H)$ then

$$u(t) = u(0) + \int_0^t v(\tau)\, d\tau$$

has the derivative $u'(t) = v(t)$ almost everywhere.

A proof may be found in [3, p. 88]. The following result goes in the opposite direction.

<u>Theorem 2.2.</u> Let $u \in L_2(\frac{d}{dt}, I, H)$ and let $v = u'(\in L_2(I, H))$. Then v is integrable on I, and

$$u(b) - u(a) = \int_a^b v(t)\, dt \quad \text{for almost all } a, b \in I . \tag{2.3}$$

In particular, $u(t)$ equals a continuous function for almost all $t \in I$. Conversely, if $v \in L_2(I, H)$ then (2.3) defines a $u \in L_2(\frac{d}{dt}, I, H)$ and $u' = v$.

This theorem plays an important part in both the mathematical formulation of the diffraction problem and in the proofs of the existence and uniqueness theorems. Moreover, it does not appear to exist in the literature. For these reasons a complete proof of the theorem is presented here. The proof makes use of a related result which is stated as

Lemma 2.1. Let $u \in L_2(\frac{d}{dt}, I, H)$ and let $v = u' (\in L_2(I, H))$. Let $K = \{t: 0 < a < t < b < T\}$ be an arbitrary subinterval of I. Then there exists a sequence $w_k \in C^1(K, H) \cap L_2(\frac{d}{dt}, K, H)$ such that

$$\lim_{k\to\infty} w_k = u \ , \quad \text{and} \quad \lim_{k\to\infty} w'_k = v$$

in $L_2(K, H)$.

The proof makes use of a function

$$\phi \in C^\infty(R^1, R^1) \ ,$$

with the properties

$$\phi(t) \geq 0 \text{ for } t \in R^1 \ , \quad \phi(t) = 0 \text{ for } |t| \geq 1 \ , \quad \int_{-\infty}^{\infty} \phi(t)\,dt = 1 \ ,$$

and the corresponding functions

$$\phi_\epsilon \in C^\infty(R^1, R^1) \text{ defined by } \phi_\epsilon(t) = \frac{1}{\epsilon}\,\phi(\frac{t}{\epsilon})$$

with the properties

$$\phi_\epsilon(t) \geq 0 \ , \quad \phi_\epsilon(t) = 0 \text{ for } |t| \geq \epsilon \ , \quad \int_{-\infty}^{\infty} \phi_\epsilon(t)\,dt = 1 \ .$$

Functions of this kind have been called "mollifiers" by K. O. Friedrichs, who introduced them to discuss generalized derivatives [2].

Given u and K as in Lemma 2.1, define

$$u_\epsilon(t) = \int_{-\infty}^{\infty} u(\tau)\,\phi_\epsilon(t-\tau)\,d\tau \ , \quad t \in K \ .$$

The integral is meaningful (involves values $u(t)$ for $t \in I$ only) provided

$$\epsilon < \epsilon_0 = \text{Min}(a, T-b) \ .$$

Now $u_\epsilon \in C^1(K, H)$ (indeed, $u_\epsilon \in C^\infty(K, H)$) and

$$u'_\epsilon(t) = \int_{-\infty}^{\infty} u(\tau)\phi'_\epsilon(t-\tau)\,d\tau \quad , \quad t \in K \ .$$

(This can be proved by using Fubini's theorem [3, p. 84] to show that the integral with respect to t of the last integral equals u_ϵ.) It follows that $u_\epsilon(t)$ and $u'_\epsilon(t)$ are bounded for $t \in K$ whence, in particular, they are square-integrable. Thus

$$u_\epsilon \in C^1(K, H) \cap L_2(\frac{d}{dt}, K, H) \ .$$

Observe that if $h \in H$ is fixed then

$$\psi(\tau) = \phi_\epsilon(t-\tau)h \in C_0^1(I, H)$$

for each $\epsilon < \epsilon_0$ and $t \in K$. Thus, by the definition of v,

$$-\int_0^T (u(\tau), \psi'(\tau))_H d\tau = \int_0^T (v(\tau), \psi(\tau))_H d\tau$$

or

$$\left(-\int_0^T u(\tau)\frac{d}{d\tau}\phi_\epsilon(t-\tau)\,d\tau, h\right)_H = \left(\int_0^T v(\tau)\phi_\epsilon(t-\tau)\,d\tau, h\right)_H$$

Since $h \in H$ is arbitrary it follows that

$$-\int_0^T u(\tau)\frac{d}{d\tau}\phi_\epsilon(t-\tau)\,d\tau = \int_0^T u(\tau)\phi'_\epsilon(t-\tau)\,d\tau = \int_0^T v(\tau)\phi_\epsilon(t-\tau)\,d\tau \ ,$$

or

$$u'_\epsilon = v_\epsilon \ .$$

Proof of Lemma 2.1. Define $w_k = u_\epsilon$, with $\epsilon = 1/k$ so that $w'_k = u'_\epsilon = v_\epsilon$. The lemma then follows from

Lemma 2.2. If $u \in L_2(I, H)$ then $\lim_{\epsilon\to 0} u_\epsilon = u$ in $L_2(K, H)$ for each proper sub-interval $K \subset I$; i.e.

$$\lim_{\epsilon\to 0} \|u_\epsilon - u\|^2_{L_2(K,H)} = \int_a^b \|u_\epsilon(t) - u(t)\|^2_H dt = 0 \ .$$

Proof. Write $f_\epsilon = u_\epsilon - u$, so

$$f_\epsilon(t) = \int_{-\infty}^{\infty} \{u(t-\tau) - u(\tau)\}\phi_\epsilon(\tau)\,d\tau \quad , \quad t \in K \ .$$

Then

$$\|f_\epsilon\|^2_{L_2(K,H)} = \int_a^b (f_\epsilon(t), \int_{-\infty}^{\infty} \{u(t-\tau)-u(t)\}\phi_\epsilon(\tau)d\tau)_H dt$$

$$\overset{*}{=} \int_a^b dt \int_{-\infty}^{\infty} (f_\epsilon(t), u(t-\tau)-u(t))_H \phi_\epsilon(\tau)d\tau$$

$$\overset{**}{=} \int_{-\infty}^{\infty} \phi_\epsilon(\tau)d\tau \int_a^b (f_\epsilon(t), u(t-\tau)-u(t))_H dt$$

$$= \int_{-\infty}^{\infty} \phi_\epsilon(\tau)(f_\epsilon(t), u(t-\tau)-u(\tau))_{L_2(K,H)} d\tau \quad .$$

Step * follows from the definition of the Bochner integral. Step ** follows from Fubini's theorem. Applying Schwarz's inequality to the last integral gives (since $\phi_\epsilon \geq 0$),

$$\|f_\epsilon\|^2_{L_2(K,H)} \leq \|f_\epsilon\|_{L_2(K,H)} \int_{-\infty}^{\infty} \phi_\epsilon(\tau) \|u(t-\tau)-u(t)\|_{L_2(K,H)} d\tau$$

Now

$$\lim_{|\tau|\to 0} \|u(t-\tau)-u(t)\|_{L_2(K,H)} = 0 \; ,$$

[3, p. 86]. Thus, given $\delta > 0$,

$$\|u(t-\tau)-u(t)\|_{L_2(K,H)} \leq \delta \text{ for } |\tau| \leq \epsilon_1 \; ,$$

whence

$$\int_{-\infty}^{\infty} \phi_\epsilon(\tau) \|u(t-\tau)-u(t)\|_{L_2(K,H)} d\tau \leq \delta \text{ for } \epsilon \leq \epsilon_1 \; .$$

Hence

$$\|f_\epsilon\|^2_{L_2(K,H)} \leq \|f_\epsilon\|_{L_2(K,H)} \delta \text{ for } \epsilon \leq \epsilon_1 \; ,$$

which implies $\lim_{\epsilon\to 0} \|f_\epsilon\|_{L_2(K,H)} = 0$.

Proof of Theorem 2.2. v is measurable and square-integrable. Hence, Schwarz's inequality implies

$$\int_0^T \|v(t)\|_H dt \leq T^{\frac{1}{2}} \left(\int_0^T \|v(t)\|^2_H dt \right)^{\frac{1}{2}} < \infty$$

and v is integrable. Next, observe that (2.3) holds when

$u \in C^1(K, H) \cap L_2(\frac{d}{dt}, K, H)$. (The rules of calculus hold for functions with values in H ; see [3, pp. 58-71].) Thus, an application of the formula

$$\int_a^b d\tau \int_a^\tau f(t)\,d\tau = \int_a^b (b-t)f(t)\,dt$$

gives

$$\int_a^b d\alpha \int_\alpha^b \{u(\beta)-u(\alpha)-\int_\alpha^\beta v(t)\,dt\}d\beta = \int_a^b (2t-a-b)\,u(t)\,dt + \int_a^b (t-a)(t-b)\,v(t)\,dt = 0 \qquad (2.4)$$

for all

$$u \in C^1(K, H) \cap L_2(\frac{d}{dt}, K, H) .$$

Now every $u \in L_2(\frac{d}{dt}, I, H)$ is the limit in the norm

$$\|u\|^2_{L_2(\frac{d}{dt}, K, H)} = \int_a^b \{\|u(t)\|^2_H + \|u'(t)\|^2_H\}dt$$

of a sequence $w_k \in C^1(K, H) \cap L_2(\frac{d}{dt}, K, H)$ by Lemma 2.1. Equation (2.3) holds for each w_k and, moreover,

$$w_k \to u \text{ in } L_2(I, H) \text{ and } w'_k \to v \text{ in } L_2(K, H) .$$

It follows easily that passage to the limit in (2.4), written for w_k , is permissible. Thus (2.4) holds for every $u \in L_2(\frac{d}{dt}, I, H)$. Finally, differentiating (2.4) with respect to a and b gives (2.3) for almost all a and b (Theorem 2.1). The last statement of Theorem 2.2 follows easily from Fubini's theorem [3, p. 84]; the proof is omitted.

An important consequence of Theorem 2.2 is

Theorem 2.3. If u and v are in $L_2(\frac{d}{dt}, I, H)$ then

$$\int_a^b (u'(t), v(t))_H dt + \int_a^b (u(t), v'(t))_H dt = (u(b), v(b))_H - (u(a), v(a))_H$$

$$\text{for } 0 \le a \le b \le T . \qquad (2.5)$$

Proof. The representations

$$u(t) = u(0) + \int_0^t u'(\tau)\,d\tau , \quad v(t) = v(0) + \int_0^t v'(\tau)\,d\tau$$

imply

$$f(t) = (u(t), v(t))_H$$

is an absolutely continuous real-valued function on I , and that

$$f'(t) = (u'(t), v(t))_H + (u(t), v'(t))_H \text{ almost everywhere}$$

(Theorem 2.2). Thus (2.5) follows from a standard theorem concerning absolutely continuous functions.

§3. A MATHEMATICAL FORMULATION OF THE DIFFRACTION PROBLEM. Consider the classes

$$\mathscr{F}_{\text{ELECTRIC}} = L_2(I, \overset{0}{L}_2(\nabla\times, \Omega)) \cap L_2(\tfrac{d}{dt}, I, L_2(\Omega)) \quad ,$$

and

$$\mathscr{F}_{\text{MAGNETIC}} = L_2(I, L_2(\nabla\times, \Omega)) \cap L_2(\tfrac{d}{dt}, I, L_2(\Omega)) \quad .$$

Fields $E \in \mathscr{F}_{\text{ELECTRIC}}$ and $H \in \mathscr{F}_{\text{MAGNETIC}}$ are square-integrable and possess square-integrable curls and time-derivatives. Moreover, the correspondences $t \to E(t)$, $t \to H(t)$ are continuous from I to $L_2(\Omega)$, by Theorem 2.2. In particular $E(0)$ and $H(0)$ are well-defined. Finally,

$$E(t) \in \overset{0}{L}_2(\nabla\times, \Omega) \text{ for almost all } t \in I \ ,$$

which generalizes the boundary condition (1.4). This suggests the

Definition. A pair E, H is the strict solution of the diffraction problem for the domain Ω and the data

$$F \text{ and } G \text{ in } L_0(Q) \ , \quad E_0 \text{ and } H_0 \text{ in } L_2(\Omega)$$

if

$$E \in \mathscr{F}_{\text{ELECTRIC}} \ , \quad H \in \mathscr{F}_{\text{MAGNETIC}} \ ,$$

$$\left.\begin{aligned} \nabla\times H - \frac{\partial E}{\partial t} &= F \\ \nabla\times E + \frac{\partial H}{\partial t} &= G \end{aligned}\right\} \text{ almost everywhere in } Q \ , \tag{3.1}$$

and

$$E(0) = E_0 \ , \quad H(0) = H_0 \text{ in } L_2(\Omega) \ .$$

It is well known that singularities can propagate in an electromagnetic field, so that in general the field at time t has no more derivatives than the initial field. Hence, if arbitrary initial values in $L_2(Q)$ are to be treated, a formulation of the diffraction problem that does not demand the existence of derivatives is needed. This can be achieved by the use of integral identities. To derive them, multiply equations (3.1) by $\Phi \in \mathscr{F}_{\text{ELECTRIC}}$ and $\Psi \in \mathscr{F}_{\text{MAGNETIC}}$, respectively, and integrate over Q . The terms involving $\nabla\times$ can be integrated by parts, giving

$$\int_Q (\nabla\times H\cdot\Phi)dxdt = \int_0^T (\nabla\times H,\Phi)_{L_2(\Omega)}dt = \int_0^T (H,\nabla\times\Phi)_{L_2(\Omega)}dt$$

and

$$\int_Q (\nabla\times E\cdot\Psi)dxdt = \int_0^T (\nabla\times E,\Psi)_{L_2(\Omega)}dt = \int_0^T (E,\nabla\times\Psi)_{L_2(\Omega)}dt$$

because $\Phi(t)$ and $E(t)$ are in $L_2^0(\nabla\times,\Omega)$ for almost all t. The terms involving $\partial/\partial t$ can be integrated by parts, by Theorem 2.3. The resulting identities are

$$\int_0^T \{(H,\nabla\times\Phi) + (E,\frac{\partial\Phi}{\partial t}) - (F,\Phi)\}dt + (E_0,\Phi(0)) - (E(T),\Phi(T)) = 0 ,$$

$$\int_0^T \{(E,\nabla\times\Psi) - (H,\frac{\partial\Psi}{\partial t}) - (G,\Psi)\}dt - (H_0,\Psi(0)) + (H(T),\Psi(T)) = 0 .$$

These identities are meaningful for fields E and H in $L_2(Q)$, provided $\Phi(T) = \Psi(T) = 0$ so that the meaningless terms $E(T), H(T)$ do not appear. This suggests the

Definition. A pair E, H is the solution with finite energy of the diffraction problem for the domain Ω and the data

$$F \text{ and } G \text{ in } L_2(Q) , \quad E_0 \text{ and } H_0 \text{ in } L_2(\Omega)$$

if

$$E \in L_2(Q) , \quad H \in L_2(Q) ,$$

and E and H satisfy the identities

$$\int_0^T \{(H,\nabla\times\Phi) + (E,\frac{\partial\Phi}{\partial t}) - (F,\Phi)\}dt + (E_0,\Phi(0)) = 0 ,$$
$$\int_0^T \{(E,\nabla\times\Psi) - (H,\frac{\partial\Psi}{\partial t}) - (G,\Psi)\}dt - (H_0,\Psi(0)) = 0 , \tag{3.2}$$

for all $\Phi \in \mathscr{F}_{ELECTRIC}$ and $\Psi \in \mathscr{F}_{MAGNETIC}$ that satisfy

$$\Phi(T) = \Psi(T) = 0 .$$

The scalar products in (3.2) are

$$(H,\nabla\times\Phi) = (H,\nabla\times\Phi)_{L_2(\Omega)} , \quad t \in I \text{ fixed; etc.}$$

Notice that F, G, E, H are in

$$L_2(Q) = L_2(I, L_2(\Omega))$$

(the identity of these spaces follows from Fubini's theorem) so that all the scalar products in (3.2) are defined for almost all $t \in I$ and are integrable on I.

If E_0 and H_0 are only locally square-integrable, then $E(t)$ and $H(t)$ can be expected to have the same property. This class of solutions is of interest in applications. (For example, plane waves are not square-integrable.) The corresponding formulation of the diffraction problem is described by the

Definition. A pair E, H is the solution with locally finite energy of the diffraction problem for the domain Ω and the data

$$F \text{ and } G \text{ in } L_2^{loc}(Q) \quad , \quad E_0 \text{ and } H_0 \text{ in } L_2^{loc}(\Omega)$$

if

$$E \in L_2^{loc}(Q) \quad , \quad H \in L_2^{loc}(Q)$$

and E and H satisfy the identities (3.2) for all $\Phi \in \mathscr{F}_{ELECTRIC}$ and $\Psi \in \mathscr{F}_{MAGNETIC}$ that are equivalent to zero outside a bounded measurable set $(K \times I) \cap Q$ and satisfy $\Phi(T) = \Psi(T) = 0$ in $L_2(Q)$.

Several explanatory comments need to be made. The set K is a bounded measurable set in R^3 which may depend on Φ and Ψ. The scalar products in (3.2) are now

$$(H, \nabla \times \Phi) = (H, \nabla \times \Phi)_{L_2(K \cap \Omega)} \quad , \quad t \in I \text{ fixed, etc.}$$

By hypothesis, E_0 and H_0 are in $L_2(K \cap \Omega)$ and F, G, E, H are in

$$L_2((K \times I) \cap Q) = L_2((K \cap \Omega) \times I) = L_2(I, L_2(K \cap \Omega))$$

for every bounded measurable $K \subset R^3$. Hence all the scalar products are defined (for almost all $t \in I$) and integrable on I.

The remainder of the paper is concerned with the existence, uniqueness, and functional properties of the three kinds of solution defined above. The results are described in the next section.

§4. THE FUNDAMENTAL THEOREMS. The basic existence and uniqueness theorems obtained in this paper may be stated as follows.

Theorem 4.1. Let Ω be an arbitrary domain in R^3 and T be an arbitrary positive number. Then

(a) the diffraction problem has a unique solution with locally finite energy for all data

$$F \text{ and } G \text{ in } L_2^{loc}(Q) \quad , \quad E_0 \text{ and } H_0 \text{ in } L_2^{loc}(\Omega) \quad .$$

(b) The diffraction problem has a (unique) solution with finite energy for all data

$$F \text{ and } G \text{ in } L_2(Q) \quad , \quad E_0 \text{ and } H_0 \text{ in } L_2(\Omega) \quad .$$

(c) The diffraction problem has a (unique) strict solution for all data

$$F \in L_2(I, \overset{0}{L}_2(\nabla\times, \Omega)) \quad , \quad G \in L_2(I, L_2(\nabla\times, \Omega))$$

and

$$E_0 \in \overset{0}{L}_2(\nabla\times, \Omega) \quad , \quad H_0 \in L_2(\nabla\times, \Omega) \quad .$$

The remaining theorems describe properties of these three classes of solutions.

Corollary 4.1. The solution with locally finite energy is independent of T ; i.e. the solutions for time-intervals $0 \le t \le T$ and $0 \le t \le T'$ with $T < T'$ agree for $0 \le t \le T$.

The same statement is true for the solution with finite energy and the strict solution, if they exist, since they are also solutions with locally finite energy.

Corollary 4.2. (a) The solution with locally finite energy defines continuous curves

$$t \to E(t) \in L_2(K \cap \Omega) \quad , \quad t \to H(t) \in L_2(K \cap \Omega)$$

for each bounded measurable set $K \subset R^3$, and $E(0) = E_0$, $H(0) = H_0$.

(b) The solution with finite energy defines continuous curves

$$t \to E(t) \in L_2(\Omega) \quad , \quad t \to H(t) \in L_2(\Omega)$$

and

$$E(0) = E_0 \quad , \quad H(0) = H_0 \quad .$$

A characteristic feature of electromagnetic radiation is its finite speed of propagation. The next theorem shows that the present model for the electromagnetic field exhibits this feature.

Theorem 4.2 (Domain of Dependence Theorem). The solution with locally finite energy (and hence also the solution with finite energy and the strict solution) satisfy the inequality

$$\int_{S_a(x_0)\cap\Omega} (|E(x,T)|^2 + |H(x,T)|^2)\,dx$$

$$\leq \int_{S_{a+T}(x_0)\cap\Omega} (|E_0(x)|^2 + |H_0(x)|^2)\,dx + 2\int_{C_a(x_0)\cap Q} (H\cdot G - E\cdot F)\,dx\,dt$$

where

$$S_a(x_0) = \{x : |x-x_0| \leq a\}$$

is an arbitrary sphere in R^3 and

$$C_a(x_0) = \{(x,t) : |x-x_0| \leq a+T-t\ ,\ 0 \leq t \leq T\}$$

is the portion of the space-time cone with vertex at $(x,t) = (x_0, a+T)$ that lies between the planes $t = 0$ and $t = T$.

An obvious corollary of Theorem 4.2 is

Corollary 4.3. If E_0 and H_0 are equivalent to zero in $S_{a+T}(x_0)\cap\Omega$ and F and G are equivalent to zero in $C_a(x_0)\cap Q$ then $E(T)$ and $H(T)$ are equivalent to zero in $S_a(x_0)\cap\Omega$.

Another important result which follows from Theorem 4.2 is

Theorem 4.3 (Energy Inequality). The solution with finite energy satisfies

$$\|E(t)\|^2 + \|H(t)\|^2 \leq e^T\{\|E_0\|^2 + \|H_0\|^2 + 2\int_0^T (\|F(\tau)\|^2 + \|G(\tau)\|^2)\,d\tau\}\ ,$$

$$0 \leq t \leq T\ ,$$

where $\|\ \|$ denotes the $L_2(\Omega)$-norm.

The most fundamental of these results are the uniqueness theorem for solutions with finite energy and the domain of dependence theorem. The other theorems will be shown to follow from them.

The remainder of the paper is organized as follows. The uniqueness theorem for solutions with finite energy is proved in §5. In §6 the domain of dependence theorem is proved for strict solutions. Using this result, the energy inequality is proved for strict solutions in §7. In §8, the existence theorem for solutions with finite energy (Theorem 4.1(b)) is shown to follow from the uniqueness theorem for these solutions and the energy inequality for strict solutions. Corollary 4.2(b), Theorem 4.2 (for solutions with finite energy) and Theorem 4.3 are then derived from the existence proof. The existence theorem for strict solutions (Theorem 4.1(c)) is derived in §9. The uniqueness and existence theorems for solutions with locally finite energy (Theorem 4.1(a)) are derived in §10 and §11, respectively, using the results of §6, §8 and §9.

§5. THE UNIQUENESS THEOREM FOR SOLUTIONS WITH FINITE ENERGY. The proof of the uniqueness theorem is based on

Lemma 5.1. If the pair E, H is a solution with finite energy for the data (F, G, E_0, H_0) then the identities

$$\left(\int_0^\tau H(t)\,dt, \nabla\times A\right) = \left(\int_0^\tau F(t)\,d\tau + E(\tau) - E_0, A\right) ,$$
$$\left(\int_0^\tau E(t)\,dt, \nabla\times B\right) = \left(\int_0^\tau G(t)\,dt - H(\tau) + H_0, B\right) , \tag{5.1}$$

hold for every $A \in L_2^0(\nabla\times;\Omega)$, every $B \in L_2(\nabla\times;\Omega)$, and almost all $\tau \in I$.

Proof. Fix $\tau \in I$ and define

$$\Phi(x,t) = \begin{cases} (\tau - t)A(x) , & 0 \le t \le \tau \\ 0 , & \tau \le t \le T , \end{cases}$$

and

$$\Psi(x,t) = \begin{cases} (\tau - t)B(x) , & 0 \le t \le \tau , \\ 0 , & \tau \le t \le T . \end{cases}$$

Then it is clear that $\Phi \in \mathscr{F}_{\text{ELECTRIC}}$ and $\Psi \in \mathscr{F}_{\text{MAGNETIC}}$. Substituting these fields in the identities (3.2) gives

$$\int_0^T \{(\tau-t)(H(t), \nabla\times A) - (\tau-t)(F(t), A) - (E(t), A)\}dt + \tau(E_0, A) = 0 ,$$

$$\int_0^T \{(\tau-t)(E(t), \nabla\times B) - (\tau-t)(G(t), B) + (H(t), B)\}dt - \tau(H_0, B) = 0 ,$$

for every $\tau \in I$. Identities (5.1) are obtained by differentiating these with respect to τ, using Theorem 2.1.

The uniqueness theorem for solutions with finite energy is equivalent to

Theorem 5.1. If the pair E, H is a solution with finite energy for data $(F, G, E_0, H_0) = (0, 0, 0, 0)$ then $E = H = 0$ in $L_2(Q)$.

Proof. If

$$E_1(\tau) = \int_0^\tau E(t)\,dt , \quad H_1(\tau) = \int_0^\tau H(t)\,dt ,$$

then Lemma 5.1 implies

$$\begin{aligned} (H_1(\tau), \nabla\times A) &= (E(\tau), A) \quad \text{for all } A \in L_2^0(\nabla\times;\Omega) , \\ (E_1(\tau), \nabla\times B) &= -(H(\tau), B) \quad \text{for all } B \in L_2(\nabla\times;\Omega) , \end{aligned} \tag{5.2}$$

for almost all $\tau \in I$. Since

$$C_0^1(\Omega, R^3) \subset L_2^0(\nabla\times;\Omega) \subset L_2(\nabla\times;\Omega)$$

(5.2) implies that

$$H_1(\tau) \in L_2(\nabla\times;\Omega) \quad \text{and} \quad \nabla\times H_1(\tau) = E(\tau) ,$$

$$E_1(\tau) \in L_2^0(\nabla\times;\Omega) \quad \text{and} \quad \nabla\times E_1(\tau) = -H(\tau) ,$$

for almost all $\tau \in I$. Hence it is permissible to take

$$A = E_1(\tau) , \quad B = H_1(\tau)$$

in (5.2). When this is done both identities yield the equation

$$(E(\tau), E_1(\tau)) + (H(\tau), H_1(\tau)) = 0$$

or

$$\left(E_1(\tau), \frac{dE_1(\tau)}{d\tau}\right) + \left(H_1(\tau), \frac{dH_1(\tau)}{dt}\right) = 0 \quad \text{for almost all } \tau \in I .$$

Integrating and using $E_1(0) = H_1(0) = 0$ gives (Theorem 2.3)

$$\|E_1(t)\|^2 + \|H_1(t)\|^2 = 0 \quad \text{for } t \in I ,$$

whence

$$E_1(t) = H_1(t) = 0 \quad \text{for } t \in I .$$

Consequently $E(t) = H(t) = 0$ for almost all $t \in I$ (Theorem (2.1), which implies $E = H = 0$ in $L_2(Q)$.

The uniqueness theorem admits a reformulation in terms of the linear mapping Λ with domain

$$D(\Lambda) = \{\Phi, \Psi: \Phi \in \mathscr{F}_{\text{ELECTRIC}}, \Psi \in \mathscr{F}_{\text{MAGNETIC}}\} \subset L_2(Q) \times L_2(Q)$$

and range

$$R(\Lambda) \subset W = L_2(Q) \times L_2(Q) \times L_2(\Omega) \times L_2(\Omega)$$

defined by

$$\Lambda(\Phi, \Psi) = (\nabla\times \Psi - \frac{\partial\Phi}{\partial t}, \nabla\times \Phi + \frac{\partial\Psi}{\partial t}, \Phi(0), \Psi(0)) \ .$$

The result is stated as

Theorem 5.2. $R(\Lambda)$ is dense in the Hilbert space W ; i.e. the closure of $R(\Lambda)$ in W is

$$\overline{R(\Lambda)} = W \ .$$

Proof. $\overline{R(\Lambda)}$ is a closed linear subspace of W . Thus if $\overline{R(\Lambda)} \neq W$ then there exists a non-zero element

$$(A, B, A_0, B_0) \in W$$

which is orthogonal to $\overline{R(\Lambda)}$; i.e.,

$$\begin{aligned} &(\nabla\times\Psi - \frac{\partial\Phi}{\partial t}, A)_{L_2(Q)} + (\nabla\times\Phi + \frac{\partial\Psi}{\partial t}, B)_{L_2(Q)} \\ &+ (\Phi(0), A_0)_{L_2(\Omega)} + (\Psi(0), B_0)_{L_2(\Omega)} = 0 \end{aligned} \qquad (5.3)$$

for all $\Phi, \Psi \in D(\Lambda)$. In this identity take first, $\Psi(t) \equiv 0$ and $\Phi(0) = 0$, second, $\Phi(t) \equiv 0$ and $\Psi(0) = 0$. The resulting identities are

$$\int_0^T \{(B, \nabla\times\Phi) - (A, \frac{\partial\Phi}{\partial t})\}dt = 0 \ ,$$

$$\int_0^T \{(A, \nabla\times\Psi) + (B, \frac{\partial\Psi}{\partial t})\}dt = 0 \ ,$$

for all $\Phi \in \mathscr{F}_{ELECTRIC}$, $\Psi \in \mathscr{F}_{MAGNETIC}$ with $\Phi(0) = \Psi(0) = 0$. These identities state that the pair $B, -A$ is a solution with finite energy of the "backwards" diffraction problem with sources $F = G = 0$ and "initial" values $B(x, T) = -A(x, T) = 0$. Thus $A = B = 0$ in $L_2(Q)$ by Theorem 5.1. Then (5.3) with $A = B = 0$, $\Phi(t) \equiv \Phi_0 \in L_2^0(\nabla\times;\Omega)$ and $\Psi(t) \equiv 0$ gives

$$(\Phi_0, A_0)_{L_2(\Omega)} = 0 \ ,$$

whence $A_0 = 0$ (because $L_2^0(\nabla\times;\Omega)$ is dense in $L_2(\Omega)$) and similarly $B_0 = 0$. Thus

$$(A, B, A_0, B_0) = (0, 0, 0, 0)$$

contrary to hypothesis. It follows that $\overline{R(\Lambda)} = W$.

It is evident from the above proof that the uniqueness theorem is entirely equivalent to the proposition $\overline{R(\Lambda)} = W$.

§6. THE DOMAIN OF DEPENDENCE THEOREM. In this section Theorem 4.2 is proved for fields $E \in \mathscr{F}_{\text{ELECTRIC}}$, $H \in \mathscr{F}_{\text{MAGNETIC}}$. The result is stated as

Theorem 6.1. If $E \in \mathscr{F}_{\text{ELECTRIC}}$ and $H \in \mathscr{F}_{\text{MAGNETIC}}$ then

$$\int_{S_a(x_0)\cap\Omega} \{|E(x,T)|^2 + |H(x,T)|^2\}dx \le \int_{S_{a+T}(x_0)\cap\Omega} \{|E(x,0)|^2+|H(x,0)|^2\}dx \tag{6.1}$$

$$+ \int_{C_a(x_0)\cap\Omega} \{H\cdot(\nabla\times E + \frac{\partial H}{\partial t}) - E\cdot(\nabla\times H - \frac{\partial E}{\partial t})\}dxdt$$

for every $x_0 \in R^3$ and every $a > 0$.

Proof. Let $\phi_\delta(\tau)$ be a real-valued function of the real variable τ with the properties

$$\phi_\delta \in C^1(-\infty,\infty) \ , \quad \phi'_\delta(\tau) \ge 0 \ ,$$

$$\phi_\delta(\tau) = 0 \text{ for } \tau \le -\delta \ , \quad \phi_\delta(\tau) = 1 \text{ for } \tau \ge \delta \ ,$$

$$0 \le \phi_\delta(\tau) \le 1 \text{ for all } \tau \ ,$$

and define

$$\phi(x,t) = \phi_\delta(\tau) \text{ where } \tau = \tau(x,t) = a+T - t - |x-x_0| \ . \tag{6.2}$$

Obviously, $\tau(x,t) \in C^\infty$ for $x \ne x_0$. Thus, $\phi(x,t) \in C^1(\overline{Q})$ provided $\delta < a$. Obviously, $\phi(x,t) = 0$ outside of the compact set $C_{a+\delta}(x_0)$. The proof of (6.1) makes use of the fields

$$A(x,t) = \phi(x,t)E(x,t) \ , \quad B(x,t) = \phi(x,t)H(x,t) \ . \tag{6.3}$$

Their use is justified by the following two lemmas.

Lemma 6.1. If $\phi \in C^1(\overline{Q})$ and has compact support and $E \in L_2(\frac{d}{dt}, I, L_2(Q))$ then $A = \phi E \in L_2(\frac{d}{dt}, I, L_2(\Omega))$ and

$$\frac{dA}{dt} = \frac{\partial\phi}{\partial t}E + \phi\frac{dE}{dt} \ .$$

Proof. The fields A and $C = \frac{\partial\phi}{\partial t}E + \phi\frac{dE}{dt}$ are both in $L_2(I, L_2(\Omega))$, since ϕ and $\partial\phi/\partial t$ are bounded and measurable in $\overline{Q}$. The proof is completed by verifying that $C = dA/dt$. To this end let $\Phi \in C_0^1(I, L_2(\Omega))$. Then

$$\int_0^T (C, \Phi)\,dt = \int_0^T (\phi \frac{dE}{dt}, \Phi)\,dt + \int_0^T (\frac{\partial\phi}{\partial t} E, \Phi)\,dt$$

$$= \int_0^T (\frac{dE}{dt}, \phi\Phi)\,dt + \int_0^T (E, \frac{\partial\phi}{\partial t}\Phi)\,dt$$

$$\overset{*}{=} -\int_0^T (E, \frac{\partial\phi}{\partial t}\Phi + \phi\frac{d\Phi}{dt})\,dt + \int_0^T (E, \frac{\partial\phi}{\partial t}\Phi)\,dt$$

$$= -\int_0^T (\phi E, \frac{d\Phi}{dt})\,dt = -\int_0^T (A, \frac{d\Phi}{dt})\,dt$$

which proves that $C = dA/dt$. The steps in the calculation are easy to justify. The definition of dE/dt is used at $*$.

Lemma 6.2. If $\phi \in C^1(\bar{\Omega})$ and has compact support and $E \in L_2(\nabla\times;\Omega)$ then $A = \phi E \in L_2(\nabla\times;\Omega)$ and

$$\nabla\times A = \nabla\phi \times E + \phi\nabla\times E \quad . \tag{6.4}$$

Proof. The fields A and $C = \nabla\phi \times E + \phi\nabla\times E$ are both in $L_2(\Omega)$, since ϕ and $\nabla\phi$ are bounded and measurable in $\bar{\Omega}$. The proof is completed by verifying that $C = \nabla\times A$. To this end let $\Phi \in C_0^1(\Omega)$. Then

$$\int_\Omega C\cdot\Phi dx = \int_\Omega \nabla\phi\times E\cdot\Phi dx + \int_\Omega \phi(\nabla\times E)\cdot\Phi dx$$

$$= \int_\Omega \nabla\phi\times E\cdot\Phi dx + \int_\Omega E\cdot\nabla\times(\phi\Phi)\,dx$$

$$= \int_\Omega \nabla\phi\times E\cdot\Phi dx + \int_\Omega E\cdot\nabla\phi\times\Phi dx + \int_\Omega \phi E\cdot\nabla\times\Phi dx$$

$$= \int_\Omega (\phi E)\cdot\nabla\times\Phi dx = \int_\Omega A\cdot\nabla\times\Phi dx \quad .$$

Corollary 6.1. If $\phi \in C^1(\bar{Q})$ and has compact support and $E \in L_2(I; L_2(\nabla\times;\Omega))$ then $A = \phi E \in L_2(I; L_2(\nabla\times;\Omega))$ and

$$\nabla\times A = \nabla\phi\times E + \phi\nabla\times E \quad .$$

Proof. Lemma 6.2 implies that $A(t) \in L_2(\nabla\times;\Omega)$ and

$$\nabla\times A(t) = \nabla\phi(t)\times E(t) + \phi(t)\nabla\times E(t)$$

for almost all $t \in I$. Obviously $\nabla \times A \in L_2(Q)$, since ϕ and $\nabla\phi$ are bounded and measurable on $\overline{Q}$.

Proof of Theorem 6.1 (continued). Let $E \in \mathscr{F}_{\text{ELECTRIC}}$, $H \in \mathscr{F}_{\text{MAGNETIC}}$ and define ϕ , A , and B by (6.2) and (6.3). Then $E(t) \in L_2^0(\nabla\times;\Omega)$ and $B(t) \in L_2(\nabla\times;\Omega)$ for almost all $t \in I$ (by Cor. 6.1) whence

$$\int_\Omega \{B(x,t)\cdot\nabla\times E(x,t) - E(x,t)\cdot\nabla\times B(x,t)\} = 0 \quad \text{for almost all } t \in I .$$

Using (6.4) to evaluate $\nabla\times B$ and then integrating with respect to t gives

$$\int_Q (H\cdot\nabla\times E - E\cdot\nabla\times H)\phi\, dxdt = \int_Q (H\cdot E\times\nabla\phi)\, dxdt \quad . \tag{6.5}$$

Next, Lemma 6.1 and Theorem 2.3 imply

$$\int_0^T \{(E, \phi\frac{dE}{dt}) + (H, \phi\frac{dH}{dt}) + (E, \frac{\partial\phi}{\partial t}E) + (H, \frac{\partial\phi}{\partial t}H)\}dt$$

$$= \int_0^T \{(E, \frac{dA}{dt}) + (H, \frac{dB}{dt})\}$$

$$= -\int_0^T (\frac{dE}{dt}, \phi E)\,dt + (E(T), \phi(T)E(T)) - (E(0), \phi(0)E(0))$$

$$- \int_0^T (\frac{dH}{dt}, \phi H)\,dt + (H(T), \phi(T)H(T)) - (H(0), \phi(0)H(0))$$

whence

$$\int_Q (E\cdot\frac{dE}{dt} + H\cdot\frac{dH}{dt})\phi\, dxdt = \frac{1}{2}\int_\Omega (|E(x,T)|^2 + |H(x,T)|^2)\phi(x,T)\,dx$$
$$-\frac{1}{2}\int_\Omega (|E(x,0)|^2 + |H(x,0)|^2)\phi(x,0)\,dx - \frac{1}{2}\int_Q (|E|^2+|H|^2)\frac{\partial\phi}{\partial t}dxdt. \tag{6.6}$$

Now add equations (6.5) and (6.6) and write, for brevity,

$$F = \nabla\times H - \frac{dE}{dt} \; , \quad G = \nabla\times E + \frac{dH}{dt} \; .$$

The result is

$$2\int_Q (H\cdot G - E\cdot F)\phi\,dxdt = \int_\Omega (|E(x,T)|^2+|H(x,T)|^2)\phi(x,T)\,dx$$

$$- \int_\Omega (|E(x,0)|^2+|H(x,0)|^2)\phi(x,0)\,dx \tag{6.7}$$

$$+ \int_Q \left\{2H\cdot E\times\nabla\phi - (|E|^2+|H|^2)\frac{\partial\phi}{\partial t}\right\}dxdt \quad .$$

Now

$$\nabla\phi(x,t) = \phi'_\delta(\tau)\nabla\tau = -\phi'_\delta(\tau)\frac{x-x_0}{|x-x_0|} = -\phi'_\delta(\tau)U \ ,$$

where U is a unit vector, and

$$\frac{\partial\phi(x,t)}{\partial t} = -\phi'_\delta(\tau) \quad .$$

Thus, the last integral has the integrand

$$2H\cdot E\times\nabla\phi - (|E|^2+|H|^2)\frac{\partial\phi}{\partial t} = \phi'_\delta(\tau)(-2H\times E\cdot U+|E|^2+|H|^2)$$

$$= \phi'_\delta(\tau)\{|E+H\times U|^2+(H\cdot U)^2\}\geq 0 \ ,$$

since $\phi'_\delta \geq 0$. Hence (6.7) implies

$$2\int_Q (H\cdot G - E\cdot F)\phi\,dxdt \tag{6.8}$$

$$\geq \int_\Omega (|E(x,T)|^2+|H(x,T)|^2)\phi(x,T)\,dx - \int_\Omega (|E(x,0)|^2+|H(x,0)|^2)\phi(x,0)\,dx \ .$$

Finally, if $\delta\to 0$ then $\phi(x,t)$ tends to the characteristic function of $C_a(x_0)$ on Q , and $|\phi(x,t)|\leq 1$ everywhere. Thus passage to the limit $\delta = 0$ in (6.8) is legitimate and yields (6.1).

Making $a\to\infty$ in Theorem 6.1 gives

Corollary 6.2. If $E\in\mathscr{F}_{\text{ELECTRIC}}$ and $H\in\mathscr{F}_{\text{MAGNETIC}}$ then

$$\|E(T)\|^2_{L_2(\Omega)} + \|H(T)\|^2_{L_2(\Omega)} \leq \|E(0)\|^2_{L_2(\Omega)} + \|H(0)\|^2_{L_2(\Omega)}$$

$$+ 2\int_Q \{H\cdot(\nabla\times E + \frac{\partial H}{\partial t}) - E\cdot(\nabla\times H - \frac{\partial E}{\partial t})\}dxdt \ .$$

§7. THE ENERGY INEQUALITY. The purpose of this section is to prove

Theorem 7.1. If $E \in \mathscr{F}_{\text{ELECTRIC}}$ and $H \in \mathscr{F}_{\text{MAGNETIC}}$ then

$$\| E(t)\|^2+\| H(t)\|^2 \le e^T\left[2\int_0^T (\| \nabla\times H-\frac{\partial E}{\partial t}\|^2+\| \nabla\times E+\frac{\partial H}{\partial t}\|^2)\,dt+\| E(0)\|^2+\| H(0)\|^2\right]$$

for every $t \in I$. (Here $\| \ \|$ denotes the $L_2(\Omega)$-norm.)

Proof. Put

$$f(t) = \int_0^t (\| E(\tau)\|^2 + \| H(\tau)\|^2)\,d\tau \quad , \text{ so } f'(t) = \| E(t)\|^2 + \| H(t)\|^2 \ .$$

Then Cor. 6.2, with T replaced by $t \in I$, may be written

$$f'(t) - f'(0) \le 2\int_0^t \{(H, G) - (E, F)\}d\tau$$

with

$$F = \nabla\times H - \frac{\partial E}{\partial t} \ , \quad G = \nabla\times E + \frac{\partial H}{\partial t} \ .$$

Successive applications of Schwarz's inequality to the integral give

$$f'(t) - f'(0) \le 2\left(\int_0^t \| H\| \ \| G\|\,d\tau + \int_0^t \| E\| \ \| F\|\,d\tau\right)$$

$$\le 2\left\{\left(\int_0^t \| G\|^2 d\tau\right)^{\frac{1}{2}}\left(\int_0^t \| H\|^2 d\tau\right)^{\frac{1}{2}} + \left(\int_0^t \| F\|^2 d\tau\right)^{\frac{1}{2}}\left(\int_0^t \| E\|^2 d\tau\right)^{\frac{1}{2}}\right\}$$

$$\le 2\sqrt{f(t)}\left\{\left(\int_0^T \| F\|^2 d\tau\right)^{\frac{1}{2}} + \left(\int_0^T \| G\|^2 d\tau\right)^{\frac{1}{2}}\right\}.$$

Application of the elementary inequalities

$$2ab \le a^2 + b^2 \quad \text{and} \quad (a^{\frac{1}{2}} + b^{\frac{1}{2}})^2 = a+b + 2\sqrt{ab} \le 2(a+b)$$

to the last expression gives

$$f'(t)-f'(0) \le f(t) + 2\int_0^T (\| F\|^2 + \| G\|^2)\,d\tau$$

or

$$f'(t) \le f(t) + K \ , \quad K = f'(0)+ 2\int_0^T (\| F\|^2+\| G\|^2)\,d\tau$$

for all $t \in I$. Integration of this inequality, with the initial condition $f(0) = 0$, gives

$$f(t) \le K(e^t-1) \ , \quad f'(t) \le Ke^t \quad \text{for } t \in I$$

which is equivalent to the energy inequality.

§8. THE EXISTENCE THEOREM FOR SOLUTIONS WITH FINITE ENERGY. The proofs of Theorem 4.1(b), Corollary 4.2(b) and Theorem 4.3 are completed in this section. The existence statement of Theorem 4.1(b) asserts the existence of a solution with finite energy for all data

$$(F, G, E_0, H_0) \in W .$$

The proof is based on the uniqueness theorem, as formulated in Theorem 5.2, and the energy inequality (Theorem 7.1). By Theorem 5.2 there exists a sequence

$$E_n, H_n \in D(\Lambda) = \mathscr{F}_{\text{ELECTRIC}} \times \mathscr{F}_{\text{MAGNETIC}}$$

such that

$$\Lambda(E_n, H_n) = (\nabla\times H_n - \frac{\partial E_n}{\partial t}, \nabla\times E_n + \frac{\partial H_n}{\partial t}, E_n(0), H_n(0) \to (F, G, E_0, H_0)$$

in W , i.e.

$$\left.\begin{aligned} \nabla\times H_n - \frac{\partial E_n}{\partial t} &\equiv F_n \to F \\ \nabla\times E_n + \frac{\partial H_n}{\partial t} &\equiv G_n \to G \end{aligned}\right\} \text{ in } L_2(Q)$$

and

$$\left.\begin{aligned} E_n(0) &\to E_0 \\ H_n(0) &\to H_0 \end{aligned}\right\} \text{ in } L_2(\Omega) .$$

Applying Theorem 7.1 to the differences $E_m - E_n$, $H_m - H_n$ gives

$$\|E_m(t) - E_n(t)\|^2 + \|H_m(t) - H_n(t)\|^2 \leq e^T[2\|F_m - F_n\|^2_{L_2(Q)} + 2\|G_m - G_n\|^2_{L_2(Q)}$$
$$+ \|E_m(0) - E_n(0)\|^2 + \|H_m(0) - H_n(0)\|^2] . \tag{8.1}$$

It follows that $E_n(t)$ and $H_n(t)$ are Cauchy sequences in $L_2(\Omega)$ for each $t \in I$. Thus the limits

$$E(t) = \lim_{n\to\infty} E_n(t) , \quad H(t) = \lim_{n\to\infty} H_n(t) \tag{8.2}$$

exist in $L_2(\Omega)$, for each $t \in I$, by the Riesz-Fischer theorem. Making $m\to\infty$ in (8.1) gives

$$\| E(t) - E_n(t) \|^2 + \| H(t) - H_n(t) \|^2$$

$$\leq e^T [2 \| F - F_n \|^2_{L_2(Q)} + 2 \| G - G_n \|^2_{L_2(Q)} + \| E_0 - E_n(0) \|^2 + \| H_0 - H_n(0) \|^2] \, , \tag{8.3}$$

$$t \in I \, ,$$

which shows that the convergence in (8.2) is uniform in t. It follows that

$$\lim_{n\to\infty} E_n = E \, , \qquad \lim_{n\to\infty} H_n = H \quad \text{in } L_2(Q) \, . \tag{8.4}$$

If $\Phi \in \mathscr{F}_{\text{ELECTRIC}}$ and $\Phi(T) = 0$ then

$$\int_0^T (H_n, \nabla\times \Phi)\,dt = \int_0^T (\nabla\times H_n, \Phi)\,dt$$

and

$$\int_0^T (E_n, \frac{\partial\Phi}{\partial t})\,dt = -\int_0^T (\frac{\partial E_n}{\partial t}, \Phi)\,dt - (E_n(0), \Phi(0)) \, ,$$

whence by addition

$$\int_0^T \{(H_n, \nabla\times \Phi) + (E_n, \frac{\partial\Phi}{\partial t})\}dt = \int_0^T (F_n, \Phi)\,dt - (E_n(0), \Phi(0)) \, .$$

Similarly, if $\Psi \in \mathscr{F}_{\text{MAGNETIC}}$ and $\Psi(T) = 0$ then

$$\int_0^T \{(E_n, \nabla\times \Psi) - (H_n, \frac{\partial\Psi}{\partial t})\}dt = \int_0^T (G_n, \Psi)\,dt + (H_n(0), \Psi(0)) \, .$$

Making $n\to\infty$ in these identities and using (8.4) and the convergence of the data gives identities (3.2); i.e. the pair E, H is the solution with finite energy for the data (F, G, E_0, H_0). This completes the proof of Theorem 4.1(b).

Proof of Corollary 4.2(b). For each n the curves

$$t \to E_n(t) \in L_2(\Omega) \, , \quad t \to H_n(t) \in L_2(\Omega)$$

are continuous (Theorem 2.2). Hence Corollary 4.2(b) follows from the uniform convergence of $E_n(t)$ to $E(t)$ and $H_n(t)$ to $H(t)$.

Proof of Theorem 4.3. The energy inequality holds for each of the pairs E_n, H_n by Theorem 7.1. Making $n\to\infty$ in these inequalities gives Theorem 4.3.

Proof of Theorem 4.2 for Solutions with Finite Energy. The domain of dependence inequality (6.1) holds for each of the pairs E_n, H_n.

Making $h \to \infty$ in these inequalities gives Theorem 4.2 for the corresponding solution with finite energy.

§9. THE EXISTENCE OF STRICT SOLUTIONS. The purpose of this section is to prove the existence statement of Theorem 4.1(c). The strict solution, when it exists, must coincide with the solution with finite energy whose existence has been proved. Hence it is sufficient to prove

Theorem 9.1. Let

$$F \in L_2(I, \overset{0}{L}_2(\nabla\times;\Omega)) \quad , \quad G \in L_2(I, L_2(\nabla\times,\Omega))$$

and

$$E_0 \in \overset{0}{L}_2(\nabla\times,\Omega) \quad , \qquad H_0 \in L_2(\nabla\times,\Omega) \quad .$$

Then the solution with finite energy for the data (F, G, E_0, H_0) is also a strict solution.

The proof makes use of

Lemma 9.1. Let the pair E, H be the solution with finite energy corresponding to data $(F, G, E_0, H_0) \in W$. Then writing

$$E_1(t) = \int_0^t E(\tau)\,d\tau \quad , \quad H_1(t) = \int_0^t H(\tau)\,d\tau \quad , \text{ etc.}$$

as in §5,

$$E_1 \in \mathscr{F}_{\text{ELECTRIC}} \quad , \quad H_1 \in \mathscr{F}_{\text{MAGNETIC}} \tag{9.1}$$

and the pair E_1, H_1 is the strict solution for the data

$$(F_1(t) - E_0, G_1(t) + H_0, 0, 0) \quad ;$$

i.e.

$$\left.\begin{cases} \nabla\times H_1(x,t) - E(x,t) = F_1(x,t) - E_0(x) \\ \nabla\times E_1(x,t) \quad H(x,t) = G_1(x,t) + H_0(x) \end{cases}\right\} \text{for almost all } (x,t) \in Q \; . \tag{9.2}$$

Proof. By Lemma 5.1 the following identities hold for almost all $t \in I$

$$\begin{aligned} (H_1(t), \nabla\times A) &= (F_1(t) + E(t) - E_0, A) \quad , \quad \text{all } A \in \overset{0}{L}_2(\nabla\times,\Omega) \quad , \\ (E_1(t), \nabla\times B) &= (G_1(t) - H(t) + H_0, B) \quad , \quad \text{all } B \in L_2(\nabla\times,\Omega) \quad . \end{aligned} \tag{9.3}$$

Since $C_0^1(\Omega) \subset \overset{0}{L}_2(\nabla\times,\Omega) \subset L_2(\nabla\times,\Omega)$, these identities imply that $\nabla\times H_1(t)$ and $\nabla\times E_1(t)$ exist in $L_2(\Omega)$, for almost all $t \in I$, and have the values indicated in (9.2). These equations imply that

$\nabla\times E_1$ and $\nabla\times H_1$ are in $L_2(Q)$. Moreover

$$E_1(t) \in \overset{0}{L}_2(\nabla\times, \Omega) \quad \text{for almost all} \quad t \in I ,$$

by the second identity of (9.3). Finally, E_1 and H_1 are in $L_2(\frac{d}{dt}, I, L_2(\Omega))$, by Theorem 2.2, and (9.1) follows.

Another lemma that is used in the proof of Theorem 9.1 is

Lemma 9.2. If $\Phi \in L_2(I, L_2(\nabla\times, \Omega))$ then $\Phi_1 \in L_2(I, L_2(\nabla\times, \Omega))$ and

$$\nabla\times \Phi_1(t) = \int_0^t \nabla\times \Phi(\tau)\, d\tau .$$

Proof. If $A \in C_0^1(\Omega)$ then

$$(\Phi_1(t), \nabla\times A) = \int_0^t (\Phi(\tau), \nabla\times A)\, d\tau = \int_0^t (\nabla\times \Phi(\tau), A)\, d\tau = \left(\int_0^t \nabla\times \Phi(\tau)\, d\tau, A\right)$$

Proof of Theorem 9.1. Let the pair $\widetilde{E}$, $\widetilde{H}$ be the solution with finite energy for the data

$$(\widetilde{F}, \widetilde{G}, \widetilde{E}_0, \widetilde{H}_0) = (-\nabla\times G, \nabla\times F, \nabla\times H_0, -\nabla\times E_0) \in W .$$

Then, by Lemma 9.1 (equations (9.2)) and Lemma 9.2,

$$\widetilde{E}(t) = \widetilde{E}_0 - \widetilde{F}_1(t) + \nabla\times \widetilde{H}_1(t) = \nabla\times H_0 + \int_0^t \nabla\times G(\tau)\, d\tau + \nabla\times \widetilde{H}_1(t)$$

$$= \nabla\times (H_0 + G_1(t) + \widetilde{H}_1(t)) ,$$

and

$$\widetilde{H}(t) = \widetilde{H}_0 + \widetilde{G}_1(t) - \nabla\times \widetilde{E}_1(t) = -\nabla\times E_0 + \int_0^t \nabla\times F(\tau)\, d\tau - \nabla\times \widetilde{E}_1(t)$$

$$= \nabla\times (-E_0 + F_1(t) - \widetilde{E}_1(t))$$

for almost all $t \in I$. These may be written

$$\widetilde{E}(t) = \nabla\times \mathscr{H}(t) , \quad \widetilde{H}(t) = -\nabla\times \mathscr{E}(t) \tag{9.4}$$

where

$$\mathscr{E}(t) = E_0 - F_1(t) + \widetilde{E}_1(t) ,$$
$$\mathscr{H}(t) = H_0 + G_1(t) + \widetilde{H}_1(t) . \tag{9.5}$$

Theorem 9.1 now follows from

Lemma 9.3. The pair $\mathscr{E}, \mathscr{H}$ is the strict solution of the diffraction problem for the data (F, G, E_0, H_0) .

Indeed, since strict solutions are also solutions with finite energy, Lemma 9.3 implies

$$E = \mathscr{E} \quad , \qquad H = \mathscr{H}$$

by the uniqueness theorem (Theorem 5.1).

Proof of Lemma 9.3. $\mathscr{E}$ and $\mathscr{H}$ are in $L_2(\frac{d}{dt}, I, L_2(\Omega))$ by (9.5) and Theorem 2.2. Also, (9.5) implies

$$\mathscr{E}(t) \in L_2^0(\nabla \times, \Omega) \quad \text{for almost all} \quad t \in I \ ,$$

since E_0 , $F_1(t)$ and $\widetilde{E}_1(t)$ all have this property ($\widetilde{E}_1$ by Lemma 9.1). Finally, (9.4) implies that $\mathscr{E}(t)$ and $\mathscr{H}(t)$ have square-integrable curls. Combining these results gives

$$\mathscr{E} \in \mathscr{F}_{\text{ELECTRIC}} \ , \qquad \mathscr{H} \in \mathscr{F}_{\text{MAGNETIC}} \ .$$

Next, (9.4) and (9.5) imply

$$\left.\begin{aligned} \frac{\partial \mathscr{E}(t)}{\partial t} &= -F(t) + \widetilde{E}(t) = -F(t) + \nabla \times \mathscr{H}(t) \\ \frac{\partial \mathscr{H}(t)}{\partial t} &= G(t) + \widetilde{H}(t) = G(t) - \nabla \times \mathscr{E}(t) \end{aligned}\right\} \text{for almost all} \quad t \in I \ ,$$

i.e. $\mathscr{E}$ and $\mathscr{H}$ satisfy Maxwell's equations (3.1) with source terms F and G . Finally (9.5) implies

$$\mathscr{E}(0) = E_0 \ , \qquad \mathscr{H}(0) = H_0 \ .$$

This completes the proof.

§10. THE UNIQUENESS OF SOLUTIONS WITH LOCALLY FINITE ENERGY. The purpose of this section is to prove the uniqueness statement of Theorem 4.1(a) and Corollary 4.1. The uniqueness statement is equivalent to

Theorem 10.1. If the pair E, H is a solution with locally finite energy for data $(F, G, E_0, H_0) = (0, 0, 0, 0)$ then $E = H = 0$ in $L_2^{loc}(Q)$.

Proof. E and H satisfy the identity

$$\int_0^T \{(H, \nabla \times \Phi + \frac{\partial \Psi}{\partial t}) + (E, \frac{\partial \Phi}{\partial t} - \nabla \times \Psi)\} dt = 0 \ , \qquad (10.1)$$

obtained by subtracting identities (3.2), for all fields $\Phi \in \mathscr{F}_{ELECTRIC}$, $\Psi \in \mathscr{F}_{MAGNETIC}$ that are equivalent to zero outside a bounded measurable set $(K \times I) \cap Q$ and satisfy $\Phi(T) = \Psi(T) = 0$. This suggests choosing Φ and Ψ as the solutions of the "backwards" diffraction problem

$$\nabla \times \Psi - \frac{\partial \Phi}{\partial t} = F \equiv \begin{cases} -E & \text{in } (K \times I) \cap Q \\ 0 & \text{elsewhere} \end{cases},$$

$$\nabla \times \Phi + \frac{\partial \Psi}{\partial t} = G \equiv \begin{cases} H & \text{in } (K \times I) \cap Q \\ 0 & \text{elsewhere} \end{cases},$$

with

$$\Phi(T) = \Psi(T) = 0 ,$$

and K an arbitrary bounded measurable set. Then (10.1) would give

$$\int_{(K \times I) \cap Q} (|E|^2 + |H|^2)\, dxdt = 0 \tag{10.2}$$

for all bounded measurable $K \subset R^3$, which implies $E = H = 0$ in $L_2^{loc}(Q)$. However, the pair Φ, Ψ is known to exist as a solution with finite energy only, and hence may not be allowable in (10.1). To remedy this let F_n and G_n be sequences of functions in $C_0^1((K \times I) \cap Q)$ such that

$$F_n \to F \,, \quad G_n \to G \text{ in } L_2((K \times I) \cap Q) \,. \tag{10.3}$$

(It is well known that such functions are dense in L_2). Then the backwards diffraction problem with data $(F_n, G_n, 0, 0)$ has a strict solution pair Φ_n, Ψ_n by Theorem 9.1. (The data obviously satisfy the hypotheses of Theorem 9.1.) Moreover,, Φ_n and Ψ_n are equivalent to zero outside a bounded measurable set by Theorem 6.1, since the data have this property; and $\Phi_n(T) = \Psi_n(T) = 0$. Thus the pair Φ_n, Ψ_n is allowable in (10.1) and gives

$$\int_{(K \times I) \cap Q} \{H \cdot G_n - E \cdot F_n\} dxdt = 0 \quad \text{for } n = 1, 2, \ldots \,.$$

Making $n \to \infty$ and using the property (10.3) and the definition of F and G gives (10.2), which completes the proof.

Proof of Corollary 4.1. The solution with locally finite energy for the time-interval $0 \le t \le T'$ with $T' > T$ is also a solution for the time-interval $0 \leq t \leq T$. Hence, the two solutions coincide for $0 \leq t \leq T$, by the uniqueness theorem.

§11. THE EXISTENCE OF SOLUTIONS WITH LOCALLY FINITE ENERGY. The existence statement of Theorem 4.1(a), Corollary 4.2(a) and Theorem 4.2 are proved in this section.

Proof of the Existence Statement of Theorem 4.1(a). Divide R^3 into unit cubes with vertices at the points with integer coordinates and let

$$C_n = \{x : 0 \leq x_i - k_i^n \leq 1 \text{ for } i = 1, 2, 3\}, \quad n = 1, 2, \ldots$$

be an enumeration of the cubes that intersect Ω . Write

$$\Omega_n = \Omega \cap C_n, \quad \text{so } \Omega = \Omega_1 \cup \Omega_2 \cup \cdots,$$

and

$$Q_n = \Omega_n \times I, \quad \text{so } Q = Q_1 \cup Q_2 \cup \cdots .$$

Define

$$F_n(x, t) = \begin{cases} F(x, t), & (x, t) \in Q_n \\ 0, & \text{elsewhere} \end{cases}, \quad G_n(x, t) = \begin{cases} G(x, t), & (x, t) \in Q_n \\ 0, & \text{elsewhere} \end{cases}$$

and

$$E_0^n(x) = \begin{cases} E_0(x), & x \in \Omega_n \\ 0, & \text{elsewhere} \end{cases}, \quad H_0^n(x) = \begin{cases} H_0(x), & x \in \Omega_n \\ 0, & \text{elsewhere} \end{cases}$$

so

$$F = \sum_{n=1}^{\infty} F_n, \quad G = \sum_{n=1}^{\infty} G_n, \quad E_0 = \sum_{n=1}^{\infty} E_0^n, \quad H_0 = \sum_{n=1}^{\infty} H_0^n .$$

Then F_n and G_n are in $L_2(Q)$ and E_0^n and H_0^n are in $L_2(\Omega)$ for each n . Let the pair E_n, H_n denote the corresponding solution with finite energy. E_n and H_n are equivalent to zero outside the set

$$(\Omega \cap \{x : -T \leq x_i - k_i^n \leq 1 + T \text{ for } i = 1, 2, 3\}) \times I$$

by the domain of dependence theorem for solutions with finite energy (proved at the end of §8). Hence, the sums

$$E(x, t) = \sum_{n=1}^{\infty} E_n(x, t), \quad H(x, t) = \sum_{n=1}^{\infty} H_n(x, t)$$

are finite for each $(x, t) \in Q$ and define fields E and H in $L_2^{loc}(Q)$.

Suppose that $\Phi \in \mathscr{F}_{\text{ELECTRIC}}$, $\Psi \in \mathscr{F}_{\text{MAGNETIC}}$, $\Phi(T) = \Psi(T) = 0$ and Φ and Ψ are equivalent to zero outside $(K \times I) \cap Q$ where K is bounded and measurable. Let $n_1, \ldots, n_p$ be the indices n for which E_n and H_n are not both equivalent to zero on $(K \times I) \cap Q$. Then

$$\int_0^T \{(H_n, \nabla\times \Phi) + (E_n, \frac{\partial \Phi}{\partial t}) - (F_n, \Phi)\}dt + (E_0^n, \Phi(0)) = 0$$

and

$$\int_0^T \{(E_n, \nabla\times \Psi) - (H_n, \frac{\partial \Psi}{\partial t}) - (G_n, \Psi)\}dt - (H_0^n, \Psi(0)) = 0 ,$$

the scalar products being

$$(H_n, \nabla\times \Phi) = (H_n, \nabla\times \Phi)_{L_2(K\cap\Omega)} , \text{ etc.}$$

Summing the identities for $n = n_1, \ldots, n_p$ then gives identities (3.2). Thus the pair E, H is the solution with locally finite energy for the data (F, G, E_0, H_0).

Proof of Corollary 4.2(a). This follows from the existence proof and Corollary 4.2(b) since on any set $K \cap \Omega$ with K bounded and measurable, $E(t)$ and $H(t)$ are sums of a finite number of solutions with finite energy.

Proof of Theorem 4.2. This has been proved for solutions with finite energy at the end of §8. If the pair E, H is a solution with locally finite energy consider the fields

$$\widetilde{E}(x, t) = \phi(x, t)\, E(x, t) , \quad \widetilde{H}(x, t) = \phi(x, t)\, H(x, t)$$

where $\phi \in C^1(R^4)$ and has compact support, and $\phi(x, t) \equiv 1$ on $C_a(x_0) \cap Q$. It is easy to verify that the pair $\widetilde{E}, \widetilde{H}$ is a solution with finite energy for the data

$$\widetilde{F} = \phi F + \nabla\phi \times H - \frac{\partial \phi}{\partial t} E ,$$

$$\widetilde{G} = \phi G + \nabla\phi \times E + \frac{\partial \phi}{\partial t} H ,$$

$$\widetilde{E}_0 = \phi(0)\, E_0 , \quad \widetilde{H}_0 = \phi(0)\, H_0 .$$

Hence the domain of dependence inequality holds for $\widetilde{E}, \widetilde{H}$. This inequality is identical with the corresponding one for E, H because $\phi(x, t) \equiv 1$ on $C_a(x_0) \cap Q$, whence

$$\widetilde{E} = E , \ \widetilde{H} = H , \ \widetilde{F} = F , \ \widetilde{G} = G \ \text{ in } C_a(x_0) \cap Q .$$

ACKNOWLEDGMENT

I should like to express my appreciation to Professor C. R. DePrima of the California Institute of Technology for a number of stimulating discussions, during the preparation of this paper, which led to simplification and improvement of some of the results.

REFERENCES

1. Bouwkamp, C. J., A note on singularities occurring at sharp edges in electromagnetic diffraction theory, Physica XII, No. 7(1946) 467-474.
2. Friedrichs, K. O., The identity of weak and strong extensions of differential operators, Trans. Amer. Math. Soc., Vol. 55, No. 1 (1944) 132-151.
3. Hille, E. and Phillips, R. S., Functional Analysis and Semi-Groups, Amer. Math. Soc. Colloquium Publications, Vol. XXXI (1957).
4. Ladyzhenskaya, O. A., On non-stationary operator equations and their application to linear problems of mathematical physics, Mat. Sbornik, Vol. 45(87) (1958) 123-158 (Russian)
5. Lions, J.-L., Problèmes mixtes abstraits, Proceedings of the International Congress of Mathematicians, Edinburgh 1958, Cambridge University Press (1960).
6. Lions, J.-L., (a book on initial-boundary value problems, to be published by Springer-Verlag).
7. Phillips, R. S., Dissipative operators and hyperbolic systems of partial differential equations, Trans. Amer. Math. Soc., Vol. 90, No. 2(1959) 193-254.
8. Riesz, F. and Sz.-Nagy, B., Functional Analysis, F. Ungar Publ. Co., New York (1955).
9. Rohkind, I. I., Non-stationary diffraction of electromagnetic waves, Vestnik Leningrad Univ., Vol. 13, No. 7 (1958) 109-204 (see Mathematical Reviews, v. 20(1959) p. 731).
10. Vishik, M. and Ladyzhenskaya, O. A., Boundary value problems for partial differential equations and certain classes of operator equations, Uspehi Mat. Nauk (N. S.) 11(1956), No. 6(72), 41-97 (Russian = A. M. S. Translation, series 2, Vol. 10, pp. 223-281).

ACKNOWLEDGMENTS

[illegible] California Institute [illegible]

REFERENCES

1. [illegible] Phys. Rev. [illegible]

2. [illegible] Amer. Math. Soc. [illegible]

3. [illegible]

4. [illegible]

5. [illegible] Proceedings of the [illegible]

6. [illegible]

7. [illegible]

8. [illegible] Numerical Analysis [illegible]

9. [illegible]

10. [illegible]

ALBERT E. HEINS

Function-theoretic Aspects of Diffraction Theory

INTRODUCTION. The analytical studies of diffraction theory have brought forth many interesting function-theoretic problems. Probably the earliest significant investigation of this type is to be found in Sommerfeld's studies [1] of multi-valued wave and potential functions. From his work, there followed the first solution of the problem of the diffraction of a wave by a half plane. It was almost a half a century later that the second significant step took place. In the early 1940's the method which Wiener and Hopf [2] used in the study of a certain class of convolution integral equations was applied to a large and interesting group of integral equations which arose in diffraction and scattering theory. Among other things, these efforts produced another solution of the half plane problem and simultaneously provided a major generalization to it. During the same period, Lewy [3] produced the solution of certain problems arising in the linearized theory of gravity-waves and his methods have found their way into the study of scattering by a wedge.

What is common to this group of problems aside from the fact that it arises from the study of diffraction and scattering of waves? A common mathematical tool has been used—that is the theory of analytic continuation from the theory of analytic functions of a single complex variable. In Sommerfeld's work we find studies of the continuation of a multi-valued function from one sheet of a Riemann surface to the other sheet (or sheets). In the method of Wiener and Hopf [4], we find another version of analytic continuation. In this case, we have the fact that we know that elements of two analytic functions are analytic in two different half planes and these two half planes have a common strip of analyticity. These analytic functions do not arise from representations of solutions of the wave equation, but rather from the Fourier transforms of known and unknown functions in the integral equation. It is possible to rearrange these analytic functions so that the resulting equation represents an entire function of algebraic growth, and one may then invoke the Liouville theorem.

In the work of Lewy, essential use is made of the reflection principle. Laplace's equation in two independent variables plus boundary conditions on the sides of a wedge are reduced to a non-homogeneous ordinary differential equation with constant coefficients (in the complex domain).

We now turn to another group of problems in which the methods of analytic continuation promises to play an important role, and which we shall describe in some detail in the later sections of this paper. There is in three dimensional potential theory and wave motion a class of geometries which are axially symmetric. To this class belong such configurations as the circular disk, the circular ring, the spherical cap, etc. We require solutions of Laplace's equation or the wave equation which satisfy certain boundary conditions on the body (and these boundary conditions need not be independent of the polar angle with respect to the axis of symmetry) as well as certain conditions at infinity. Here we shall make use of the well-known fact that for solutions of either of these equations which are regular on the geometric axis of symmetry, it is possible to determine the solution as soon as the solution (or a non-vanishing radial derivative of it) is known on the axis. On the one hand, for example, we have the "real" representation* for some unknown boundary element on the disk—the so-called Helmholtz representation. On the other hand, we have a "complex"# representation in terms of the function on the axis of revolution which has been continued into the complex plane—that is the Poisson representation [5], [6]. By blending these two representations, one arrives at another integral equation which oftentimes gives interesting information. We shall limit ourselves to the geometry of the circular disk since time will not permit us any further detail.

2. THE CIRCULAR DISK—POTENTIAL THEORY. We examine here the problem of a circular disk of radius a maintained at unit potential with no external field. This implies the solution of the partial differential equation

$$\frac{\partial^2 V}{\partial r^2} + \frac{1}{r}\frac{\partial V}{\partial r} + \frac{\partial^2 V}{\partial z^2} = 0 \ , \quad r = \sqrt{x^2 + y^2}$$

subject to the boundary condition $V = 1$ on the disk and $V \to 0$, $\sqrt{r^2 + z^2} \to \infty$. It is well known from the Helmholtz representation that

$$V(r, z) = \frac{1}{4\pi} \int_0^a \int_0^{2\pi} \frac{\sigma(t, \theta') \, t \, dt \, d\theta'}{\sqrt{t^2 + r^2 - 2tr\cos(\theta - \theta') + z^2}}$$

where $\sigma(t, \theta')$ is the discontinuity in the z derivative of V on the disk and a is the radius of the disk. It was shown by Copson [7] in 1947 that this integral equation could be reduced to one which involved two successive convolutions. However, one of these convolutions is contained in the Poisson representation, a useful tool as we shall see later [8].

In view of the fact that V is independent of θ , so is σ . Furthermore on the z axis $(z>0)$, we have

$$V(0,z) = \frac{1}{4\pi}\int_0^a\int_0^{2\pi}\frac{\sigma(t)\,t\,dt\,d\theta'}{\sqrt{t^2+z^2}} = \frac{1}{2}\int_0^a\frac{\sigma(t)\,t\,dt}{\sqrt{t^2+z^2}} \tag{2.1}$$

However, according to the Poisson integral representation

$$V(r,z) = \frac{1}{\pi}\int_0^{\pi} V(0, z+ir\cos\theta)\,d\theta \tag{2.2}$$

and this is clearly dependent on the function $V(0,z)$. Hence if we could eliminate $V(0,z)$ between (2.1) and (2.2) we would have a third representation for $V(r,z)$ which might be useful. From (2.2) using the boundary condition on the disk we get

$$1 = \frac{1}{\pi}\int_0^{\pi} V(0, ir\cos\theta)\,d\theta = \frac{1}{\pi}\int_{-r}^{r}\frac{V(0,it)\,dt}{\sqrt{r^2-t^2}} = \frac{1}{\pi}\int_0^{r}\frac{[V(0,it)+V(0,-it)]\,dt}{\sqrt{r^2-t^2}} \tag{2.3}$$

This equation becomes, when we write $t^2=\beta$ and $r^2=\alpha$,

$$\frac{1}{2\pi}\int_0^{\alpha}\frac{[V(0,i\sqrt{\beta})+V(0,-i\sqrt{\beta})]\,d\beta}{\sqrt{\beta}\,\sqrt{\alpha-\beta}} = 1 ,$$

a Volterra integral equation. Clearly, $V(0,i\sqrt{\beta})+V(0,-i\sqrt{\beta})$ is real for $\beta>0$ and we find immediately that

$$V(0,it)+V(0,-it) = 2\,\mathrm{Re}\,V(0,it) = 2, \quad 0\le t<a .$$

Now let us return to (2.1). If we continue $V(0,z)$ into the domain of the complex variable $z=\rho+i\tau$ and let $\rho\to 0^+$, we have for $0<t<\tau<a$

$$V(0,i\tau) = \frac{1}{2}\left[\frac{1}{i}\int_0^{\tau}\frac{\sigma(t)\,t\,dt}{\sqrt{\tau^2-t^2}} + \int_{\tau}^{a}\frac{\sigma(t)\,t\,dt}{\sqrt{t^2-\tau^2}}\right] .$$

The argument of the $\sqrt{t^2+z^2}$ for z complex has been chosen to be zero for z on the real axis. Accordingly, when $0<t<\tau<a$, the argument of $\sqrt{t^2+z^2}$ is $\pi/2$ and is zero when $0<\tau<t<a$. Now

$$\mathrm{Re}[V(0, i\tau)] = \frac{1}{2}\int_{\tau}^{a} \frac{\sigma(t)\,t\,dt}{\sqrt{t^2-\tau^2}}$$

since $\sigma(t)$ is real. Hence, we get

$$\int_{\tau}^{a} \frac{\sigma(t)\,t\,dt}{\sqrt{t^2-\tau^2}} = 2 \,, \quad 0 \le \tau < a$$

for which we find the solution

$$\sigma(r) = \frac{4}{\pi\sqrt{a^2-r^2}} \,, \quad 0 \le r < a \,.$$

The corresponding Neumann problem proceeds in much the same fashion. We use as a Helmholtz representation

$$V(r, \theta, z) = \frac{1}{4\pi} \int_0^a \int_0^{2\pi} [V(t, \theta', 0)] \frac{\partial}{\partial z'} \frac{1}{\rho} t\,dt\,d\theta' \tag{2.4}$$

where $[V(r, \theta, 0)]$ is the discontinuity of V on the disk and $\rho = \sqrt{t^2 + r^2 - 2rt\cos(\theta-\theta') + (z-z')^2}$. The z' derivative of $1/\rho$ is evaluated at $z' = 0$. Now due to the $z-z'$ dependence of ρ, we may replace $\partial/\partial z'$ by $-\partial/\partial z$ so that (2.4) may be rewritten as

$$V(0, \theta, z) = -\frac{1}{4\pi} \frac{\partial}{\partial z} \int_0^a \int_0^{2\pi} \frac{[V]\,t\,dt\,d\theta'}{\sqrt{t^2 + z^2}}$$

and for solutions which are independent of θ, this reduces to

$$\bar{V}(0, z) = -\frac{1}{2} \frac{\partial}{\partial z} \int_0^a \frac{[\bar{V}]\,t\,dt}{\sqrt{t^2 + z^2}} \tag{2.5}$$

where

$$\bar{V}(0, z) = \frac{1}{2\pi} \int_0^{2\pi} V(0, \theta, z)\,d\theta \,.$$

Equation (2.5) may be rewritten as

$$\int_0^z \bar{V}(0, \lambda)\,d\lambda + C = -\frac{1}{2}\int_0^a \frac{[\bar{V}]\,t\,dt}{\sqrt{t^2 + z^2}}$$

where C is a constant of integration. Save for the integral on the left side of this equation, it has the same character as the one which we use in the Dirichlet problem. Suppose we continue z into the domain of the complex variable $z = \rho + i\tau$ and let $\rho \to 0^+$, $0 \le \tau < a$.

Then

$$\int_0^{\tau} \bar{V}(0, i\lambda)\, i d\lambda + C = -\frac{1}{2}\left[\int_0^{\tau} \frac{[\bar{V}]\, t\, dt}{i\sqrt{\tau^2-t^2}} + \int_{\tau}^{a} \frac{[\bar{V}]\, t\, dt}{\sqrt{t^2-\tau^2}}\right] .$$

From this last equation, we obtain (noting that $[\bar{V}]$ is real)

$$\frac{1}{2}\int_{\tau}^{a} \frac{[\bar{V}]\, t\, dt}{\sqrt{t^2-\tau^2}} = -C + \int_0^{\tau} \operatorname{Im} \bar{V}(0, i\lambda)\, d\lambda \quad . \tag{2.6}$$

A knowledge of $\operatorname{Im}\bar{V}(0,i\lambda)$ will determine the left side of this equation. From the Poisson integral representation, we have

$$\frac{\partial \bar{V}(r, z)}{\partial z} = \frac{1}{\pi}\int_{-r}^{r} \frac{dt}{\sqrt{r^2-t^2}} \frac{\partial \bar{V}}{\partial z}(0, z + it)$$

$$= \frac{2}{\pi}\int_0^{r} \frac{1}{\sqrt{r^2-t^2}} \frac{\partial}{\partial z} \operatorname{Re} \bar{V}(0, z + it)\, dt$$

$$= \frac{2}{\pi}\int_0^{r} \frac{1}{\sqrt{r^2-t^2}} \frac{\partial}{\partial t} \operatorname{Im} \bar{V}(0, z + it)\, dt \quad .$$

Hence, the Poisson integral representation produces $\operatorname{Im}\bar{V}(0, it)$ in the Neumann problem and equation (2.6) may be solved for $[\bar{V}]$. Depending on specific situations, there may be order requirements on $[\bar{V}]$ which will serve to evaluate the constant C .

This method we have described enables us to solve potential problems of this type which are not independent of θ . Heins and MacCamy [10, 11] have described a differential operator which enables one to find each Fourier harmonic about the z axis by the above method, but we shall not pursue this point here.

As a final aspect of such axially symmetric representations, we consider forms of the type

$$V(r, z) = \frac{1}{\pi}\int_{-a}^{a} \frac{f(t)\, dt}{\sqrt{r^2 + (z+it)^2}} \tag{2.7}$$

where for the time being we don't specify $f(t)$ except for the fact that this integral has a meaning. It is clear that $V(r, z)$ satisfies the Laplace equation which is independent of θ . We shall show that (2.7) is a product of the Helmholtz and Poisson representations. Observe first that for the Dirichlet problem, $\operatorname{Re} V(0, i\tau) = 0$, $|\tau| > a$ and accordingly, for complex z ,

$$V(0, z) = \frac{1}{\pi}\int_{-i\infty}^{i\infty} \frac{\operatorname{Re}[V(0, t)]\, dt}{t-z} + i\gamma$$

$$= -\frac{1}{\pi}\int_{-a}^{a} \frac{\operatorname{Re}[V(0, it)]\, dt}{it-z} + i\gamma$$

since an analytic function may be given in terms of its real part on the boundary of the domain (in this case the half plane $\mathrm{Re}\, z \geq 0$). γ is an arbitrary real constant. Hence

$$\begin{aligned} V(r, z) &= \frac{1}{\pi}\int_0^{\pi} V(0, z + ir\cos\theta)\, d\theta \\ &= \frac{1}{\pi}\int_0^{\pi} d\theta \left[-\frac{1}{\pi}\int_{-a}^{a} \frac{\mathrm{Re}[V(0, i\tau)]\, d\tau}{i\tau - z - ir\cos\theta} + i\gamma \right] \\ &= -\frac{1}{\pi}\int_{-a}^{a} \frac{\mathrm{Re}[V(0, i\tau)]\, d\tau}{\sqrt{(z+i\tau)^2 + r^2}} + i\gamma \, . \end{aligned}$$

Accordingly we can identify $f(t)$ in (2.7) with $-\mathrm{Re}[V(0, it)]$ in (2.8) if $\mathrm{Re}\, V(0, it)$ is even in t and $\gamma = 0$. It is not difficult to justify this calculation.

The representation (2.7) deserves some comment. Expressions of this type have been given without derivation and some writers admit that it is a fortunate guess. It has also been claimed that (2.7) has advantages over (2.2) and (2.3) since it involves only one convolution. The fact is that to determine the physically interesting parameter $\partial V/\partial z$ at $z = 0$, $0 \leq r \leq a$ one first has to determine the $\mathrm{Re}\, V(0, i\tau)$ $0 \leq r \leq a$ and then one has to return to the continuation of the Helmholtz representation to the complex domain which involves a second convolution integral. It would appear to the writer that the results are equivalent and the advantages in the present procedure are that the results are expressed in physical parameters directly rather than auxiliary quantities and furthermore special coordinate systems are avoided. In this connection, the work of Love [12], 1949, should be noted.

The results which we described here may be extended to curves, rather than slit cross sections—although whether we can solve the resulting integral equations is a question we will discuss elsewhere. For segments of circular arcs the answer is in the affirmative (Collins [10]).

3. THE CIRCULAR DISK—DIFFRACTION THEORY. Here we are concerned upon a disk of radius a §. Subject to the Sommerfeld radiation condition and appropriate edge conditions on the disk, we are required to solve the scalar wave equation

$$\frac{\partial^2 V}{\partial r^2} + \frac{1}{r}\frac{\partial V}{\partial r} + \frac{1}{r^2}\frac{\partial^2 V}{\partial \theta^2} + \frac{\partial^2 V}{\partial z^2} + k^2 V = 0$$

when a Dirichlet condition is satisfied on the disk—that is $V = 0$ on the disk $0 \leq r \leq a$, $z = 0$. If we assume for the time being that the incident wave has a propagation normal which is perpendicular to the disk, we obtain the Helmholtz representation

$$V(r, \theta, z) = \exp(ikz) + \frac{1}{4\pi}\int_0^a\int_0^{2\pi} \frac{\exp[ik\sqrt{r^2+t^2-2tr\cos(\theta-\theta')+z^2}]}{\sqrt{r^2+t^2-2tr\cos(\theta-\theta')+z^2}}\sigma(t,\theta')t\,dt\,d\theta'$$

where $\sigma(t, \theta)$ is the discontinuity in the normal derivative of $V(r,\theta,z)$ on the disk. In view of the fact that we have axially symmetric excitation—that is, one which is independent of θ, we know that σ and V are independent of θ. Hence for a point on the z axis we have

$$V(0, \theta, z) = \exp(ikz) + \frac{1}{4\pi}\int_0^a\int_0^{2\pi} \frac{\exp[ik\sqrt{t^2+z^2}]}{\sqrt{t^2+z^2}}\sigma(t,\theta')t\,dt\,d\theta' .$$

Upon taking into account the independence on θ of V and σ, this reduces to

$$\bar{V}(0, z) = \exp(ikz) + \frac{1}{2}\int_0^a \frac{\exp[ik\sqrt{t^2+z^2}]}{\sqrt{t^2+z^2}}\bar{\sigma}(t)\,t\,dt \tag{3.1}$$

where

$$\bar{V}(0, z) = \frac{1}{2\pi}\int_0^{2\pi} V(0,\theta,z)\,d\theta$$

and

$$\bar{\sigma}(r) = \frac{1}{2\pi}\int_0^{2\pi}\sigma(r,\theta)\,d\theta .$$

Equation (3.1) is similar to the one we obtained for the Dirichlet problem for the disk in potential theory.

If we now try to proceed as we did in Section 2 and continue z into the domain of the complex variable $z = \rho + i\tau$, we find that we cannot compute $\bar{V}(0, i\tau) + \bar{V}(0, -i\tau)$, $\rho \to 0^+$ in the same manner. In fact $\bar{V}(0, i\tau) + \bar{V}(0, -i\tau)$ is not real since $\bar{\sigma}$ is not real. Nevertheless, this quantity may be obtained without trouble. Let us write $z^2 = -\alpha$, $t^2 = \beta$. Then

$$\bar{V}(0, \sqrt{-\alpha}) = \exp(ik\sqrt{-\alpha}) + \frac{1}{4}\int_0^{a^2} \frac{\exp[ik\sqrt{\beta-\alpha}]}{\sqrt{\beta-\alpha}}\bar{\sigma}(\sqrt{\beta})\,d\beta .$$

$\bar{V}(0, \sqrt{-\alpha})$ is now analytic in the plane cut from $0 < \alpha < \infty$. We choose the branches of $\sqrt{-\alpha}$ and $\sqrt{\beta-\alpha}$ of argument zero for $\alpha < 0$ and $\alpha < \beta$ respectively. Then for $0 < \alpha < a^2$ and the cuthaving been approached from above, we get

$$\bar{V}(0, -i\sqrt{|\alpha|}) = \exp(k\sqrt{|\alpha|}) + \frac{1}{4}\int_0^{\alpha} \frac{\exp[k\sqrt{\alpha-\beta}]}{-i\sqrt{\alpha-\beta}}\bar{\sigma}(\sqrt{\beta})\,d\beta$$

$$+ \frac{1}{4}\int_{\alpha}^{a^2} \frac{\exp[ik\sqrt{\beta-\alpha}]}{\sqrt{\beta-\alpha}}\bar{\sigma}(\sqrt{\beta})\,d\beta ,$$

Hence

$$\bar{V}(0, -i\sqrt{|\alpha|}) + \bar{V}(0, i\sqrt{|\alpha|}) = 2\cosh(k\sqrt{|\alpha|})$$

$$+\frac{i}{2}\int_0^{a^2} \frac{\sinh k\sqrt{\alpha-\beta}}{\sqrt{\alpha-\beta}}\,\bar{\sigma}(\sqrt{\beta})\,d\beta + \frac{1}{2}\int_\alpha^{a^2} \frac{\cos k\sqrt{\beta-\alpha}}{\sqrt{\beta-\alpha}}\,\bar{\sigma}(\sqrt{\beta})\,d\beta \qquad (3.2)$$

In order to find $\bar{V}(0, i\sqrt{|\alpha|}) + \bar{V}(0, -i\sqrt{|\alpha|})$ we recall the Poisson representation for an axially symmetric solution of the wave quation. Here we have that

$$\begin{aligned}\bar{V}(r, z) &= \frac{1}{\pi}\int_0^{\pi} \cos(kr\sin\psi)\bar{V}(0, z + ir\cos\psi)\,d\psi \\ &= \frac{1}{\pi}\int_{-r}^{r} \frac{\cos(k\sqrt{r^2-t^2})}{\sqrt{r^2-t^2}}\,[\bar{V}(0, z+it)]\,dt \\ &= \frac{1}{\pi}\int_0^{r} \frac{\cos(k\sqrt{r^2-t^2})}{\sqrt{r^2-t^2}}[\bar{V}(0, z+it) + \bar{V}(0, z-it)]\,dt \;.\end{aligned}$$

Since $\bar{V}(r, 0) = 0$, $0 \leq r \leq a$, this last equation implies that

$$\bar{V}(0, it) + \bar{V}(0, -it) = 0 \;, \quad 0 \leq t < a \;.$$

Hence (3.2) reduces to

$$\int_\alpha^{a^2} \frac{\cos(k\sqrt{\beta-\alpha})}{\sqrt{\beta-\alpha}}\,\bar{\sigma}(\sqrt{\beta})\,d\beta + i\int_0^{a^2} \frac{\sinh(k\sqrt{\alpha-\beta})}{\sqrt{\alpha-\beta}}\,\bar{\sigma})\sqrt{\beta})\,d\beta = -4\cosh k\sqrt{\alpha}$$

$$0 < \alpha < a^2 \;. \qquad (3.3)$$

Now if we write $a^2 - \beta = \mu$ and $a^2 - \alpha = \lambda$, equation (3.3) assumes the form

$$\int_0^{\lambda} \frac{\cos(k\sqrt{\lambda-\mu})}{\sqrt{\lambda-\mu}}\,\bar{\sigma}(\sqrt{a^2-\mu})\,d\mu + i\int_0^{a^2} \frac{\sinh(k\sqrt{\mu-\lambda})}{\sqrt{\mu-\lambda}}\,\bar{\sigma}(\sqrt{a^2-\mu})\,d\mu$$

$$= -4\cosh(k\sqrt{a^2-\lambda}) \;, \quad 0 < \lambda < a^2 \;. \qquad (3.4)$$

It is possible to invert the first integral in (3.4) so that we obtain a regular Fredholm integral equation of the second kind, a fact first noted by Jones [14] in 1956. Indeed a elementary calculation given

$$\bar{\sigma}(\sqrt{a^2-\lambda}) + \frac{i}{\pi}\frac{d}{d\lambda}\int_0^{\lambda} \frac{\cosh(k\sqrt{\lambda-\mu})}{\sqrt{\lambda-\mu}} d\mu \int_0^{a^2} \frac{\sinh(k\sqrt{\rho-\mu})}{\sqrt{\rho-\mu}} \bar{\sigma}(\sqrt{a^2-\rho})\, d\rho$$

$$= -\frac{4}{\pi}\frac{d}{d\lambda}\int_0^{\lambda} \cosh(k\sqrt{a^2-\mu}) \frac{\cosh(k\sqrt{\lambda-\mu})}{\sqrt{\lambda-\mu}}\, d\mu \ .$$

This may be reduced to

$$\sigma(\sqrt{a^2-\lambda}) + \frac{i}{\pi}\frac{d}{d\lambda}\int_0^{a^2} \bar{\sigma}(\sqrt{a^2-\rho})\, d\rho \int_{\sqrt{\rho}-\sqrt{\lambda}}^{\sqrt{\rho}+\sqrt{\lambda}} \frac{\sinh k\tau}{\tau}\, d\tau$$

$$-\frac{4}{\pi}\frac{d}{d\lambda}\int_0^{\lambda} \cosh(k\sqrt{a^2-\mu}) \frac{\cosh(k\sqrt{\lambda-\mu}}{\sqrt{\lambda-\mu}}\, d\mu$$

and finally to

$$g(\alpha) + \frac{i}{\pi}\int_0^{a} g(\beta)\, d\beta \left[\frac{\sinh k(\alpha+\beta)}{\alpha+\beta} + \frac{\sinh k(\alpha-\beta)}{\alpha-\beta}\right]$$

$$= -\frac{4}{\pi}\frac{d}{d\alpha}\int_0^{\alpha} \frac{\cosh(k\sqrt{\alpha^2-\beta^2})\,\cosh(k\sqrt{a^2-\beta^2})\,\beta\, d\beta}{\sqrt{\alpha^2-\beta^2}} \qquad (3.5)$$

where $g(\alpha) = \alpha\bar{\sigma}(\sqrt{a^2-\alpha^2})$. Equation (3.5) has a regular kernel and permits a solution for k small by the usual iteration process.

It is possible to apply these methods to the Neumann boundary condition as well as to non-normal excitation (see [10, 11]). Some progress has also been made with the vector problem. There are also representations which may be employed for the planar infinite strip. In this case trigonometric functions are replaced by Bessel functions in (3.3), but the inversion operation described above leads to an awkward equation.

NOTES

*All variables of integration are real.

#This integral has a representation as a line integral in the complex plane.

§Spherical wave excitation may be handled with equal ease.

Hence if there is dependence on θ, we expand V and σ into a Fourier series and treat each component separately. See [10, 11].

Publication supported by the Horace Rackham School of Graduate Studies of the University of Michigan.

BIBLIOGRAPHY

1. Sommerfeld, A., Mathematische Theorie der Diffraction, Mathematische Annalen 47, 317-374 (1896).

2. Wiener, N. and Hopf, E., Über eine Klasse singulärer Integralgleichungen, Sitzungsberichte der Preussichten Akademie, Mathematisch-Physikalische Klasse, 696-706 (1931).

3. Lewy, H., Water waves on sloping beaches, Bulletin of the American Mathematical Society, 52, 737-775 (1946).

4. Heins, A. E., The Scope and Limitations of the Method of Wiener and Hopf, Communications on Pure and Applied Mathematics IX 447-466 (1956).

5. Henrici, P., A survey of I. N. Vekua's theorey of elliptic partial differential equations with analytic coefficients, Zeitschrift fur Angewandte Mathematik und Physik, 8, 169-202 (1957).

6. Temple, G., Whittaker's work on the integral representation of harmonic functions. Proceedings of the Edinburgh Mathematical Society, 11, 11-24(1958).

7. Copson, E. T., On the problem of the electrified disk, Proceedings of the Edinburgh Mathematical Society (3) 8, 14-19(1947).

8. Heins, A. E., and MacCamy, R. C., On mixed boundary value problems for axially symmetric potentials. Journal of Mathematical Analysis and Applications, I, 331-333 (1960).

9. Heins, A. E. and MacCamy, R. C., Axially symmetric solutions of elliptic differential equations. Tech. Rep. No. 24, AF OSR, Contract No. AF49(638)-227, Carnegie Institute of Technology, November, 1958 (to appear shortly).

10. Heins, A. E. and MacCamy, R. C., On the scattering of waves by a disk, Tech. Rep. No. 43, Contract No. DA-36-061-ORD-491, June, 1959.

11. Heins, A. E. and MacCamy, R. C., On the scattering of waves by a disk, Zeitschrift fur Angewandte Mathematik und Physik XI, 249-264(1960).

12. Love, E. R., The electrostatic field of two equal circular coaxial conducting disks. Quart. J. of Mech. and Appl. Math. 2, 428-451 (1949).

13. Collins, W. D. On the solution of some axisymmetric boundary value problems by means of integral equations. Quart. J. Mech. and Appl. Math. 12, 232-241 (1959).

14. Jones, D. S. A new method for calculating scattering with particular reference to the circular disk. Com. Pure and Appl. Math. IX 713-746(1956).

N. MARCUVITZ

Abstract Operator Methods in Electromagnetic Diffraction

1. INTRODUCTION: Although abstract operator procedures are familiar to quantum field theorists in connection with quantum theoretic scattering problems[1], etc., their use in classical electromagnetic field theory, albeit not unfamiliar, has not been widespread.[2] In the following, abstract techniques will be briefly illustrated for both the formulation and solution of electromagnetic scattering problems in free space and in waveguides. The essence of a diffraction problem lies in the determination of a far scattered field from a prescribed incident field. In abstract terms the desired relation is provided by a transformation operator, the explicit evaluation of which is the central problem of the abstract operator theory. Solution of this problem requires the inversion of an operator characterizing both the scattering region and the scatterer.

Explicit inversion of an operator can be effected abstractly, i. e. in a "coordinate" independent manner, only if the structure of the operator can be exhibited in an abstract manner. Since operators descriptive of a scatterer and of its environment generally have too complex a structure to be displayed abstractly in any complete way, it is not to be expected that scattering problems can be solved completely in abstract terms. For general classes of scattering problems it is possible, however, to exhibit certain abstract features of the relevant operators and to derive abstractly therefrom the information corresponding to these features. A number of examples of such abstract procedures are included below. In the absence of any abstract indication of operator structure, an operator formalism becomes for the most part a notational procedure that, nevertheless, may not be lacking in interest if some systematization of viewpoint is achieved thereby.

In steady state electromagnetic problems, one is interested in inferring at every point $\underline{r}$ the electric field $\underline{E}(\underline{r})$ and the magnetic field $\underline{H}(\underline{r})$ from a knowledge of the electric and magnetic current densities $\underline{J}_e(\underline{r})$ and $\underline{J}_m(\underline{r})$, respectively. For scattering problems these current densities are not known explicitly everywhere, but are dependent upon unknown equivalent surface electric currents $\underline{H}(\underline{r}) \times \underline{n}$ and surface magnetic currents $\underline{n} \times \underline{E}(\underline{r})$ flowing on obstacle and aperture discontinuity surfaces (with normal $\underline{n}$) that generate the scattering. Alternatively, if the scattering is caused by a volume discontinuity in both the relative dyadic dielectric constant $\underline{\varepsilon}(\underline{r})$ and permeability $\underline{\mu}(\underline{r})$, then assuming and supressing a steady state time dependence $\exp(-i\omega t)$, the unknown equivalent volume electric and magnetic currents characterizing the scatterer are $-i\omega(\underline{\varepsilon}-1)\circ\underline{E}$ and $i\omega(\underline{\mu}-1)\circ\underline{H}'$, respectively.

To introduce abstract notation, one defines "abstract vectors" Ψ and θ by their representatives:

$$\Psi \to \begin{pmatrix} \underline{E}(\underline{r}) \\ i\,\underline{H}(\underline{r}) \end{pmatrix} \quad \text{and} \quad \theta \to \begin{pmatrix} \underline{J}_e(\underline{r}) \\ i\,\underline{J}_m(\underline{r}) \end{pmatrix} . \tag{1}$$

Implicit in this notation is the concept of a product space comprising a hilbert space, with components distinguished by the "index" $\underline{r}$, and a finite six dimensional space, with three ordinary vector components of electric type and three of magnetic type. The relationship between the abstract wave vector Ψ and the source vector θ is provided by the Maxwell operator M whose representative in the same basis as employed in (1) is the 2 by 2 matrix with dyadic elements

$$M \to i\begin{pmatrix} -k\underline{\varepsilon} & \nabla\times\underline{1} \\ \nabla\times\underline{1} & -k\underline{\mu} \end{pmatrix} \tag{2}$$

where ∇ is the ordinary vector gradient operator, $\underline{1}$ is the unit dyadic, and $k = \omega/c$, c being the velocity of light in vacuum. The Maxwell field equations are synthesized by the single abstract equation

$$M\Psi = -\theta \tag{3a}$$

whence by straightforward matrix multiplication of the representatives (1) and (2), of Ψ and M , there is inferred the familiar component form[3]

$$\begin{pmatrix} -ik\underline{\varepsilon}\cdot\underline{E} & -\nabla\times\underline{H} \\ i\nabla\times\underline{E} & k\underline{\mu}\cdot\underline{H} \end{pmatrix} = -\begin{pmatrix} \underline{J}_e \\ i\underline{J}_m \end{pmatrix} . \tag{3b}$$

Equation (3a), if supplemented by known boundary conditions on the field components of Ψ , provides an implicit and unique definition of Ψ in terms of θ . The boundary constraints are contained in the statement

$$\Psi \subset D \tag{3c}$$

i. e. Ψ lies in a domain D of elements identifiable by suitable differentiability properties within a given volume and by stated limiting properties on surfaces bounding this volume.

The algebraic structure of the Maxwell operator M is made more manifest by rewriting (2) in the form

$$M = i(\Gamma_p - kW) \tag{4}$$

where

$$\Gamma_p \rightarrow \begin{pmatrix} 0 & \nabla \times \underline{1} \\ \nabla \times \underline{1} & 0 \end{pmatrix} \quad \text{and} \quad W \rightarrow \begin{pmatrix} \varepsilon & 0 \\ 0 & \mu \end{pmatrix} \quad .$$

On introduction of the ordinary momentum operator $p = -i\nabla$, the "spin triadic" $\underline{S} = i\,\underline{1} \times \underline{1}$, and the Pauli matrix

$$\sigma \rightarrow \begin{pmatrix} 0 & 1 \\ 1 & 0 \end{pmatrix} ,$$

one observes that $\Gamma_p = \underline{p} \cdot \underline{S}\sigma$, $\sigma^2 = 1$, and that the abstract operator

$$\Gamma_p^2 = \nabla\nabla - \nabla^2 \underline{1} = \nabla \times (\nabla \times \underline{1}) \tag{5}$$

is evidently representable by a diagonal 2×2 matrix with the indicated identical elements. The triadic $\underline{S}$ is recognizable as an angular momentum operator with spin one, as is manifest in its properties

$$\underline{S} \times \underline{S} = i\underline{S} \quad \text{and} \quad \underline{S}^2 = -\underline{1} \quad .$$

Further discussion of the algebraic properties of M is contingent on special knowledge of the structure of the medium operator W. Although in particular cases the latter is expressible simply in terms of the complete set of "Pauli matrices", of which σ is but one, no attempt will be made to display this information herein.

Solution of an abstract equation of the type (3) is effected by introduction of a green s operator G, inverse to M, defined formally by

$$MG = 1 = GM \quad . \tag{6}$$

On premultiplication of Eq. (3a) by G and use of the right-hand operator relation in (6), one formally obtains the solution to (3) in the form

$$\Psi = -G\theta \quad . \tag{7}$$

Formal verification of the solution (7) follows on premultiplication with M whence the original Eq. (3a) is regained if the left-hand side of (6) is utilized. Whenever, as in scattering problems, there exists non-vanishing solutions Φ of

$$M\Phi = 0 \ , \tag{8}$$

the operator M becomes singular in that it does not possess an inverse on the subspace spanned by the Φ . In this event the right-hand operator relation in (6) is modified to

$$1 - \Phi\Phi = GM \ ,$$

with $\Phi\Phi$ denoting the identity operator for the subspace in question, whence repeating the previous procedure one now obtains as the formal solution to Eq. (3)

$$\Psi = c\Phi - G\theta \ , \tag{9}$$

c being a numerical constant. In view of the previously noted dependence in scattering problems of θ on Ψ , it is manifest that Eq. (9) is not the solution to Eq. (3) but rather an "integral" form of the latter.

Depending on whether the scatterer is of the obstacle or aperture type, or a volume discontinuity in $\underline{\varepsilon}$ and $\underline{\mu}$, one recalls that the representative of the equivalent current vector θ in the basis (1) is

$$\theta \rightarrow \begin{pmatrix} \underline{H} \times \underline{n} \\ i\underline{n} \times \underline{E} \end{pmatrix}_S \quad \text{or} \quad \theta \rightarrow \begin{pmatrix} -i\omega(\underline{\varepsilon}-\underline{1}) \cdot \underline{E} \\ -\omega(\underline{\mu}-\underline{1}) \cdot \underline{H} \end{pmatrix} \tag{10}$$

where the index S implies non-vanishing values only at the obstacle or aperture locations. The dependence on Ψ is evident and can be made explicit by introduction of an abstract ("potential") operator V by:

$$\theta = V\Psi \tag{11}$$

where in view of (10) the operator V has as its representative

$$V = i\underline{n} \times \underline{1}\sigma \rightarrow \begin{pmatrix} 0 & i\underline{n} \times \underline{1} \\ 1\,\underline{n} \times \underline{1} & 0 \end{pmatrix} \delta(\underline{r}-\underline{r}_s) \tag{12a}$$

or

$$V \rightarrow \begin{pmatrix} -i\omega(\underline{\varepsilon}-\underline{1}) & 0 \\ 0 & +i\omega(\underline{\mu}-\underline{1}) \end{pmatrix} \tag{12b}$$

with δ denoting the three dimensional Dirac delta function and with $\underline{r}_s$ defining the location of the obstacle or aperture surfaces. For scattering problems Eq. (9) thus takes the form

$$\Psi = \Phi - GV\Psi \tag{13}$$

the arbitrary constant c being chosen as unity. If one can determine an abstract operator T, related to V by

$$\theta = T\Phi = V\Psi \tag{14}$$

the explicit solution for Ψ becomes

$$\Psi = (1 - GT)\Phi \ . \tag{15}$$

It is the determination of the operator T that constitutes the central problem of electromagnetic diffraction. However, rather than pursue further the formal procedure under discussion, it is appropriate at this point to impart more substance to the abstract formalism by a more precise definition of some of the algebraic operations employed in Eqs. (6)-(15).

2. VECTOR AND OPERATOR ALGEBRA. The combinatorial facility required for solution of the problem posed by Eq. (3) is based upon the known abstract algebra of vectors and operators on a vector hilbert space[4]. By way of review and of notational clarification some of the salient features of abstract algebra and of representations in various bases will be sketched. The hilbert space in question is spanned by elements, i.e. abstract vectors, of the type Ψ whose representative in a "natural basis" within this space is given as in (1) above. All elements on the space are assumed to obey the associative, distributive, and commutative axioms of addition. In consequence of this, and the infinite dimensionality of the hilbert space, one infers the existence in this space of an infinite number of independent elements Φ_j in terms of which any Ψ can be represented by superposition as

$$\Psi = \sum_j a_j \Phi_j \ . \tag{16}$$

The composite index j distinguishes the various elements of the set Φ_j, the summation sign implies addition (or integration) over the "complete" set, and the scalars a_j constitute the representatives of the element Ψ with respect to the basis Φ_j, viz: $\Psi \rightarrow (a_j)$. If the representative of Φ_j in the natural basis is denoted as

$$\Phi_j \rightarrow \begin{pmatrix} \underline{\mathscr{E}}_j(\underline{r}) \\ i\underline{\mathscr{H}}_j(\underline{r}) \end{pmatrix} \tag{17}$$

there follows from Eqs. (16) and (1) the component representations

$$\underline{E}(\underline{r}) = \sum_j a_j \underline{\mathscr{E}}_j(\underline{r}) \quad .$$

$$\underline{H}(\underline{r}) = \sum_j a_j \underline{\mathscr{H}}_j(\underline{r}) \quad ,$$

To any vector Ψ within a specified domain D of the hilbert space in question one can associate by means of an operator A a new abstract vector $A\Psi$ lying within a range R of the space. The complete characterization of the operator A requires specification of both its domain and range. In the natural basis an abstract operator will have as its representative a 2 by 2 matrix each of whose elements $\underline{\underline{A}}_{ij}$ are dyadics, viz:

$$A \rightarrow \begin{pmatrix} \underline{\underline{A}}_{11}(\underline{r},\underline{r}') & -i\underline{\underline{A}}_{12}(\underline{r},\underline{r}') \\ i\underline{\underline{A}}_{21}(\underline{r},\underline{r}') & \underline{\underline{A}}_{22}(\underline{r},\underline{r}') \end{pmatrix} \tag{18}$$

where $\underline{r}$ and $\underline{r}'$ distinguish points of the relevant physical space. In consequence, by matrix multiplication, the representative of $A\Psi$ in the natural basis is expressible in terms of the representatives (1) and (18) as

$$A\Psi \rightarrow \begin{pmatrix} \iiint[\underline{\underline{A}}_{11}(\underline{r},\underline{r}')\cdot\underline{E}(\underline{r}') + \underline{\underline{A}}_{12}(\underline{r},\underline{r}')\cdot\underline{H}(\underline{r}')]d\tau' \\ \iiint[\underline{\underline{A}}_{21}(\underline{r},\underline{r}')\cdot\underline{E}(\underline{r}') + \underline{\underline{A}}_{22}(\underline{r},\underline{r}')\cdot\underline{H}(\underline{r}')]\,d\tau' \end{pmatrix} \tag{19}$$

where the triple integration with respect to the volume element $d\tau'$ is extended over the physical space.

The definition of the operator M in (2) and its operation on Ψ in (3b) appears to be at variance with the operator definition in (18) and the matrix multiplication in (19). If M is represented, however, in the form

$$M \rightarrow i \begin{pmatrix} -k\underline{\underline{\varepsilon}}\,\delta(\underline{r}-\underline{r}') & \nabla\times\underline{\underline{1}}\,\delta(\underline{r}-\underline{r}') \\ \nabla\times\underline{\underline{1}}\,\delta(\underline{r}-\underline{r}') & -k\underline{\underline{\mu}}\,\delta(\underline{r}-\underline{r}') \end{pmatrix} \quad ,$$

the compatibility of (3b) and (19) is manifest. The presence of the delta function $\delta(\underline{r}-\underline{r}')$ in its representative stamps M as singular, i.e. unbounded, among operators of the type (18). Unbounded operators are distinguished from those of the bounded variety in that the domain of the latter is the entire hilbert space whereas that of the former is in general smaller, as noted under (3c) in the case of the operator M . For unbounded derivative operators of the type M the dictates of simplicity suggest elision of the delta function.

The abstract operators of interest obey the usual associative and distributive axioms of addition and multiplication, commutativity obtaining only in the case of addition. Further operator properties flow from the introduction of scalar products of two elements Ψ and Φ , the representatives of which have been noted in (1) and (17). The hermitean product is defined by:

$$(\Phi, \Psi) = \iiint [\underline{\mathscr{E}}^*(\underline{r}) \cdot \underline{E}(\underline{r}) + \underline{\mathscr{H}}^*(\underline{r}) \cdot \underline{H}(\underline{r})]\, d\tau \qquad (20a)$$

and the symmetric product by:

$$(\Phi, \Psi) = \iiint [\underline{\mathscr{E}}(\underline{r}) \cdot \underline{E}(\underline{r}) - \underline{\mathscr{H}}(\underline{r}) \cdot \underline{H}(\underline{r})]\, d\tau \qquad (20b)$$

where the integration is extended over the entire volume of the physical space. From Φ and $A\Psi$ one forms the products:

$$(\Phi, A\Psi) = (A^+\Phi, \Psi) \qquad (21a)$$

and alternatively,

$$(\Phi \cdot A\Psi) = (A'\Phi \cdot \Psi) \quad . \qquad (21b)$$

The equating of the well-defined left-hand members of Eqs. (21) with the corresponding members on the right provides a definition of the hermitean adjoint A^+ and the symmetric adjoint A' . Implicit in these definitions are statements of the domains D_A, D_{A^+}, $D_{A'}$, of the various operators and the requirements for Eqs. (21) that $\Psi \subset D_A$ and that $\Phi \subset D_{A^+}$ or $D_{A'}$ for (21a) or (21b).

Useful inferences from Eqs. (21) for the case of the operator Γ_p of Eq. (4) are:

$$\Gamma_p^+ = \Gamma_p \text{ and } \Gamma_p' = \Gamma_p \qquad (22)$$

provided $D_{\Gamma_p} = D_{\Gamma_p^+} = D_{\Gamma_p'}$ is appropriately defined. Similarly, but more directly, one observes for the operator W that

$$W^+ = W \text{ if } \tilde{\underline{\varepsilon}}^* = \underline{\varepsilon} \ , \ \tilde{\underline{\mu}}^* = \underline{\mu} \qquad (23a)$$

or

$$W' = W \text{ if } \tilde{\underline{\varepsilon}} = \underline{\varepsilon} \ , \ \tilde{\underline{\mu}} = \underline{\mu} \qquad (23b)$$

with $\sim$ and $*$ denoting transpose and conjugate dyadics, respectively. Other properties following from (21) for two operators A and B are

$$(AB)^+ = B^+A^+ \quad \text{and} \quad (AB)' = B'A' \tag{24}$$

with the implied provisions $R_B \subset D_A$, $R_{A^+} \subset D_{B^+}$, and $R_{A'} \subset D_{B'}$.

For subsequent considerations it is purposeful to introduce in addition to the scalar products (20a and b) other products on a somewhat different hilbert space. Thus for the two vector elements Φ and Ψ one defines another hermitean product

$$[\Phi, \Psi] = \iint [\underline{\mathscr{E}}^*(\underline{r}) \cdot \underline{E}(\underline{r}) + \underline{\mathscr{H}}^*(\underline{r}) \cdot \underline{H}(\underline{r})]\, dS \tag{25a}$$

and a symmetric product

$$[\Phi \cdot \Psi] = \iint [\underline{\mathscr{E}}(\underline{r}) \cdot \underline{E}(\underline{r}) - \underline{\mathscr{H}}(\underline{r}) \cdot \underline{H}(\underline{r})]\, dS \tag{25b}$$

where in this instance the integration is extended over a prescribed surface within the physical space of interest. Furthermore, in a procedure isomorphic to that in Eqs. (21), one associates with an operator A an hermitean adjoint A^+ by

$$[\Phi, A\Psi] = [A^+\Phi, \Psi] \tag{26a}$$

and a symmetric adjoint A' by

$$[\Phi \cdot A\Psi] = [A'\Phi \cdot \Psi] \,, \tag{26b}$$

each defined on appropriate domains of the hilbert space in question.

A significant relation between the products (20) and (25) is highlighted by noting that for the operator V of (12a):

$$(\Phi, V\Psi) = \iint [\underline{\mathscr{E}}^*(\underline{r}) \cdot \underline{H}(\underline{r}) \times \underline{n} + \underline{\mathscr{H}}^*(\underline{r}) \cdot \underline{n} \times \underline{E}(\underline{r})]\, dS = [\Phi, \Gamma_n \Psi] \tag{27a}$$

$$(\Phi \cdot V\Psi) = \iint [\underline{\mathscr{E}}(\underline{r}) \cdot \underline{H}(\underline{r}) \times \underline{n} - \underline{\mathscr{H}}(\underline{r}) \cdot \underline{n} \times \underline{E}(\underline{r})]\, dS = [\Phi \cdot \Gamma_n \Psi] \tag{27b}$$

where $\underline{n}$ is the normal to the surface of integration, and

$$\Gamma_n = i\underline{n} \times \underline{1}\sigma \,. \tag{28a}$$

The operator Γ_n and the related operator

$$\Gamma_{p_t} = \underline{\nabla}_t \times \underline{1}\sigma \tag{28b}$$

appear in the Maxwell operator M of Eq. (4), viz:

$$M = i(\Gamma_{p_t} - kW + \frac{1}{i}\frac{\partial}{\partial n}\Gamma_n) = -i(L - \frac{1}{i}\frac{\partial}{\partial n}\Gamma_n) \tag{29}$$

and display a decomposition of Γ_p into components transverse (t) and normal (n) to the surface under consideration. One can infer from Eqs. (25) and (26) that the operator L, implicitly defined in (29), possesses the property

$$L^+ = L \tag{30a}$$

or

$$L' = L \tag{30b}$$

provided (23a) or (23b) is applicable, and in the same manner that

$$\Gamma_n^+ = \Gamma_n \tag{31a}$$

but

$$\Gamma_n' = -\Gamma_n \ . \tag{31b}$$

3. GREEN's OPERATORS, REPRESENTATIONS. In view of the algebraic preliminaries of the previous section, it is now possible to ascertain properties of the Green's operator defined in Eq. (6) and as well to effect its evaluation in a number of instances. Making explicit the Maxwell operator M, one first rewrites the left-hand Eq. (6) as

$$i(\Gamma_p - kW)\,G = 1 \tag{32}$$

with $R_G = D_M$ appropriately defined. Also, on forming the hermitean or symmetric adjoints, one re-expresses by (24) the right-hand Eq. (6) either as:

$$-i(\Gamma_p^+ - k^* W^+)\,G^+ = 1 \tag{33a}$$

or

$$i(\Gamma_p' - kW')\,G' = 1 \tag{33b}$$

with suitable specification of $R_{G^+} = D_{M^+}$ or $R_{G'} = D_{M'}$. In bounded, reciprocal, and non-dissipative electromagnetic regions $\Gamma_p = \Gamma_p^+$, $W = W^+$, $k = k^*$, and $D_M = D_{M^+}$. Hence, on comparison of Eqs. (32) and (33a), one observes that

$$G = -G^+ \ ; \tag{34a}$$

whereas in unbounded regions $k \neq k^*$, and the relation (34a) is modified to

$$G(k) = -G(k^*)^+ \ . \tag{34b}$$

For regions of infinite extent $\Gamma_p = \Gamma_p'$, and if the medium and boundaries are such that $W = W'$ and $D_M = D_{M'}$ one infers by comparison of (32) and (33b) that

$$G = G' \quad . \tag{35}$$

The physical significance of the above properties becomes more apparent with the expression by (18) of the matrix representative of G in the natural basis as

$$G \rightarrow \begin{pmatrix} \underline{Z}(\underline{r}, \underline{r}') & -i\underline{T}_e(\underline{r}, \underline{r}') \\ i\underline{T}_m(\underline{r}, \underline{r}') & \underline{Y}(\underline{r}, \underline{r}') \end{pmatrix} \tag{36}$$

whence by (19) the field solution (7) in the presence of prescribed current sources becomes, in component form,

$$\begin{aligned} \underline{E}(\underline{r}) &= -\iiint \underline{Z}(\underline{r}, \underline{r}') \cdot \underline{J}_e(\underline{r}') d\tau' - \iiint \underline{T}_e(\underline{r}, \underline{r}') \cdot \underline{J}_m(\underline{r}') d\tau' \\ \underline{H}(\underline{r}) &= -\iiint \underline{T}_m(\underline{r}, \underline{r}') \cdot \underline{J}_e(\underline{r}') d\tau' - \iiint \underline{Y}(\underline{r}, \underline{r}') \cdot \underline{J}_m(\underline{r}') d\tau' \quad . \end{aligned} \tag{37}$$

Equations (37) display the physical meaning of the matrix elements (36) as conventional dyadic Green's functions; moreover, by way of example, the symmetry property (35) implies that

$$\underline{Z}(\underline{r}, \underline{r}') = \widetilde{\underline{Z}(\underline{r}', \underline{r})}, \ \underline{Y}(\underline{r}, \underline{r}') = \widetilde{\underline{Y}(\underline{r}', \underline{r})} \ , \ \underline{T}_e(\underline{r}, \underline{r}') = \widetilde{-\underline{T}_m(\underline{r}'\underline{r})} \tag{38}$$

which is recognized as a familiar reciprocity property of the electromagnetic field.

The case of free space, wherein $W = 1$ and D_M is the domain of suitably continuous functions which for $\text{Im } k > 0$ vanish at infinity, provides an instance in which the dyadic structure of the Green's operator defined in (32) can be readily obtained in an abstract algebraic manner. In this instance via permitted algebraic operations one rewrites (32) in the successive forms

$$\begin{aligned} G &= -i \frac{1}{\Gamma_p - k} = -i \frac{(\Gamma_p + k + \frac{\nabla\nabla}{k})}{(\Gamma_p + k + \frac{\nabla\nabla}{k})} \frac{1}{(\Gamma_p - k)} \\ &= -i(\Gamma_p + k + \frac{\nabla\nabla}{k}) \cdot \frac{1}{-(\nabla^2 + k^2)} \\ &\rightarrow -i(\Gamma_p + k + \frac{\nabla\nabla}{k}) \frac{\ell^{ik|\underline{r}-\underline{r}'|}}{4\pi|\underline{r}-\underline{r}'|} \quad . \end{aligned} \tag{39}$$

The last stage in the "rationalization" of the denominator follows from (5); the representative of the resulting inverse operator from its recognition as the free space scalar Green's function whose range is D_M and which satisfies

$$-(\nabla^2+k^2)\frac{e^{ik|\underline{r}-\underline{r}'|}}{4\pi|\underline{r}-\underline{r}'|} = \delta(\underline{r}-\underline{r}') \quad .$$

From the explicit display of dyadic structure in (39), one notes by comparison with (36) the natural basis representatives

$$\begin{aligned} \underline{Z}(\underline{r},\underline{r}') &= \underline{Y}(\underline{r},\underline{r}') = -ik(\underline{1} + \frac{\nabla\nabla}{k^2})\frac{e^{ik|\underline{r}-\underline{r}'|}}{4\pi|\underline{r}-\underline{r}'|} \\ \underline{T}_e(\underline{r},\underline{r}') &= -\underline{T}_m(\underline{r},\underline{r}') = \nabla\times\underline{1}\,\frac{e^{ik|\underline{r}-\underline{r}'|}}{4\pi|\underline{r}-\underline{r}'|} \end{aligned} \qquad (40)$$

which, bearing in mind the normalization[3] of the present paper, are recognized as the familiar dyadic green's functions for free space. For regions other than free space the range of G and that of the scalar inverse operator in (39) are not so readily related, and hence the representative of the latter is not as easily identified as in (39).

Representations of the green's operator in rather arbitrary regions can be achieved from knowledge of complete sets of orthogonal wave vectors. One such set is provided by the possible solutions of Eq. (8), viz:

$$(\Gamma_p - k_j W)\Phi_j = 0 \qquad (41)$$

with Φ_j in a domain characteristic of the region in question. Equation (41) manifestly poses an eigenvalue problem with $k_j = |\underline{k}_j|$ playing the role of eigenvalue and Φ_j that of the associated eigenvector. The ordinary "momentum" vector $\underline{k}_j$ characterizes the spatial periodicities of Φ_j in three mutually perpendicular directions.

For the hermitean case wherein $\Gamma_p = \Gamma_p^+$ and $W = W^+$, on formation of the hermitean scalar product of (41) with another eigenvector Φ_i, there is derived through conventional algebraic manipulation the orthonormality property:

$$(W\Phi_i, \Phi_j) = \delta_{ij} \quad . \qquad (42)$$

The kronecker delta $\delta_{ij} = 0$ if $\underline{k}_i \neq \underline{k}_j$ and $= 1$ if $\underline{k}_i = \underline{k}_j$. In view of (42) and the implied completeness of the Φ_j the representation (16) of an arbitrary element Ψ in the hilbert space can now be made definitive. One observes that

$$a_j = (W\Phi_j, \Psi)$$

whence (43a)

$$\Psi = \sum_j \Phi_j (W\Phi_j, \Psi) \quad ,$$

the summation sign implying a three-fold sum (or integral) with respect to both the triple index j and three different "mode" types. Since (43a) is applicable to any Ψ in the hilbert space, the appearance of Ψ may be suppressed, thereby yielding a representation of the identity operator in the form

$$1 = \sum_j \Phi_j \, W \, \Phi_j \tag{43b}$$

whose operational interpretation on the relevant hilbert space is provided by (43a). It should be noted from (43b) that the elements of the 2×2 matrix representative of the identity operator on the natural basis provide a number of dyadic completeness relations, not all of these in general being independent or non-trivial. In the basis Φ_j the matrix representative of the identity operator (43b) is evidently δ_{ij} .

Representation of the green's operator in terms of the Φ_j can be effected by operation of the identity operator upon G , whence

$$G = \sum_j \Phi_j (W\Phi_j, G) \quad . \tag{44a}$$

For the case $\Gamma_p = \Gamma_p^+$ and $W = W^+$, the hermitean product in (44a) is evaluated by forming the product of (32) and Φ_j

$$(\Phi_j, i(\Gamma_p - kW)G) = \Phi_j \quad ,$$

thence utilizing adjointness properties and (41), one obtains

$$G = \sum_j \frac{\Phi_j \Phi_j}{i(k_j - k)} \tag{44b}$$

whose 2×2 matrix representative in the natural basis provides rather general representations of the dyadic green's functions of (36). For regions whose extent in at least one direction is infinite, the possible eigenvalues k_j of (41) constitute a continuous spectrum; hence the green's operator representation in (44b) is not particularly convenient because of the many Φ_j with $|\underline{k}_j|$ in the vicinity of k . In these instances one either reduces the triple "sum" in (44b) to a more desirable double sum, or equivalently, employs a more appropriate basis to achieve a rapidly convergent representation of G .

In uniform waveguide regions wherein there exists a direction z of translational invariance, it is possible to delineate a subset of the Φ_j of (41) for which $|\underline{k}_j| = k$, i.e. whose eigenvalues lie on the shell k of the $\underline{k}_j$ space. Translational invariance implies an exponential z dependence that, for eigenvectors Φ_α on the shell k , will be made explicit in the notation

$$\Phi_\alpha(z) = \overline{\Phi}_\alpha e^{i\kappa_\alpha z}$$

with $\overline{\Phi}_\alpha$ the abstract vector referred to the transverse surface $z = 0$, and κ_α the wavenumber indicate of the periodicity along z . In view of the decomposition (29) of the operator M into components transverse and parallel to the direction $\underline{n}$ (in the present instance z), one can elide the z dependence of $\Phi_\alpha(z)$ and rewrite Eq. (4) as

$$(L - \kappa_\alpha \Gamma_z)\overline{\Phi}_\alpha = 0 \tag{45}$$

with $\overline{\Phi}_\alpha$ contained within a domain characteristic of the guide walls. Equation (45) poses an eigenvalue problem in which κ_α is the eigenvalue and $\overline{\Phi}_\alpha$ the eigenvector.

If, by way of example, the guide is such that the symmetric adjointness property (30b) of L obtains, then since $\Gamma_z' = -\Gamma_z$, formation of the scalar product (25b) of (45) with $\overline{\Phi}_\beta$ permits derivation of the orthogonality properties

$$[\Gamma_z \overline{\Phi}_\alpha \cdot \overline{\Phi}_\beta] = N_\alpha \delta_{\alpha,-\beta} = -[\overline{\Phi}_\alpha \cdot \Gamma_z \overline{\Phi}_\beta] \tag{46}$$

where by (27b) the indicated scalar product implies a surface integration over the guide cross-section and evidently involves only the transverse parts of $\overline{\Phi}_\alpha$ and $\overline{\Phi}_\beta$. The customary interpretation of the kronecker delta $\delta_{\alpha,-\beta}$ as unity if $\alpha = -\beta$ and zero otherwise again applies. It should be observed that the double index α distinguishes a Φ_α with wavenumber $\kappa_\alpha = \sqrt{k^2 - \underline{k}_{t\alpha}^2}$, the transverse wavenumber vector $\underline{k}_{t\alpha}$ being indicative of the spatial periodicity of $\overline{\Phi}_\alpha$ along two directions transverse to z ; hence, $\alpha = -\beta$ implies identity not only of κ_α and $-\kappa_\beta$ but also of $\underline{k}_{t\alpha}$ and $-\underline{k}_{t\beta}$. For consistency with the normalization (42) to unity of the Φ_j , the normalization N_α for the subset $\overline{\Phi}_\alpha$ cannot be equated to unity. A useful inference from (46) is that $N_\alpha = -N_{-\alpha}$.

It will be assumed that the transverse part of the set Φ_α of possible solutions to the eigenvalue Eq. (45) provides a complete set for the representation of any transverse wave vector on the guide cross-section. If ϕ_α is the transverse part of $\overline{\Phi}_\alpha$ and ψ is an arbitrary transverse wavevector in an appropriate hilbert space, then in view of the completeness of the ϕ_α

$$\psi = \sum_\alpha b_\alpha \phi_\alpha \tag{47a}$$

where by (46) the coefficients in this double sum are:

$$b_\alpha = \frac{1}{N_\alpha}[\bar{\Phi}_{-\alpha}\cdot \Gamma_z\psi] = \frac{1}{N_\alpha}[\phi_{-\alpha}\cdot \Gamma_z\psi] \ . \tag{47b}$$

An interesting representation obtained from (47) is

$$\Gamma_z\psi = \sum_\alpha \frac{1}{N_\alpha}\Gamma_z\phi_\alpha[\phi_{-\alpha}\cdot \Gamma_z\psi] \tag{48a}$$

which provides, on the appropriate hilbert space of transverse wave-vectors, the representation of the transverse identity operator

$$1_t = \sum_\alpha \frac{1}{N_\alpha}\Gamma_z\phi_\alpha\phi_{-\alpha} \ . \tag{48b}$$

For uniform guides with reflection symmetry along z both $+\alpha$ and $-\alpha$ wavevectors are admissible and hence, in view of $N_\alpha = -N_{-\alpha}$ the representation (48b) can be rewritten as:

$$1_t = \sum_{+\alpha} \frac{1}{N_\alpha}(\Gamma_z\phi_\alpha\phi_{-\alpha} - \Gamma_z\phi_{-\alpha}\phi_\alpha) \ , \tag{49}$$

the sum in (49) being extended only over the $+\alpha$ eigenvectors. This relation permits a simple representation of the Green's operator for a uniform reflection symmetric waveguide. Noting the decomposition (29), one re-expresses the defining Eq.(32) for G in the form

$$-i(L - \frac{1}{i}\frac{\partial}{\partial z}\Gamma_z)G(z,z') = 1\,\delta(z-z') \tag{50}$$

wherein the dependence on z has been made explicit and where the range of G is appropriate to the waveguide in question. Equation (50) implies for all $z \neq z'$ that $G(z,z')$ satisfies the homogeneous equation and at $z = z'$ possesses the discontinuity

$$[\Gamma_z G(z,z')1_t]_{z'-}^{z'+} = 1_t \tag{51}$$

where the bracket implies the difference between the values of the bracketed quantity at $z = z'+0$ and $z'-0$; this discontinuity requirement follows on integration of the independent transverse part of (50) over an infinitesimal z interval centered at z' . For the case $W = 1$ use of the symmetry property (35) and the range requirement of vanishing $G(z,z')$ for $z \rightarrow +\infty$ if $\text{Im}\, k > 0$ leads to the representation of the Green's operator G in terms of the Φ_α as

$$G(z,z') = \sum_{+\alpha} C_\alpha\,\Phi_{\pm\alpha}(z)\,\Phi_{\mp\alpha}(z') - 1_z\frac{\delta(z-z')}{ik} , \tag{52a}$$

where the upper and lower signs on the α subscripts apply for z greater and less than z' , respectively, and where 1_z is an operator whose 2×2 matrix representation in the natural basis is diagonal with identical dyadic elements $\underline{z}_0 \underline{z}_0$ (note $\underline{1} = \underline{1}_t + \underline{z}_0 \underline{z}_0$) . Since the summation is extended only over $+\alpha$, it is manifest that the sum in Eq. (52) satisfies the homogeneous equation and boundary conditions for $z \neq z'$; and also the last term on the right is the longitudinal correction permitting applicability of the representation to $z = z'$. Substitution of (52a) into (51) yields

$$\sum_{+\alpha} C_\alpha (\Gamma_z \phi_\alpha \phi_{-\alpha} - \Gamma_z \phi_{-\alpha} \phi_\alpha) = 1_t$$

and comparison with (49) leads to the identification

$$C_\alpha = \frac{1}{N_\alpha} \ . \tag{52b}$$

The representation (52) together with (17) permits an alternative evaluation of the matrix representative (36) of G in the form:[5]

$$\begin{aligned}
\underline{Z}(\underline{r}, \underline{r}') &= \sum_{+\alpha} \frac{1}{N_\alpha} \mathscr{E}_{\pm\alpha}(\underline{r}) \mathscr{E}_{\mp\alpha}(\underline{r}') - \underline{z}_0 \underline{z}_0 \frac{\delta(z-z')}{ik} \\
\underline{T}_m(\underline{r}, \underline{r}') &= \sum_{+\alpha} \frac{1}{N_\alpha} \mathscr{H}_{\pm\alpha}(\underline{r}) \mathscr{E}_{\mp\alpha}(\underline{r}') \\
\underline{T}_e(\underline{r}, \underline{r}') &= -\sum_{+\alpha} \frac{1}{N_\alpha} \mathscr{E}_{\pm\alpha}(\underline{r}) \mathscr{H}_{\mp\alpha}(\underline{r}') \\
\underline{Y}(\underline{r}, \underline{r}') &= -\sum_{+\alpha} \frac{1}{N_\alpha} \mathscr{H}_{\pm\alpha}(\underline{r}) \mathscr{H}_{\mp\alpha}(\underline{r}') - \underline{z}_0 \underline{z}_0 \frac{\delta(z-z')}{ik} \ .
\end{aligned} \tag{53}$$

A more definitive result is achieved on insertion into (53) of explicit solutions Φ_α of Eq. (45) and hence of the $\mathscr{E}_\alpha$ and $\mathscr{H}_\alpha$. Known solutions for a uniform guide with perfectly conducting walls are of two types:

$$\Phi'_\alpha \rightarrow (\Gamma_p + \frac{\Gamma_p^2}{k}) \begin{pmatrix} \underline{F}'_\alpha(\underline{r}) \\ 0 \end{pmatrix} , \quad N'_\alpha = -\frac{2\kappa'_\alpha}{k} \tag{54a}$$

$$\Phi''_\alpha \rightarrow (\Gamma_p + \frac{\Gamma_p^2}{k}) \begin{pmatrix} 0 \\ i\underline{F}''_\alpha(\underline{r}) \end{pmatrix} , \quad N''_\alpha = \frac{2k}{\kappa''_\alpha} \tag{54b}$$

where suppressing the superscript ' and ''

$$\underline{F}_\alpha(\underline{r}) = f_\alpha(\rho) \frac{e^{i\kappa_\alpha z}}{-ik_{t\alpha}} \underline{z}_0$$

and the f_α and $k_{t\alpha}$ satisfy the scalar eigenvalue equations

$$(\nabla_t^2 + k_{t\alpha}^2) f_\alpha(\underline{\rho}) = 0$$

with f'_α vanishing on the guide periphery if $k_{t\alpha} \neq 0$ (otherwise constant), and the normal derivative of f''_α vanishing thereon for all $k_{t\alpha}$. Solutions of (45) in non-uniform geometries can be effected in a manner similar to that in (54).

Although only a few illustrations of the variety of possible bases have been indicated in this section, it is of importance to recognize that the utility of any abstract procedure is dependent upon the knowledge of appropriate sets of wavevectors Φ_j. The latter are characterized by completeness and orthogonality properties that relate both to the volume and to various surfaces of a scattering region.

4. THE T-OPERATOR. In Section 1 it was noted that the essence of an electromagnetic scattering problem lies in the determination of an operator T defined by (14). It should be observed from Eq. (15) that knowledge of T provides a field solution Ψ everywhere within the scattering region. But, if as is usual only the "far" scattered fields are of interest, it is evident that T contains an excess of information. This observation is made more explicit by noting from (15) and (52) that matrix representatives $(\Phi_\alpha, T\Phi_\beta)$ only on the shell k, rather than on the entire k space, are required for description of the far field.

An explicit defining equation for T can be readily derived from the basic scattering equation (13) and then formally solved. In successive steps one obtains by operation on (13) with the operator V of (12),

$$V\Psi = V\Phi - VGV\Psi$$

or in the light of definition (14),

$$T\Phi = V\Phi - VGT\Phi$$

from which, because of its validity for all Φ in the hilbert space spanned by the Φ; one has

$$T = V - VGT . \tag{55}$$

By simple algebraic manipulation there results from (55) the solutions:

$$T = (1 + VG)^{-1}V \tag{56a}$$

or

$$T = V - VGV + VGVGV - \cdots \tag{56b}$$

or

$$T = V(1 + GV)^{-1} \tag{56c}$$

or

6)

$$T = \frac{(1 + VG)^{-1} V e^{\mathrm{Tr}\ \ln(1 + VG)}}{e^{\mathrm{Tr}\ \ln(1 + VG)}} \tag{56d}$$

Equations (56) constitute formal solutions of the diffraction problem but their utility is dependent upon one's ability to evaluate operator representatives in known bases.

Both the operators V and G are known in the natural basis, the former (12) and the latter (36) being characteristic, respectively, of the scatterer and the scattering region. The iterative solution (56b) can therefore be readily evaluated in the natural basis, but in most cases the rapidity and domain of convergence of the resulting series is poor; an improved result is obtained from a similar expansion of the Fredholm solution (56d) but the rapidity of convergence is usually still inadequate. The evaluation of the representative of (56a) or (56c) in the natural basis requires the ability to solve in essence an integral equation, in general a prohibitively difficult procedure. Alternatively, if there is known a complete basis of orthogonal eigenvectors with respect to which the matrix representative of VG or GV is diagonal, a simple evaluation of the solutions (56a) or (56c) is possible. Generally, such a basis cannot be easily ascertained for the operator G, but is frequently possible for a simpler but related operator G_0. In this latter circumstance one introduces the decomposition

$$G = G_0 + G_1 \tag{57}$$

and exploits this abstract structure to display the simplicity associated with the operator G_0.

On substitution of (57) into the defining Eq. (55) and reordering terms, one obtains

$$(1 + VG_0)T = V(1 - G_1T)$$

whence on making the ansatz

$$T = T_0(1 - G_1T) \tag{58}$$

on the left-hand side only, there results

$$((1 + VG_0)T_0 - V)(1 - G_1T) = 0 \ . \tag{59}$$

Subject to the proviso

$$(1 - G_1T) \neq 0 \ , \tag{60}$$

that permits factoring of this operator from (50), there is obtained

$$T_0 = V(1 - G_0 T_0) \ . \tag{61}$$

The solutions of (58) and (61), viz:

$$T_0 = (1 + VG_0)^{-1} V \tag{62a}$$

$$T = (1 + T_0 G_1)^{-1} T_0 \ , \tag{62b}$$

constitute a dual set of operator relations equivalent to (56).

The simplicity of the decomposition (57) cloaks a quite general abstract procedure with wide applicability. For electromagnetic diffraction a rigorous abstract perturbation procedure is provided whereby a scattering problem associated with a region characterized by G is expressed in terms of a simpler region described by G_0 . A further noteworthy feature is that the range of validity of this abstract procedure is clearly delimited by (60). These operator interpretations are made more explicit in terms of wave equations. The definition by $T_0 \Phi = V\Psi_0$ of a new wavevector Ψ_0 permits the observation from (61) that

$$\Psi_0 = \Phi - G_0 V \Psi_0 \ , \tag{63a}$$

whence Ψ_0 characterizes the scattering associated with a wave Φ incident on a scatterer V in a region described by G_0 . In a similar manner use of the definition $T_0 G_1 = V\hat{G}_1$ [7] in (58) permits the inference

$$\Psi = \Psi_0 - \hat{G}_1 V \Psi \tag{63b}$$

and hence the interpretation of the desired Ψ as arising from the action of Ψ on the scatterer V in a region $\hat{G}_1$. The limitation implied by (60) can likewise be interpreted; one first observes from (56c) that

$$1 - G_1 T = 1 - G_1 V(1 + GV)^{-1} = (1 + G_0 V)(1 + GV)^{-1}$$

whence the proviso (60) reduces to either

$$(1 + G_0 V) \neq 0 \tag{64a}$$

$$(1 + GV)^{-1} \neq 0 \ . \tag{64b}$$

In view of the relations

$$(1 + G_0 V)\Psi_0 = \Phi$$

$$(1 + GV)^{-1} \Phi = \Psi$$

manifest from (63a) and (13), one infers that the limitation (64a) of the decomposition procedure is operative whenever in the region G_0 there exists a "resonance" (i.e. $\det(1 + G_0 V) = 0$) wherein there is a finite excitation Ψ_0 even in the absence of an incident wave Φ ; on the other hand the limitation (64b) does not appear to be operative since in the original region described by G , it implies the possibility of no excitation Ψ for every incident wave Φ , a seemingly physically untenable possibility. It is of interest to remark parenthetically that approximate representative forms of the abstract limitation (64a) have arisen in specific perturbation analyses by Noble[8], Twersky, et al, which can be subsumed under the abstract procedure being discussed.

There are many avenues of approach in the decomposition (57) to the choice of a G_0 appropriate to a given scattering problem. On the one hand G_0 may satisfy the same equation (32) as G but have a different range; alternatively, the defining equation may be different but the range the same. The appropriate choice is dependent on the parameters descriptive of the scattering problem. In the former instance it is significant to observe that the defining equation for G_1 is homogeneous, viz:

$$i(\Gamma_p - kW)G_1 = 0$$

with a consequent need of only the Φ_α for its representation.

The equivalent static procedure for solution of a scattering problem is illustrative of the second instance mentioned above. In this case G_0 is defined by a static Green's operator

$$i\Gamma_p G_0 = 1$$

with the same range as G , and is capable of ready evaluation. With scatterers of appropriate geometry this choice permits a simple evaluation of the matrix representation of the solution (62a) for T_0 when a basis can be ascertained in which VG_0 is diagonal. For example, in the case of a capacitive window in rectangular waveguide it can be shown, if only transverse-transverse parts of T_0 and G_0 are considered, that (62a) reduces to $T_0 = G_0^{-1}$. In this case, which is discussed in a non-abstract manner in Sec. 3.5c of the <u>Waveguide Handbook</u>, [9] the matrix representative of T_0 can be readily evaluated in the appropriate diagonal basis (provided by the modes of the conformally mapped guide in the <u>Handbook</u>) and thence re-evaluated in the basis (provided by the modes of the original guide) of interest for the solution (62b). With the knowledge of the latter matrix representative (the Z_{mn} and T_{mo} of the <u>Handbook</u>) the T solution (62b) cast in the form (58), is characterized by a set of "static" network equations (cf. Eqs. (84) of Sec. 3.5c of the <u>Handbook</u>) which can be rapidly solved to arbitrary accuracy by a successive approximation procedure. The use in this example of different bases for (62a) and (62b) is typical of many diffraction problems.

FOOTNOTES

1. Cf. J. Schwinger, Phys. Rev., vol. 93, no. 3, Feb. 1, 1954; note Eq. (19), et. seq.

2. Cf. however, K. Furutsu, Jour. Phys. Soc. Japan, vol. 8, no. 4, July 1953.

3. Note that the normalization employed is such that $\sqrt{\mu_0/\varepsilon_0} = 1$, where ε_0, μ_0 are the dielectric constant and permeability of vacuum. The conventional normalization is regained if the $\underline{H}$ and $\underline{J}_e$ of the text are replaced by $\sqrt{\mu_0/\varepsilon_0}\,\underline{H}$ and $\sqrt{\mu_0/\varepsilon_0}\,\underline{J}_e$, respectively.

4. Cf. B. Friedman, Principles of Applied Mathematics, J. Wiley (1956).

5. Cf. N. Marcuvitz and J. Schwinger, Journal of Appl. Phys., Vol. 22, no. 6, June 1951.

6. This "Fredholm solution" is dependent on the knowledge in abstract of the determinant of $(1+VG)$ following from the identity $\ln\det(1+VG) = \mathrm{Tr}\,\ln(1+VG)$, where Tr is the trace (spur) operation. For a singular determinant a slight modification must be introduced.

7. Note that if $G_1 = \sum_{\alpha\beta} A_{\alpha\beta}\Phi_\alpha\Phi_\beta$, then $T_0 G_1 = V\sum_{\alpha\beta} A_{\alpha\beta}\Psi_{o\alpha}\Phi_\beta = V\hat{G}_1$

8. Cf. B. Noble, "Integral Equation Perturbation Methods in Low Frequency Diffraction," this Symposium; V. Twersky, "On Scattering of Waves by Two Objects," this symposium.

9. N. Marcuvitz, "Waveguide Handbook", McGraw-Hill Book Co., (1951); vol. 10. Radiation Laboratory Series.

JOSEPH KELLER

Diffraction by Polygonal Cylinders

§1. INTRODUCTION. Let us consider the initial boundary value problem for the two dimensional wave equation in a finite or infinite region of the xy plane. This problem has previously been solved explicitly for a small number of regions of special shape. We shall solve it explicitly for any region bounded by any number of straight line segments. To do so we shall utilize the finite propagation speed associated with the wave equation to show that the solution at any point P and time t is expressible in terms of a finite sequence of simpler problems. These simpler problems are initial boundary value problems for the entire space, the half space and the angular sector. Since they can be solved explicitly, so can the original problem. An account of previous work on these and related problems is given in the excellent book of F. G. Friedlander [2].

As t increases, the number of simpler problems which must be solved also increases and their initial data, which depend upon the solutions of the preceding problems, become more complicated. Nevertheless the singularities of the solution can be analyzed since they propagate along the bicharacteristics of the wave equation. We shall show that a diffracted singularity is produced whenever a singularity is incident upon a vertex of the boundary. We shall determine the diffracted singularity and show that it is weaker than the incident one. We describe this by saying that diffraction is a smoothing process.

Finally we shall use our results concerning singularities to determine the high frequency asymptotic expansion of solutions of the reduced wave equation in the same region. We shall see that this expansion is exactly what is predicted by the Geometrical Theory of Diffraction [1].

The title of this article results from the custom of calling initial boundary value problems for the wave equation "diffraction problems." The polygonal cylinders are three dimensional cylinders whose two dimensional cross-sections are the polygonal lines constituting the boundary of the region under consideration.

§2. FORMULATION OF THE PROBLEM. Let D_0 be a finite or infinite region of the xy plane bounded by a finite or infinite number of straight line segments and let B_0 denote this boundary. Let $D = D_0 \times I$ where I is the interval $[0, \infty]$ of the t axis and let $B = B_0 \times I$. We shall call B the boundary of D and D_0 the initial domain. We seek a solution $u(x, y, t)$ of the wave equation in D which has prescribed initial data on D_0 and prescribed boundary values on B. These conditions may be written as follows by letting P denote the point (x, y).

$$u_{xx}(P, t) + u_{yy}(P, t) - u_{tt}(P, t) = 0, \qquad (P, t) \text{ in } D \tag{1}$$

$$u(P, 0) = G(P), \qquad P \text{ in } D_0 \tag{2}$$

$$u_t(P, 0) = g(P), \qquad P \text{ in } D_0 \tag{3}$$

$$u(P, t) = h(P, t), \qquad (P, t) \text{ in } B. \tag{4}$$

In order that this problem possess a smooth solution, it is necessary that the prescribed functions G, g and h be sufficiently smooth. In addition these data must be compatible on B_0, where B and D_0 meet. In case the given data are not sufficiently smooth, we shall seek a weak solution of (1)-(4). The problem in which the normal derivative of u is prescribed on B rather than u itself, and that in which u is prescribed on some boundary segments and the normal derivative of u on others, can also be solved by the method to be described below.

3. SOLUTION OF THE PROBLEM. In order to solve the problem, it is convenient to take D_0 to be an open point set. It is also convenient to call the endpoints of the line segments in B_0 vertices and to assume that each line segment contains its endpoints. We now define the optical distance between two points P and Q in D_0 as the greatest lower bound (infinum) of the lengths of all paths from P to Q in D_0. In terms of this definition, we define the optical distance between two line segments as the infinum of the optical distances between pairs of points, one of which belongs to each segment. We now define the length $2a$ as the infinum of the optical distances between pairs of vertices and between pairs of non-intersecting segments in B_0. If both "sides" of a line segment in B_0 bound D_0, we treat the two sides as distinct line segments; in fact, we may do so for every line segment in B_0.

Because the propagation speed in (1) is unity, the optical distance between two points is the time required for a signal or disturbance to travel from one point to the other. Therefore $2a$ is the infinum of the times required for a signal to travel from one vertex of B_0 to another, or between two non-intersecting segments of B_0 . We now assume that a is positive : $a > 0$. This condition is necessarily satisfied if B_0 consists of a finite number of segments.

Let $D_a = D_0 \times [0, a)$ where $[0, a)$ is the interval of the t axis from 0 to a excluding $t = a$. We shall now show how to solve the problem (1)-(4) explicitly for (P, t) in D_a . To do so we divide D_a into three regions

$$D_a = D_a^0 + D_a^1 + D_a^2 . \quad (5)$$

A point (P, t) of D_a is in D_a^j if the proper backward characteristic cone from (P, t) intersects j line segments of B_0 , $j = 0, 1, 2$. From the definition of a , it is not possible for this cone to intersect more than two such segments. By the proper backward characteristic cone we mean that component of the cone which contains (P, t) when the cone is subdivided by the boundary B . Equivalently we may say that (P, t) is in D_a^j if the optical distance from P to exactly j boundary segments is less than or equal to t .

For points in D_a^0 the solution $u(P, t)$ is just the solution of the pure initial value problem for the entire plane with arbitrary initial data outside D_0 . This solution is given explicitly by a well-known formula. For points in D_a^1 the solution is just that for the initial-boundary value problem in a half-plane. The boundary of that half-plane is the infinite straight line a segment of which is intersected by the proper backward characteristic cone from (P, t) . The boundary data on this line outside the segment are arbitrary, as are the initial data on the half-plane outside D_0 . The solution $u(P, t)$ in D_a^1 is also given by a well-known formula. Finally, for points in D_a^2 the solution is that for the initial-boundary value problem in an angular sector. The boundaries of the sector are the two semi-infinite straight lines whose segments intersect the proper backward characteristic cone from (P, t) . The boundary data on the lines outside the segments are arbitrary and so are the initial data in the sector outside D_0 . An explicit formula for $u(P, t)$ in D_a^2 can be obtained by Fourier or Laplace transformation of the time periodic solutions of the angular sector problem given by Sommerfeld and by Macdonald. However, a direct solution of the time dependent problem for the sector was given by I. Kay [3] by means of separation of appropriate variables in xyt space. Another direct solution, more convenient for some purposes, was obtained by M. B. Firedman [4] who applied Green's theorem appropriately in xyt space, using a convenient Green's function. His solution utilizes the finite parts of divergent integrals, introduced by J. Hadamard [5]. This method of solution was first used by F. G. Friedlander [6] to solve the problem of diffraction by a half-plane (which is a semi-infinite line in xy space).

We have now shown how the solution $u(P, t)$ of (1)-(4) can be found explicitly for (P, t) in D_a. The continuity properties of the solution are exactly those of the solution of the sector problem. From the solution in D_a the data $u(P, a)$ and $u_t(P, a)$ can be found as limits of $u(P, t)$ and $u_t(P, t)$ at $t = a$. Then the solution can be obtained in the next interval of length a by the same process. By continuing in this way, the solution can be found explicitly for any P and any $t \geqq 0$.

4. PROPAGATION OF SINGULARITIES. It is well known that a singularity in the initial data gives rise to singularities in the solution which propagate along the bicharacteristics emanating from the locus of the initial singularity. When a bicharacteristic carrying a singularity intersects the boundary at a regular point, the singularity propagates along the reflected bicharacteristic. We must now determine what happens when a bicharacteristic carrying a singularity intersects a vertex of the boundary. The clue to the answer is contained in the result of J. B. Keller and A. A. Blank [7]. They analyzed the field produced by a plane Heaviside or step pulse incident upon a vertex. They found that in addition to the expected reflected discontinuities, the resulting field was singular on the circle (or cone) $r = t$, where r denotes distance from the vertex and t denotes time measured from the instant at which the incident discontinuity reached the vertex. On this diffracted cone the field was continuous except where the cone was tangent to the characteristics carrying the incident and reflected discontinuities. Except at these places, all the derivatives of the field of order less than one-half were also continuous across the cone while derivatives of order one-half and greater were singular. Thus a discontinuous incident field gave rise to a diffracted field with a singular derivative of order one-half.

This particular result leads us to expect a similar result in general. Specifically, we expect that an incident singularity will give rise to a diffracted singularity on the diffracted characteristic cone with its apex at the point in xyt space where the incident singularity hits the vertex. We also expect the diffracted singularity to be one-half order weaker than the incident one in the sense that the diffracted field will have a continuous derivative of order $\alpha + \frac{1}{2}$ if the incident field has a continuous derivative of order α.

We shall now verify this conjecture for the case of a plane pulse incident upon a vertex. Later we shall consider the general case. Let r and θ be polar coordinates in the xy plane with origin at the vertex. Let the two line segments bounding the angular sector under consideration lie along $\theta = -\pi/2$ and $\theta = 3\pi/2 - \gamma$. Let the incident field $u_i(r, \theta, t)$ be a plane wave traveling in the direction $-\alpha$, which we write as

$$u_i(r, \theta, t) = f[t + r\cos(\theta - \alpha)] \quad . \tag{6}$$

The special case in which f is the Heaviside function $H(z)$, which is either 1 or 0 according as z is positive or negative, is the one treated by Keller and Blank [7]. Let us denote their solution by $v(r, \theta, t)$. Then by considering f to be a superposition of Heaviside functions, we see that the solution corresponding to u_i is, if f' vanishes fast enough at $-\infty$,

$$u(r, \theta, t) = \int_{-\infty}^{t} f'(z) v(r, \theta, t-z) dz \quad . \tag{7}$$

The solution v can be written as the sum of the incident and reflected fields plus a diffracted field v_d . Near the diffracted cone $t = r$, the diffracted field has the singular form

$$\begin{aligned} v_d(r, \theta, t) &\sim (t-r)^{\frac{1}{2}} r^{-\frac{1}{2}} D(\theta, \alpha, \gamma) 2\pi^{\frac{1}{2}} \qquad t \geqq r , \quad \theta \neq -\alpha, \pi+\alpha \\ &\sim 0 \qquad\qquad\qquad\qquad t < r . \end{aligned} \tag{8}$$

Here $D(\theta, \alpha, \gamma)$ is given by

$$D(\theta, \alpha, \gamma) = \frac{e^{i\pi/4} \sin\pi/n}{n(2\pi)^{1/2}} \left[\left(\cos\frac{\pi}{n} - \cos\frac{\theta-\alpha}{n} \right)^{-1} - \left(\cos\frac{\pi}{n} - \cos\frac{\theta+\alpha+\pi}{n} \right)^{-1} \right] \tag{9}$$

In (9), $n = 2-\gamma\pi^{-1}$. Thus the diffracted part u_d of u is

$$\begin{aligned} u_d(r, \theta, t) &\sim r^{-\frac{1}{2}} D(\theta, \alpha, \gamma) 2\pi^{\frac{1}{2}} \int_{-\infty}^{t-r} f'(z)(t-r-z)^{\frac{1}{2}} dz \\ &= r^{-\frac{1}{2}} D(\theta, \alpha, \gamma) \pi^{\frac{1}{2}} \int_{-\infty}^{t-r} f(z)(t-r-z)^{-\frac{1}{2}} dz \quad . \end{aligned} \tag{10}$$

In integrating by parts we have assumed that $f(z)$ vanishes rapidly enough at $-\infty$. The last result can be rewritten in terms of fractional integration as

$$u_d(r, \theta, t) \sim r^{-\frac{1}{2}} D(\theta, \alpha, \gamma) \, I_t^{\frac{1}{2}} f(t-r) \quad . \tag{11}$$

This formula shows that for an incident plane pulse the diffracted wave is one-half order smoother than the incident wave, as we expected, except at $\theta = \pi + \alpha$ and $\theta = \alpha$, where the diffracted wave front is tangent to the incident and reflected wavefronts, respectively.

It is instructive to derive the result (11) in another way which utilizes periodic solutions. To this end we rewrite (6) in terms of a

Fourier integral with amplitude $A(k)$

$$u_i(r, \theta, t) = f[t + r\cos(\theta-\alpha)] = \int_{-\infty}^{\infty} A(k)e^{-ikt} e^{-ikr\cos(\theta-\alpha)} dk. \tag{12}$$

If we denote by $w(kr, \theta, \alpha)$ the solution of the diffraction problem with the incident field $e^{-ikr\cos(\theta-\alpha)}$, then the solution corresponding to u_i incident is

$$u(r, \theta, t) = \int_{-\infty}^{\infty} A(k)e^{-ikt} w(kr, \theta, \alpha)\, dk . \tag{13}$$

In particular the diffracted field u_d is given by (13) with w replaced by its diffracted part w_d.

$$u_d(r, \theta, t) = \int_{-\infty}^{\infty} A(k)e^{-ikt} w_d(kr, \theta, \alpha)\, dk . \tag{14}$$

Since the singularities of u_d are determined by the behavior of its Fourier transform for large values of $|k|$, it suffices to replace w_d by its asymptotic form for large kr which is

$$w_d(kr, \theta, \alpha) \sim \frac{e^{ikr + i\pi/4}}{(kr)^{\frac{1}{2}}} D(\theta, \alpha, \gamma) . \tag{15}$$

Thus (14) becomes

$$u_d(r, \theta, t) \sim \frac{D(\theta, \alpha, \gamma)e^{i\pi/4}}{r^{\frac{1}{2}}} \int_{-\infty}^{\infty} A(k) \frac{e^{-ik(t-r)}}{k^{\frac{1}{2}}} dk \tag{16}$$

$$= \frac{D(\theta, \alpha, \gamma)}{r^{\frac{1}{2}}} e^{i\pi/4} e^{-i\pi/4} I_t^{\frac{1}{2}} \int_{-\infty}^{\infty} A(k)e^{-ik(t-r)} dk$$

$$= \frac{D(\theta, \alpha, \gamma)}{r^{\frac{1}{2}}} I_t^{\frac{1}{2}} f(t-r) .$$

This is again the desired result (11).

The same result (11) can be deduced for an arbitrary incident pulse, or equivalently for arbitrary initial data, which is singular along a smooth curve. To deduce it one may examine the explicit solution of the problem of diffraction by a wedge in the form given by M. B. Friedman [4]. This has been done by R. Kalechofsky (unpublished). The analysis involves the determination of the singular behavior of several integrals.

§5. ASYMPTOTIC EXPANSION OF PERIODIC SOLUTIONS. The solutions of the wave equation which are periodic in the time are of considerable interest. Usually special solutions of this type, called time harmonic, are investigated since other periodic solutions can be constructed from them by Fourier superposition. The harmonic solutions are of the form

$$u(x, y, t) = v(x, y) e^{-i\omega t} .$$

The constant ω is called the angular frequency of the solution. If the solution corresponds to a source $F(x, y) e^{-i\omega t}$ then this source term appears on the right side of the wave equation (1) as an inhomogeneous term. From this equation it follows that the function $v(x, y)$ satisfies the inhomogeneous reduced wave equation

$$\Delta v + \omega^2 v = F(x, y) \qquad x, y \text{ in } D_0 . \qquad (17)$$

In addition, if $h(P, t) = 0$, it follows from (4) that v satisfies the boundary condition

$$v(x, y) = 0 \qquad x, y \text{ in } B_0 . \qquad (18)$$

In any parts of the domain D_0 which extend to infinity, v also satisfies appropriate radiation conditions.

Let us consider the problem of obtaining the asymptotic expansion of v for large values of ω. A method for dealing with this problem was introduced by R. K. Luneburg [8] and developed by M. Kline [9] and R. M. Lewis [10]. It is based upon representing a solution of an initial-boundary value problem for the inhomogeneous wave equation in terms of a corresponding solution of the homogeneous wave equation, by means of Duhamel's principle. When the source is time-harmonic, it is to be expected that the solution will become time-harmonic as t becomes infinite if the domain extends to infinity. This fact has been proved by C. S. Morawetz (unpublished) for any three dimensional domain which is the exterior of a star-shaped body. The resulting time-harmonic solution, and thus $v(x, y)$, is represented as a Fourier integral of the solution $U(x, y, t)$ of an appropriate initial-boundary value problem for the homogeneous wave equation. From this integral the asymptotic expansion of $v(x, y)$ for large ω is obtained. The terms in this expansion are found to correspond to the singularities of $U(x, y, t)$ considered as a function of t. Since we have just determined these singularities, we can use them to construct the asymptotic expansion of $v(x, y)$.

Let us denote by $t_j = \psi_j(x, y)$, $j = 1, 2, \ldots,$ the values of t at which $U(x, y, t)$ is singular at x, y. Then we have (see M. Kline [11], p. 597)

$$v(x, y) \sim \sum_{j=1} U_j(x, y, \omega) e^{i\omega\psi_j(x, y)} . \qquad (19)$$

The $U_j(x, y, \omega)$ are asymptotic series in ω which are given by equation (1.3) of reference [11] in terms of the form of $U(x, y, t)$ near $t = t_j$. We can calculate the leading term in each U_j since we have found the leading term in $U(x, y, t)$ near $t = t_j$. On those characteristics which reach x, y, t without touching the boundary, the singularity of U is determined solely by the initial data and can be easily computed by well-known formulas. The same is true of singularities on characteristics which have hit the boundaries at regular points a finite number of times, provided that the reflection coefficient, -1, is included for each reflection.

The singularity on a characteristic which has hit one or more edges can be determined by repeated use of (11). Each such diffraction results in the multiplication of the leading term in the diffracted field by another factor of the form $r^{-\frac{1}{2}}D(\theta, \alpha, \gamma)$ and another one-half order integration with respect to t. According to the equation for U_j in reference [11], each one-half order integration of $U(x, y, t)$ results in another factor $\omega^{-\frac{1}{2}} e^{i\pi/4}$ in the expression for U_j. The net result is that each diffraction introduces a factor of the form $(\omega r)^{-\frac{1}{2}} e^{i\pi/4}D(\theta, \alpha, \gamma)$ into the expression for the leading term in U_j. But this is exactly the prescription of the Geometrical Theory of Diffraction [12] in this case. Thus we have shown that the theory correctly yields the leading term in the asymptotic expansion of $v(x, y)$ associated with each diffracted ray in cases of diffraction by polygonal cylinders.

The geometrical theory just referred to has been applied to diffraction by an infinite slit in an infinite screen in reference [12] and to diffraction by a thick screen and by a step, in a report by J. E. Burke and the author [13]. Since these diffracting objects are polygonal cylinders, the present considerations justify the theory in these cases.

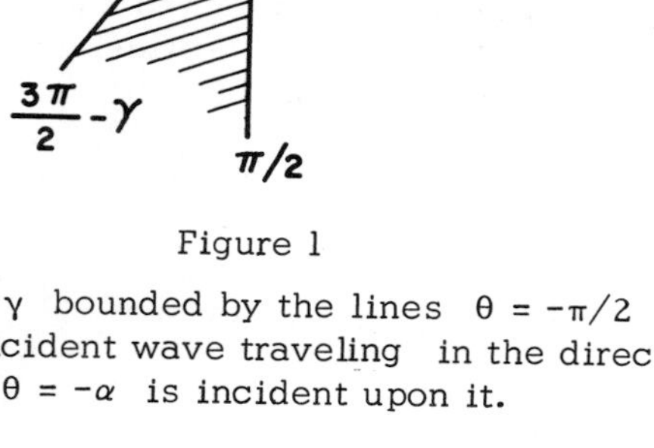

Figure 1

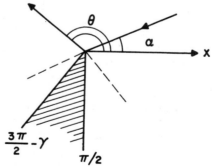

A wedge of angle γ bounded by the lines $\theta = -\pi/2$ and $\theta = 3\pi/2 - \gamma$. An incident wave traveling in the direction $\theta = -\alpha$ is incident upon it.

REFERENCES

1. Keller, J. B. A geometrical theory of diffraction, in Calculus of Variations and its Applications, Vol. VIII, Proceedings of Symposia on Applied Mathematics, edited by L. M. Graves, McGraw-Hill, New York, 1958.

2. Friedlander, F. G. Sound Pulses, Cambridge Univ. Press (1958).

3. Kay, I. Diffraction of an arbitrary pulse by a wedge, Comm. Pure Appl. Math. 6, 419-434 (1953).

4. Friedman, M. B. The method of the Green's function applied to the diffraction of pulses by wedges, Tech. Rep. 18, Dept. of Civil Eng. and Eng. Mech., Columbia Univ., Nov. 1956.

5. Hadamard, J. Lectures on Cauchy's Problem, Yale Univ. Press (1923).

6. Friedlander, F. G. On the half plane diffraction problem, Quart. Jour. Mech. Appl. Math. 4, 344-57 (1951).

7. Keller, J. B. and Blank, A. A. Diffraction and reflection of pulses by wedges and corners, Comm. Pure Appl. Math. 4, 75-94 (1951).

8. Luneburg, R. K. The Mathematical Theory of Optics, Lecture Notes, Brown Univ., 1944; Propagation of Electromagnetic Waves, Lecture Notes, New York Univ., 1948.

9. Kline, M. Asymptotic solution of linear hyperbolic partial differential equations, Jour. Rat. Mech. Anal. 3, 315-342 (1954).

10. Lewis, R. M. Asymptotic expansion of steady-state solutions of symmetric hyperbolic linear differential equations, J. Math. Mech. 7, 593-628 (1958).

11. Kline, M. Asymptotic solutions of Maxwell's equations involving fractional powers of the frequency, Comm. Pure. Appl. Math. 8, 595-614(1955).

12. Keller, J. B. Diffraction by an aperture, Jour. Appl. Phys. 28, 426-444 (1957).

13. Burke, J. E. and Keller, J. B. Diffraction by a thick screen, a step and related axially symmetric objects, Engineering Report EDL-E48, Electronics Defense Labs., Sylvania Electric Products, Inc., Mountain View, Calif., March 1960.

N. A. LOGAN and K. S. YEE

A Mathematical Model for Diffraction by Convex Surfaces

1. THE GREEN'S FUNCTION $D(x, y, y_0, q)$

This paper is concerned with the theory and application of the Green's function $D(x, y, y_0, q)$ defined by

Differential Equation:

$$\frac{\partial^2 D}{\partial y^2} + i\frac{\partial D}{\partial x} + yD = -\delta(x)\delta(y-y_0) \qquad 0 \le y, y_0 < \infty \qquad (1.1)$$

$$0 < x < \infty$$

Boundary Condition:

$$\left(\frac{\partial D}{\partial y} + qD\right)\Bigg|_{y=0} = 0 \qquad (1.2)$$

Radiation Condition:

$$\lim_{y \to \infty}\left[\frac{1}{\sqrt[4]{y}}\left(\frac{\partial D}{\partial y} - i\sqrt{y}\,D\right)\right] = 0 \qquad (1.3)$$

The solution of this problem involves the Airy functions

$$\left(\frac{d^2}{dt^2} - t\right) w_{1,2}(t) = 0 \qquad (1.4)$$

$$w_{1,2}(t) = \sqrt{\pi}\,[\,Bi(t) \pm iAi(t)\,] = \frac{1}{\sqrt{\pi}}\int_0^\infty \exp(-\tfrac{1}{3}x^3 + xt)\,dx$$

$$\pm \frac{i}{\sqrt{\pi}}\int_0^\infty \exp[-i(\tfrac{1}{3}x^3 + xt)]\,dx \qquad (1.5)$$

$$v(t) = \frac{1}{2i}[\,w_1(t) - w_2(t)\,] = \sqrt{\pi}\,Ai(t) = \frac{1}{\sqrt{\pi}}\int_0^\infty \cos(\tfrac{1}{3}x^3 + xt)\,dx \qquad (1.6)$$

It is possible to express this Green's function in the form of a Fourier integral or in the form of a normal mode expansion.

$$D(x,y,y_0,q) = \frac{1}{2\pi}\int_{-\infty}^{\infty} \exp(ixt)\left[w_1(t-y_>)v(t-y_<) - \frac{v'(t)-q\,v(t)}{w_1'(t)-qw_1(t)} w_1(t-y_0)\,w_1(t-y)\right]dt$$

$$= -i\sum_{s=1}^{\infty} \frac{\exp(ixt_s)\,w_1(t_s-y_0)\,w_1(t_s-y)}{[w_1'(t_s)]^2 - t_s[w_1(t_s)]^2} \qquad (1.7)$$

where

$$w_1'(t_s) - q\,w_1(t_s) = 0 \,. \qquad (1.8)$$

In some of the applications it is convenient to renormalize $D(x,y,y_0,q)$ in order to employ a function $V(x,y,y_0,q)$ which has the property $V(0,0,0,0) = 2$.

$$V(x,y,y_0,q) = 2\sqrt{-i\pi x}\; D(x,y,y_0,q) \qquad (1.9)$$

$$\frac{\partial^2 V}{\partial y^2} + i\frac{\partial V}{\partial x} + \left(y - \frac{i}{2x}\right)V = 0 \qquad (1.10)$$

$$\cdot\left(\frac{\partial V}{\partial y} + qV\right)_{y=0} = 0 \qquad (1.11)$$

When $y_0 \to \infty$, it is convenient to express $D(x,y,y_0,q)$ in the form

$$D(x,y,y_0,q) \xrightarrow[y_0\to\infty]{} \frac{\exp\left(i\frac{2}{3}y_0^{3/2} + i\frac{\pi}{4}\right)}{2\sqrt{\pi}\;\sqrt[4]{y_0}}\, E(x-\sqrt{y_0},y,q) \qquad (1.12)$$

$$E(\xi,y,q) = \frac{1}{\sqrt{\pi}}\int_{-\infty}^{\infty} \exp(i\xi t)\left[v(t-y) - \frac{v'(t)-q\,v(t)}{w_1'(t)-q\,w_1(t)}\, w_1(t-y)\right]dt \qquad (1.13)$$

$$\frac{\partial^2 E}{\partial y^2} + i\frac{\partial E}{\partial \xi} + yE = 0\,, \quad \left(\frac{\partial E}{\partial y} + qE\right)_{y=0} = 0 \qquad (1.14)$$

It is often convenient to decompose $E(\xi,y,q)$ into a "plane wave" field $E_0(\xi,y)$ and a reflected field $P(\xi,y,q)$.

$$E_0(\xi,y) = \frac{1}{\sqrt{\pi}}\int_{-\infty}^{\infty} \exp(i\xi t)\,v(t-y)\,dt$$

$$= \exp(i\xi y - i\xi^3/3) \qquad (1.15)$$

$$P(\xi, y, q) = -\frac{1}{\sqrt{\pi}} \int_{-\infty}^{\infty} \exp(i\xi t) \frac{v'(t)-q\,v(t)}{w'_1(t)-q\,w_1(t)} w_1(t-y)\,dt \qquad (1.16)$$

2. THE RADIO PROBLEM

The function $V(x, y, y_0, q)$ is well known in the theory of the propagation of the ground wave around the earth's surface under the conditions of "normal refraction" (i.e., in the absence of ducts and atmospheric inhomogeneities). As an example, we cite the problem of finding the Hertz potential for a vertically-directed, electric dipole located at $z = r_0$ on the polar axis in the region exterior to a sphere of radius a.

Let the Hertz potential in free space be

$$U_0 = \frac{e^{ikR}}{4\pi R} \qquad R = \sqrt{\rho^2 + (z-r_0)^2}\ . \qquad (2.1)$$

The field in the presence of the sphere must satisfy the equations

$$(\nabla^2 + k^2)U = \frac{\delta(\theta)\delta(r-r_0)}{2\pi r_0^2 \sin\theta} \qquad (2.2)$$

$$\frac{\partial U}{\partial r} + k[(\frac{2}{ka})^{1/3} q]U = 0 \qquad \text{at } r = a\ . \qquad (2.3)$$

The solution is generally given in the form

$$U \sim \frac{e^{iks}}{4\pi s} \sqrt{\frac{\theta}{\sin\theta}}\ V(x, y, y_0, q) \qquad (2.4)$$

$$x = \left(\frac{k}{2a^2}\right)^{1/3} s\ , \quad y = \left(\frac{2k^2}{a}\right)^{1/3} h\ , \quad y_0 = \left(\frac{2k^2}{a}\right)^{1/3} h_0 \qquad (2.5)$$

$$s = a\theta\ , \quad h = r-a\ , \quad h_0 = r_0 - a\ . \qquad (2.6)$$

The attenuation function $V(x, y, y_0, q)$ is often written in a form which employs a so-called "height-gain" function $f_s(y)$.

$$V(x, y, y_0, q) = 2\sqrt{i\pi x} \sum_{s=1}^{\infty} \frac{\exp(ixt_s)}{t_s - q^2} f_s(y) f_s(y_0) \qquad (2.7)$$

$$f_s(y) = \frac{w_1(t_s - y)}{w_1(t_s)} = 1 - qy + \frac{1}{2} t_s y^2 + \cdots\ . \qquad (2.8)$$

$$f_s(y) \xrightarrow[y \gg |t_s|]{} \frac{\exp\left[i\left(\frac{2}{3} y^{3/2} - \sqrt{y}\, t_s - \frac{\pi}{4}\right)\right]}{\sqrt[4]{y}\, w_1(t_s)} \{1 + i \frac{t^2}{4\sqrt{y}} + \cdots\} \tag{2.9}$$

3. LIMITING FORMS OF THE DIFFRACTION FUNCTION

In the applications it is convenient to give special attention to three limiting forms of the diffraction function.

The attenuation function is defined by

$$\begin{aligned} V_0(\xi, q) &= \frac{1}{2} V(\xi, 0, 0, q) \\ &= \sqrt{\pi\xi}\, \exp(i\frac{\pi}{4}) \sum_{s=1}^{\infty} \frac{\exp(i\xi t_s)}{t_s - q^2} \\ &= \frac{\exp(-i\frac{\pi}{4})}{2} \sqrt{\frac{\xi}{\pi}} \int_{-\infty}^{\infty} \exp(i\xi t) \frac{w_1(t)}{w'_1(t) - q\, w_1(t)}\, dt \end{aligned} \tag{3.1}$$

The current distribution function is defined by

$$\begin{aligned} V_1(\xi, q) &= \lim_{y_0 \to \infty} \left\{ \frac{\sqrt[4]{y_0}}{\sqrt{\xi + \sqrt{y_0}}} \exp\left(-i\frac{2}{3} y_0^{3/2}\right) V(\xi + \sqrt{y_0}, 0, y_0, q) \right\} \\ &= i2\sqrt{\pi} \sum_{s=1}^{\infty} \frac{\exp(i\xi t_s)}{(t_s - q^2)\, w_1(t_s)} \\ &= \frac{1}{\sqrt{\pi}} \int_{-\infty}^{\infty} \exp(i\xi t) \frac{1}{w'_1(t) - q\, w_1(t)}\, dt \end{aligned} \tag{3.2}$$

The reflection coefficient function is defined by

$$\begin{aligned} V_{11}(\xi, q) &= \lim_{\substack{y \to \infty \\ y_0 \to \infty}} \left\{ \frac{\sqrt[4]{y_0 y}}{\sqrt{\xi + \sqrt{y} + \sqrt{y_0}}} \exp\left[-i\frac{2}{3}(y^{3/2} + y_0^{3/2})\right] V(\xi + \sqrt{y} + \sqrt{y_0}, y, y_0, \right. \\ &= \exp(i\frac{3\pi}{4})\, 2\sqrt{\pi} \sum_{s=1}^{\infty} \frac{\exp(i\xi t_s)}{(t_s - q^2)[w_1(t_s)]^2} \\ &= -\frac{\exp(i\frac{\pi}{4})}{\sqrt{\pi}} \int_{-\infty}^{\infty} \exp(i\xi t) \frac{v'(t) - q\, v(t)}{w'_1(t) - q\, w_1(t)}\, dt \end{aligned} \tag{3.3}$$

The functions $V_0(\xi, q)$, $V_1(\xi, q)$ can be shown to be solutions of the integral equations

$$V_0(\xi,q) = e^{-i\frac{1}{12}\xi^3} - \frac{e^{-i\frac{\pi}{4}}}{2}\sqrt{\frac{\xi}{\pi}}\int_0^{\xi} V_0(x,q)\,e^{-i\frac{1}{12}(\xi-x)^3}\{(\xi-x)-2iq\}\frac{dx}{\sqrt{x(\xi-x)}} \tag{3.4}$$

$$V_1(\xi,q) = 2e^{-i\frac{1}{3}\xi^3} - \frac{e^{-i\frac{\pi}{4}}}{2\sqrt{\pi}}\int_{-\infty}^{\xi} V_1(x,q)\,e^{-i\frac{1}{12}(\xi-x)^3}\{(\xi-x)-2iq\}\frac{dx}{\sqrt{x(\xi-x)}} . \tag{3.5}$$

The limiting form for $V(x,y,y_0,q)$ which was given for the case $y\to\infty$, $y_0\to\infty$ is not useful when x is comparable with $\sqrt{y}+\sqrt{y_0}$. In this "horizon" region one needs to employ a form involving a Fresnel integral. As a preliminary step to giving a representation for this case we make the definitions

$$V_2(\xi,q) = V_{11}(\xi,q) - \frac{\exp(i\frac{\pi}{4})}{2\sqrt{\pi}\,\xi} \tag{3.6}$$

$$K(\tau) = \frac{1}{\sqrt{\pi}}\exp(-i\tau^2-i\frac{\pi}{4})\int_{\tau}^{\infty}\exp(is^2)\,ds \underset{\tau\to\infty}{\longrightarrow} \frac{\exp(i\frac{\pi}{4})}{2\sqrt{\pi}\,\tau} \tag{3.7}$$

$$\mu K(\mu\xi) + V_2(\xi,q) \underset{\substack{\mu\to\infty\\ \xi>0}}{\longrightarrow} V_{11}(\xi,q) \tag{3.8}$$

We can then show that in the "horizon" region,

$$V(x,y,y_0,q) \underset{\substack{y\to\infty\\ y_0\to\infty}}{\longrightarrow} H(x,y,y_0) + \sqrt[4]{\frac{x^2}{y\,y_0}}\exp[i\tfrac{2}{3}(y^{3/2}+y_0^{3/2})]V_2(\xi,q) \tag{3.9}$$

$$\begin{aligned} H(x,y,y_0) &= \sqrt[4]{\frac{x^2}{y\,y_0}}\exp[i\tfrac{2}{3}(y^{3/2}+y_0^{3/2})]\,\mu K(\tau) \qquad \xi>0 \\ &= \sqrt[4]{\frac{x^2}{y\,y_0}}\exp[i\tfrac{2}{3}(y^{3/2}+y_0^{3/2})]\,[-\mu K(-\tau)] \\ &\quad + \exp\left\{i\left[-\frac{x^3}{12}+\frac{x}{2}(y+y_0)+\frac{(y-y_0)^2}{4x}\right]\right\} \qquad \xi<0 \end{aligned} \tag{3.10}$$

$$\xi = x-\sqrt{y}-\sqrt{y_0}\,, \qquad \tau=\mu\xi\,, \qquad \mu = \sqrt{\frac{\sqrt{y}\sqrt{y_0}}{\sqrt{y}+\sqrt{y_0}}} \tag{3.11}$$

4. THE LINE-OF-SIGHT REGION

For points well above the horizon it is convenient to separate the Green's function $D(x, y, y_0, q)$ into a free space field $D_0(x, y, y_0)$ and a reflected field $R(x, y, y_0, q)$

$$D(x, y, y_0, q) = D_0(x, y, y_0) + R(x, y, y_0, q) \tag{4.1}$$

$$D_0(x, y, y_0) = \frac{e^{i\frac{\pi}{4}}}{2\sqrt{\pi x}} \exp\left[-i\frac{x^3}{12} + i\frac{x}{2}(y + y_0) + i\frac{y-y_0{}^{\,2}}{4x}\right] \tag{4.2}$$

$$R(x, y, y_0, q) = -\frac{1}{2\pi}\int_{-\infty}^{\infty} \exp(ixt)\frac{v'(t) - q\,v(t)}{w'_1(t) - q\,w_1(t)}\, w_1(t-y)\, w_1(t-y_0)dt\ . \tag{4.3}$$

The method of stationary phase can be used to show that

$$R(\zeta+\zeta_0, \zeta^2+2\mu\zeta, \zeta_0^2+2\mu\zeta_0, q) \xrightarrow[\mu \gg 1]{} -\frac{\exp(i\frac{\pi}{4})}{2\sqrt{\pi}}\ \frac{q-i\mu}{q+i\mu}\sqrt{\frac{\mu}{2\zeta\zeta_0+\mu(\zeta+\zeta_0)}}\exp(iw^*) \tag{4.4}$$

where

$$w^* = \frac{2}{3}(\zeta^3+\zeta_0^3) + 2\mu(\zeta^2+\zeta_0^2) + \mu^2(\zeta+\zeta_0) \quad . \tag{4.5}$$

This result is valid for arbitrary values of ζ and ζ_0 .

If we require that both ζ and ζ_0 be very large, but leave μ unrestricted, we must use the reflection coefficient function $V_{11}(\xi, q)$.

$$R(\zeta+\zeta_0, \zeta^2+2\mu\zeta, \zeta_0^2+2\mu\zeta_0, q) \xrightarrow[\zeta, \zeta_0 \gg 1]{} \frac{\exp(i\frac{\pi}{4})}{\sqrt{2\pi}\sqrt{2\zeta\zeta_0+\mu(\zeta+\zeta_0)}}\, V_{11}(-2\mu, q)\exp(iw^* - i\frac{2}{3} \tag{4.6}$$

$$V_{11}(-2\mu, q) \xrightarrow[\mu \gg 1]{} -\frac{q-i\mu}{q+i\mu}\sqrt{\frac{\mu}{2}}\exp(i\frac{2}{3}\mu^3) \tag{4.7}$$

$$V_{11}(-2\mu, q) \xrightarrow[\substack{\mu \gg 1 \\ q \to \infty}]{} -\sqrt{\frac{\mu}{2}}\exp[i(\frac{2}{3}\mu^3 - \frac{2\mu}{q})] \tag{4.8}$$

The cases $q = \infty$ and $q = 0$ are of particular importance in the applications. For these cases we have the further results

$$V_{11}(\xi, \infty) \xrightarrow[\xi \to -\infty]{} \frac{\sqrt{-\xi}}{2}\exp\left(-i\frac{\xi^3}{12}\right)\left\{1 - i\frac{2}{\xi^3} + \frac{20}{\xi^6} + i\frac{560}{\xi^9} - \frac{25520}{\xi^{12}} - i\frac{1601600}{\xi^{15}} + \cdots\right\} \tag{4.9}$$

$$V_{11}(\xi,0) \xrightarrow[\xi\to-\infty]{} -\frac{\sqrt{-\xi}}{2}\exp\left(-i\frac{\xi^3}{12}\right)\left\{1+i\frac{2}{\xi^3}-\frac{28}{\xi^6}-i\frac{896}{\xi^9}+\frac{43120}{\xi^{12}}+i\frac{2754752}{\xi^{15}}+\cdots\right\} \tag{4.10}$$

The case in which the source is at a very great distance (i.e., $y_0 \to \infty$) is very important. It is convenient to treat this case by employing the reflected field $P(\xi,\zeta,q)$ associated with the "plane wave" problem (see Eq. 1.16).

$$R(x,y,y_0,q) \xrightarrow[y_0\to\infty]{} \frac{\exp\left(i\frac{2}{3}y_0^{3/2}+i\frac{\pi}{4}\right)}{2\sqrt{\pi}\;\sqrt[4]{y_0}}\left[1-i\frac{1}{4\sqrt{y_0}}\;\frac{\partial^2}{\partial\xi^2}+\cdots\right]P(\xi,y,q) \tag{4.11}$$

$$\xi = x-\sqrt{y_0} \tag{4.12}$$

$$P(\xi,y,q) = -\frac{1}{\sqrt{\pi}}\int_{-\infty}^{\infty}\exp(i\xi t)\frac{v'(t)-q\,v(t)}{w'_1(t)-q\,w_1(t)}\;w_1(t-y)\,dt \tag{4.13}$$

When $\sqrt{y}-\xi > 0$, the expression for the field $P(\xi,y,q)$ can be evaluated by the method of stationary phase

$$P(\xi,y,q) \xrightarrow[p\gg 1]{} -\frac{q-ip}{q+ip}\sqrt{\frac{p}{\sigma}}\exp\left[i\left(\frac{\sigma^3}{12}+\frac{\sigma^2 p}{4}-\frac{\sigma p^2}{4}+\frac{p^3}{4}\right)\right] \tag{4.14}$$

$$p = \frac{1}{3}\left(\sqrt{\xi^2+3y}-2\xi\right) \tag{4.15}$$

$$\sigma = \sqrt{\xi^2+3y}\quad . \tag{4.16}$$

In order to find an asymptotic expansion for $P(\xi,y,q)$ it is convenient to use the differential equation for the complex amplitude $A(p,\sigma,q)$ defined by

$$P(\xi,y,q) = \exp\left[i\left(\frac{\sigma^3}{12}+\frac{\sigma^2 p}{4}-\frac{\sigma p^2}{4}+\frac{p^3}{4}\right)\right]A(p,\sigma,q) \tag{4.17}$$

We can show that $A(p,\sigma,q)$ is a solution of

$$\frac{1}{4\sigma^2}\frac{\partial^2 A}{\partial p^2}+\frac{9}{4\sigma^2}\frac{\partial^2 A}{\partial\sigma^2}+\frac{3}{2\sigma^2}\frac{\partial^2 A}{\partial\sigma\partial p}-\frac{3}{4\sigma^3}\frac{\partial A}{\partial p}+\left(2i-\frac{9}{4\sigma^3}\right)\frac{\partial A}{\partial\sigma}+\frac{i}{\sigma}A = 0\;. \tag{4.18}$$

If we assume that

$$A(p,\sigma,q) = \sqrt{\frac{p}{\sigma}} \sum_{n=0}^{\infty} \frac{A_n(p,q)}{\sigma^n} \xrightarrow[\sigma\to\infty]{} \sqrt{\frac{2}{\sigma}}\, V_{11}(-2p,q)\exp(-i\tfrac{2}{3}p^3)\ , \quad (4.19)$$

the differential equation leads to the recursion formula

$$\begin{aligned} A_{n+1}(p,q) = -\frac{i}{2(n+1)} \Bigg\{ & \left[\frac{1}{4}\frac{d^2A_n}{dp^2} + \frac{1}{4p}\frac{dA_n}{dp} - \frac{1}{16p^2}A_n\right] \\ & - \left[\frac{3}{2}n\frac{dA_{n-1}}{dp} + \frac{3n}{4p}A_{n-1}\right] \\ & + \left[\frac{45}{16} + \frac{9}{4}(n-2)(n+1)A_{n-2}\right]\Bigg\} \end{aligned} \quad (4.20)$$

$$A_0(p,q) = \sqrt{\frac{2}{p}}\, V_{11}(-2p,q)\exp(-i\tfrac{2}{3}p^3) \qquad A_m = 0 \ \text{if}\ m < 0\ . \quad (4.21)$$

5. THE SHADOW REGION

When $x > \sqrt{y} + \sqrt{y_0}$ it is convenient to use the normal mode representation for $D(x,y,y_0,q)$. It is convenient to define $x = \sqrt{y} + \sqrt{y_0}$ to be the horizon. For points well below the horizon (i. e., $x \gg \sqrt{y} + \sqrt{y_0}$), only one term in the normal mode expansion contributes significantly to the sum. As one approaches the horizon from the shadow side one must use an increasing number of terms. For heights not exceeding several natural units (i. e., y and y_0 not greater than 5) it has been found that the use of up to twenty terms is sufficient to come within the horizon to the vicinity of the first minima. This property is illustrated in Fig. 1

The location of the roots $t_s(q)$ in the complex t-plane are well known for the cases $q = 0$ and $q = \infty$.

$$w_1'(t_s^0) = 0$$
$$t_s^0 = \beta_s \exp(i\tfrac{\pi}{3})$$
$$A_i'(-\beta_s) = 0$$

s	β_s	$Ai(-\beta_s)$
1	1.01879 29716 47471	+0.53565 66560 15700
2	3.24819 75821 79837	-0.41901 54780 32564
3	4.82009 92111 78736	+0.38040 64686 28153
4	6.16330 73556 39487	-0.35790 79437 12292
5	7.37217 72550 47770	+0.34230 12444 11624

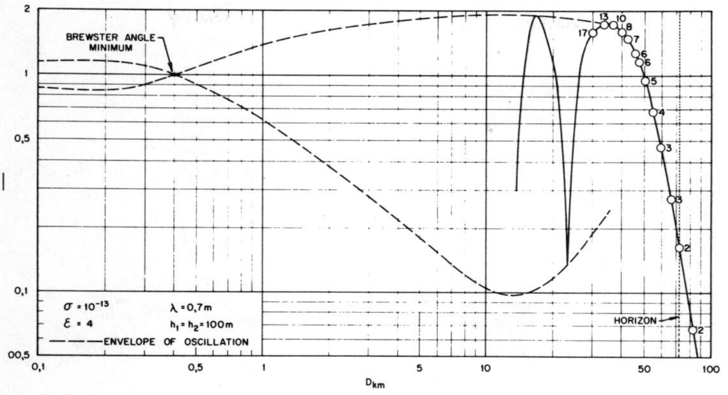

Figure 1
VARIATION OF FIELD STRENGTH NEAR THE HORIZON
The circles O indicate number of terms required in residue series
(After Van der Pol and Bremmer Phil. Mag. 27, 270, 1939)

$$w_1(t_s^{\infty}) = 0$$

$$t_s^{\infty} = \alpha_s \exp(i\frac{\pi}{3})$$

$$Ai(-\alpha_s) = 0$$

s	α_s	$Ai'(-\alpha_s)$
1	2.33810 74104 59767	+0.70121 08227 20691
2	4.08794 94441 30971	-0.80311 13696 54864
3	5.52055 98280 95551	+0.86520 40258 94152
4	6.78670 80900 71759	-0.91085 07370 49602
5	7.94413 35871 20853	+0.94733 57094 41568

Much attention has been given to the study of the propagation of vertically-polarized, electromagnetic waves over the convex interface between free space and a highly conducting homogeneous obstacle. In this case, the impedance parameter q has a phase of the order of 45°. We refer to these as the "Watson modes." In the theory of the propagation of vertically-polarized, electromagnetic waves over a convex interface of a perfect conductor which is (a) slightly rough, (b) covered with a thin dielectric layer, or (c) corrugated, the impedance parameter q has a phase of the order of 0°. We refer to these as the "Elliott modes." In Fig. 2 we illustrate the position of the dominant modes for which the imaginary part of t_s is small.

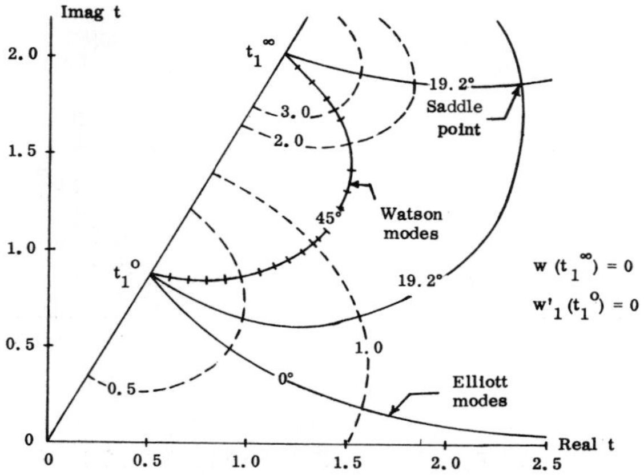

Figure 2

THE LOGARITHMIC DERIVATIVE $q = w_1'(t)/w_1(t)$

(— phase ---- modulus)

In this figure we observe that when q has a phase of the order of 19.2° two modes coalesce at a saddle point. There are an infinite number of these critical points t_s^c. These saddlepoints have the properties

$$t_s^c = q^2 \tag{5.1}$$

$$[w_1'(t_s^c)]^2 = t_s^c[w_1(t_s^c)]^2 \tag{5.2}$$

$$\left.\begin{aligned} t_s^c &\xrightarrow[s\to\infty]{} \left[\frac{3\pi}{8}(4s+1)\right]^{2/3} \exp\left(i\frac{\pi}{3} \pm i\theta_s\right), \\ \theta_s &= \frac{4}{3\pi}\,\frac{1}{(4n+1)}\left\{\log\frac{3}{4} + 2\log[(4n+1)\pi]\right\} \end{aligned}\right\} \tag{5.3}$$

There are three important types of representations for the roots t_s. They can be readily derived by observing that $t_s(q)$ satisfies a Riccati equation.

$$\frac{dt_s}{dq} = \frac{1}{t_s - q^2} \tag{5.4}$$

Three useful representations for $t_s(q)$ can be derived from this equation.

$$t_s(q) = t_s^0 + \frac{1}{t_s^0} q - \frac{1}{2(t_s^0)^3} q^2 + \left(\frac{1}{3(t_s^0)^2} + \frac{1}{2(t_s^0)^5}\right) q^3 - \left(\frac{7}{12(t_s^0)^4} + \frac{5}{8(t_s^0)^7}\right) q^4 + \cdots \tag{5.5}$$

$$t_s(q) = t_s^\infty + \frac{1}{q} + \frac{1}{3} t_s^\infty \frac{1}{q^3} + \frac{1}{4} \frac{1}{q^4} + \frac{1}{5}(t_s^\infty) \frac{1}{q^5} + \frac{7}{18}(t_s^\infty) \frac{1}{q^6} + \cdots \tag{5.6}$$

$$t_0(q) = q^2 + \frac{1}{2q} + \frac{1}{8} \frac{1}{q^4} + \frac{5}{32} \frac{1}{q^7} + \frac{11}{32} \frac{1}{q^{10}} + \cdots \tag{5.7}$$

$$0^\circ \leq \arg q < 30^\circ$$

We observe that t_0 corresponds to t_1 for $0^\circ \leq \arg q < 19.2^\circ$, t_0 t_2 for $19.2^\circ < \arg q < 23.4^\circ$, etc. This property is illustrated by Fig. 3.

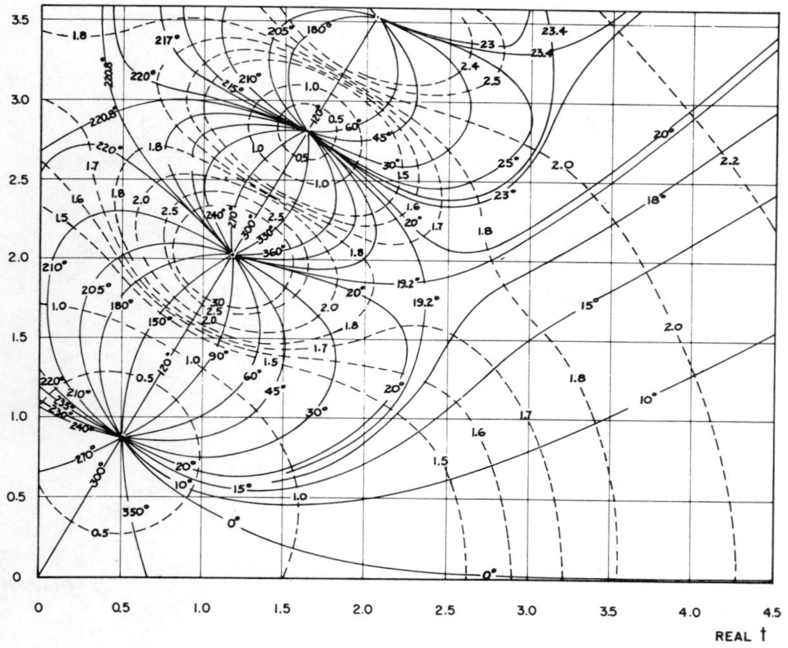

Figure 3

THE LOGARITHMIC DERIVATIVE $q = w_1'(t)/w_1(t)$ (—phase, ---modulus)

The behavior of the height factors $w_1(t-y)$ is illustrated in Fig. 4. From the location of the roots t_s for Watson modes, we find that for $y > 1$ the height factor behaves in a relatively simple manner. The complex behavior of $w_1(t_s-y)$ for small values of y can be interpreted in terms of a leaky waveguide. The region of complex behavior corresponds to the region inside the waveguide. The simple behavior for $y \gg 1$ corresponds to the radiation region.

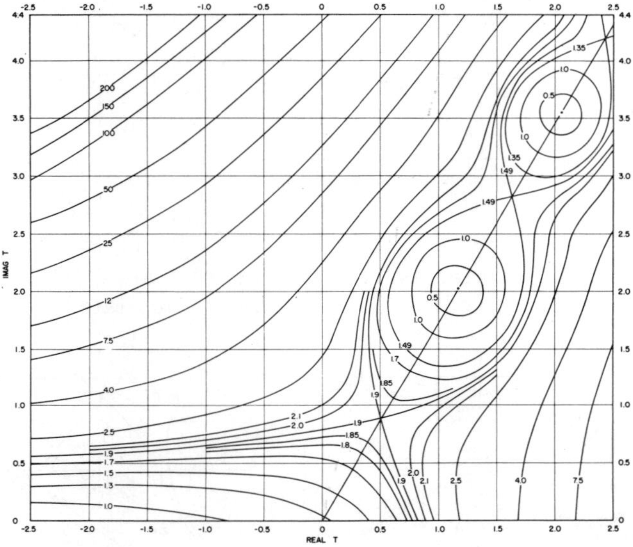

Figure 4

THE MODULUS OF THE AIRY FUNCTION $w_1(t)$

The leaky waveguide concept is illustrated in Fig. 5.

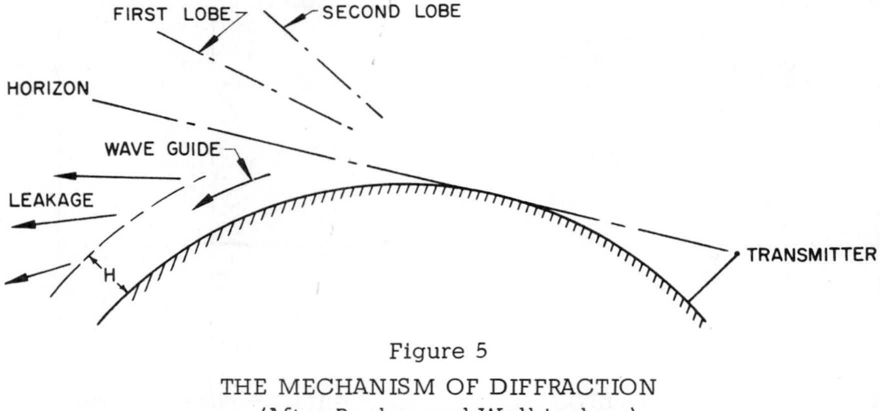

Figure 5

THE MECHANISM OF DIFFRACTION
(After Booker and Walkinshaw)

6. NUMERICAL RESULTS FOR $V(x, y, y_0, q)$

The first extensive computations of $V(x, y, y_0, q)$ were made in 1937-1939 by van der Pol and Bremmer. Fig. 1 is typical of their end results.

In the early days of World War II, Pryce and Domb expressed the normal mode expansion in terms of the Airy integral $Ai(z)$ and made extensive calculations for

$$t = \exp(-i\frac{\pi}{4})q = 0(0.1)1.0$$

$$\frac{1}{t} = \exp(i\frac{\pi}{4})(\frac{1}{q}) = 0(0.1)1.0$$

The location of the roots t_s for these values of the modulus of q are shown in Fig. by marks on the curve for $\arg q = 45°$. Their calculations were based on using up to five terms in the residue series. Unlike the previous work of van der Pol and Bremmer, these authors published tables of the eigenvalues a_s and the eigenfunctions $Ai[-a_s + h_1 \exp(-i\frac{\pi}{3})]$ which were defined by

$$V(d,h_1,h_2,\sqrt{it}) = 2\sqrt{\pi d}\exp(-i\frac{\pi}{12})\sum_{s=1}^{\infty}\frac{\exp[(-\frac{\sqrt{3}}{2}+i\frac{1}{2})a_s d]}{a_s[A(-a_s)]^2+[A'(-a_s)]^2} A[-a_s+h_1\exp(-i\frac{\pi}{3})]$$

$$V(d,h_1,h_2,\sqrt{it}) = 2\sqrt{\pi d}\exp(-i\frac{\pi}{12})\sum_{s=1}^{\infty}\frac{\exp[(-\frac{\sqrt{3}}{2}+i\frac{1}{2})a_s d]}{a_s[Ai(-a_s)]^2+[Ai'(-a_s)]^2} Ai[-a_s+h_1\exp(-i\frac{\pi}{3})]\, Ai[-a_s+h_2\exp(-i\frac{\pi}{3})] \quad (6.1)$$

$$Ai'(-a_s) - t\exp(-i\frac{\pi}{6})Ai(-a_s) = 0 \quad (6.2)$$

$$Ai(z) = \frac{1}{\pi}\int_0^{\infty}\cos(\frac{1}{3}t^3 + zt)\,dt \quad (6.3)$$

In 1949, Belkina published some tables of $V(x, y, 0, q)$ and $V_1(x, q)$ for some selected values of q which occur when radio waves propagate over a lossy dielectric sphere. The tables were constructed for

$$q = i\,n^{5/6}(i + \alpha n)^{-1/2}$$

$$\alpha = 0.00(0.01)0.03 \ , \quad \log_e n = -0.9(0.2)2.9 \ .$$

In 1955, van der Pol and Bremmer cooperated with the Mathematical Centre, Amsterdam (A. van Wyngaarden, Director) in the preparation of an extensive Atlas of curves which are equivalent to $V(x, y, y_0, q)$

$$E_0 = 787,000\frac{1}{2\sqrt{\pi}}|A(m, m_1, m_2, b| \text{ microvolts per meter} \quad (6.4)$$

$$A(m, m_1, m_2, b) = 2\sqrt{\pi m}\ \exp(i\frac{3\pi}{4})\sum_{s=1}^{\infty}\frac{h_2(\mu_s+m_1^2)h_2(\mu_s+m_2^2)\exp(i\mu_s m)}{\mu_s[h_2(\mu_s)]^2+[h_2'(\mu_s)]^2} \tag{6.5}$$

$$h_2(\mu_s) + b\,h_2'(\mu_s) = 0 \tag{6.6}$$

$$h_2(z) = (\frac{2}{3}z^{3/2})^{1/3} H_{1/3}^{(2)}(\frac{2}{3}z^{3/2}) \tag{6.7}$$

It is a straightforward exercise to show that

$$A(m, m_1, m_2, b) = \overline{\{V(m, m_1^2, m_2^2, \bar{b}^{-1}\}} \tag{6.8}$$

$$\left[\left(\frac{1}{2m_1}\frac{\partial}{\partial m_1}\right)^2 - i\frac{\partial}{\partial m} + \left(m_1^2 + \frac{i}{2m}\right)\right]A(m, m_1, m_2, b) = 0 \tag{6.9}$$

$$\left(\frac{b}{2m_1}\frac{\partial A}{\partial m_1} + A\right)_{m_1=0} = 0 \tag{6.10}$$

where the $\bar{V}$ and $\bar{b}$ denote the complex conjugates of V and b. We observe that the differential equation satisfied by $V(x, y, y_0, q)$ is somewhat simpler than that satisfied by $A(m, m_1, m_2, b)$.

In 1957, the Ministry of Postal Services (Radio Research Laboratories) in Tokyo issued an even more extensive Atlas.

Unfortunately, both the 1955 Atlas and the 1957 Atlas contain only graphs. In many applications it would be more desirable to have tables of $V(x, y, y_0, q)$ which are prepared for specific values of the natural units x, y, y_0, and q. These units were first suggested in the early 1940's by Pryce and Domb who realized that by using these natural units the calculations for one set of values of the geometrical and physical parameters could then be readily rescaled for another set of parameters.

In 1957, Belkina and Azrilyant published an extensive set of tables and graphs for $V(x, y, y_0, 0)$ and $V(x, y, y_0, \infty)$. These tables were, for the most part, constructed by summing no more than five terms in the normal mode expansion.

The tables of $V(x, y, y_0, 0)$ are very valuable in the computation of fields diffracted around a perfectly conducting surface when the field is vertically polarized. They are also useful for the study of propagation around the earth's surfaces for frequencies up to 1 kilocycle over sea water and up to 50 kilocycles over typical land. For small values of q which are associated with these problems for these frequency ranges, we can use the approximation

$$V(x, y, y_0, q) \sim V(x, y, y_0, 0) + (\sqrt{y} + \sqrt{y_0} - x)\,qV^{(-1)}(x, y, y_0, 0) \tag{6.11}$$

$$V^{(-1)}(x,y,y_0,0) = 2\sqrt{i\pi x}\sum_{s=1}^{\infty}\frac{1}{it_s^0}\,\frac{\exp(ixt_s^0)\,w_1(t_s^0-y)\,w_1(t_s^0-y_0)}{t_s^0[\,w_1(t_s^0)\,]^2}$$

$$= \sqrt{x}\left[\int_0^x \frac{1}{\sqrt{\xi}}V(\xi, y, y_0, 0)\,d\xi + \lim_{x\to 0}\frac{V^{(-1)}(x, y, y_0, 0)}{\sqrt{x}}\right] \tag{6.12}$$

provided y and y_0 are both large and $(\sqrt{y}+\sqrt{y_0}-x)q$ is small. It is interesting to observe that for points on the horizon, (i. e., $x = \sqrt{y}+\sqrt{y_0}$) this first order correction term vanishes and a higher order approximation is required.

For $qy < y^2 < 1$, we need to use different asymptotic forms

$$y < 1\ , \qquad |q| \ll 1\ , \quad y_0 > 1$$

$$V(x,y,y_0,q) \sim \left[1 - qy - iy^2\frac{\partial}{\partial x}\right]\left[V(x, 0, y_0, 0) + (\sqrt{y_0}-x)\,qV^{(-1)}(x, 0, y_0, 0)\right] \tag{6.13}$$

$$y < 1\ , \qquad |q| \ll 1\ , \quad y_0 < 1$$

$$V(x, y,y_0,q) \sim \left[1-q(y+y_0) - i(y^2+y_0^2)\frac{\partial}{\partial x}\right]\left[V(x, 0,0,0) - xqV^{(-1)}(x, 0,0,0)\right]. \tag{6.14}$$

It is convenient to define the one-parameter functions

$$v(x) = V_0(x, 0) \tag{6.15}$$

$$g(x) = V_1(x, 0) \tag{6.16}$$

$$q(x) = -\exp(-i\tfrac{\pi}{4})\,V_2(x, 0) \tag{6.17}$$

and the functions

$$v^{(-1)}(x) = \sqrt{-i\pi x}\sum_{s=1}^{\infty}\frac{\exp(ixt_s^0)}{(t_s^0)^2} \tag{6.18}$$

$$g^{(-1)}(x) = 2\sqrt{\pi}\sum_{s=1}^{\infty}\frac{\exp(ixt_s^0)}{(t_s^0)^2\,w_1(t_s^0)} \tag{6.19}$$

$$q^{(-1)}(x) = -2\sqrt{\pi}\sum_{s=1}^{\infty}\frac{\exp(ixt_s^0)}{[\,t_s^0\,w_1(t_s^0)\,]^2} \tag{6.20}$$

We can then use the results

$$V_0(x, q) \sim v(x) - xq\,v^{(-1)}(x) \tag{6.21}$$

$$V_1(x, q) \sim g(x) - xq\,g^{(-1)}(x) \qquad (6.22)$$

$$V_2(x, q) \sim \exp(-i\tfrac{3}{4}\pi)\,[q(x) - xq\,q^{(-1)}(x)] \qquad (6.23)$$

provided $|q| < 0.3$. Tables of $v(x)$, $g(x)$, $v^{(-1)}(x)$, $g^{(-1)}(x)$, $q(x)$ and $q^{(-1)}(x)$ have been prepared by the present authors.

The discussion above has demonstrated the importance of the tables of $V(x, y, y_0, 0)$ and reveal that tables should also be constructed for $V^{(\pm 1)}(x, y, y_0, 0)$.

$$\left.\begin{array}{l} V(x, y, y_0, 0) \\ V^{(-1)}(x, y, y_0, 0) \\ V^{(1)}(x, y, y_0, 0) \end{array}\right\} = 2\sqrt{i\pi x}\sum_{s=1}^{\infty}\left\{\begin{array}{c} 1 \\ (it_s^0)^{-1} \\ (it_s^0) \end{array}\right\} \frac{\exp(ixt_s^0)\,w_1(t_s^0 - y)\,w_1(t_s^0 -}{t_s^0[w_1(t_s^0)]^2} \qquad (6.24)$$

where $$w_1'(t_s^0) = 0$$

For $y = y_0 = 0$; $y \to \infty$, $y_0 = 0$; $y \to \infty$, $y_0 \to \infty$ the 1959 tables of the present authors can be used to evaluate the functions $V^{(\pm 1)}(x, y, y_0, 0)$.

The special case $V(x, y, y_0, \infty)$ is of far greater practical importance. This case was extensively studied by Pryce and Domb in the early 1940's. In 1947, Pekeris published a paper which deals with the special cases we have denoted by $V_0(x, q)$, $V_1(x, q)$, and $V_2(x, q)$. The numerical results in Pekeris' paper were confined to the case $q = \infty$. Although there is considerable difference in the notation used by Pekeris and that which we have adopted, we can relate Pekeris' results to the functions

$$u(x) = \lim_{q\to\infty} \{2iq^2 x V_0(x, q)\} \qquad (6.25)$$

$$f(x) = \lim_{q\to\infty} \{-q\,V_1(x, q)\} \qquad (6.26)$$

$$p(x) = \lim_{q\to\infty} \{-\exp(-i\tfrac{\pi}{4})\,V_2(x, q)\} \qquad (6.27)$$

For $q \to \infty$, we can use the approximations

$$V(x, y, y_0, q) \sim \exp[i(x - \sqrt{y} - \sqrt{y_0})\,\tfrac{1}{q}]\,V(x, y, y_0, \infty) \qquad (6.28)$$

$$V_0(x, q) \sim \frac{\exp(ix/q)}{i\,2q^2}\,u(x) \qquad (6.29)$$

$$V_1(x, q) \sim -\frac{\exp(ix/q)}{q}\,f(x) \qquad (6.30)$$

$$V_2(x, q) \sim -\exp[i(\frac{x}{q} + \frac{\pi}{4})]\, p(x) \quad (6.31)$$

These approximations are very reliable for $|q| > 5$. For the problem of propagation of vertically polarized waves around the earth's surface this corresponds to frequencies above 10 megacycles over typical land and above 300 megacycles over typical sea. These results can be used for horizontally polarized fields for virtually all frequencies. These important applications make it very important to continue computational work on $V(x, y, y_0, \infty)$.

7. THE PRINCIPLE OF THE LOCAL FIELD IN THE PENUMBRA

In the pioneering work of van der Pol and Bremmer in the late 1930's, the attenuation function $V(x, y, y_0, q)$ was quite adequate because of the low antenna heights and relatively long wave lengths which were of interest. However, after the development of radar in the early 1940's it became very important to treat the case of very short wavelengths and very great heights. The first problem to be vigorously attacked was that of predicting the high altitude coverage of ground-based radars. In 1941, Burrows and Gray (in a notation different from that which we are using) expressed the results of the van der Pol-Bremmer theory for this case in the form

$$U \sim \frac{\exp(ika\theta)}{4\pi a\theta}\sqrt{\frac{\theta}{\sin\theta}}\,\exp(i\frac{2}{3}y^{3/2})\,V_1(x - \sqrt{y}, q) \quad (7.1)$$

$$x = (\frac{ka}{2})^{1/3}\theta \;, \quad y = (\frac{2}{ka})^{1/3}k(r-a) \;, \quad q = i(\frac{ka}{2})^{1/3}\frac{k}{k_2}\sqrt{1-\frac{k^2}{k_2^2}} \quad (7.2)$$

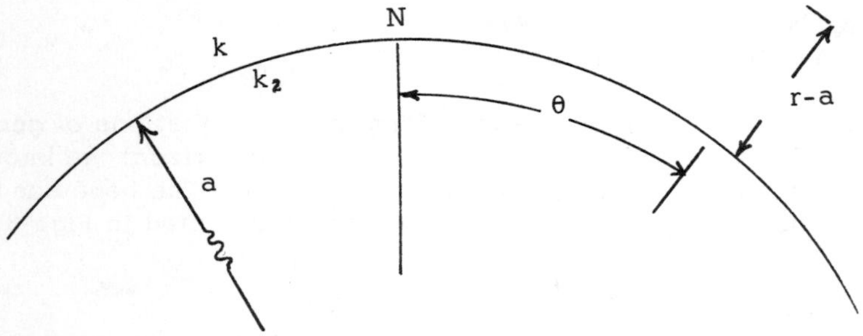

Figure 6

SOURCE ON SURFACE OF SPHERICAL INTERFACE

In 1944, Fock published a similar result (in the same notation we have used) and gave a table of $V_1(\xi, 0)$ for $\xi = -4.5(0.1)4.5$. It was long overlooked that Burrows and Gray gave a curve for $V_1(\xi, 0)$ and $V_1(\xi, \infty)$ for $\xi > 0$ in their original paper. The quantity plotted in the graph was defined by

$$F_L(q) = \left[\frac{(t_1 - q^2)\, w_2(t_1)}{\sqrt[3]{4}\, w_2'(t_1^\infty)}\, V_1\left(\frac{|t_1^\infty|}{|t_1|}\, \frac{L}{\sqrt[3]{2}}, q\right)\right] \tag{7.3}$$

The curves are for $q = 0$ and $q = \infty$ with $L \geq 0$.

These results of Burrows-Gray and Fock are only valid for natural units of height y of the order of two to five. For larger heights, it is desirable to use the reciprocity principle and use the fields on the surface which are induced by a plane wave. This problem was studied by Fock in 1945. Fock called his results "The Principle of the Local Field in the Penumbra Region." According to this principle: "The transition from light to shadow on the surface of the body takes place in a narrow strip along the boundary of the geometrical shadow. The width of this strip is of the order of $\sqrt[3]{\lambda a^2/\pi}$ where a is the radius of curvature of the normal section of the body in the plane of incidence." The principle is expressed in the following formulae.

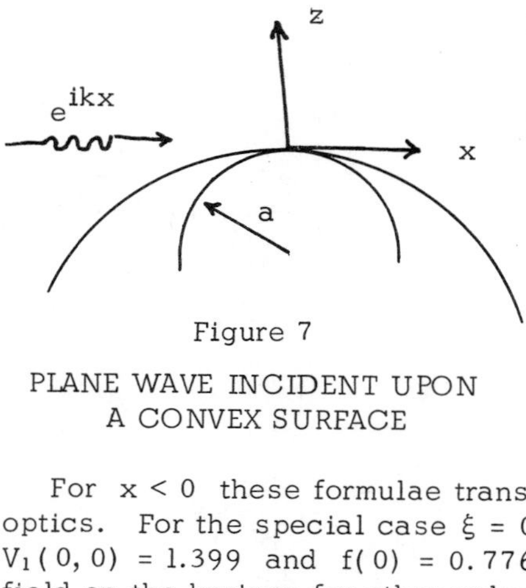

Figure 7

PLANE WAVE INCIDENT UPON A CONVEX SURFACE

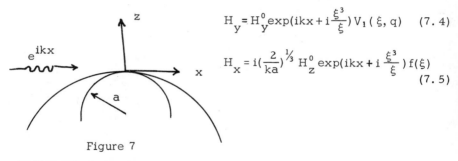

$$H_y = H_y^0 \exp(ikx + i\frac{\xi^3}{\xi})\, V_1(\xi, q) \tag{7.4}$$

$$H_x = i\left(\frac{2}{ka}\right)^{1/3} H_z^0 \exp(ikx + i\frac{\xi^3}{\xi})\, f(\xi) \tag{7.5}$$

For $x < 0$ these formulae transform into the equations of geometric optics. For the special case $\xi = 0$ (i.e., the horizon) we know that $V_1(0, 0) = 1.399$ and $f(0) = 0.776 \exp(-i\pi/3)$. The behavior for the field on the horizon for other values of q is depicted in Fig. 8.

8. A REFLECTION FORMULA

The Fock principle provides the transition from light to shadow for points on the surface when the source is at a very great distance. We will now consider a generalization which is valid for arbitrary locations of the source and receiver provided they are in the line-of-sight region.

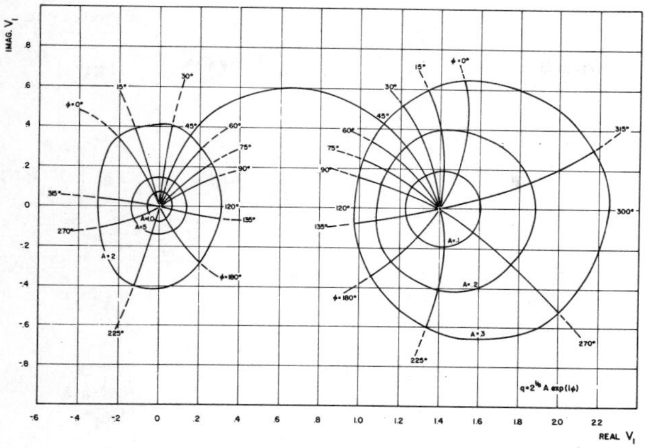

Figure 8

$$V_1(0,q) = \frac{1}{\sqrt{\pi}} \int_{-\infty}^{\infty} \frac{1}{w_1'(t) - q w_1(t)}\, dt$$

In the work of van der Pol and Bremmer, and most later authors, this region was treated by starting from the exact solution of the problem.

Differential equation:

$$\nabla^2 U + k^2 U = \frac{\delta(r-r_0)\,\delta(\theta)}{2\pi r^2 \sin\theta} \tag{8.1}$$

Boundary condition:

$$\frac{\partial}{\partial r}(rU) \text{ and } k^2 U \quad \text{continuous across } r = a \tag{8.2}$$

Periodic Condition:

$$U(\theta \pm 2m\pi) = U(\theta) \tag{8.3}$$

Radiation condition:

$$\lim_{r\to\infty} \left\{ r \left[\frac{\partial U}{\partial r} - ikU \right] \right\} = 0 \tag{8.4}$$

$$k^2 = \omega^2 \varepsilon_0 \mu_0 \quad \text{for } r > a \; ; \quad k_1^2 = \omega^2 \varepsilon_1 \mu_0 + i\omega\mu_0\sigma \, , \text{ for } r < a \, . \tag{8.5}$$

The classical methods for the solution of a problem of this type involve an expansion of the field in a series of spherical harmonics. The resulting representation for $U(\theta, r, r_0, \Gamma)$ involves a complex combination of spherical Hankel functions

$$U(\theta, r, r_0, \Gamma) = \frac{ik}{8\pi}\frac{1}{(kr)(kr_0)}\sum_{n=0}^{\infty}(2n+1)\left\{\zeta_n^{(1)}(kr_>)\zeta_n^{(2)}(kr_<) - \frac{\zeta_n^{(2)'}(ka)+\Gamma\zeta_n^{(2)}(ka)}{\zeta_n^{(1)'}(ka)+\Gamma\zeta_n^{(1)}(ka)}\zeta_n^{(1)}(kr)\zeta_n^{(1)}(kr_0)\right\}P_n(\cos\theta) \quad (8.6)$$

$$\zeta_n^{(1,2)}(x) = \sqrt{\frac{\pi x}{2}}\,H_{n+\frac{1}{2}}^{(1,2)}(x) \quad , \quad \psi_n(x) = \sqrt{\frac{\pi x}{2}}\,J_{n+\frac{1}{2}}(x) \quad (8.7)$$

$$\Gamma = -\frac{k}{k_1}\frac{\psi_n'(k_1 a)}{\psi_n(k_1 a)} \sim i\frac{k}{k_1}\sqrt{1-\left(\frac{k}{k_1}\right)^2} \quad (8.8)$$

The classical procedure involves the transformation of the sum into an integral. From the integral, one extracts an integral which can be evaluated by the method of stationary phase to yield the reflected wave. Before we consider the form taken by this result, we must make some geometrical definitions.

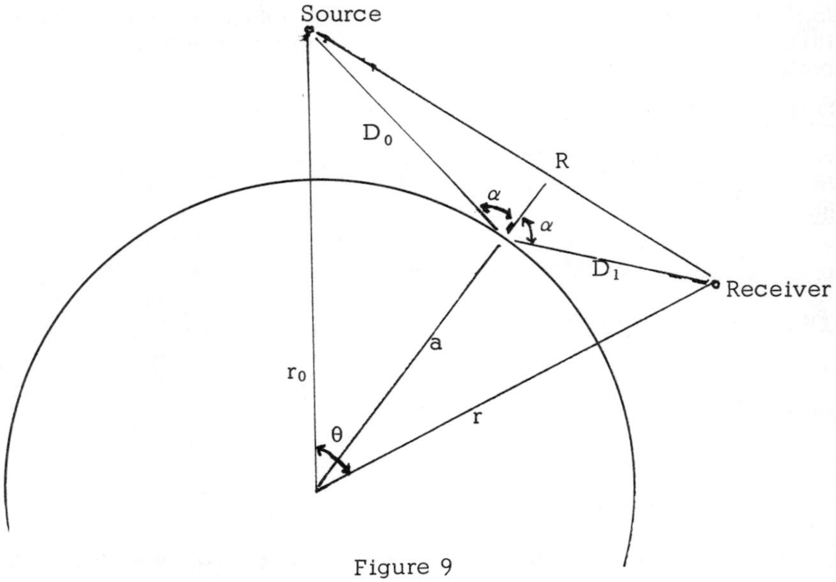

Figure 9

REFLECTION FROM A CONVEX SURFACE

The angle α is the angle of incidence. The distances D_0 and D_1

are the distances to the point of reflection of the source and the receiver, respectively.

The result obtained by the method of stationary phase is of the form

$$U(\theta,r,r_0,\Gamma) \sim \frac{\exp(ikR)}{4\pi R} - \frac{ik}{4\pi}\frac{1}{(kr)(kr_0)}\int_{-\infty+i0}^{\infty+i0}(n+\tfrac{1}{2})\frac{\zeta_n^{(2)\prime}(ka)+\Gamma\zeta_n^{(2)}(ka)}{\zeta_n^{(1)\prime}(ka)+\Gamma\zeta_n^{(1)}(ka)}$$

$$\zeta_n^{(1)}(kr)\,\zeta_n^{(1)}(kr_0)[P_n(\cos\theta)-i\frac{2}{\pi}Q_n(\cos\theta)]\,dn$$

$$\sim\frac{\exp(ikR)}{4\pi R}+\left\{\frac{1}{4\pi}\sqrt{\frac{a\sin\alpha}{rr_0\sin\theta}}\;\frac{\cos\alpha+i\Gamma}{\cos\alpha-i\Gamma}\right.\quad\text{times}$$

$$\left.\sqrt{\frac{a\cos\alpha}{2D_0D+a(D_0+D)\cos\alpha}}\right\}\exp[ik(D_0+D)] \tag{8.9}$$

Van der Pol and Bremmer showed that this formula agrees with the approximation based on the attenuation function provided the comparison is made in the vicinity of the first and second lobe just above the horizon. However, for points well above the horizon the attenuation function fails to agree with the stationary phase (geometrical optics) result.

It would be interesting to seek a formula which agrees with the classic result involving $V(x, y, y_0, q)$ for points near the horizon, but which is in better agreement with the stationary phase result for points well above the horizon. Such a formula has been found in the course of studies made by the present authors. It involves the reflected field $R(x, y, y_0, q)$ which was discussed earlier. However, it is more convenient to define a complex amplitude $S(\mu, \zeta, \zeta_0, q)$ which has the property

$$S(\mu,\zeta,\zeta_0,q) = \exp(-iw^*)\,R(\zeta+\zeta_0,\ \zeta^2+2\mu\zeta,\ \zeta_0^2+2\mu\zeta_0,\ q)$$

$$\xrightarrow[\mu\to\infty]{} -\frac{1}{2}\sqrt{\frac{i}{\pi}}\;\frac{q-i\mu}{q+i\mu}\sqrt{\frac{\mu}{2\zeta\zeta_0+\mu(\zeta+\zeta_0)}} \tag{8.10}$$

$$w^* = \frac{2}{3}(\zeta^3+\zeta_0^3)+2\mu(\zeta^2+\zeta_0^2)+\mu^2(\zeta+\zeta_0)$$

The new formula for the region of direct visibility then takes the form

$$U(\theta,r,r_0,\Gamma) = \frac{\exp(ikR)}{4\pi R}+\sqrt{\frac{-ik}{8\pi}}\left(\frac{2}{ka}\right)^{1/3}\sqrt{\frac{a\sin\alpha}{rr_0\sin\theta}}\exp\{ik(D_0+D)\}S(\mu,\zeta,\zeta_0,q) \tag{8.11}$$

$$\zeta_0 = \left[\frac{ka}{a}\right]^{1/3} \frac{D_0}{a} \qquad \mu = \left[\frac{ka}{2}\right]^{1/3} \cos\alpha \tag{8.12}$$

$$\zeta = \left[\frac{ka}{2}\right]^{1/3} \frac{D}{a}$$

For points well above the horizon, $\mu \to \infty$ as $ka \to \infty$ since $\cos\alpha > 0$. Therefore, we observe that with the above definitions of ζ_0, ζ and μ our new formulation agrees with the classical results obtained from a stationary phase evaluation of the exact solution. The new formulation has the advantage, however, of leading to results which are useful up to the horizon. In fact, it can even be used in the region just beyond the horizon.

From properties we have already given for $R(x, y, y_0, q)$ we find that $S(\mu, \zeta, \zeta_0, q)$ has the properties

$$S(\mu, \zeta, \zeta_0, q) \underset{\substack{\zeta > 1 \\ \zeta_0 > 1 \\ \mu > 0}}{\longrightarrow} \sqrt{\frac{i}{2\pi}} \frac{\exp(-i\frac{2}{3}\mu^3)}{\sqrt{2\zeta\zeta_0 + \mu(\zeta+\zeta_0)}} V_{11}(-2\mu, q) \tag{8.13}$$

$$S(\mu, \zeta, \zeta_0, q) \underset{\substack{\zeta \to \infty \\ \zeta_0 \to \infty \\ \mu \to 0}}{\longrightarrow} \frac{1}{2}\sqrt{\frac{i}{\pi}} \frac{1}{\sqrt{\zeta\zeta_0}} \exp(-i\frac{2}{3}\mu^3)[-\eta K(-\tau) + V_2(-2\mu, q)] \tag{8.14}$$

where

$$\tau = -2\mu\eta, \qquad \eta = \sqrt{\frac{\zeta\zeta_0}{\zeta+\zeta_0}} \tag{8.15}$$

These formulae provide a useful extension of the classical reflection formulae. The representation involving the Fresnel integral is of very great practical importance in the region near the horizon.

On the horizon, $\mu = 0$, the field takes the form

$$U(\theta, r, r_0, \Gamma) = \frac{\exp(ikR)}{8\pi R} + \frac{1}{2\pi}\left(\frac{ka}{2}\right)^{1/3} \sqrt{2kDD_0} \sqrt{\frac{a}{r r_0 \sin\theta}} V_2(0, q) \exp[ik(D+$$

$$\underset{\substack{r_0 \to \infty \\ r \to \infty}}{\longrightarrow} \left\{\frac{1}{2} + 2\left(\frac{ka}{2}\right)^{1/3} \sqrt{\frac{D+D_0}{2kDD_0}} V_2(0, q)\right\} \frac{\exp(ikR)}{4\pi R} \tag{8.16}$$

The factor "1/2" is the familiar Fresnel field factor for the field on the shadow boundary. The effects of the curvature of the surface are contained in the term involving $V_2(0, q)$. In Fig. 10, we illustrate the behavior of $V_2(0, q)$ as a function of q .

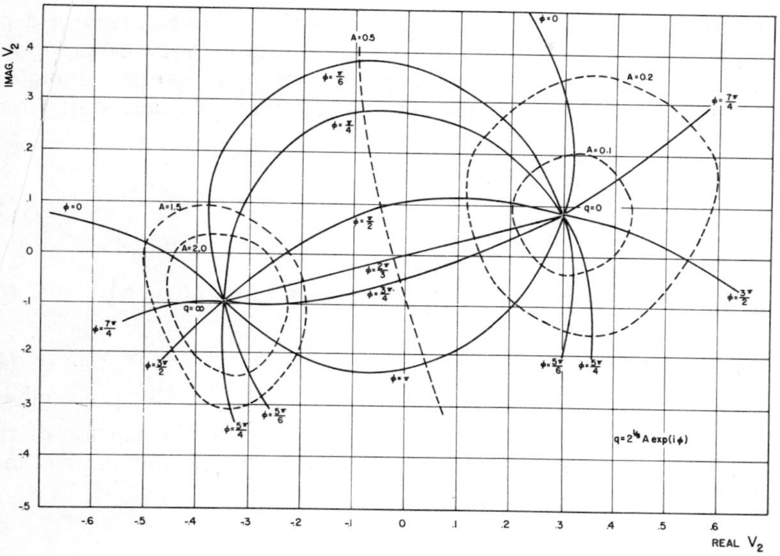

Figure 10

$$V_2(0,q) = \lim_{\xi\to 0}\left\{-\frac{\exp(i\pi/4)}{\sqrt{\pi}}\int_{-\infty}^{\infty}\exp(i\xi t)\frac{v'(t)-q\,v(t)}{w_1'(t)-qw_1(t)}\,dt - \frac{\exp(i\pi/4)}{2\sqrt{\pi}\,\xi}\right\}$$

The reflection formulae which we have discussed thus far have been derived for the case of an axially symmetric source above a spherical surface. We can give a very similar result for the case of a line source above a circular cylinder. For this case, we can again use Fig. 9 and define μ, ζ, ζ_0 and q as in the case of the sphere. The result is of the form

$$C(\theta,r,r_0,\Gamma) = \frac{\exp[i(kR+\frac{\pi}{4})]}{\sqrt{8\pi kR}} + \frac{1}{2}\left(\frac{2}{ka}\right)^{1/3} S(\mu,\zeta,\zeta_0,q)\exp[ik(D+D_0)] \qquad (8.17)$$

$$C(\theta,r,r_0,\Gamma) \xrightarrow[\mu\to\infty]{} \frac{\exp[i(kR+\frac{\pi}{4})]}{\sqrt{8\pi kR}} + \left\{\sqrt{\frac{i}{8\pi k}}\;\frac{\cos\alpha + i\Gamma}{\cos\alpha - i\Gamma}\sqrt{\frac{a\cos\alpha}{2DD_0 + a(D+D_0)\cos\alpha}}\;\exp[ik(D+D_0)]\right\} \qquad (8.18)$$

$$C(\theta,r,r_0,\Gamma) \xrightarrow[\substack{\mu\to 0\\ r\to\infty\\ r_0\to\infty}]{} \left\{\frac{1}{2} + 2\left(\frac{ka}{2}\right)^{1/3}\sqrt{\frac{D+D_0}{2kDD_0}}\, V_2(0,q)\right\}\frac{\exp[i(kR+\frac{\pi}{4})]}{\sqrt{8\pi kR}} \qquad (8.19)$$

The case $r_0 \to \infty$ corresponds to the problem of reflection of a plane wave by a cylinder. This problem has been studied very frequently in recent years. For this problem it is convenient to use the complex amplitude $A(p, \sigma, q)$ which we defined earlier. We can start from the results above and use the approximations

$$\frac{\exp(ikR)}{\sqrt{8\pi kR}} \sim \frac{\exp(ikr_0)}{\sqrt{8\pi kr_0}}\exp(-ikr\cos\theta) \qquad (8.20)$$

$$S(\mu,\zeta,\zeta_0,q) \xrightarrow[\zeta_0\to\infty]{} \frac{1}{2}\sqrt{\frac{i}{\pi\zeta_0}}\exp(-iw^0)A(\mu, 2\zeta+\mu, q) \qquad (8.21)$$

$$w^0 = \frac{2}{3}\zeta_0^3 + 2\mu\zeta^2 + \mu^2\zeta_0 \qquad (8.22)$$

However, it is more interesting to start from a transformation of the Laplacian operator which was used in a paper by Keller, Lewis and Seckler.

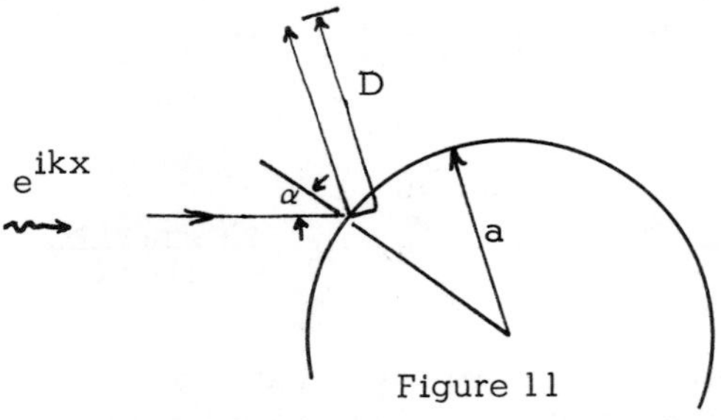

Figure 11

THE VARIABLES α AND D

$$s = D + \frac{a}{2}\cos\alpha \qquad \beta = \pi - 2\alpha \qquad (8.23)$$

$$\nabla^2 = \left(1+\frac{u}{s^2}\right)\frac{\partial^2}{\partial s^2} + \left(\frac{1}{s} - \frac{w}{s^2} - \frac{u}{s^3}\right)\frac{\partial}{\partial s} - \frac{2v}{s^2}\frac{\partial^2}{\partial s\partial\beta} + \frac{1}{s^2}\frac{\partial^2}{\partial\beta^2} + \frac{v}{s^3}\frac{\partial}{\partial\beta} \qquad (8.24)$$

$$u = \frac{9}{16}a^2\cos^2{}^{\beta}/_2 \qquad v = -\frac{3}{4}a\cos{}^{\beta}/_2 \qquad w = \frac{3}{8}a\sin{}^{\beta}/_2 \qquad (8.25)$$

If we make a change of scale from s to σ and $\sin\beta/2$ to p, we can use a perturbation procedure to solve this problem

$$p = \left(\frac{ka}{2}\right)^{1/3} \sin \beta/2 \qquad \sigma = 2\left(\frac{ka}{2}\right)^{1/3} \frac{s}{a} \tag{8.26}$$

The Helmholtz's equation takes the form

$$(\nabla^2 + k^2)\Phi = \left[\left(\frac{ka}{2}\right)^{4/3} L_0 + \left(\frac{ka}{2}\right)^{2/3} L_1 + \left(\frac{ka}{2}\right)^{0} L_2\right]\Phi \tag{8.27}$$

Let Φ be represented in the form

$$\Phi = \left[\Phi_0 + \left(\frac{2}{ka}\right)^{2/3} \Phi_1 + \left(\frac{2}{ka}\right)^{4/3} \Phi_2 + \cdots\right] \exp[ik(D - a\cos\alpha)] \tag{8.28}$$

where

$$L_0 = \frac{9}{\sigma^2}\frac{\partial^2}{\partial\sigma^2} + \frac{1}{\sigma^2}\frac{\partial^2}{\partial p^2} + \frac{6}{\sigma^2}\frac{\partial^2}{\partial\sigma\partial p} - \frac{3}{\sigma^3}\frac{\partial}{\partial p} + \left(8i - \frac{9}{\sigma^3}\right)\frac{\partial}{\partial\sigma} + \frac{4i}{\sigma} . \tag{8.29}$$

We then find that

$$L_0\Phi_0 = 0 , \quad \Phi_0 = A(p, \sigma, q) . \tag{8.30}$$

The leading term in the expansion of the wave function is found to satisfy the equation which has $A(p, \sigma, q)$ as its solution. We can express the field in the form

$$\Phi(\theta, r, \Gamma) \sim \exp(ikx) + A(p, \sigma, q)\exp[ik(D - a\cos\alpha)] \tag{8.31}$$

This asymptotic estimate has the properties

$$\Phi(\theta, r, \Gamma) \xrightarrow[p\to\infty]{} \exp(ikx) - \frac{q - ip}{q + ip}\sqrt{\frac{p}{\sigma}}\exp[ik(D - a\cos\alpha)] \tag{8.32}$$

$$\Phi(\theta, r, \Gamma) \xrightarrow[p\to 0]{} \left\{\frac{1}{2} + \left(\frac{ka}{2}\right)^{1/3}\sqrt{\frac{2}{kD}}\, V_2(0, q)\right\}\exp(ikx) \tag{8.33}$$

The previous study of the reflection formula made by Keller, Lewis, and Seckler involved a representation for $\Phi(\theta, r, \Gamma)$ in the form of an asymptotic expansion in inverse integral powers of (ka) which became useless for $p \to 0$. These new results have the considerable advantage of being useful for $p \to 0$ as well as $p \to \infty$.

For $\sigma \to p$, we obtain the field on the surface of the cylinder. This leads to

$$\begin{aligned}\Phi(\theta, a, \Gamma) &\sim [1 + A(p, p, q)]\exp(ika\cos\theta) \\ &= V_1(-p, q)\exp\left[i\left(ka\cos\theta - \frac{p^3}{3}\right)\right]\end{aligned} \tag{8.34}$$

This is precisely the formula obtained by Fock in his principle of the local field in the penumbra.

9. A DIFFRACTION FORMULA

We have given a reflection formula which permits us to raise the source and receiver to arbitrary heights provided they are in the region of direct visibility. We turn now to the case when the receiver is below the horizon. We will give a result which reduces to the original results of van der Pol and Bremmer when both heights are very small in comparison with the radius of the earth.

A paper by Wu and Seshadri provides a suitable starting point. Let us denote the radius of curvature of the surface of a cylinder by $\tau(s)$ in order to emphasize that it is a function of the arc length s. Let t be the distance from the receiver to the surface measured along the tangent to the surface. From the paper of Wu and Seshadri we can find the expression for the Laplacian in these coordinates

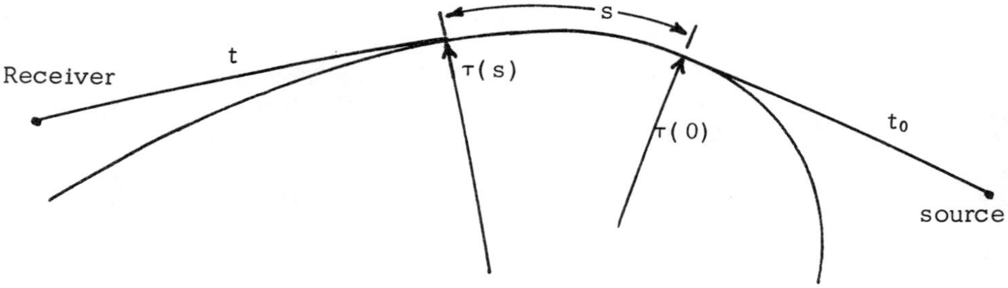

Figure 12

DEFINITIONS OF t, t_0 AND s

$$(\nabla^2+k^2)\psi = \left(\frac{\partial^2}{\partial x^2} + \frac{\partial^2}{\partial y^2} + k^2\right)\psi$$

$$= \left\{\frac{\tau^2}{t^2}\left(\frac{\partial}{\partial s} - \frac{\partial}{\partial t}\right)^2 + \left(\frac{\tau^2}{t^3} + \frac{\tau\tau'}{t^2}\right)\left(\frac{\partial}{\partial s} - \frac{\partial}{\partial t}\right) + \frac{1}{t}\frac{\partial}{\partial t} + k^2\right\}\psi = 0 \tag{9.1}$$

Let us now replace the variables s and t by new variables x and y and use a perturbation procedure to solve for ψ.

$$x = \left(\frac{k}{2}\right)^{1/3} \int_0^s \frac{1}{[\tau(u)]^{2/3}}\, du \tag{9.2}$$

$$y = \left(\frac{k}{2}\right)^{1/3} \frac{t}{[\tau(s)]^{2/3}}, \quad y_0 = \left(\frac{k}{2}\right)^{1/3} \frac{t_0}{[\tau(0)]^{2/3}} \tag{9.3}$$

$$\psi(s,t) = \left(\sum_{n=0}^{\infty} \psi_n k^{-n/3}\right) \exp[ik(t_0+s+t)] \left[\frac{1}{2}\left(\frac{2}{k\tau(0)}\right)^{1/6}\left(\frac{2}{k\tau(s)}\right)^{1/6}\right] \tag{9.4}$$

We can then show that ψ_0 satisfies a familiar equation

$$\frac{\partial^2\psi_0}{\partial x^2} + \frac{\partial^2\psi_0}{\partial y^2} - 2\frac{\partial^2\psi_0}{\partial y \partial x} + 4iy^2\frac{\partial\psi_0}{\partial y} - \frac{1}{y}\frac{\partial\psi_0}{\partial y} + \frac{1}{y}\frac{\partial\psi_0}{\partial x} + 2iy\psi_0 = 0 \tag{9.5}$$

$$\psi_0(x,y) = \exp[-i\frac{2}{3}(y^3 + y_0^3)]\, D(x+y+y_0, y^2, y_0^2, q) \tag{9.6}$$

$$\left(\frac{\partial^2}{\partial\zeta^2} + i\frac{\partial}{\partial\xi} + \zeta\right) D(\xi, \zeta, \zeta_0, q) = 0 \quad . \tag{9.7}$$

For the case of a line source in the presence of the cylinder, we find the asymptotic estimate

$$\psi(s,t) \sim \frac{1}{2}\left[\frac{2}{k\tau(0)}\right]^{1/6}\left[\frac{2}{k\tau(s)}\right]^{1/6} D(x+y+y_0, y^2, y_0^2, q) \exp\{i[k(t+s+t_0] - i\frac{2}{3}y^3 - i\frac{2}{3}y_0^3\}$$

$$\xrightarrow[\substack{x<0 \\ y_0 \neq 0}]{} \frac{\exp[i(kR + \frac{\pi}{4})]}{\sqrt{8\pi kR}} + (\text{reflected wave}) \tag{9.8}$$

This result leads to the classical result of van der Pol and Bremmer when $t_0 \ll a$, $t \ll a$. In order to show this correspondence we let $\tau(s) = a$ and consider the following relations.

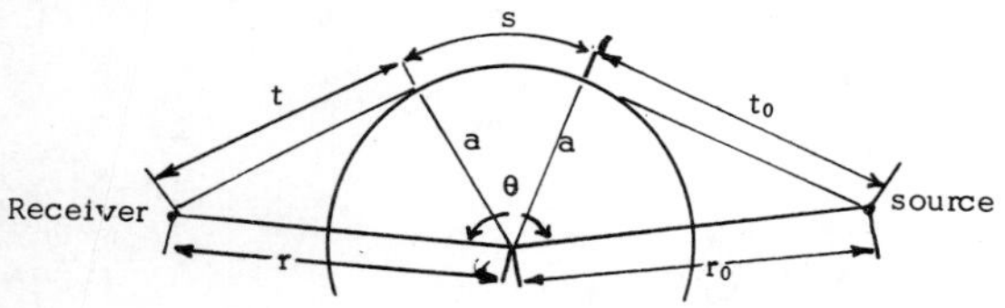

$$t = \sqrt{r^2 - a^2}$$

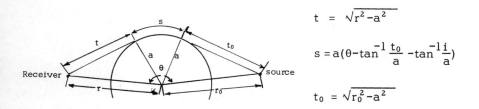

$$s = a(\theta - \tan^{-1}\frac{t_0}{a} - \tan^{-1}\frac{t}{a})$$

$$t_0 = \sqrt{r_0^2 - a^2}$$

Figure 13

RELATIONS FOR A SURFACE OF CONSTANT CURVATURE.

We can show that

$$y_0 = \left(\frac{ka}{2}\right)^{1/3}\frac{\sqrt{r_0^2-a^2}}{a} \xrightarrow[r_0\to a]{} \left(\frac{ka}{2}\right)^{1/3}\frac{\sqrt{2ah_0}}{a}, \quad h_0 = r_0 - a \tag{9.9}$$

$$y = \left(\frac{ka}{2}\right)^{1/3}\frac{\sqrt{r^2-a^2}}{a} \xrightarrow[r\to a]{} \left(\frac{ka}{2}\right)^{1/3}\frac{\sqrt{2ah}}{a}, \quad h = r - a \tag{9.10}$$

$$s = a\theta - (t_0+t) + \frac{1}{3a^2}(t_0^3 + t^3) + \cdots \xrightarrow[r\to a]{} a\theta - t_0 - t \quad . \tag{9.11}$$

We then find that

$$x = \left(\frac{ka}{2}\right)^{1/3}\frac{s}{a} \xrightarrow[r\to a]{} \left(\frac{ka}{2}\right)^{1/3}\theta - y - y_0 \tag{9.12}$$

$$k(t+s+t_0) - \frac{2}{3}(y^3 + y_0^3) \xrightarrow[r\to a]{} ka\theta - \frac{k}{5a^4}(t^5 + t_0^5) \sim ka\theta \tag{9.13}$$

$$\psi(s,t) \xrightarrow[r,\, r_0\to a]{} \frac{1}{2}\left(\frac{2}{ka}\right)^{1/3}\exp(ika\theta)\,D(\xi, \zeta^2, \zeta_0^2, q) \tag{9.14}$$

$$\xi = \left(\frac{ka}{2}\right)^{1/3}\theta, \quad \zeta = \left(\frac{ka}{2}\right)^{1/3}\sqrt{\frac{2h}{a}}, \quad \zeta_0 = \left(\frac{ka}{2}\right)^{1/3}\sqrt{\frac{2h_0}{a}} \tag{9.15}$$

This is the two-dimensional analog of the results we have referred to as the "radio problem." In order to solve the three-dimensional problem of an axially symmetric source above a sphere we need only write

$$U(r,\theta) \sim \sqrt{\frac{-ika}{2\pi r r_0 \sin\theta}}\,\psi(s,t)$$

$$\xrightarrow[\substack{r\to a\\ r_0\to a}]{} \sqrt{\frac{-ik}{2\pi a \sin\theta}}\,\psi(s,t)$$

$$= \frac{\exp(ika\theta)}{4\pi a\theta}\sqrt{\frac{\theta}{\sin\theta}}\,V(\xi, \zeta, \zeta_0, q) \tag{9.16}$$

since

$$V(\xi, \zeta, \zeta_0, q) = 2\sqrt{-i\pi\xi}\,D(\xi, \zeta, \zeta_0, q) \ . \tag{9.17}$$

Let us express our modification of the classical solution of the "radio problem" in the form

$$U(r,\theta) = \frac{\exp[ik(t_0+s+t) - i\frac{2}{3}(y_0^3+y^3)]}{4\pi a\theta(1-\frac{t+t_0}{a\theta})^{\frac{1}{2}}}\sqrt{\frac{\theta}{\sin\theta}}\,V(x+y+y_0, y^2, y_0^2, q) \tag{9.18}$$

$$x = (\frac{ka}{2})^{1/3}\frac{s}{a}, \quad y = (\frac{ka}{2})^{1/3}\frac{t}{a}, \quad y_0 = (\frac{ka}{2})^{1/3}\frac{t_0}{a}. \tag{9.19}$$

This extended result is valid with no restriction on the heights above the surface. However, the basic function which is employed is precisely the same as has already been studied and tabulated.

Let us now turn to the case in which $t_0 \to \infty$. We want to show that for $t = 0$ and $t_0 \to \infty$, our new formulation is in agreement with Keller's "geometric theory of diffraction." We must first express $V_{11}(\xi, q)$ and $V_1(\xi, q)$ in terms of the special representation for the Airy integral which has been employed by Keller and Franz.

$$A(q) = \int_0^\infty \cos(\tau^3 - q\tau)\,d\tau = \frac{\pi}{\sqrt[3]{3}}\,Ai\left(-\frac{q}{\sqrt[3]{3}}\right) \tag{9.20}$$

$$V_1(\xi, q) = \pi\sum_{s=1}^{\infty}\frac{\exp\left(-\frac{\sqrt{3}-i}{2}\frac{q_s}{\sqrt[3]{3}}\xi\right)A(q_s)}{q_s[A(q_s)]^2+3[A'(a_s)]^2} \tag{9.21}$$

$$V_{11}(\xi, q) = \frac{\sqrt{\pi^3}}{2\sqrt[3]{3}}\exp(i\frac{\pi}{12})\sum_{s=1}^{\infty}\frac{\exp\left(-\frac{\sqrt{3}-i}{2}\frac{q_s}{\sqrt[3]{3}}\xi\right)}{q_s[A(q_s)]^2+3[A'(q_s)]^2} \tag{9.22}$$

If we now use the properties

$$\exp(-i\frac{2}{3}y_0^3)\,D(x+y_0, 0, y_0^2, q) \xrightarrow[y_0\to\infty]{} \frac{1}{2}\sqrt{\frac{i}{\pi y_0}}\,V_1(x, q) \tag{9.23}$$

$$\exp[-i\frac{2}{3}(y^3+y_0^3)]\,D(x+y+y_0, y^2, y_0^2, q) \xrightarrow[\substack{y\to\infty\\ y_0\to\infty}]{} \frac{1}{2}\sqrt{\frac{i}{\pi y\,y_0}}\,V_{11}(x, q) \tag{9.24}$$

we find that

$$\psi(s, 0) \xrightarrow[t_0\to\infty]{} \left\{\frac{\exp(ikt_0 + i\frac{\pi}{4})}{\sqrt{8\pi k\,t_0}}\right\}\left[\frac{\tau(0)}{\tau(s)}\right]^{1/6} V_1(x, q)\exp(iks) \tag{9.25}$$

$$\psi(s, t) \xrightarrow[\substack{t_0\to\infty\\ t\to\infty}]{} \left\{\frac{\exp[ik(t+t_0) + i\frac{\pi}{4}]}{\sqrt{4\pi kt\,kt_0}}\right\}\left(\frac{k\tau(0)}{2}\right)^{1/6}\left(\frac{k\tau(s)}{2}\right)^{1/6} V_{11}(x, q)\exp(iks) \tag{9.26}$$

$$x = \left(\frac{k}{2}\right)^{1/3} \int_0^s \frac{1}{[\tau(u)]^{2/3}}\, du \tag{9.27}$$

These results are identical with those of Keller's theory. However, by replacing the series used by Keller by the functions $V_1(x, q)$ and $V_{11}(x, q)$, we have extended Keller's results for the umbra region so as to obtain a result for the penumbra region.

10. THE NORMAL REFRACTION PROBLEM

We have shown that the diffraction function $D(x, y, y_0, q)$ can be employed as a mathematical model for the study of the diffraction of waves by a convex surface when the radius of curvature is large compared with the wavelength. This summary of applications of $D(x, y, y_0, q)$ would not be complete without observing that this function can be used in another wide class of problems. Let us compare the geometry of the convex surface problem

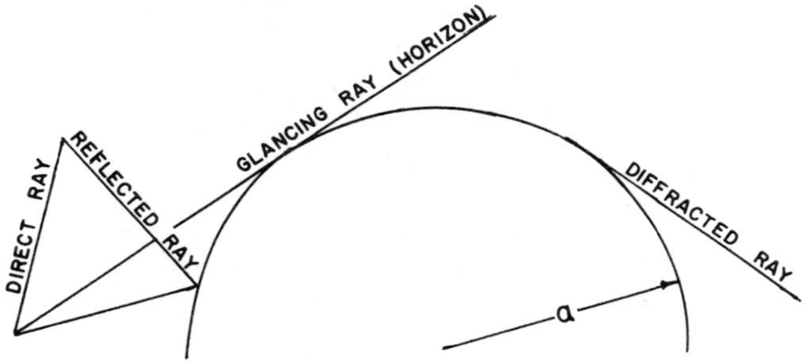

Figure 14

DIFFRACTION BY A CONVEX SURFACE

with the geometry of the normal refraction problem where the index of refraction increases monotonically with height above a plane surface.

As an example, let us consider a problem which has been studied by Pekeris. Consider the case of waves propagating above the surface $z = h$ above which the index of refraction varies with z according to the law $n^2(z) = 1-(\nu^2 - 1/4)(kz)^{-2}$. We can show that Pekeris' exact solution can be expressed in terms of $D(x, y, y_0, q)$ in the following manner.

$$\left\{\nabla^2 + \left[k^2 - \frac{\nu^2 - 1/4}{z^2}\right]\right\}\psi = 0 , \tag{10.1}$$

$$\left(\frac{\partial\psi}{\partial z} + ikZ\psi\right)_{z=h} = 0 . \tag{10.2}$$

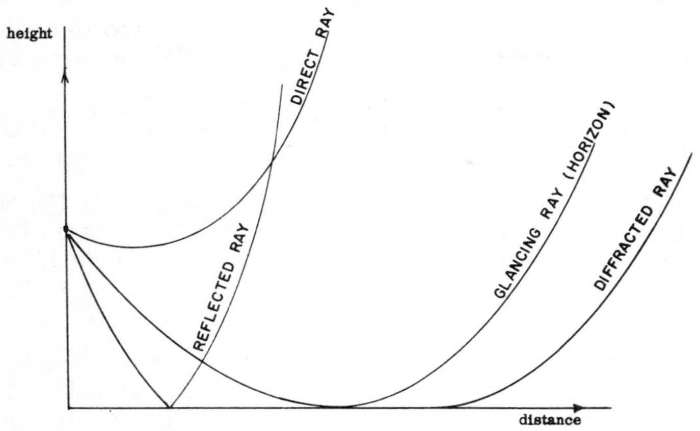

Figure 15

DIFFRACTION BY MONOTONICALLY INCREASING INDEX OF REFRACTION

The exact solution is

$$\Psi(\rho, z) = \frac{i\sqrt{z_1 z_2}}{16} \int_{-i\infty}^{\infty} H_0^{(1)}(\sqrt{k^2-\beta^2}\,\rho)\Big[H_\nu^{(1)}(\beta z_>)\, H_\nu^{(2)}(\beta z_<) -$$

$$\frac{H_\nu^{(2)\prime}(\beta h) + (iZ + \frac{1}{2\beta h})H_\nu^{(2)}(\beta h)}{H_\nu^{(1)\prime}(\beta h) + (iZ + \frac{1}{2\beta h})H_\nu^{(1)}(\beta h)}\, H_\nu^{(1)}(\beta z_1)\, H_\nu^{(1)}(\beta z_2)\Big]\, d\beta \qquad (10.3)$$

We can show that

$$\psi(\rho, z) \sim \frac{\sqrt{z_1 z_2}}{4h}\left(\frac{2}{\nu}\right)^{1/3} H_0^{(1)}(\sqrt{k^2-(\nu/h)^2}\,\rho)\, D(\xi, \zeta_1, \zeta_2, q) \qquad (10.4)$$

where

$$\left.\begin{aligned} \xi &= \left(\frac{\nu}{2}\right)^{1/3}\left(\frac{\nu}{k_0 h^2}\right)\rho & \zeta_1 &= \left(\frac{2}{\nu}\right)^{1/3}\beta(z_1-h) \\ q &= i\left(\frac{\nu}{2}\right)^{1/3}\left(Z-\frac{i}{2\nu}\right) & \zeta_2 &= \left(\frac{2}{\nu}\right)^{1/3}\beta(z_2-h) \end{aligned}\right\} \qquad (10.5)$$

Similar results can be found for other laws for the index of refraction provided the index of refraction increases monotonically with height. One can also use $D(x, y, y_0, q)$ for some problems involving convex surfaces above which the index of refraction has a behavior such that the ray paths are a composite of those depicted above.

11. REFERENCES AND NOTES

This paper is a condensation of a series of reports which are being prepared by the authors. The following company reports have been distributed to various institutions interested in wave propagation:

N. A. Logan, General Research in Diffraction Theory, Vol. I. LMSD Report 288087, Lockheed Aircraft Corporation, Missiles and Space Division, Sunnyvale, December, 1959, 363 pp.

N. A. Logan, et. al., General Research in Diffraction Theory, Vol. II, LMSD Report 288088, Lockheed Aircraft Corporation, Missiles and Space Division, Sunnyvale, December, 1959, 268 pp.

Further reports are in preparation.

In writing this paper, and in the preparation of the reports listed above, the authors make few claims to originality of material. All too frequently, we have thought that we had found new results only to find a little later that essentially the same results have been given by others. To the best of our knowledge, we are the first writers to use the extended forms involving $R(\zeta+\zeta_0, \zeta^2 + 2\mu\zeta, \zeta_0^2 + 2\mu\zeta_0, q)$ in the region of direct visibility and $D(x+y+y_0, y^2, y_0^2, q)$ in the shadow region.

The authors' main contributions have been to keep themselves well read in the periodical literature, and to arrange in a logical manner what we regard as the most significant concepts which have sprung from these researches. It would not be possible to acknowledge all the papers which have contributed to our understanding of these problems.

In order to guide our readers through some of the literature which we have consulted, we have prepared the following bibliographic notes. The list is far from being complete, but we hope that it will provide a starting point for readers who wish to learn more about these problems.

Most of the results in Section 1 can be found in the papers of V. A. Fock. A collection of Fock's papers is available in English.

Diffraction, Refraction, and Reflection of Waves: Thirteen papers by V. A. Fock, Air Force Cambridge Research Center Report AFCRC-TN-57-102, June, 1957, (ASTIA Document No. AD117276).

The function $V(x, y, y_0, q)$ is employed in numerous references. Unfortunately, it is known by a variety of notations. In General Research in Diffraction Theory, Vol. I, Logan has made a comparison of some of the more common notations.

The "radio problem" in Section 2 was first solved in this manner in the classic papers of van der Pol and Bremmer.

B. van der Pol and H. Bremmer, "Diffraction of Electromagnetic

Waves from an Electrical Point Source Round a Finitely Conducting Sphere with Applications of Radio-Telegraphy and the Theory of the Rainbow," Part I: Phil. Mag., Vol. 24, 1937, pp. 141-176; Part II: Phil. Mag., Vol. 24, 1937, pp. 825-864; Part III: Phil. Mag., Vol. 25, 1938, pp. 817-837.

B. van der Pol and H. Bremmer, "Further Note on the Propagation of Radio Waves Over a Finitely Conducting Spherical Earth," Phil. Mag., Vol. 27, 1939, pp. 261-275.

A summary of these papers, together with some extensions of the theory, can be found in Bremmer's treatise.

H. Bremmer, Terrestial Radio Waves, Elsevier, New York, 1949.

The reader is urged to supplement the study of Bremmer's treatise by consulting the excellent, and somewhat more detailed, discussions in the original papers of van der Pol and Bremmer.

The limiting forms in Section 3 can be found in Fock's papers in a notation which is similar to that which we have employed. The function $V_0(\xi, q)$ for $q = 0$ was employed as early as 1910 in a series of papers by Nicholson.

J. W. Nicholson, "On the Bending of Electric Waves Round the Earth," Part I, Phil. Mag., Vol. 18, 1910, pp. 757-760; Part II, Phil. Mag., Vol. 20, 1910, pp. 157-172; Part III, Phil. Mag., Vol. 21, 1911, pp. 62-68; Part IV, Phil. Mag., Vol. 21, 1911, pp. 281-295.

The function $V_1(\xi, q)$ was first used in a paper by Burrows and Gray.

C. R. Burrows and M. C. Gray, "The Effect of the Earth's Curvature on Ground-Wave Propagation," Proc. IRE 5, Vol. 29, 1941, pp. 16-24.

All three limiting cases were considered by Pekeris in a much neglected paper.

C. L. Pekeris, "The Field of a Microwave Dipole Antenna in the Vicinity of the Horizon," J. Appl. Phys., Vol. 18, 1947, pp. 667-680, 1025-1027.

The integral equation for $V_0(\xi, q)$ was first discussed by Hufford.

G. A. Hufford, "An Integral Equation Approach to the Problem of Wave Propagation over an Irregular Surface," Quarterly of Applied Mathematics, Vol. IX, 1952, pp. 391-404.

It was then rediscovered by Feinberg.

IA. L. Al'Pert, V. L. Ginzburg, and E. L. Feinberg, Radiowave Propagation, State Printing House for Technical-Theoretical

Literature, Moscow, 1953. See Chapter 10, Eq. 50.15. (This chapter has been translated by Morris Friedman, Inc., Needham Heights, Mass.)

The integral equation for $V_1(\xi, q)$ was encountered by Cullen.

J. A. Cullen, "Surface Currents Induced by Short-Wavelength Radiation," Phys. Rev., Vol. 109, 1958, pp. 1863-1867.

However, the homogeneous integral equation had been used as early as 1952 by Franz and Deppermann.

W. Franz and K. Deppermann, "Theory of Diffraction by a Cylinder as Affected by the Surface Wave," Annalen der Physik, Vol. 10, 1952, pp. 361-373.

The decomposition in Eq. (3.9) of the field into a Fresnel integral plus a term containing $V_2(\xi, q)$ was affected as early as 1947 by Pekeris.

C. L. Pekeris, "The Field of a Microwave Dipole Antenna in the Vicinity of the Horizon," J. Appl. Phys., Vol. 18, 1947, pp. 667-680, 1025-1027.

The decomposition was later rediscovered by Fock.

V. A. Fock, "Fresnel Diffraction by Convex Bodies," Uspekhi Fizicheskikh Nauk, Vol.43, 1951, pp. 587-599.

Pekeris gave a table of a function equivalent to $V_2(\xi, \infty)$. Calculations for $V_2(\xi, 0)$ and $V_2(\xi, \infty)$ were made by Rice who also rediscovered the Fresnel integral decomposition.

S. O. Rice, "Diffraction of Plane Radio Waves by a Parabolic Cylinder-Calculation of Shadows behind Hills," Bell Syst. Tech. J., Vol. 33, 1954, pp. 417-504.

The stationary phase evaluation of $R(x, y, y_0, q)$ given in Eq. (4.4) of Section 4 can be found in Fock's paper,

V. A. Fock, "Field of a Vertical and Horizontal Dipole Raised Above the Surface of the Earth," Zh. Tekh. Fiz., Vol. 19, 1949, pp. 916-929;

or in a paper by Pryce.

M. H. L. Pryce, "The Diffraction of Radio Waves by the Curvature of the Earth," Advances in Phys., Vol. 2, 1953, pp. 67-95.

The corresponding stationary phase result for $P(\xi, y, q)$ given in Eq. (4.14) may be found in Fock's paper

V. A. Fock, "The Field of a Plane Wave in the Vicinity of a Conducting Body," Izvestiia Akademii Nauk (Ser. Fiz.), Vol. 10, 1946, pp. 171-186.

The recursion formula for $A_n(p, q)$ given in Eq. (4.20) can be found by suitable extensions of a paper by Keller, Lewis and Seckler.

J. B. Keller, R. M. Lewis and B. D. Seckler, "Asymptotic Solution of Some Diffraction Problems," New York University, Institute of Mathematical Sciences, Research Report EM-81, 1955. Also published in Comm. Pure and Applied Math., Vol. 9, 1956, pp. 207.

The illustration in Fig. 1 in Section 5, which shows the behavior of the field near the horizon, has been based upon an illustration in the classic paper:

B. van der Pol and H. Bremmer, "Further Note on the Propagation of Radio Waves over a Finitely Conducting Spherical Earth," Phil. Mag., Vol. 27, 1939, pp. 261-275.

The illustrations in Figs. 2 and 3 which show the locations in the t-plane of the roots of $w_1'(t_s) - qw_1(t_s) = 0$ as a function of q, were prepared by B. L. Gardner and R. L. Mason while working under the direction of the present authors. A similar, but much less complete, illustration was given in the paper

W. Franz and P. Beckmann, "Creeping Waves for Objects of Finite Conductivity," Trans. Inst. Radio Engrs., Vol. AP-4, 1956, pp. 203-208.

The expansions for $t_s(q)$ in powers of q and (1/q) in Eqs. (5.5) and (5.6) were first studied in the 1938-1939 papers of van der Pol and Bremmer. Further terms in these series are given in a recent paper

J. R. Johler and L. C. Walters, "Propagation of a Ground Wave Pulse Around a Finitely Conducting Spherical Earth from a Damped Sinusoidal Source Current," Trans. Inst. Radio Engrs., Vol. AP-7, 1959, pp. 1-10.

The expansion for the root $t_0(q)$ in Eq. (5.7) was given incorrectly by Furutsu and Wait in the papers:

K. Furutsu, "On the Excitation of the Waves of Proper Solutions," Trans. Inst. Radio Engrs., Vol. AP-7, 1959, pp. S-209-S218.

J. R. Wait, "On the Excitation of Electromagnetic Surface Waves on a Curved Surface," Trans. Inst. Radio Engrs., Vol. AP-8, 1960, pp. 445-448.

The correctness of the expansion given in the text is readily established by inserting the expansion into Riccati's equation. Furutsu apparently recognized the importance of the saddle points where $t_s = q^2$, but he failed to locate them correctly. Our designations for the root t_0, and its relation to $t_s(q)$ for $s \geq 1$, does not agree exactly with the definitions used by Wait.

The "Watson modes" are those discussed in Bremmer's treatise and other papers which deal with propagation over the earth's surface. The "Elliott modes" are discussed in the above-mentioned paper by Wait. A list of references related to the applications of these modes can be found in

R. S. Elliott, "Spherical Surface Wave Antennas," Trans. Inst. Radio Engrs. Vol. AP-4, 1956, pp. 422-428.

The illustration in Fig. 4 of the behavior of the modulus of $w_1(t)$ was prepared for the present authors by B. L. Gardner. The preparation of this illustration was greatly facilitated by the availability of the comprehensive tables of the Airy functions which were prepared under the direction of H. H. Aiken and W. H. Furry during World War II.

Harvard University, "Tables of the Modified Hankel Functions of Order One-Third and of Their Derivatives," Annals of the Computation Laboratory of Harvard University, Vol. II, Harvard University Press, Cambridge, Mass., 1945. (Gives tables of $h_2(x+iy) = (12)^{1/6}\pi^{-\frac{1}{2}}$ since result is $h_2(z) = \frac{\sqrt[6]{12}}{\sqrt{\pi}} e^{i\frac{2\pi}{3}} w_2(-z)$ $\exp(i2\pi/3)w_1(-x+iy)$ and $h_2'(x+iy)$ for $\Delta x=\Delta y=0.1$ for $x^2+y^2<36$.)

This illustration is somewhat more suitable for use with these problems than the comprehensive map of $|H^{(1)}_{1/3}(z)|$ which was constructed by C. Kropveld and T. Lohuis and which appears as Fig. 13 in Bremmer's 1949 treatise.

The computations of Domb and Pryce which are referred to in Section 6 are described in the paper:

C. Domb and M. H. L. Pryce, "The Calculation of Field Strengths Over a Spherical Earth," J. I. E. E., Vol. 94, Part III, 1947, pp. 325-339.

C. Domb, "Tables of Functions Occurring in the Diffraction of Electromagnetic Waves by the Earth," Advances in Physics, Quarterly Supplement of Phil. Mag. Vol. 5, 1953, pp. 96-102..

A list of the unpublished reports prepared by this group during 1941-1945 is given in Logan's General Research in Diffraction Theory, Vol. I.

Belkina's tables are available in the translation:

M. G. Belkina, Tables to Calculate the Electromagnetic Field in the Shadow Region for Various Soils. Soviet Radio Press, Moscow, 1949, Translated by Morris D. Firedman, ASTIA Document No. AD 110298, 1956.

The complete Bibliographic description of the C. C. I. R. Atlas is as follows:

Atlas of Ground-Wave Propagation Curves for Frequencies Between 30 Mc/s and 300 Mc/s, (C. C. I. R. Resolution No. 11) Union internationale des Télécommunications, Geneva, 1955.

The Japanese *Atlas* is known as

Atlas of Radio Wave Propagation Curves for Frequencies Between 30 and 10,000 Mc/s, The Radio Research Laboratories, Ministry of Postal Services, Tokyo, 1957.

The 1957 Soviet Atlas for $q = 0$ and $q = \infty$ is unique in that both tables and graphs are employed to display the data.

P. A. Azriliant and M. G. Belkina, *Numerical Results of the Theory of Diffraction of Radio Waves Around the Earth's Surface*, Soviet Radio Press, Moscow, 1957.

Wait has published some important data and curves related to $V_1(x, q)$ and $V_2(x, q)$ for some selected values of q for which $\arg q \sim 45°$.

J. R. Wait and A. M. Conda, "Pattern of an Antenna on a Curved Lossy Surface," *Trans. Inst. Radio Engrs.*, Vol. AP-6, 1958, pp. 348-359.

J. R. Wait and A. M. Conda, "Diffraction of Electromagnetic Waves by Smooth Obstacles for Grazing Angles," *J. Research NBS*, Vol. 63D, 1959, pp. 181-197.

Some results for $V_1(x, q)$ for $\arg q = 0$ are given in

J. R. Wait and A. M. Conda, "Radiation from a Slot on a Large Corrugated Cylinder," *Electromagnetic Wave Propagation*, edited by M. Desirant and J. L. Michiels, Academic Press, 1960.

Extensive studies of $V_0(x, q)$ have been made by the U. S. National Bureau of Standards. Up to 200 terms have been used in the residue series. Some of the outstanding reports are

J. R. Johler, W. J. Kellar and L. C. Walters, "Phase of the Low Radio Frequency Ground Wave," *National Bureau of Standards Circular 573*, 1956.

J. R. Wait and H. H. Howe, "Amplitude and Phase Curves for Ground-Wave Propagation in the Band 200 cycles per second to 500 Kilocycles," *National Bureau of Standards Circular 574*, 1956.

The expression given in Eq. (7.1) in Section 7 in which U is related to $V_1(x, q)$ was first given by Fock in 1945.

V. A. Fock, "Diffraction of Radio Waves Around the Earth's Surface," *J. Phys.*, Vol. 9, 1945, pp. 255-266.

A more detailed account is given in the monograph:

V. A. Fock, *The Diffraction of Radio Waves Around the Surface* of the Earth, Acad. of Sciences of USSR., Moscow, 1946. (Translated by Morris D. Friedman, Inc., Needham Heights, Massachusetts.)

The curves of the quantity $F_L(q)$ defined in Eq. (7.3) are given in

C.R. Burrows and M.C. Gray, "The Effect of the Earth's Curvature on Ground-Wave Propagation," Proc. Inst. Radio Engrs., Vol. 29, 1941, pp. 16-24.

C.R. Burrows and S.S. Attwood, ed., Radio Wave Propagation, Academic Press, Inc., New York, 1949 (Contains bibliography of wartime reports in the propagation field.)

Fock's work on the principle of the local field in the penumbra was published in the papers:

V.A. Fock, "The Distribution of Currents Induced by a Plane Wave on the Surface of a Conductor," J. Phys., Vol. 10, 1946, pp. 130-136.

V.A. Fock, "The Field of a Plane Wave Near the Surface of a Conducting Body," J. Phys., Vol. 10, 1946, pp. 399-409.

The detailed derivation of one of the main results in the 1946 paper was published in 1958

V.A. Fock and A.A. Fedorov, "Diffraction of a Plane Electromagnetic Wave by a Pefectly Conducting Paraboloid of Revolution," Zh. Tekh. Fiz., Vol. 28, 1958, pp. 2548-2566.

The illustration of $V_1(0, q)$ was constructed by D.W. Gillett, J.G. Hillhouse and N.A. Logan.

The reflection formula given in Eq. (8.9) in Section 8 for the source above a spherical surface was first given in the classic papers of van der Pol and Bremmer.

The illustration of $V_2(0, q)$ given in Fig. 10 was constructed by R.L. Mason and N.A. Logan.

The Fresnel field results obtained by using Eq. (8.14) in Eq. (8.11) differ from those given by Wait and Conda in a previous study.

J.R. Wait and A.M. Conda, "Diffraction of Electromagnetic Waves by Smooth Obstacles for Grazing Angles," J. Research National Bureau of Standards, Vol. 63D, 1959.

The present form is more suitable for points above the horizon. The form given by Wait and Conda are more suitable for points below the horizon. Both forms agree on the horizon.

The stationary phase evaluation for $C(\theta, r, r_0, \Gamma)$ given in Eq. (8.18) can be found in Franz's monograph

W. Franz, Theorie der Beugung Elektromagnetischer Wellen, (Ergebnisse der Angewandten Mathematik, Part 4) Berlin,

Springer-Verlag, 1957.

The expression in Eq. (8.24) for the Laplacian operator in terms of the variables s and β has been taken from

J.B. Keller, R.M. Lewis and B.D. Seckler, "Asymptotic Solution of Some Diffraction Problems," New York University, Institute of Mathematical Sciences, Research Report EM-81, 1955. Also published in Comm. Pure and Applied Math., Vol. 9, 1956, pp. 207.

The expression for the Laplacian operator in terms of the variables s and t given in Eq. (9.1) has been taken from

T.T. Wu and S.R. Seshadri, The Electromagnetic Theory of Light II, Scientific Report No. 22, Contract No. AF 19(604)-786, Harvard University, 1958.

These authors were only interested in constructing normal mode solutions of the wave equation and hence the function $D(x, y, y_0, q)$ is not used in their report.

The importance of the use of the variables in the form $D(x+y+y_0, y^2, y_0^2, q)$ was demonstrated in Logan's General Research in Diffraction Theory, Vol. I., for the case of a circular cylinder.

The use in Eq. (9.2) of the variable x which involves the integral with respect to the arc length of the (-2/3) power of the radius of curvature is related to the pioneering work of Keller.

J.B. Keller, "Diffraction by a Convex Cylinder," Trans. Inst. Radio Engrs., Vol. AP-4, 1956, pp. 312-321.

However, Keller worked with special cases of the general result which involves the function $D(x, y, y_0, q)$ (See Eqs. (9.23) and (9.24). The introduction of the variable defined in this manner can also be motivated by a geometrical interpretation of some mathematical results in a much neglected paper by Friedlander.

F.G. Friedlander, Propagation of a Pulse in an Inhomogeneous Medium, New York University Report EM-76, Contract No. AF 19(122)-42, 1955.

The equation to be interpreted is Friedlander's Eq. (7.11) which is derived from a use of the W.K.B. approximation. This interesting result was omitted from Friedlander's monograph.

F.G. Friedlander, Sound Pulses, Cambridge University Press, 1958.

However, by putting $s = -i\omega$ in many of the results of Chapter 6 of Friedlander's book, one can develop a theory which is closely related to our discussion of the diffraction region.

The special form taken by $\psi(s,t)$ for r and r_0 tending to a can be obtained directly from a form of the Laplacian which has been used by Ivanov.

V. I. Ivanov, "Diffraction of Short Waves by a Smooth Cylinder, Nauchnye Doklady Vysshei Shkoly, I(6), 1958, pp. 192-196.

The technique used in Eq. (9.16) of deriving the three-dimensional (sphere) function $U(r, \Theta)$ from the two-dimensional (cylinder) function $\psi(s, t)$ by multiplying a purely geometric factor was suggested to the authors by Friedlander's discussion on page 171 of Sound Pulses.

For results related to the case $t_0 \to \infty$ and $t = 0$ or $t \to \infty$, the reader should consult the following papers:

W. Franz, "The Green's Functions of Cylinders and Spheres," Z. Naturfoschung, Vol. 9A, 1954, pp. 705-716.

W. Franz and R. Galle, "Semiasymptotic Series for the Diffraction of a Plane Wave by a Cylinder," Z. Naturfoschung, Vol. 10A, 1955, pp. 374-378.

L. Wetzel, High-Frequency Current Distributions on Conducting Obstacles, Scientific Report No. 10, Contract No. AF 19(604)-786, Harvard University, 1957.

B. R. Levy, Diffraction by an Elliptic Cylinder, Research Report EM-121, Contract No. AF 19(604)-1717, New York University, 1958, (AFCRC-TN-59-103, ASTIA Document No. AD 208235).

J. B. Keller and B. R. Levy, "Diffraction by a Smooth Object," Comm. Pure Appl. Math., Vol. 12, 1959, pp. 159-209.

J. B. Keller and B. R. Levy, "Decay Exponents and Diffraction Coefficients for Surface Waves on Surfaces of Nonconstant Curvature," Trans. Inst. Radio Engrs., Vol. AP-7, 1959, pp. S52-S61.

F. Gilbert, "Scattering of Impulsive Elastic Waves by a Smooth Convex Cylinder," J. Accoust. Soc. of Am., Vol. 32, 1960, pp. 841-857.

A perusal of this representative sample of the literature on the diffraction region provides ample evidence of the need for a set of symbols, such as $V_1(\xi, q)$ and $V_{11}(\xi, q)$, which can be used to describe the normal mode expansions. This has already been done in the Soviet literature. See, for example,

A. S. Goriainov, "An Asymptotic Solution of the Problem of Diffraction of a Plane Electromagnetic Wave by a Conducting Cylinder, Radiotekhnika i. Elektronika, Vol. 3, 1958, pp. 603-614, (See also the English translation: Radio Engineering and Electronics, Vol. 3, 1959, pp. 28-39.

Keller's results have already been expressed in terms of functions related to $V_1(\xi, q)$ and $V_{11}(\xi, q)$ by Ivanov in the paper referred to above as well as in a more recent publication.

V. I. Ivanov, "Diffraction of Short Wave Plane Electromagnetic Waves by a Convex Cylinder for the Case of Non-Perpendicular Incidence," Radioteknika i Elektronika, Vol. 5, 1960, pp. 524-528.

The results quoted from Pekeris in Section 10 have been taken from a 1946 paper based upon wartime underwater sound studies.

C. L. Pekeris, "Theory of Propagation of Sound in a Half-Space of Variable Sound Velocity Under Conditions of Formation of a Shadow Zone," J. Accoust. Soc. Am., Vol. 18, 1946, pp. 295-315.

Friedlander's monograph (and his partially published 1955 report) is a valuable reference for the class of problems considered in Section 10. One should also consult the papers by Seckler and Keller.

B. D. Seckler and J. B. Keller, "Geometrical Theory of Diffraction in Inhomogeneous Media," J. Acoust. Soc. Am., Vol. 31, 1959, pp. 192-205.

B. D. Seckler and J. B. Keller, "Asymptotic Theory of Diffraction in Inhomogeneous Media," J. Acoust. Soc. Am., Vol. 31, 1959, pp. 206-216.

The composite problem (inhomogeneous medium above a convex surface) has been considered in a recent paper by Bremmer.

H. Bremmer, "On the Theory of Wave Propagation Through a Concentrically Stratified Troposphere with a Smooth Profile," J. Research National Bureau of Standards, Vol. 64D, 1960, pp. 467-482.

Bremmer results can all be expressed in terms of $V_0(\xi, q)$, $V_1(\xi, q)$, and $V_{11}(\xi, q)$. Bremmer's paper can also be modified to lead to the use of $V(x, y, y_0, q)$ if the solutions of $F(y, \lambda)$

$$\frac{d^2F}{dy^2} + [-\lambda + k^2 f(y)]F = 0 \qquad f(y) > 0 \qquad f'(y) > 0 \qquad y > 0$$

are expressed in the form

$$F(y, \lambda) \sim \left(\frac{f_1 y}{f(y)-f_0}\right)^{1/4} w_{1,2}(-\eta_0) \exp\left[\pm i\left(\frac{2}{3}\eta_\infty^{3/2} - \frac{2}{3}kf_1^{1/2}y^{3/2} + k^{1/3}f_1^{1/6}y^{1/2}t\right)\right] \qquad \eta_0 = k^{2/3}f_1^{1/3}y - t$$

$$\frac{2}{3}\eta_\infty^{2/3} = k\int_0^y \sqrt{f(y')-f_0}\,dy' - \frac{1}{2}k^{1/3}f_1^{2/3}t\int_0^y \frac{dy'}{\sqrt{f(y')-f_0}}$$

where $f(y) = f_0 + f_1 y + \cdots$, $\lambda = k^2 f_0 + f_1^{2/3} k^{4/3} t + \cdots$

This estimate has the advantage of reducing to the results of the previous writers for $y = 0$ and $y \to \infty$ but at the same time it is useful for intermediate values of y . This extension was suggested to the authors by a comparison of the treatment of $F(y, x)$ in Friedlander's monograph with the treatment given in one of Fock's classic papers.

V. A. Fock, "Ground Wave Propagation Around the Earth Taking Diffraction and Refraction into Account," Izvestiia Akademii Nauk, (Ser. Fiz.), Vol. 12, 1948, pp. 81-97.

The authors gratefully acknowledge the valuable contributions of B. L. Gardner who rendered valuable assistance in the preparation of the manuscript and illustrations for this paper. The authors also acknowledge their indebtedness to the many members of the Electromagnetics Division who have contributed to the preparation of this paper. In particular, we acknowledge the encouragement to undertake these studies which we have received from Messrs. E. A. Blasi and J. S. LaRue, the assumption of administrative responsibility by P. D. Kennedy, the constructive criticisms of J. R. Huynen, the diligent execution of algebraic manipulations by J. G. Hillhouse and R. L. Mason, and the scores of other tasks carried out by D. W. Gillett, M. J. McCurry, C. E. Ryan, C. L. Ross, J. G. Stout and H. Tom, and other members of the Lockheed Missile and Space Division.

Finally, it is a pleasure to thank Professor R. E. Langer and the program committee for including this paper on the program. Special thanks are also due the Mathematics Research Center for the care they have taken in the preparation of the typescript from which this paper has been printed.

The work leading to this paper has been carried out as part of the Lockheed General Research Program under the sponsorship of the United States Government.

KEEVE M. SIEGEL

The Quasi-static Radar Cross Sections of Complex Bodies of Radiation

I. INTRODUCTION. The approximate procedure developed by the author many years ago to find the radar cross section of a complex shape when the wavelength is large with respect to the dimensions of the body, has withstood many experimental investigations and the results indicate that for all complex shapes yet measured, the results remain an excellent approximation. The result also shows for axially symmetric back-scattering from a perfectly conducting body of revolution that the back-scattering cross section is $\sigma = (4/\pi)k^4(vf)^2$ and that the similar result in acoustics is $(1/4)k^4(vf)^2$; k = propagation constant, $2\pi/\lambda$, v = volume and f = correction factor depending upon the length-to-width ratio. f had the form $1+e^{-y}/\pi y$, where y was a numerical constant times the length-to-width ratio; length being the maximum dimension of the body in the direction of propagation, and width being the maximum dimension of the body perpendicular to the direction of propagation. For shapes of large length-to-width ratio of $f \simeq 1$. In acoustics one obtains the same results except that one gets a contribution from the body as if there were one dipole present instead of two dipoles adding up on phase as one gets in electromagnetics. This explains the discrepancy of the factor 4 in the Rayleigh scattering from a hard body in acoustics. The numerical constants appearing in the length-to-width ratio are determined for many shapes [1]. For a finite cone the volume is $\pi(1/3)r^2h$ where r is the radius of the base and h is the altitude. y is the numerical constant times the length-to-width ratio, in this case length is h and the width is $2r$. By utilizing the Rayleigh answer obtained by Rayleigh [2] for the disc, one finds the numerical constant = one-half. Thus the Rayleigh radar cross section obtained for the finite cone is

$$\sigma = \frac{4\pi k^4 r^4 h^2}{9}\left[1 + \frac{4r\,e^{-h/4r}}{\pi h}\right]^2 \qquad (1)$$

Agreement was obtained between theory and experiment [3, 4]. Since the resonance region decreases [4], as the cone angle increases, we would expect Rayleigh theory and experiment to be in agreement for larger values of kr , or for larger cone angles, than the value of kr where agreement starts for small cone angles. Figure 1 from Ref. 4 indicates this trend is correct. We note from the Rayleigh approximation equation that we would obtain the results independent of whether we looked at the body from the left or right as long as we are on the axis of symmetry. This states that the nose-on cross section of a finite cone in the Rayleigh region must be equal to the base-on cross section. In Figure 2 we observe that this statement agrees with experiment. We have also compared these data with experiments of Keys and Primich [5], Honda, Silver and Clapp [6], and with August and Angelakos [7]. The results are given in Figure 3. Many other complex bodies of revolution have been measured, such as spheroids, intersections between cones, spheres, etc., and the results obtained are in the same essential agreement as given in the above figures. We have presented the electromagnetic data but nevertheless we find the acoustic scattering data yields similar results.

I will now discuss a method of obtaining higher order long wavelength answers in acoustics and in electromagnetics. I will do the acoustic sphere cases first as they allow us to "see through the method" quite easily, and then I will do the electromagnetic sphere answer. In the final section, I will present similar results for a capped cone.

FIGURE 1 - NOSE-ON CROSS SECTIONS FOR CONES OF HALF-ANGLE, α

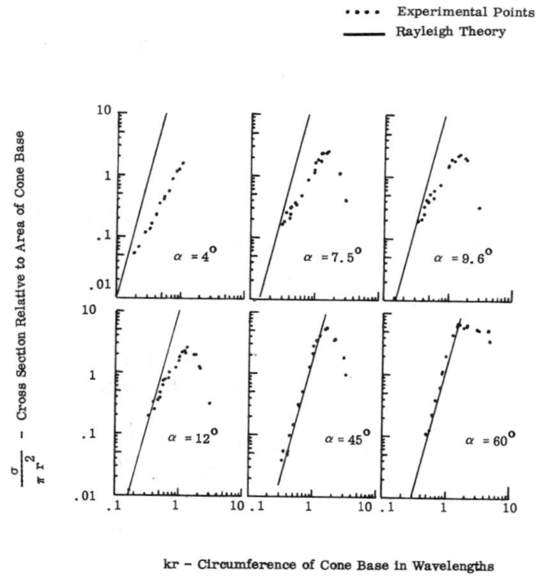

FIGURE 2 - COMPARISON OF NOSE-ON AND TAIL-ON RADAR CROSS SECTIONS OF FINITE CONES
EXPERIMENTAL DATA (RANGE OF VALUES)

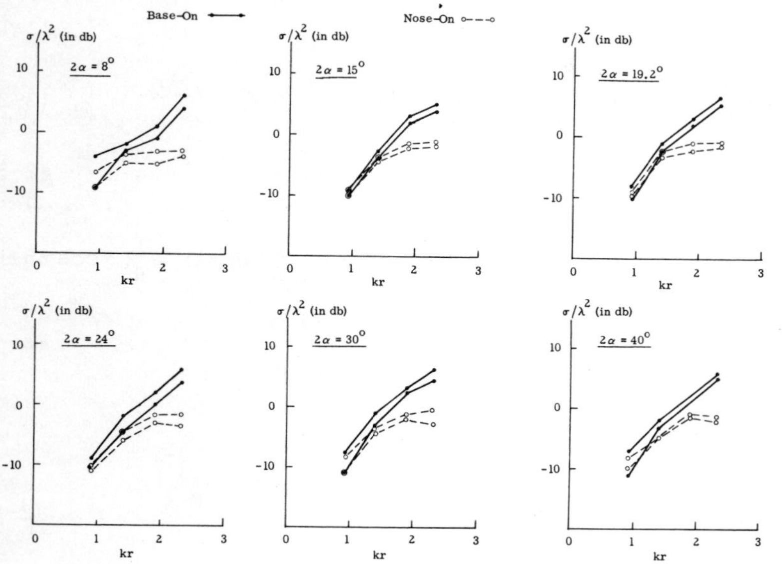

FIGURE 3
RATIO OF BASE-ON TO NOSE-ON CROSS SECTIONS OF FINITE CONES

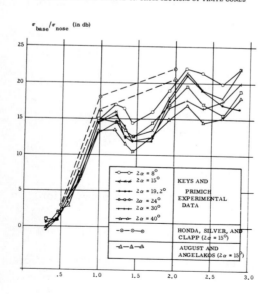

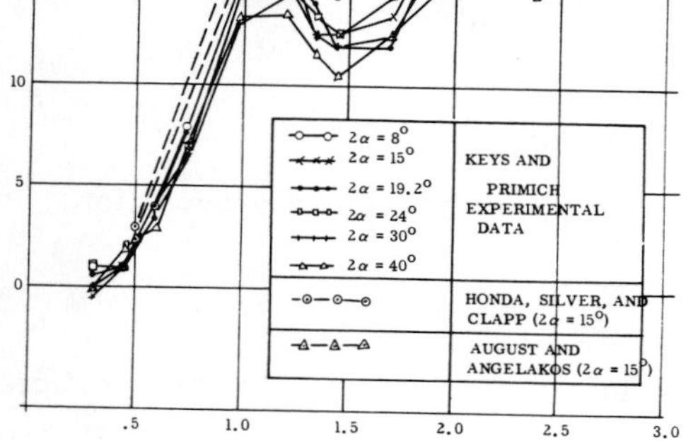

II. SCALAR RESULTS FOR A SPHERE. The following formulas will prove to be useful for this section

$$h_0(\rho) = \frac{-i}{\rho} + 1 + \frac{i\rho}{2} - \frac{\rho^2}{6} - \frac{i\rho^3}{24} \tag{2-1}$$

$$h_1(\rho) = -\frac{1}{\rho^2} - \frac{i}{2} + \frac{\rho}{3} + \frac{i\rho^2}{8} - \frac{\rho^3}{30} \tag{2-2}$$

$$h_2(\rho) = -\frac{3i}{\rho^3} - \frac{i}{2\rho} - \frac{i\rho}{8} + \frac{\rho^2}{15} + \frac{i\rho^3}{48} \tag{2-3}$$

$$P_0(x) = 1 \ , \quad P_1(x) = x = \cos\theta \ , \quad P_2(x) = \frac{1}{2}(3x^2-1) = \frac{1}{4}(3\cos 2\theta + 1) \ ,$$

$$P_3(x) = \frac{1}{2}(5x^3 - 3x) = \frac{1}{8}(5\cos 3\theta + 3\cos\theta) \ ,$$

$$P_4(x) = \frac{1}{8}(35x^4 - 30x^2 + 3) = \frac{1}{8}(-7 - 20P_2 + 35x^4) \ , \tag{2-4}$$

$$P_5(x) = \frac{15}{8}(x - \frac{14}{3}x^3 + \frac{21}{5}x^5) \ .$$

$$\lim_{r\to\infty} h_n^{(1)}(kr) \sim \frac{e^{ikr}}{kr}(-i)^{n+1} \tag{2-5}$$

The Soft Sphere

We first solve the problem of a plane wave incident on a soft sphere. The acoustic long wavelength expansion for the far field is desired.

The boundary value problem is

$$\phi^i = e^{-ikz} \tag{2-6}$$

$$\nabla^2\phi + k^2\phi = 0 \tag{2-7}$$

where

$$\phi = \phi^i + \phi^s \tag{2-8}$$

At the boundary $r = a$

$$\phi_{b(r=a)} = 0 \tag{2-9}$$

and at infinity ϕ^s satisfies the radiation condition

$$\lim_{r\to\infty} r\left(\frac{\partial\phi^s}{\partial r} - ik\phi^s\right) = 0 \tag{2-10}$$

Specifically we are interested in obtaining the coefficient of the spherically outgoing wave

$$\lim_{r\to\infty} \phi^s = \frac{e^{ikr}}{r} f_s \quad . \tag{2-11}$$

We want to find f_s as a function of k .

We know that a solution of Eq. (2-7) in the form to satisfy (2-10) and (2-11) is

$$\phi^s = \sum_{n=0}^{\infty} A_n h_n^{(1)}(kr) P_n(\cos\theta) \quad . \tag{2-12}$$

We observe that for small kr, $h_n^{(1)}$ can be approximated by a few terms in its series. We also observe for small kz that e^{-ikz} can also be approximated by a few terms in its series. Knowing this we match the common Legendre Polynomial term in each to satisfy Eq. (2-9).

Matching P_0 terms we find then if $\rho = ka$ that at the boundary each even term in z in the e^{-ikz} series has a contribution to P_0

$$\underbrace{\left(1 - \frac{\rho^2}{6} + \frac{\rho^4}{24}\cdot\frac{1}{5}\right)}_{\text{From } P_0 \text{ contribution of } e^{-ikz}} + \underbrace{A_0\left(-\frac{i}{\rho} + 1 + \frac{i\rho}{2} - \frac{\rho^2}{6}\right)}_{\text{First terms of } h_0^{(1)} \text{ the only coefficient of } P_0 \text{ in Eq. (2-12)}} = 0 \tag{2-13}$$

$$\therefore\ A_0 = -i\rho - \rho^2 + \frac{2i\rho^3}{3} + \frac{\rho^4}{6} \tag{2-14}$$

Now we match P_1 which has a contribution from odd powers of z in the incident field expansion. We find, using Eq. (2-8)

$$\underbrace{\left(-i\rho + \frac{i\rho^3}{3!}\cdot\frac{3}{5}\right)}_{\text{From odd } z \text{ in } e^{-ikz}} + A_1\underbrace{\left(-\frac{i}{\rho^2} - \frac{i}{2}\right)}_{\text{From } h_1} = 0 \tag{2-15}$$

$$A_1 = -\rho^3 + \frac{3}{5}\rho^5 \quad . \tag{2-16}$$

Now match P_2 ; we obtain

$$-\frac{\rho^2}{2}\frac{2}{3} + A_2\left(-\frac{3i}{\rho^3}\right) = 0 \tag{2-17}$$

$$A_2 = \frac{i\rho^5}{9} \quad . \tag{2-18}$$

Now utilizing Eq. (2-5) we obtain

$$f_s = -\rho\left[\left(1 - i\rho + \frac{2}{3}\rho^2 + \frac{i\rho^3}{3}\right)P_0 - \left(\rho^2 - \frac{3}{5}\rho^4\right)P_1 + \frac{\rho^4}{9}P_2\right] \tag{2-19}$$

In [8], Senior has decomposed the usual series solution and this result is in agreement with the result obtained by that method.

The Hard Sphere

We have the same boundary problem as before, except we replace Eq. (2-9) by

$$\left.\frac{\partial\phi}{\partial\ \mathrm{norm}}\right|_b = 0 \qquad (2\text{-}20)$$

For the sphere we have

$$\left.\frac{\partial\phi}{\partial r}\right|_{r=a} = 0 \quad . \qquad (2\text{-}21)$$

We again match P_0 and differentiate individual terms with respect to ρ in e^{-ikz} and in $h_2^{(1)}$ and using Eq. (2-21) we obtain

$$-\frac{\rho}{3} + \frac{\rho^3}{6}\,\frac{1}{5} + B_0\left(+ \frac{i}{\rho^2} + \frac{i}{2} - \frac{\rho}{3}\right) = 0 \qquad (2\text{-}22)$$

$$B_0 = -\frac{i\rho^3}{3} + \frac{i\rho^5}{5} - \frac{\rho^6}{9} \qquad (2\text{-}23)$$

Now we match

$$\underbrace{\left(-i + \frac{i\rho^2}{2}\,\frac{3}{5} - \frac{\rho^4}{4!}\,\frac{5}{21}\right)}_{\text{Odd terms in } \rho \text{ diff in } e^{-ikz} \text{ after coefficients of } P_1 \text{ were selected}} + \underbrace{B_1\left(\frac{2i}{\rho^3} + \frac{1}{3}\right)}_{\text{diff in } \rho \text{ from } h_1} = 0 \qquad (2\text{-}24)$$

$$B_1 = \frac{\rho^3}{2} - \frac{3}{5}\,\frac{\rho^5}{4} + \frac{i\rho^6}{12} \qquad (2\text{-}25)$$

Now matching P_2 we obtain

$$\underbrace{-\frac{2\rho}{3}}_{\text{From } z^2 \text{ in } e^{-ikz} \text{ and differentiated with respect to } \rho} + \underbrace{B_2\,\frac{9i}{\rho^4}}_{\text{From } h_2 \text{ and differentiated with respect to } \rho\ .} = 0 \qquad (2\text{-}26)$$

$$B_2 = -i\,\frac{2\rho^5}{27} \qquad (2\text{-}27)$$

Now matching Eq. (2-5) we obtain

$$f_h = \left[-\frac{1}{3}\rho^3 + \frac{1}{5}\rho^5 + \frac{1}{9}i\rho^6\right]P_0 + \left[-\frac{1}{2}\rho^3 + \frac{3}{20}\rho^5 - \frac{1}{12}i\rho^6\right]P_1 + \frac{2}{27}\rho^5 P_2\ . \qquad (2\text{-}28)$$

III. ELECTROMAGNETIC PERFECTLY CONDUCTING SPHERE. We here use the same method except the results are more complicated. The algebra of this section will be published in detail in Reference [8]. We first use the method of Hansen [9] to write down a general scattered field

$$\underline{E}^s = E_0 \sum_{n=1}^{\infty} (A_{oln} M_{oln} + B_{eln} N_{eln}) \qquad (3\text{-}1)$$

where

$$M_{oln} = \mp \frac{m}{\sin\theta} z_n(kR) P_n^m(\cos\theta) \frac{\sin}{\cos} m\phi\, i_2 - z_n(kR) \frac{\partial P_n^m}{\partial\theta} \frac{\cos}{\sin} m\phi\, i_3$$

$$N_{eln} = \frac{n(n+1)}{kR} z_n(kR) P_n^m(\cos\theta) \frac{\cos}{\sin} m\phi\, i_1$$

$$+ \frac{1}{kR}\frac{\partial}{\partial R}[R\, z_n(kR)]\, \frac{\partial}{\partial\theta} P_n^m(\cos\theta) \frac{\cos}{\sin} m\phi\, i_2$$

$$\mp \frac{m}{kR\sin\theta} \frac{\partial}{\partial R}[R\, z_n(kR)]\, P_n^m(\cos\theta) \frac{\sin}{\cos} m\phi\, i_3 \; .$$

We again match this with the incident field using the series representations for $h_n(kr)$ and $\frac{1}{kr}[kr\, h_n(kr)]'$. We find it easier to match like values of $\cos i\theta$ and this gives us polynomials in k^i and setting the coefficients of each k^j to zero we find we can evaluate the unknown constants as before. We obtain:

$$B_{e11} = i\rho^3 \{1 + \frac{3}{10}\rho^2 + \frac{2}{3} i\rho^3 - \frac{3}{14}\rho^4 + \frac{2}{5} i\rho^5 + 0(\rho^6)\}$$

$$A_{011} = -\frac{1}{2}\rho^3 \{1 - \frac{3}{5}\rho^2 - \frac{1}{3} i\rho^3 + \frac{3}{7}\rho^4 + \frac{2}{5} i\rho^5 + 0(\rho^6)\}$$

$$B_{e12} = \frac{1}{36}\rho^5 \{1 - \frac{5}{42}\rho^2 + \frac{5}{108}\rho^4 + \frac{1}{30} i\rho^5 + 0(\rho^6)\}$$

$$A_{012} = \frac{1}{54} i\rho^5 \{1 - \frac{5}{21}\rho^2 + 0(\rho^4)\}$$

$$B_{e13} = -\frac{1}{2025} i\rho^7 \{1 - \frac{7}{60}\rho^2 + 0(\rho^4)\} \qquad (3\text{-}2)$$

$$A_{013} = \frac{1}{2700}\rho^7 \{1 - \frac{7}{45}\rho^2 + 0(\rho^4)\}$$

$$B_{e14} = -\frac{1}{(420)^2}\rho^9 \{1 - \frac{153}{1540}\rho^2 + 0(\rho^4)\}$$

$$A_{014} = -\frac{1}{20(105)^2} i\rho^9 + 0(\rho^{11})$$

We now use the asymptotic expression for a far field expansion in M_{oln} and N_{eln} and this gives us the Rayleigh expansion for the perfectly conducting sphere.

For example, to exhibit the method we will repeat the first two steps. From the boundary condition we obtain the first term in B_{e11} as follows.

$$[\hat{n} \times (\underline{E}^i + \underline{E}^s)] = 0 \tag{3-3}$$

to put it in useful form

$$\hat{r} \times (A\,\hat{r} + B\hat{\theta} + c\hat{\phi}) = 0 \tag{3-4}$$

$$-c\hat{\theta} + B\hat{\phi} = 0 \tag{3-5}$$

$$\therefore \quad c = 0 \quad B = 0 \quad . \tag{3-6}$$

Now by using $B = 0$ we obtain

$$D_n \cos\theta + B'_n \frac{[kr\, h_n(kr)]'}{kr} \frac{\partial P'_n}{\partial \theta} + A_n \frac{h_n(kr)\, P'_n}{\sin\theta} = 0$$

where

$$D_n = \sum_{\ell=0}^{n-1} (-i)^\ell \frac{(kr\cos\theta)^\ell}{\ell!}$$

Now letting $n = 1$

$$\cos\theta + B'_1 \frac{i}{(ka)^3} \cos\theta = 0$$

$$B'_1 = i\rho^3 \quad .$$

Now by letting $n = 2$ we obtain

$$(1-kr\cos\theta)\cos\theta + B'_1 \frac{i}{(ka)^3}\cos\theta + B'_2 \frac{6i}{\rho^4}\, 3\cos 2\theta + A'_1 \frac{(-i)}{\rho^2} = 0 \ .$$

By using $\cos^2\theta = \frac{1}{2}(\cos 2\theta + 1)$ and Fourier matching, we obtain

$$B'_2 = \frac{\rho^5}{36} \qquad A'_1 = -\frac{1}{2}\rho^3$$

and we can see we have obtained the first terms in B_{e11} and A_{o11} and B_{e12} . This method continues the same way until the coefficients in Eq. (3-2) are all obtained.

IV. SOME SCALAR RESULTS FOR AN ARBITRARY AXIALLY SYMMETRIC SHAPE PARTICULARIZED FOR A CAPPED CONE.

Let us consider a soft, arbitrary, axially symmetric shape. We will note the symmetry restriction can be removed. It is put in to simplify the algebra a bit. Choose any point in or near the shape and consider that point as a center of a sphere. Construct a sphere which completely covers the arbitrary shape but which physically does not exist. Now let us consider a solution to the scalar wave equation which satisfies the following boundary value problem. The incident field is a plane wave,

$$\phi^i = e^{-ikz} . \qquad (4-1)$$

The total field consists of an incident field and a scattered field,

$$\phi = \phi^i + \phi^s . \qquad (4-2)$$

This field satisfies the scalar wave equation

$$\nabla^2 \phi + k^2 \phi = 0 . \qquad (4-3)$$

The boundary absorbs the energy and is considered perfectly soft

$$\phi \big|_b = 0 . \qquad (4-4)$$

The scattered field satisfies the radiation condition

$$\lim_{r \to \infty} r\left(\frac{\partial \phi^s}{\partial r} - ik\phi^s\right) = 0 . \qquad (4-5)$$

The scattered far field can be decomposed as

$$\phi^s = \frac{e^{ikr}}{r} f_s . \qquad (4-6)$$

We choose a scattered field to satisfy eqs. (4-3), (4-5) and (4-6)

$$\phi^s = \sum_{n=0}^{\infty} A_n h'_n(kr) P_n(\mu) . \qquad (4-7)$$

We now consider ourselves on the mathematical sphere and we take a limit as the wavelength becomes very large ($k \to 0$). The field on the sphere then must approach a static field and in the limit satisfies the following boundary value problem:

$$\phi_p^i = 1$$

$$\nabla^2 \phi_p = 0$$

$$\phi_p = 1 + \phi_{s,p}^s$$

$$\phi\big|_b = 0 \tag{4-8}$$

$$\lim_{r\to\infty} r\frac{\partial \phi_p^s}{\partial r} = 0$$

$$\phi^s = \frac{1}{r} f_{s,p} \; .$$

We observe that the boundary value problem in $V = -\phi_{s,p}^s$ (where the upper "s" stands for "scattered", the lower "s" stands for "soft and the "p" stands for "potential") satisfies the following potential problem:

$$\nabla^2 V = 0$$

$$V\big|_b = 1$$

$$\lim_{r\to\infty} r\left(\frac{\partial V}{\partial r}\right) = 0 \tag{4-9}$$

$$\lim_{r\to\infty} V = \frac{1}{r} g(\theta, \phi) = 0 \; .$$

Since we are looking for a V on the mathematical sphere which is exterior to the arbitrary shape, we can always express such a V as

$$V = \sum_{n=0}^{\infty} - \frac{B_n}{r^{n+1}} P_n(\mu) \; ;$$

$$\therefore \quad \phi_{s,p}^s = \sum \frac{B_n}{r^{n+1}} P_n(\mu) \; . \tag{4-10}$$

Thus for k small enough on the mathematical sphere we obtain from (4-7) and (4-10),

$$\lim_{k\to 0} \sum A_n h_n^{(1)}(kr) P_n(\mu) = \sum_{n=0}^{\infty} \frac{B_n}{r^{n+1}} p_n(\mu) \; . \tag{4-11}$$

We now match $P_0(\mu)$ terms and we find

$$\lim_{k\to 0} A_0 h_0'(kr) = \frac{B_0}{r} . \quad (4\text{-}12)$$

By use of (2-1) we obtain

$$A_0 \frac{(-i)}{kr} = \frac{B_0}{r}$$
$$\therefore \quad A_0 = ikB_0 . \quad (4\text{-}13)$$

Matching the nth term

$$A_n h_n^{(1)}(kr) = \frac{B_n}{r^{n+1}} .$$

Using the dominant pole in $h_n^{(1)}$,

$$\frac{A_n(-i)(-1)^n 2^n \sqrt{\pi}}{(kr)^{n+1}\Gamma(-n+\frac{1}{2})} = \frac{B_n}{r^{n+1}}$$
$$\therefore \quad B_n = \frac{A_n(-i)(-1)^n 2^n \sqrt{\pi}}{k^{n+1}\Gamma(-n+\frac{1}{2})} , \quad (4\text{-}14)$$

$$A_n = \frac{iB_n k^{n+1}(\Gamma(-n+\frac{1}{2}))(-1)^n}{2^n \sqrt{\pi}} . \quad (4\text{-}15)$$

Thus by (4-7),

$$\phi^s = \sum_{n=0}^{\infty} i \frac{B_n k^{n+1}(\Gamma(-n+\frac{1}{2}))(-1)^n}{2^n \sqrt{\pi}} P_n(\mu) h_n^{(1)}(kr) . \quad (4\text{-}16)$$

But by (2-5),

$$f_s^s = \sum_{n=0}^{\infty} \frac{iB_n k^n(\Gamma(-n+\frac{1}{2}))(-1)^n(-i)^{n+1}}{2^n\sqrt{\pi}} \frac{e^{ikr}}{r} P_n(\mu)$$

which simplifies to

$$f_s^s = \sum_{n=0}^{\infty} \left(\frac{ik}{2}\right)^n \frac{B_n\Gamma(-n+\frac{1}{2})}{2^n\sqrt{\pi}} P_n(\mu)\frac{e^{ikr}}{r} . \quad (4\text{-}17)$$

Since the B_n are coefficients of the potential problem, they are k independent and thus from the potential solution alone it is possible (for a not-too-simple shape) to derive contributions to the scattering coefficients of all order. The sphere being such a symmetric shape had almost all its $B_n \equiv 0$. Thus it is the simplicity of the problems already solved which has deluded some into not realizing for a complex shape the potential solution contributes to the first-order terms in all k^n. This does not give all the contributions to each k^n though it gives some contribution to all k^n for almost all shapes. To obtain the correction factors to B_n for an arbitrary shape, we must first point out where these correction factors come from. When we matched the $h_n'(kr)$ terms we only matched the leading term in each rather than the sum. Thus to obtain the corrections to the B_n we match in more and more of the series of the $h'_n(kr)$ and more terms in the incident field. The incident field can be expanded

$$e^{-ikz} = \sum_{j=0}^{\infty} \frac{(-ikr\cos\theta)^2}{j!} \quad . \tag{4-18}$$

This gives us integer exponents k^j to match in the scattered field but unfortunately also gives us $\cos^2\theta$. We must expand each $\cos^2\theta$ into a series of $P_\ell(\cos\theta)$. The result is that to obtain all the coefficients in $h_0^{(1)}(kr)$ we would have to use all the odd coefficients in the plane wave expansion (4-18) as each $\cos^{2n}\theta$ yields a contribution to $P_0(\cos\theta)$ and that is the coefficient of $h_0^{(1)}(kr)$. As we can see from looking back at the sphere, this is not as severe a problem as it might be at first sight, as the higher terms in $h_0^{(1)}$ and for that matter in $h_n(1)$ combine with the higher terms in the plane wave expansion and only contribute to higher and higher exponents in k^n. In practice, one would decide to obtain an accurate result for a particular value of n and then stop. The sphere is an instructive example of this process. If we look at eq. (2-13) we observe that only the first term was required to give us first-order result for the soft sphere. By analysis of the match process it is clear that only a few terms can contribute to any order in k. The hard sphere is a good example of the second term in the incident field contributing to the first-order result in k. We note from (2-28) where in the hard sphere case two terms contributed to the first order in k, one from P_0, and the other from P_1. The number of terms which contribute to a particular order in k increases with the value of the exponent. Of course the potential for the sphere only contributes directly to one term in the scattered field because of its symmetry and the Rayleigh answer is trivially arrived at,

$$\nabla^2 V = 0$$

$$V_{r=a} = 1$$

$$\lim_{r\to\infty} r \frac{\partial V}{\partial r} = 0 \;;$$

$$\therefore\; V = \sum -\frac{B_n P_n(\cos\theta)}{a^{n+1}} = -1$$

$$B_0 = a$$

$$B_j = 0 \qquad j \neq 0 \qquad (4\text{-}19)$$

$$\phi^s_{s,p} = -\frac{a}{r}$$

$$f_s = -a$$

$$\sigma = 4\pi |f_s|^2 = 4\pi a^2 \;.$$

This result is in agreement with (2-19).

Now it is interesting to note that though most of the terms of the incident field are not other than trivial solutions in the long wavelength limit to Laplace's equation, nevertheless they can be matched term by term with solutions which are non-trivial solutions. This is harder to state than it is to show by example. That is, we will consider a term a solution to Laplace's equation if $\lim_{k\to 0} \nabla^2\phi = 0$ and that this will suffice as matching a potential solution. In this manner each individual term in the incident field is considered a solution. For example

$$e^{-ikz} = 1 - ikr\cos\theta - \frac{(kr)^2\cos^2\theta}{2!}$$

1 is a solution of $\nabla^2 1 \equiv 0$,

$-ikr\cos\theta$ is a solution of $\nabla^2 r\cos\theta \equiv 0$,

$-\frac{(kr)^2\cos^2\theta}{2!}$ is a solution in the above limit sense as

$$\lim_{k\to 0} -\frac{(kr)^2\cos^2\theta}{2!} = 0 \;.$$

Now $\frac{r^2\cos^2\theta}{2}$ has a part which is a solution in the ordinary sense as

$$\cos^2\theta = \frac{2P_2(\cos\theta)}{3} + \frac{1}{3} \;.$$

Thus we find $-k^2r^2/3\ P_2(\cos\theta)$ is a solution in the ordinary sense and the remainder (always of lower order in $P_n(\mu)$) is a solution in the limit sense. The remainder here is $-k^2r^2P_0/6$.

In the scattered field in the ordinary solution sense we have

$$-\frac{i}{kr}P_0(\cos\theta) \quad \text{from} \quad h_0^{(1)}(kr)$$

$$-\frac{i}{(kr)^2}P_1(\cos\theta) \quad \text{from} \quad h_1^{(1)}(kr)$$

$$-\frac{i(-1)^n 2^n\sqrt{\pi}}{\rho^{n+1}\Gamma(-n-\frac{1}{2})}P_n(\cos\theta) \quad \text{from} \quad h'_n(kr) \quad .$$

Now for the hard sphere we find we match at the boundary a solution in the ordinary sense with a solution in the limit sense. That is, the first non-vanishing radial derivative in r in the incident field which is a coefficient of P_0 comes from $(-k^2r^2/6)P_0(\cos\theta)$ which will match the radial derivative of $(-i/kr)P_0(\cos\theta)$. To go through the first Rayleigh term for the hard sphere we then obtain

$$-\frac{k^2a}{3}P_0(\cos\theta)+\frac{iA_0}{ka^2}P_0(\cos\theta) = 0$$

$$-ikP_1(\cos\theta)+\frac{i^2}{k^2a^3}A_1P_1(\cos\theta) = 0$$

$$\therefore\ A_0 = -i\frac{k^3a^3}{3}$$

$$A_1 = \frac{k^3a^3}{2}$$

$$\phi_h^s = \sum_{n=0}^{\infty} A_n h_n^{(1)}(kr)P_n(\mu)$$

$$\phi_h^s = -i\frac{k^3a^3}{3}\frac{e^{ikr}}{kr}(-i)P_0(\cos\theta)+\frac{k^3a^3}{2}\frac{e^{ikr}}{kr}(-i)^2P_1(\cos\theta)$$

$$f_h^s = -\frac{k^2a^3}{3}P_0-\frac{k^2a^3}{2}P_1 \ ,$$

which agrees to this order with (2-28).

We now will discuss the soft-capped cone, but the hard-capped cone provides no additional difficulty.

Darling (Ref. 10) has obtained a potential solution for the capped cone. The Dirichlet problem he solved was our V problem,

$$\nabla^2 V = 0$$

$$V\big|_{\text{boundary}} = 0$$

$$\lim_{r \to \infty} r\left(\frac{\partial V}{\partial r}\right) = 0 \ .$$

He also solved a particular Neumann problem which by proper transformation can be put in the potential form that we need to solve the hard-cone problem. Darling's solution is of the form

$$V = \sum_{n=0}^{\infty} C_n \frac{P_n(\cos\theta)}{r^{n+1}} \ .$$

The C_n are defined as the nth component of τ where τ is given by

$$\tau = (I - N_1 M)^{-1}(B + N_2 A) \ ,$$

where I is the identity, A and B are column vectors, M, N_1 and N_2 are matrices, j is a row index and k is a column index.

$$N_1 = (1-\mu_0^2)\frac{2j+1}{2} \frac{a^{n_i+j+1} P_j(\mu_0) \left.\frac{\partial P_{n_k}(x)}{\partial x}\right|_{x=\mu_0}}{(n_k-j)(n_k+j+1)}$$

$$N_2 = (1-\mu_0^2)\frac{2j+1}{2} \frac{P_j(\mu_0) \left.\frac{\partial P_{n_k}(x)}{\partial x}\right|_{x=\mu_0}}{(n_k-j)(n_k+j+1)\, a^{n_k-j}}$$

$$M = \frac{P_k(\mu_0)}{\left.\frac{\partial P_x(\mu_0)}{\partial x}\right|_{x=n_j} (n_j+k+1)\, a^{n_j+k+1}}$$

$$A = \frac{a^{n_j+1}}{\left.\frac{\partial P_x(\mu_0)}{\partial x}\right|_{x=n_j} (n_j+1)}$$

$$B = \frac{2j+1}{2} a^{j+1} \frac{(\mu_0^2-1) P'_j(\mu_0)}{j(j+1)} \qquad j > 0$$

$$B = \frac{1}{2} a(\mu_0 + 1) \qquad j = 0 \ .$$

Thus,

$$\phi_s^s = \sum_{n=0}^{\infty} \frac{i\, C'_n k^{n+1}\, \Gamma(-n+\frac{1}{2})}{(-2)^n \sqrt{\pi}} h_n^{(1)}(kr)\, P_n(\mu)$$

where $C'_n = -C_n$.

Now to obtain f_s^s for the capped cone,

$$f_s^s = \sum_{n=0}^{\infty} \frac{i\, C'_n k^{n+1}\, \Gamma(-n+\frac{1}{2})}{(-2)^n \sqrt{\pi}} \frac{(-1)^{n+1}}{k}$$

$$f_s^s = \sum_{n=0}^{\infty} \frac{(-ik)^n C'_n\, \Gamma(-n+\frac{1}{2})}{(-2)^n \sqrt{\pi}} .$$

This result has now yielded a key contribution to every value in the power series expansion in k . By use of the limit potential solution trick as given, we can now pick up as many of the unknown correction sets of coefficients as desired. The writer has not been able to find any way to prove he can always obtain all of them, but the algebra on particular brute force examples has yielded what seems to be correct results. Although this paper is quite "rough", it is hoped that the importance of the potential solution has been stressed concerning its usefulness in obtaining contributions to higher order terms in convergent expansions and also in asymptotic expansions at long wavelengths without the necessity of solving new boundary value problems at each step or without being forced to integrate special functions.

REFERENCES

1. Siegel, K. M., Far Field Scattering from Bodies of Revolution, Applied Science Research, Section B. Vol. 7(1959), and Comments on Far Field Scattering from Bodies of Revolution, Applied Science Research, Section B., Vol. 8(1960).

2. Lord Rayleigh, On the Incidence of Aerial and Electromagnetic Waves on Small Obstacles, Phil. Mag., Vol. 44, p. 28(1897).

3. Brysk, H., Hiatt, R. E., Weston, V. H., and Siegel, K. M., The Nose-on Radar Cross Section of Finite Cones, Canadian Journal of Physics, Vol. 37(1959).

4. Crispin, J. W, Jr., Siegel, K. M., and Sleator, F. B., The Resonance Region. To be published by URSI (International Scientific Radio Union).

5. Keys, J. E., and Primich, R. I., The Radar Cross Section of Right Circular Metal Cones-I, Defence Research Telecommunications Establishment Report 1010(May 1959).

6. Honda, J S., Silver, S., and Clapp, F. D., Scattering of Microwaves by Figures of Revolution, University of California Electronics Research Laboratory Report, Issue No. 232, Series No. 60 (March 1959).

7. August, G., and Angelakos, D. J., Back Scattering from Cones, The University of California Electronics Research Laboratory Report, Series No. 60, Issue 252 (September 1959).

8. Crispin, J. W., Jr., Harrison, B. A., LeBaron, E., Plonus, M., Senior, T. B. A., Siegel, K. M., Vincent, K., and Weston, V. H., Diffraction and Scattering by Regular Bodies - 1: The Sphere, The University of Michigàn Radiation Laboratory Report 3648-1-T. To be published.

9. Stratton, J. A., Electromagnetic Theory, McGraw-Hill, New York (1941).

10. Darling, D. A., Some Relations Between Potential Theory and the Wave Equation, The University of Michigan Radiation Laboratory Report 2871-5-T (December 1960).

RONOLD W. P. KING

Dipoles in Dissipative Media

INTRODUCTION. The single antenna and arrays of antennas in a dissipative medium are analytically and experimentally interesting. Applications include communicating from a submerged submarine or from a mine shaft, and carrying out geophysical explorations with antennas directly imbedded in the earth or lowered into air-filled holes. Of more recent interest is the use of antennas as probes in the study of ionized regions and plasma sheaths by means of rockets. In general, the regions involved do not consist of a single, homogeneous and isotropic medium. There may be two distinct layers such as the sea or the earth and the air above it; alternatively, as in the interior of the earth, or in a plasma sheath in the ionosphere, the medium may have continuously varying properties or it may be stratified in one way or another. Experimental and theoretical studies of bare and insulated antennas and arrays in and over dissipative and dielectric media that are isotropic, have continuously varying properties, or are stratified in a regular manner are in progress. However, this report is limited to a study of the properties of single antennas of moderate length in an infinite, homogeneous, isotropic, dissipative medium.

Investigations that relate to antennas in dissipative media may be separated into two groups: (a) those which are concerned only with the electromagnetic field at large distances from a source, so that in the interest of simplicity, the antenna may be idealized far beyond practical availability; (b) those that treat the circuit properties of the antenna itself as well as the field that it generates. The source used in the former group usually consists of a Hertzian dipole or infinitesimal doublet that is represented mathematically by a periodically varying electric moment concentrated at a point. Physically, such a doublet may be visualized as made up of equal positive and negative charges oscillating back and forth in opposite directions along a line in the limit as the charges become infinite and the length of their path vanishes. In the second group are studies of thin cylindrical antennas and of biconical structures immersed in dissipative media. The antenna may be in direct contact with the conducting medium or it may be surrounded by an intervening layer of insulation. Note that a sufficiently short antenna is the physically realizable approximation of an infinitesimal doublet, insofar as the distant field is concerned.

An early study of the radiation of a Hertzian dipole immersed in a dissipative medium was made by C. T. Tai [1], who obtained the electromagnetic field and the Poynting vector in the well-known forms for doublets in air, but with the permittivity and propagation constants both complex instead of real. He noted that the total power transferred into a dissipative medium, as obtained from an integration of the normal component of the Poynting vector over a sphere with its center at the doublet, becomes infinite when the radius of the sphere is reduced to zero and concluded that "it is impossible to speak of the total power radiated by a Hertzian dipole when the latter is in direct contact with a dissipative medium." He then proceeded to analyze the doublet enclosed in an insulating sphere [2]. Actually, the power transferred across a spherical surface that encloses charges oscillating along a line is not obviously defined in the limit as the radius of the enclosing sphere vanishes. Indeed, it is shown in a later section that the power radiated by an electrically short dipole in a dissipative medium cannot be obtained by integrating the normal component of the Poynting vector over a spherical surface. It may be remarked in passing that the infinitesimal doublet has been used as an idealized source in numerous fairly recent studies of the electromagnetic field in a conducting half-space [3, 4, 5, 6], since the properties of a finite radiating system could in this way be avoided.

The integral equation and its formal solution for the current in a cylindrical antenna of finite length immersed in a dissipative medium was formulated by Tai [7] in a manner paralleling the analysis of King and Middleton [8] for an antenna in the air. The essential difference is that the previously real permittivity and propagation constant have become complex, with a resulting complication of the kernel and of integrals that occur in the iteration. Owing to a lack of tabulated functions, Tai did not evaluate his formal solution. Indeed, the analytical difficulty associated with the infinite admittance of the delta-function generator—which was not well understood at the time—led him to drop further work on the cylinder and turn his attention to the more tractable problem of the insulated biconical antenna in a dissipative medium. Tai's work on the dipole has been extended somewhat by Macrakis [9], Harrison [10], and Harrison and Denton [11] who made approximate evaluations of the impedance; more recently King and Harrison [12], and King, Harrison, and Denton [13], have carried out complete analyses of the circuit properties respectively of the half-wave dipole and of the electrically short antenna in a dissipative medium. These studies are based on the approximate method proposed by King [14] for the solution of the integral equation for the current in a cylindrical antenna. The present investigation is directed to the determination of the circuit properties of a thin cylindrical antenna of moderate but arbitrary length and to a consideration of the complete electromagnetic fields generated by the currents in such antennas.

REVIEW OF THE THEORY OF CYLINDRICAL ANTENNAS IN AIR. Since the analysis of the properties of an antenna in a dissipative medium is a considerable complication of the problem of the same antenna in a perfect dielectric, it is well to review briefly the extensive theory of the cylindrical antenna in air. A simple, physically realizable circuit consists of a cylindrical conductor, center-driven from a balanced two-wire transmission line, as shown in Fig. 1a. Since the currents in the antenna and in the line satisfy two simultaneous integral equations, their determination is a formidable problem. If the two conductors of the transmission line are very close together, the significant interaction of the line and the antenna is confined to a small region near their actual junction. For the line, this may be approximated by a reactive network of lumped elements characteristic of the line combined with the impedance Z_0 of the antenna also as a lumped element, as shown in Fig. 1b. From the

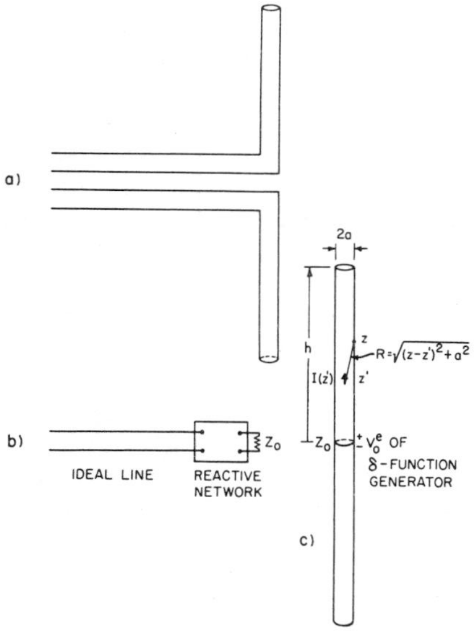

Figure 1 - a) Antenna driven from two-wire line
b) Approximately equivalent line
c) Approximate antenna

point of view of the antenna, the driving field across the end of the feeding line, which is distributed over a short length of the antenna, may be treated as an impressed field that is concentrated in a ring around the center of the antenna, in the form $E_z^e(z)\delta(z)$, where $\delta(z)$ is the Dirac delta function. Clearly, this emf is equivalent to a discontinuity in scalar potential across a pair of knife edges separated by a vanishingly small distance at $z = 0$. Such an idealized generator at the center of the antenna evidently includes an infinite capacitance across the knife edges, so that the input susceptance must also be infinite. It was shown by Wu and King [15] that in principle the infinite current associated with this capacitance may be subtracted out. Moreover, since it is confined to an extremely short distance adjacent to the knife edges, it is in practice automatically omitted from the total current when this is determined approximately by any method of solution that represents the current by a few terms in a series of continuous functions. Thus, the practical problem may be approximated by an isolated cylindrical antenna with a delta-function generator at its center, as shown in Fig. 1c. The impedance of this antenna, after the knife-edge current has been subtracted out or omitted, is the lumped load for a transmission line with a suitable terminal-zone network. The nature of the lumped, corrective networks required for different connections to various types of lines is discussed elsewhere [16].

The serious attempt to determine the distribution of current in a thin cylindrical antenna by analytical means rather than by assuming it empirically, as is still commonly done in the so-called emf method, begins with the work of L. V. King [17], and especially of Hallén [18] whose integral equation is the basis of most modern theories. For a perfectly conducting tube of very small wall thickness and radius a that extends from $z = -h$ to $z = h$, the integral equation may be expressed in the form

$$4\pi \mu_0^{-1} A_z(z) = \int_{-h}^{h} I(z') K(z, z') dz'$$

$$= \frac{-j4\pi}{\zeta_0} [C \cos k_0 z + \tfrac{1}{2} V_0^e \sin k_0 |z|] \quad (1)$$

where, as shown in Fig. 1c, $I(z')$ is the total axial current at z'. If $I(z)$ includes currents on the inner and outer surfaces of the tube, it follows that

$$I(h) = 0 \quad . \quad (2)$$

V_0^e at the center of the antenna is that of an idealized delta-function generator. $A_z(z)$ is the vector potential at the surface of the cylinder. It is in the Lorentz gauge that satisfies the Sommerfeld radiation condition. The kernel K is given by

$$K(z, z') = \frac{1}{2\pi} \int_{-\pi}^{\pi} \frac{e^{-jk_0 R}}{R} d\theta' \doteq \frac{e^{-jk_0 R_1}}{R_1} \quad (3)$$

where

$$R = \sqrt{(z-z')^2 + (2a \sin\frac{\theta'}{2})^2}, \quad R_1 = \sqrt{(z-z')^2 + a^2} \quad (4)$$

As usual, μ_0 is the permeability; $\zeta_0 \doteq 120\pi$ ohms is the characteristic impedance of free space; $k_0 = \omega/c$ is the wave number. C is a constant to be determined from the boundary condition (2).

Approximate solutions of integral equations substantially like (1) have been obtained by Hallén and others by a method of iteration which depends implicitly on the observation that the ratio $A_z(z)/I(z)$ of the vector potential to the current along the antenna is approximately constant and predominantly real. Solutions of this type appear in the form:

$$I(z) = \frac{j2\pi V_0^e}{\zeta_0\psi}\left[\frac{M_0(z) + M_1(z)/\psi + M_2(z)/\psi^2 + \cdots}{F_0(h) + F_1(h)/\psi + F_2(h)/\psi^2 + \cdots}\right] \tag{5}$$

where

$$M_0(z) = \sin k_0(h - |z|), \quad F_0(h) = \cos k_0 h . \tag{6}$$

The first-order terms, $M_1(z)$ and $F_1(h)$ may be expressed in terms of generalized sine and cosine integrals, the higher order terms are more complicated and must be evaluated by numerical methods. Unfortunately, even with the most sophisticated definition of the expansion parameter ψ, at least a second-order solution is required in order to obtain quantitative accuracy for antennas with electrical lengths in the range $0 \le k_0 h \le 2\pi$. A solution of this type is that of King and Middleton [8, 19] in which ψ is defined to be the absolute value of the function

$$\psi(z) = M_0^{-1}(z)\int_{-h}^{h} M_0(z')K(z,z')dz' \tag{6}$$

at the point where $M_0(z)$ has its greatest value in the range $0 \le z \le h$. Extensive computations of the impedances [19] of cylindrical antennas in the range of electrical half-lengths given by $0 \le k_0 h \le 7$ show the second-order King-Middleton values to be in good agreement with experiment. The distributions of current for selected lengths have also been computed, but the second-order formula is far too complicated for the convenient evaluation of electromagnetic fields. For this purpose the rather crude zero-order term has been used.

The quantitative accuracy of second-order results calculated from (5) in the King-Middleton form have been verified theoretically on the one hand by the comparable variational solutions of the integral equation (1) by Storer [20] and Tai [21]; and, on the other hand, by the detailed study of the integral equation with Fourier series methods by Duncan and Hinchey [22]. These investigators converted the integral equation into a set of simultaneous equations with the Fourier coefficients of the current distribution as the unknowns and then carried out calculations to the 25th-order. The numerical results for

$k_0 h = \pi/2$ and π and with $h/a = 60$ and 500π differ by only about 2% or less from the King-Middleton values. Significantly, even with a solution of such high order, there is still no sign of the large current associated with the knife edges at the driving point of the delta-function generator.

The reason for the rather slow convergence of the series in (5) even with a rather carefully selected expansion parameter has been traced by Wu [23] to the method of evaluation of the arbitrary constant C in terms of the boundary condition (2). Unfortunately, it is precisely at $z = h$ where the ratio of vector potential to current departs most from the assumed constant value—it actually becomes infinite at this point. It is the zero-order form of C, namely, $C = -(V_0^e/2)\tan k_0$ which leads to the zero-order distribution, $\sin k_0(h - |z|)$. It turns out that, for the input current and the current along most of the antenna, a better value of C would be: $C = -(V_0^e/2)\tan k_0(h + \delta)$ where δ is a small length that increases with the radius of the antenna. Evidently, such a value of C leads to a small non-vanishing zero-order current at $z = h$ in violation of (2). Primarily owing to the rather poor approximation in the zero-order value of C, the solution (5) even in second-order does not maintain its accuracy as the length of the antenna is increased. In order to handle specifically the very long antenna, Wu [23] developed an asymptotic solution of the integral equation (1) based on the Wiener-Hopf technique and a method of evaluating C which properly locates the distribution of current along the antenna, instead of requiring it to vanish at the end. The impedance of long antennas has been computed from the new formula by Beaton and Wu [24] for electrical lengths up to $k_0 h = 30$. The new theory does not yield a simple expression for the current for use in the evaluation of electromagnetic fields. However, the radiation field can be obtained directly from the Fourier transform of the current.

The major characteristics of the radiation field of dipoles in air may be determined with reasonable accuracy from the simple sinusoidal distribution that is the leading term in the iterated solutions for the current. However, this zero-order current has the serious defect that its value at the driving point is at best a rough approximation of the correct input current. Moreover, if it is used to calculate the radiated power with the Poynting-vector theorem, the result may be in error by as much as 50%, if it is assumed to apply to center-driven antennas with practically significant radii. It follows that even if the field patterns calculated from a sinusoidally distributed current are an acceptable approximation, the power apparently supplied to the antenna at its terminals and the power radiated may be grossly in error and mutually inconsistent. If the input admittance is known accurately from a higher-order theory, these difficulties are not serious for antennas in air, since the correct total power supplied is then available and it is known without further calculation that this is equal to the power radiated. When an antenna is immersed in a conducting medium the problem is much more complicated, since power is dissipated throughout the medium.

What is required for the quantitatively accurate respresentation of the circuit and field properties of dipole antennas and arrays is a formula for the current that is sufficiently simple to permit the evaluation of the field and at the same time sufficiently accurate to yield good approximations of the input admittance and of the radiated power. Such a formula has been derived by Storer [10] by variational methods and by King [14] with a modified iterative procedure. Since the former is not conveniently applied to more than one antenna, and a future study of coupled antennas in dissipative media is contemplated, attention is focussed on the latter, which is as useful for parallel arrays as for a single antenna.

The required relatively simple formula for the current is obtained as the approximate solution of a rearranged form of the integral equation (1), viz.,

$$4\pi\mu_0^{-1}[A_z(z) - A_z(h)] = \int_{-h}^{h} I(z')K_d(z, z')dz' = \frac{j4\pi}{\zeta_0 F_0(h)}[UF_{0z} + \tfrac{1}{2}V_0^e M_{0z}] \qquad (7)$$

where the new kernel is

$$K_d(z, z') = K(z, z') - K(h, z') \qquad (8)$$

and

$$U = \frac{-j\omega}{k_0} A_z(h) = \frac{-j\zeta_0}{4\pi} \int_{-h}^{h} I(z')K(h, z')dz \quad . \qquad (9)$$

The shorthand symbols

$$F_{0z} = \cos k_0 z - \cos k_0 h \quad . \qquad (10)$$

and

$$M_{0z} = \sin k_0 (h - |z|) \qquad (11)$$

are used, together with $F_0(h)$ which is defined in (6). The advantages of the rearranged form (7) of the integral equation (1) are several. The integral is, as indicated, proportional to the vector potential difference rather than to the vector potential itself, so that it vanishes at $z = h$ as does the current. The right-hand member of the equation is the sum of two terms that are individually related to well-known distributions of current and vector potential difference. The shifted cosine, F_{0z}, is a close approximation of the current and the vector potential difference along an unloaded receiving antenna in the plane wave front of a distant transmitting antenna. The sine term , M_{0z}, is the zero-order distribution along a center-driven antenna; it is much more exactly the distribution of both current and vector potential along an ideal two-wire transmission line with an open end at $z = h$ and a delta-function generator at $z = 0$. These facts suggest that F_{0z} may be interpreted as an approximation of the distribution of current or of the vector potential difference that is maintained by the interaction of the more widely separated elements in an antenna, whereas M_{0z} is the distribution maintained by a generator when, as in the transmission line, there is no significant interaction between widely separated current elements. This interpretation is confirmed by the fact that in (7) M_{0z} has the amplitude coefficient V_0^e, the actual driving voltage of the generator, whereas the coefficient U of F_{0z} is proportional to that part of the vector potential that has been subtracted out on the left because it is active along the entire antenna. In general and as a first approximation, a concentrated generator excites a current with the distribution M_{0z}; a distributed field excites a current with the distribution F_{0z}.

An approximate solution of (7) may be obtained if the integral is separated into two parts of which the one varies like M_{0z}, and the other like F_{0z}. This separation is easily accomplished by inspection, once the kernel has been expanded as follows:

$$K_d(z, z') = K_{dR}(z, z') + jK_{dI}(z, z') \tag{12a}$$

where

$$K_{dR}(z, z') = \frac{1}{2\pi}\left[\frac{\cos k_0 R}{R} - \frac{\cos k_0 R_h}{R_h}\right] d\theta' \doteq \frac{\cos k_0 R_1}{R_1} - \frac{\cos k_0 R_{1h}}{R_{1h}} \tag{12b}$$

and

$$K_{dI}(z, z') = -\frac{1}{2\pi}\int_{-\pi}^{\pi}\left[\frac{\sin k_0 R}{R} - \frac{\sin k_0 R_h}{R_h}\right] d\theta \doteq -\left[\frac{\sin k_0 R_1}{R_1} - \frac{\sin k_0 R_{1h}}{R_{1h}}\right]. \tag{12c}$$

The subscript h on R and R_1 denotes the values defined in (4) with $z = h$. Since R and R_1 become very small and $K_{dR}(z, z')$ correspondingly very large when z' is near z, it follows that the principal contributions to the part of the integral that has $K_{dR}(z, z')$ as kernel come from elements of current very near $z' = z$. This means that the part $A_{zR}(z)$ of $A_z(z)$ that depends on $K_{dR}(z, z')$ varies like $I(z)$. On the other hand, since $K_{dI}(z, z')$ is very small when z' is near z, the principal contributions to that part $A_{zI}(z)$ of $A_z(z)$ that depends on $K_{dI}(z, z')$ come from all the elements of current that are at some distance from z. If it is now assumed that the current is the sum of two parts,

$$I(z) = I_U(z) + I_V(z) \tag{13}$$

which by definition have the leading terms

$$I_U(z) \sim F_{0z} \;;\; I_V(z) \sim M_{0z} \tag{14}$$

it is clear that (7) may be separated reasonably into the following parts:

$$\int_{-h}^{h} [I_U(z')K_d(z,z') + jI_V(z')K_{dI}(z,z')]dz' \doteq \frac{j4\pi U}{\zeta_0 F_0(h)} F_{0z} \tag{15}$$

$$\int_{-h}^{h} I_V(z')K_{dR}(z,z')dz' \doteq \frac{j2\pi V_0^e}{\zeta_0 F_0(h)} M_{0z} \quad . \tag{16}$$

Each of these integral equations may now be solved by iteration in the King-Middleton manner, and their solutions for $I_U(z)$ and $I_V(z)$ combined in (18) to give $I(z)$. The formula for the current so obtained may then be substituted in (9) in order to evaluate the constant U in terms of V_0^e. The result is

$$I(z) = \frac{j2\pi V_0^e}{\zeta_0 \psi_{dR}} \left[\frac{\sin k_0(h-|z|) + T(h)(\cos k_0 z - \cos k_0 h)}{\cos k_0 h} \right] + \text{higher order terms} \tag{17}$$

The indeterminate form obtained when $k_0 h = \pi/2$ may be evaluated to give

$$I(z) = \frac{j2\pi V_0^e}{\zeta_0 \psi_{dR}} [\sin k_0|z| - 1 + T'(\tfrac{\lambda}{4})\cos k_0 z] + \text{higher order terms.} \tag{18}$$

The real expansion parameter ψ_{dR} and the complex constant $T(h)$ are expressed in terms of tabulated sine, cosine, and exponential integrals. They are functions of h/a and $k_0 h$. Explicit formulas and numerical values are in the literature [14, 25]. The higher order terms in (17) and (18) involve essentially the same integrals as the corresponding terms in the King-Middleton solution (5), but their contributions to $I(z)$, at least in the first- and second-order terms, are very much smaller. It follows that the quasi-zero-order terms in (17) and (18) have an accuracy that lies somewhere between the first- and the second-order solution in the form (5) in the range $0 \le k_0 h < 3\pi/2$. Moreover, the error is largely in the susceptive part of the current in a small region very near the driving point. As a specific example, consider a half-wave antenna with $h/a = 75$. The distribution of current as obtained from (18) is shown in Fig. 2. The corresponding admittance and impedance are

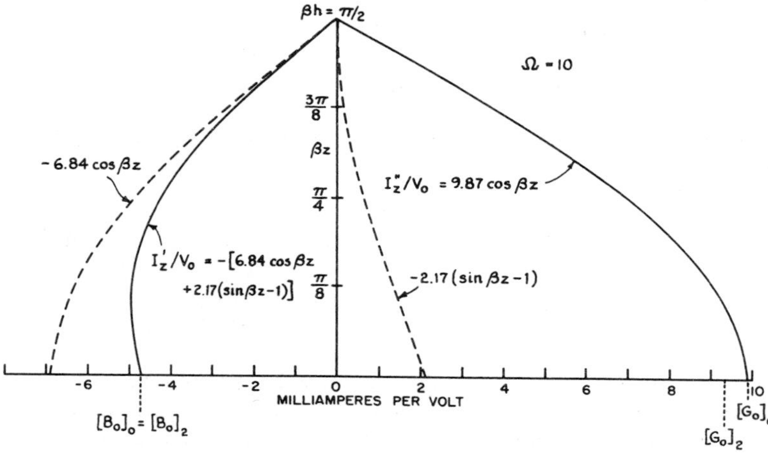

Figure 2. Quasi-zeroth-order current

$$[Y_0]_0 = (9.87 - j4.67) \times 10^{-3} \text{mhos}; \; [Z_0]_0 = 82.8 + j39.2 \text{ ohms}.$$

The second-order theoretical values (which are in good agreement with experiment) are:

$$[Y_0]_2 = (9.38 - j4.52) \times 10^{-3} \text{mhos}; \; [Z_0]_2 = 86.5 + j41.7 \text{ ohms}.$$

The values obtained by the emf method independent of h/a are

$$Y_{emf} = (10.22 - j5.94) \times 10^{-3} \text{mhos}; \; Z_{emf} = 73.13 + j42.5 \text{ ohms}.$$

As compared with the second-order value, the admittance given by (18) for the half-wave dipole is about 5% in error in the conductance, 3% in the susceptance; the corresponding errors in the values obtained by the emf method are 9% and 31%. For greater lengths the results of the emf method deteriorate very rapidly.

It may be concluded that (17) and (18) combine reasonable accuracy with simplicity in both the distribution of current and the admittance.

The Cylindrical Antenna in a Dissipative Medium

1. THE GENERAL CASE. The physical problem under consideration is to determine the current in a highly conducting cylindrical antenna immersed in a homogeneous, isotropic, dissipative medium of great extent. The antenna is center-driven, for example, from a shielded-pair

line that lies in the neutral plane. As with the antenna in air, it is convenient to approximate this configuration by an ideal line with the impedance of the antenna and a suitable terminal-zone network as a lumped load. For this purpose the antenna is imagined center-driven by a delta-function generator. In this case, the knife edges of the generator terminals are equivalent to an infinite admittance that includes both a capacitance and a conductance. The infinite current that is associated with the charging of the knife-edge capacitance and that crosses from one edge to the other by way of the dissipative medium may again be subtracted out in principle, since it is confined to an extremely short distance on each side of the generator. In practice, it is excluded from a solution that approximates the current in the antenna by a series of continuous functions.

The integral equation for a perfectly conducting cylindrical antenna immersed in an infinite, homogeneous, isotropic, dissipative medium and center-driven by a delta-function generator is formally like the equation for the same antenna in air if the complex dielectric factor $\xi = \epsilon_e - j\frac{\sigma_e}{\omega}$ is substituted for ϵ_0 and μ replaces μ_0. It is assumed that μ is real. This is equivalent to the replacement of the real wave number $k_0 = \omega\sqrt{\mu_0\epsilon_0}$ by the complex propagation constant

$$k = \beta - j\alpha = \omega\sqrt{\mu\epsilon_e}\,\sqrt{1 - jp} = \omega\sqrt{\mu\epsilon_e}[f(p) - jg(p)] \tag{19}$$

where $p = \sigma_e/\omega\epsilon_e$ and $f(p) = \cosh(\frac{1}{2}\sinh^{-1}p)$, $g(p) = \sinh(\frac{1}{2}\sinh^{-1}p)$. Note that $\mu = \mu_0\mu_r$, $\epsilon_e = \epsilon_0\epsilon_{er}$ where in the form (19) it is implied that $\epsilon_{er} > 0$. Tables of the functions $f(p)$ and $g(p)$ are available in the literature [26]. In addition, the real characteristic impedance $\zeta_0 = \sqrt{\mu_0/\epsilon_0} = \omega\mu_0/k_0$ is replaced by the complex value

$$\zeta = \sqrt{\frac{\mu}{\xi}} = \frac{\omega\mu}{k} = \zeta_\alpha e^{j\varphi} \tag{20a}$$

where

$$\zeta_\alpha = \frac{\omega\mu}{\sqrt{\beta^2 + \alpha^2}} , \quad \varphi = \tan^{-1}\frac{\alpha}{\beta} \tag{20b}$$

In these relations ϵ_e and σ_e are the real effective permittivity and conductivity, respectively. In terms of the complex permittivity $\epsilon = \epsilon' - j\epsilon''$ and the complex conductivity $\sigma = \sigma' - j\sigma''$ the real, effective values are given by

$$\epsilon_e = \epsilon_0\epsilon_{er} = \epsilon' - \frac{\sigma''}{\omega} , \quad \sigma_e = \sigma' + \omega\epsilon'' \tag{21}$$

In the rearranged form (7) the integral equation is

$$\int_{-h}^{h} I(z')K_{kd}(z,z')\,dz' = \frac{j4\pi\omega\mu}{kF_k(h)}\left[U_k F_{kz} + \tfrac{1}{2}V_0^e M_{kz}\right] \quad (22)$$

where

$$U_k = \frac{-j\omega\mu}{4\pi k}\int_{-h}^{h} I(z')K_k(h,z')\,dz' \quad (23)$$

$$F_k(h) = \cos kh = \cos\beta h \cosh\alpha h + j\sin\beta h \sin\alpha h \quad (24)$$

$$F_{kz} = \cos kz - \cos kh$$

$$= (\cos\beta z \cosh\alpha z - \cos\beta h \cosh\alpha h) + j(\sin\beta z \sinh\alpha z - \sin\beta h \sinh \quad (25)$$

$$M_{kz} = \sin k(h - |z|)$$

$$= \sin\beta(h - |z|)\cosh\alpha(h - |z|) - j\cos\beta(h - |z|)\sinh\alpha(h - |z|) \quad (26)$$

The kernels are given by

$$K_{kd}(z,z') = K_k(z,z') - K_k(h,z') \doteq \frac{e^{-jkR_1}}{R_1} - \frac{e^{-jkR_{1h}}}{R_{1h}} \quad (27)$$

The difference kernel may be separated into two parts as follows

$$K_{kR}(z,z') = K_{kR}(z,z') + jK_{kI}(z,z') \quad (28a)$$

where

$$K_{kR}(z,z') = \frac{\cos\beta R_1 \cosh\alpha R_1}{R_1} - \frac{\cos\beta R_h \cosh\alpha R_h}{R_h} \quad (28b)$$

$$K_{kI}(z,z') = -R_1^{-1}[\sin\beta R_1(\cosh\alpha R_1 - \sinh\alpha R_1) + j\cos\beta R_1 \sinh\alpha R_1]$$

$$+ R_{1h}^{-1}[\sin\beta R_{1h}(\cosh\alpha R_{1h} - \sinh\alpha R_{1h}) + j\cos\beta R_{1h}\sinh\alpha R_{1h}] \quad (29c)$$

Note that $K_{kI}(z,z')$ is not real when $\alpha \neq 0$; it does reduce to the real $K_{dI}(z,z')$ when $\alpha = 0$. This equation (22) has a much more complicated kernel than (7) and the right member is also more involved, since the distribution terms F_{kz} and M_{kz} are complex, and contain the additional parameter α .

The type of solution desired for the current in an antenna in a dissipative medium is one corresponding to (17) for the antenna in air that provides good approximations of both the distribution of current and the admittance in a form that is sufficiently simple to permit the direct integration of the integrals for the electromagnetic field. It is in order to obtain such a solution that the form (22) of the integral equation was chosen. The approximate solution of this equation may be carried out in a manner closely paralleling the procedure described for the antenna in air. Indeed, the kernel (27) has already been separated into two parts such that the one $K_{kR}(z, z')$, is very large when z' is near z so that the principal contributions to $Z_{zR}(z)$ are from the currents near z; and the other, $K_{kI}(z, z')$, is relatively small near $z' = z$ so that the principal contributions to $A_{zI}(z)$ are from currents at some distance from z. As before in (13), the current may be expressed as the sum of two terms and the integral equation appropriately separated into two parts as in (15) and (16):

$$\int_{-h}^{h} [I_U(z')K_{kd}(z, z') + jI_V(z')K_{kI}(z, z')]dz' \doteq \frac{j4\pi kU_k}{\omega\mu F_k(h)} F_{kz} \tag{29}$$

$$\int_{-h}^{h} I_V(z')K_{kR}(z, z')dz \doteq \frac{j2\pi kV_0^e}{\omega\mu F_k(h)} M_{kz} \quad . \tag{30}$$

These equations may be solved separately by iteration and the resulting solutions added to obtain $I(z)$ in terms of V_0^e and U_k. U_k may then be expressed in terms of V_0^e with the substitution of $I(z)$ in (24). The solution for the current is

$$I(z) = \frac{j2\pi kV_0^e}{\omega\mu\psi_{kR}\cos kh} [\sin k(h - |z|) + T_k(h)(\cos kz - \cos kh)] + \begin{Bmatrix}\text{higher}\\ \text{order}\\ \text{terms}\end{Bmatrix} \tag{31}$$

where ψ_{kR} is a complex expansion parameter and $T_k(h)$ a complex constant that depends on h/a, βh, and α/β. Unfortunately, the integral functions that occur in $T_k(h)$ are not in general available in tabulated form. However, explicit evaluation has been carried out for the half-wave dipole [12] in a moderately conducting medium such that $\beta h = \pi/2$ and $\alpha h < 1$ and for the electrically short dipole [13] in an arbitrary medium defined by $\beta h \leq 0.3$, $\alpha \leq \beta$. Computations of the admittance of long antennas from Wu's formula [24] for a dissipative medium are in progress.

2. THE HALF-WAVE DIPOLE. For the half-wave dipole, the approximations $\cosh \alpha h \doteq 1$ and $\sinh \alpha h \doteq \alpha h$ are made and (31) reduced to the form

$$\frac{I(z)}{V_0^e\sqrt{\epsilon_{er}}} = \frac{-j2\pi(1-j\alpha/\beta)}{\zeta_0\psi_{kR}}[\sin\beta|z| - 1 + T'_k(\tfrac{\lambda}{4})\cos\beta z]$$

$$+ \text{ higher order terms} \tag{32}$$

where

$$T'_k(\tfrac{\lambda}{4}) = -[1 + T_k(\tfrac{\lambda}{4})][\frac{1-j\alpha h}{j\alpha h}] \ . \tag{33}$$

The normalized current $I(z)/V_0^e\sqrt{\epsilon_{er}}$ is shown in Fig. 3 with $I(z) = I''_z + jI'_z$ as a function of z with $2\alpha/\beta = \sigma_e/\omega\epsilon_0\epsilon_{er}$ as a parameter. The normalized impedance $Z\sqrt{\epsilon_{er}}$ and admittance $Y/\sqrt{\epsilon_{er}}$ are shown in Fig. 4a. Both the distributions of current and the impedance are in agreement with experimental results obtained by Iizuka. It may be added that measurements have been made with larger values of $\sigma_e/\omega\epsilon_0\epsilon_{er}$ than those used in the theoretical calculations represented in Fig. 4a. These indicate that the resistance curve in Fig. 4a reaches a maximum as $\sigma_e/\omega\epsilon_0\epsilon_{er}$ is increased further and then bends down to approach zero. The corresponding distributions of current change from concave outward as in Fig. 3 to concave inward as $\sigma_e/\omega\epsilon_0\epsilon_{er}$ is increased.

The normalized impedance of a half-wave dipole in a dissipative medium in the form $Z\Delta$ is shown in Fig. 4b as a function of α/β. It has been evaluated from Wu's asymptotic theory [23] with complex

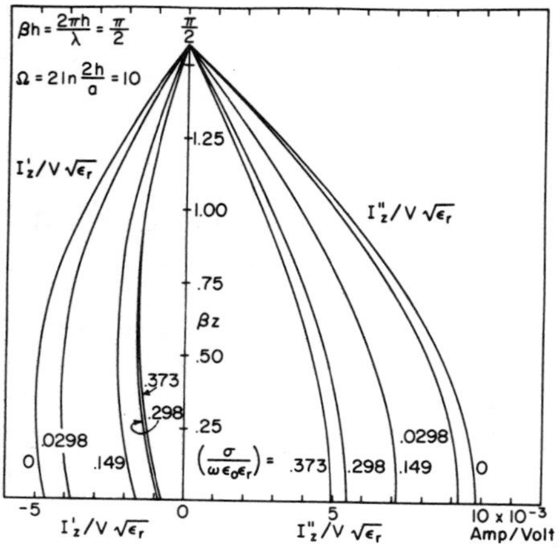

Figure 3. Normalized current $I_z = I''_z + j\,I'_z$ in half-wave dipole in medium with conductivity σ and dielectric constant $\epsilon = \epsilon_0\epsilon_r$

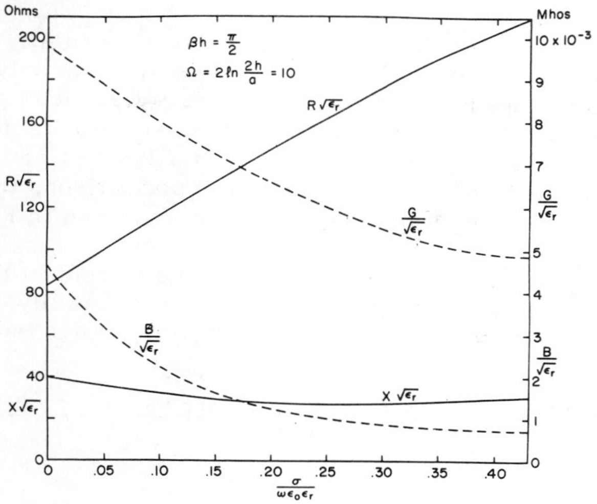

Figure 4a. Impedance and admittance of a dipole with electrical half length $\beta h = \pi/2$ when immersed in a medium with conductivity σ and dielectric constant $\epsilon = \epsilon_0 \epsilon_r$; $\beta = \omega\sqrt{\mu\epsilon} = 2\pi/\lambda$

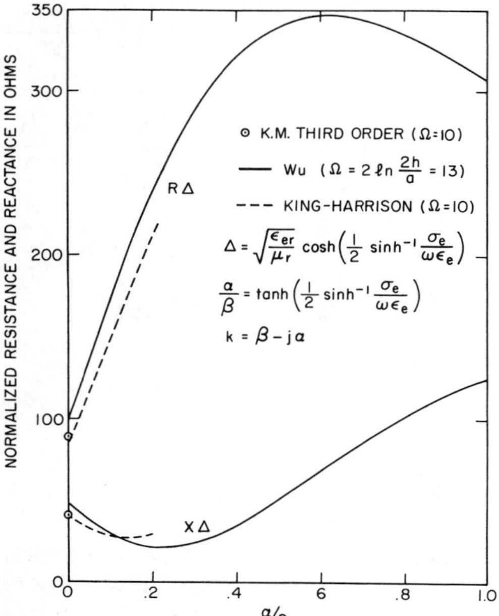

Figure 4b. Normalized impedance of half-wave dipole in a dissipative medium

$k = \beta - j\alpha$. The dimensionless parameter $\Delta = (\epsilon_{er}/\mu_r)^{\frac{1}{2}} f(p)$ where $f(p)$ and p are defined following (19). Wu's formula is intended for electrically long antennas, but yields values that are only about 6% too large when $\beta h = \pi/2$ and $\Omega = 2\ln(2h/a) = 13$. It is seen in Fig. 4b that the resistance reaches a maximum when α/β is near 0.6. Note that as $\sigma_e/\omega\epsilon_0\epsilon_{er} \to \infty$, $\Delta \to \zeta_0\sqrt{\sigma_e/2\omega\mu} \to \infty$; it follows that in this limit $Z \to 0$. For purposes of comparison, the normalized resistance and reactance from Fig. 4a are also shown in Fig. 4b.

3. THE ELECTRICALLY SHORT ANTENNA. The current in the electrically short antenna defined by $\alpha h < 1$, $\beta h < 1$ is readily obtained from (31) as a series in powers of βh and αh . The first few terms are:

$$I(z) = \frac{j2\pi k h V_0^e}{\zeta\psi_{dR}} \left\{ \left(1 + \frac{k^2h^2}{3}\right)\left(1 - \frac{|z|}{h}\right) + \frac{(3\ln 2 - 1)k^2h^2 - jk^3h^3}{3(\Omega - 3)}\left(1 - \frac{z^2}{h^2}\right) \right\} \tag{34}$$

The corresponding admittance is

$$Y_0(k) = G_0(k) + jB_0(k) \tag{35a}$$

where

$$G_0(k) = \frac{2\pi}{\zeta_e\psi_{dR}} \left\{ \frac{2\alpha}{\beta}\left[\beta h + (2\beta^3 h^3 F/3)\left(1 - \frac{\alpha^2}{\beta^2}\right)\right] + \frac{\beta^4 h^4}{3(\Omega - 3)}\left(1 - 10\frac{\alpha^2}{\beta^2} + 5\frac{\alpha^4}{\beta^4}\right) \right\} \tag{35b}$$

$$B_0(k) = \frac{2\pi}{\zeta_e\psi_{dR}} \left\{ \beta h\left(1 - \frac{\alpha^2}{\beta^2}\right) + \frac{\beta^3h^3F}{3}\left(1 - 6\frac{\alpha^2}{\beta^2} + \frac{\alpha^4}{\beta^4}\right) - \frac{\beta^4h^4\alpha}{3(\Omega - 3)\beta}\left(5 - 10\frac{\alpha^2}{\beta^2} + \frac{\alpha^4}{\beta^4}\right) \right\} \tag{35c}$$

In these formulas

$$F = 1 + \frac{3\ln 2 - 1}{\Omega - 3} = 1 + \frac{1.08}{\Omega - 3} \tag{36}$$

and

$$\Omega = 2\ln(2h/a) . \tag{37}$$

Also

$$\zeta = \frac{\omega\mu}{k} , \quad \zeta_e = \frac{\omega\mu}{\beta} = \frac{\sqrt{\mu/\epsilon_e}}{f(p)} = \frac{\zeta_0}{\Delta} \tag{38}$$

where $f(p)$ is defined following (19). These expressions are general and apply to all values of α and β that satisfy the relations $\beta h \leq 0.3$ $\alpha h \leq 0.3$. The fact that it is necessary to retain terms up to and including fourth powers of the small quantity βh is an indication of the complicated nature of the admittance of an antenna in a dissipative medium with no restriction on α . The reason is obvious: if $\alpha = 0$

as in a perfect dielectric, the leading terms are

$$G_0(k_0) \doteq \frac{2\pi\beta^4 h^4}{3\zeta_e \psi_{dR}(\Omega-3)} \qquad B_0(k_0) \doteq \frac{2\pi\beta h}{\zeta_e \psi_{dR}} . \tag{39}$$

On the other hand, when $\alpha = \beta$ as in salt water,

$$G_0(k) \doteq \frac{4\pi\beta h}{\zeta_e \psi_{dR}} \qquad B_0(k) \doteq \frac{4\pi F\beta^3 h^3}{3\zeta_e \psi_{dR}} \tag{40}$$

where F is defined in (36). Note that $G_0(k_0)$ in (39) is a pure radiation conductance; it is very small compared with the susceptance. In (40) $G_0(k)$ is determined entirely by dissipation in the medium, the contribution from radiation is negligible; $G_0(k)$ is very large compared with $B_0(k)$. It is clear from the general expression (35a) that the radiation conductance predominates for only a very small range of α near zero. This indicates that the short dipole behaves as a radiating antenna only when α is very small; for larger values it is essentially a pair of electrodes.

The normalized impedance $\frac{Z_0(k)}{\zeta_e} = \frac{R_0(k)}{\zeta_e} + \frac{X_0(k)}{\zeta_e}$ and admittance $Y_0(k)\zeta_e = G_0(k)\zeta_e + jB_0(k)\zeta_e$ of a short antenna with $\beta h = 0.3$ and $\Omega = 10$ are shown in Fig. 5 as a function of α/β. The curves for $R_0(k)\zeta_e$ and $G_0(k)\zeta_e$ are also shown on a logarithmic scale in Fig. 6 in order to show their extremely rapid rise in the range of very small values of α/β. Note that $R_0(k)/\zeta_e$ has a maximum between $\alpha/\beta = 0.5$ and 0.6, and that in general $\alpha/\beta = \tanh(\frac{1}{2}\sinh^{-1}\frac{\sigma_e}{\omega\epsilon_e})$.

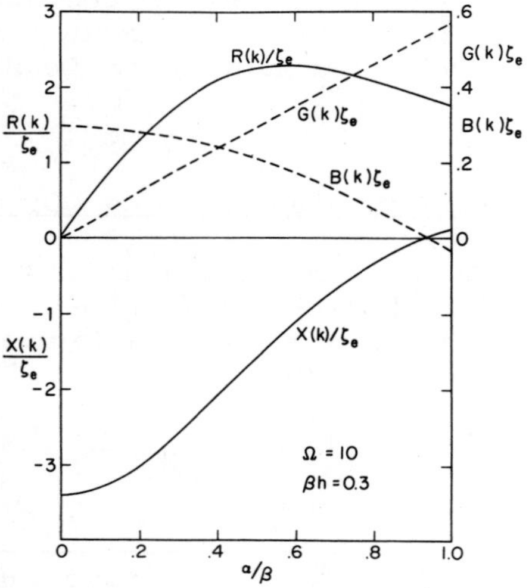

Figure 5. Normalized impedance and admittance of short antenna in dissipative medium

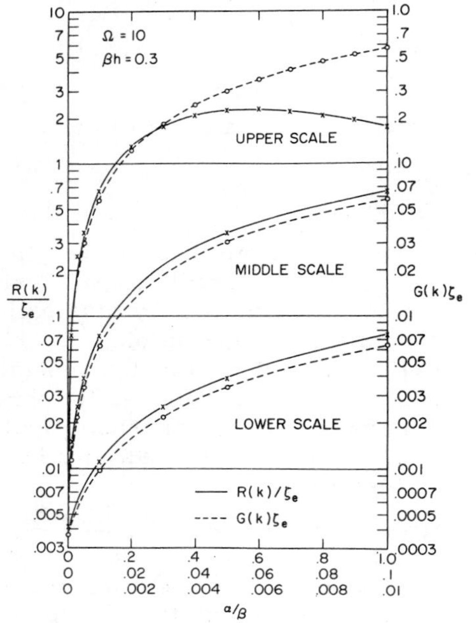

Figure 6. Normalized conductance and resistance of short antenna in dissipative medium

If the medium in which the admittance $Y_0(k)$ is measured is an ionized region such as the ionosphere, the conductance $G_0(k)$ and the susceptance $B_0(k)$ may be related directly to the concentration of electrons and to their collision frequency. Details are given elsewhere [13].

The Electromagnetic Field of an Antenna in a Dissipative Medium

1. THE GENERAL CASE AND THE FIELD AT DISTANT POINTS. The electromagnetic field of a cylindrical antenna of half-length h with a total axial current $I(z)$ when immersed in a dissipative medium may be determined from the vector potential

$$A_z(r) = \frac{\mu}{4\pi}\int_{-h}^{h} I(z')\,\frac{e^{-jkR}}{R}\,dz' \tag{41}$$

where

$$\begin{aligned} R &= \sqrt{(z-z')^2 + \rho^2 + a^2 - 2a\cos\theta'} \\ &\doteq \sqrt{(z-z')^2 + \rho^2} \end{aligned} \tag{42}$$

when expressed in the cylindrical coordinates ρ, θ, z . The formula (41) may be used to determine the vector potential at any point except within distances of the ends of the antenna comparable with its radius a . At distances $r = \sqrt{z^2 + \rho^2}$ from the center of the antenna that are large compared with the half-length h , that is, when

$$r^2 \gg h^2 \quad , \quad R \doteq r - z' \cos \theta \ , \tag{43}$$

an approximate formula for the vector potential in the radiation zone may be used. This is

$$A_z^r(r) = \frac{\mu}{4\pi} \frac{e^{-jkr}}{r} \int_{-h}^{h} I(z') e^{jkz'\cos\theta} dz' \tag{44}$$

The corresponding non-vanishing cylindrical components of the magnetic and electric fields are given by

$$B_\theta(r) = -\frac{\partial A_z(r)}{\partial \rho} \ ; \quad R_\rho(r) = \frac{jk^2}{\omega} \frac{\partial^2 A_z(r)}{\partial \rho \partial z} \ ; \quad E_z(r) = \frac{-jk^2}{\omega} \frac{1}{\rho} \frac{\partial}{\partial \rho} \rho \frac{\partial A_z(r)}{\partial \rho} \tag{45}$$

In the radiation zone the significant components are conveniently expressed in the spherical coordinates, r, Θ, Φ . They are given by

$$B_\Phi^r(r) = -jkA_z^r(r) \sin \Theta \ ; \qquad E_\Theta^r(r) = -j\omega A_z^r(r) \sin \Theta \ . \tag{46}$$

In order to determine the complete electromagnetic field it is necessary to evaluate the integral in (41) or at least the derivatives of this integral required in (45). For the radiation field at distances that satisfy (43) it is sufficient to evaluate the simpler integral in (44). A simple and reasonably accurate representation of the current in a cylindrical antenna of zero to moderate length is that given in (31). Unfortunately, if this distribution is substituted in (41) and (45) is evaluated, one of the three terms involved cannot be obtained in closed form. On the other hand, the integration of (44) is straightforward. With (46) the result is

$$\frac{\omega}{k} B^r(\vec{r}) = E_\Theta^r(\vec{r}) = \frac{V_0 e^{-jkr}}{\psi_{kr} r \cos kh} [F_m(\Theta, kh) + T_k(h) G_m(\Theta, kh)] \tag{47}$$

where

$$F_m(\Theta, kh) = \frac{\cos(kh \cos \Theta) - \cos kh}{\sin \Theta} \tag{48}$$

$$G_m(\Theta, kh) = \frac{\sin kh \cos(kh \cos \Theta) \cos \Theta - \cos kh \sin(kh \cos \Theta)}{\sin \Theta \cos \Theta} \tag{49}$$

These expressions can be separated into real and imaginary parts and the electric and magnetic fields evaluated. However, since the amplitude decreases as $e^{-\alpha r}/r$, it is evident that the range of r in which the field is significant and in which (43) is satisfied is not great unless α is sufficiently small to satisfy the conditions

$$\alpha^2h^2 \ll 1 \; , \quad \sinh \alpha h \doteq \alpha h \; , \quad \cosh \alpha h \doteq 1 \; . \tag{50}$$

Nevertheless, the general directional properties of the field not very close to the antenna may be determined from (48) and (49) even when $\alpha = \beta$. When (50) is satisfied the field factors defined in (48) and (49) become somewhat simpler. Specifically,

$$F_m(\Theta, kh) = F_{mr}(\Theta, kh) + j\alpha h F_{mi}(\Theta, kh) \tag{51a}$$

where

$$F_{mr}(\Theta, kh) = \frac{\cos(\beta h \cos \Theta) - \cos \beta h}{\sin \Theta}$$

$$F_{mi}(\Theta, kh) = \frac{\sin(\beta h \cos \Theta) \cos \Theta - \sin \beta h}{\sin \Theta} \; . \tag{51b}$$

Similarly,

$$G_m(\Theta, kh) = G_{mr}(\Theta, kh) + j\alpha h F_{mi}(\Theta, kh) \tag{52a}$$

where

$$G_{mr}(\Theta, kh) = \frac{\sin \beta h \cos(\beta h \cos \Theta) \cos \Theta - \cos \beta h \sin(\beta h \cos \Theta)}{\sin \Theta \cos \Theta} \tag{52b}$$

$$G_{mi}(\Theta, kh) = \sin \beta h \sin(\beta h \cos \Theta) \tan \Theta \; . \tag{52c}$$

Also in (47),

$$\cos kh = \cos \beta h + j\alpha h \sin \beta h \; . \tag{53}$$

When $\beta h = \pi/2$, (51) and (52) become

$$F_m(\Theta, \tfrac{1}{2}\pi - j\alpha h) = F_m(\Theta, \tfrac{\pi}{2}) + j\alpha h \left[\frac{\sin(\frac{\pi}{2} \cos \Theta) \cos \Theta - 1}{\sin \Theta}\right] \tag{54a}$$

$$G_m(\Theta, \tfrac{1}{2}\pi - j\alpha h) = F_m(\Theta, \tfrac{\pi}{2}) + j\alpha h \sin(\tfrac{\pi}{2} \cos \Theta) \tan \Theta \tag{54b}$$

where

$$F_m(\Theta, \frac{\pi}{2}) = \frac{\cos(\frac{\pi}{2}\cos\Theta)}{\sin\Theta} \qquad (54c)$$

Since from (53) $\cos kh \doteq j\alpha h$, it follows with the readily verified approximation (that is valid only when $\beta h = \pi/2$)

$$\tan\Theta \sin(\frac{\pi}{2}\cos\Theta) \doteq \frac{\pi}{2} F_m(\Theta, \frac{\pi}{2}) \qquad (55)$$

and the definition (33), that (47) becomes

$$E^r_\Theta \doteq \frac{V_0^e e^{-(\alpha + j\beta)r}}{\psi_{kr} r} \left[H_m(\Theta, \frac{\pi}{2}) + T'_k(\frac{\lambda}{4}) \left(\frac{1 - j\alpha h \pi/2}{1 - j\alpha h} \right) F_m(\Theta, \frac{\pi}{2}) \right] \qquad (56a)$$

where

$$H_m(\Theta, \frac{\pi}{2}) = \frac{\cos\Theta - \sin(\frac{\pi}{2}\cos\Theta)}{\sin\Theta\cos\Theta} \doteq (1 - \frac{\pi}{2}) F_m(\Theta, \frac{\pi}{2}). \qquad (56b)$$

This is the complete field generated by the current (32). Note that $H_m(\Theta, \frac{\pi}{2})$ is the part of the field contributed by the component of current $\sin\beta|z| - 1$. The factor $(1 - j\alpha h\,\pi/2)/(1 - j\alpha h)$ in (57) as compared with (32) is a consequence of the attenuation of the field over the small distances $z'\cos\Theta$ in $R = r - z'\cos\Theta$. The field factors $F_m(\Theta, \frac{\pi}{2})$ and $H_m(\Theta, \frac{\pi}{2})$ are shown in Fig. 7.

If the approximate relation on the right in (56b) is substituted in

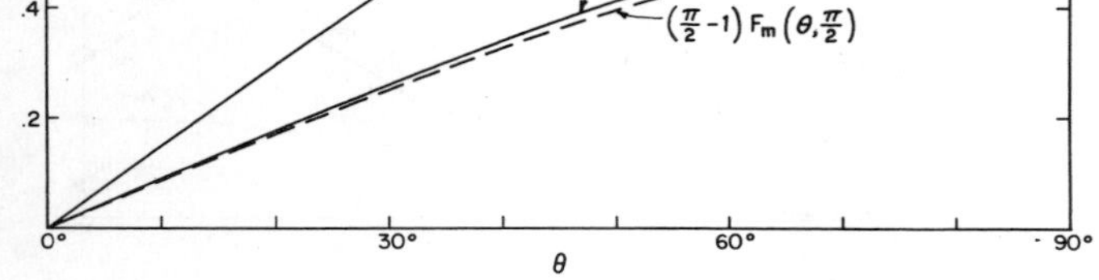

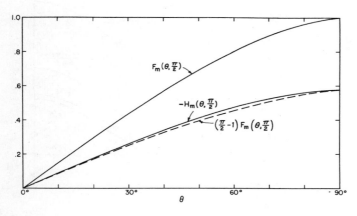

Figure 7. The field functions $F_m(\theta, \frac{\pi}{2})$ and $H_m(\theta, \frac{\pi}{2})$

(56a), the approximate electric field is given by

$$E_{\Theta}^{r} = - \frac{V_0^e e^{-(\alpha + j\beta)r}}{\psi_{kr} r} \left[1 - \frac{\pi}{2} + T_k'\left(\frac{\lambda}{4}\right)\left(\frac{1 - j\alpha h\,\pi/2}{1 - j\alpha h}\right)\right] F_m\left(\Theta, \frac{\pi}{2}\right). \quad (57)$$

This field would be maintained accurately by the current

$$\frac{I(z)}{V_0^e \sqrt{\epsilon_{er}}} = \frac{-j2\pi(1 - j\alpha/\beta)}{\zeta_0 \psi_{kr}} \left[1 - \frac{\pi}{2} + T_k'\left(\frac{\lambda}{4}\right)\right] \cos \beta z , \quad (58)$$

and only approximately by (32). Note that in (32) the input current is proportional to $[-1 + T_k'(\frac{\lambda}{4})]$ whereas in (58) it is proportional to $[1 - \frac{\pi}{2} + T_k'(\frac{\lambda}{4})]$. Since the former gives the approximately correct value, the latter is evidently in error. The explanation for this discrepancy is clear. The approximately correct current in (32) yields the approximately correct field in (56a) and the approximately correct radiated power. If the current is represented by a purely cosinusoidal distribution, its amplitude can be adjusted so that the input current is approximately correct with the factor $[-1 + T_k'(\frac{\lambda}{4})]$, or so that the field and the power radiated are approximately correct with the factor $[1 - \frac{\pi}{2} + T_k'(\frac{\lambda}{4})]$. In the former case the power radiated is too small, in the latter case the input current is too large.

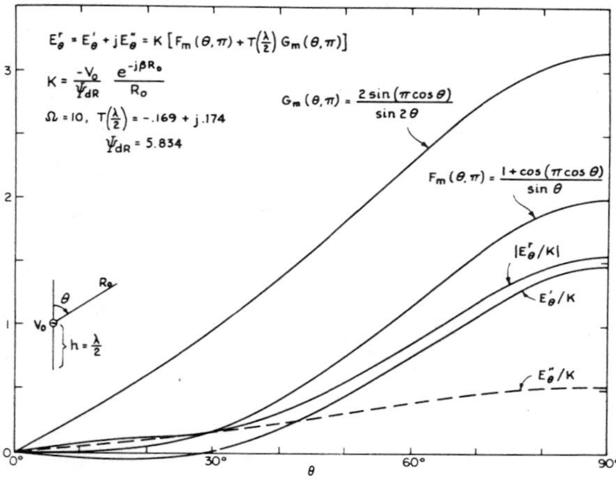

Figure 8. Vertical field pattern of full-wave center-driven antenna

Graphs of the electric field defined in (47) when $\beta h = \pi$, $\alpha = 0$, $h/a = 75$ are shown in Fig. 8. It may be concluded from the forms of (54a) and (54b) that the field patterns when αh is small do not differ greatly from those when $\alpha = 0$. Significant differences may be anticipated when αh is not small compared with one, in particular, when α is of the same order of magnitude as β. For their evaluation the complex parameter $T_k(h)$ must be computed.

2. THE FIELD NEAR THE DIPOLE; APPROXIMATE CURRENTS AND CYLINDRICAL COORDINATES. In order to determine the electromagnetic field nearer the antenna than is permitted by the condition (43) it is necessary to carry out extensive numerical computations for individual cases or to make approximations in the distribution of current in order to obtain an integrable form. Fortunately, the latter procedure is straightforward, since the term $\sin k(h-|z|)$ in the general expression for the current (31) is integrable when substituted in (41) and (45). However, it is not to be expected that a satisfactory approximation can be achieved if the entire term $T_k(h)(\cos kz - \cos kh)$ in (31) is simply omitted. In particular, it is essential that the total power supplied to the antenna be a good approximation even if the distribution of current along the antenna is somewhat in error. This may be achieved by a rearrangement of (31) in the following manner:

$$I(z) = [I(0)/A(0)][A(z) + B(z)] \tag{59a}$$

where

$$A(z) = \left[1 + T_k(h)\left(\frac{1 - \cos kh}{\sin kh}\right)\right]\left[\frac{\sin k(h-|z|)}{\cos kh}\right] \tag{59b}$$

and

$$B(z) = T_k(h)\left[\cos kz - 1 + \left(\frac{1 - \cos kh}{\sin kh}\right)\sin k|z|\right]. \tag{59c}$$

Note that

$$I(0) = V_0^e Y_0(k) = \left(\frac{j2\pi k V_0^e}{\omega \mu \psi_{kr}}\right) A(0) \tag{59d}$$

where $Y_0(k)$ is the admittance. The two parts of the current, $A(z)$ and $B(z)$, are chosen so that $B(0) = 0$ and, hence, contributes only to the distribution along the antenna and not at all to the input current and the admittance, which are determined entirely by $A(0)$. The plan is to neglect $B(z)$ in the integration to determine the electromagnetic field since it contains the term that has not been integrated in closed form. The anticipated error is, therefore, that made by the omission of $B(z)$. Investigation shows that $A(z)$ along is quite a good approximation when $|I(0)| \geq |I(z)|$ as when $\beta h \leq \pi/2$ with $\alpha = 0$ and very poor when $\beta h \sim \pi$ with $\alpha = 0$. When $\beta h = \pi/2$ and $(\alpha h)^2 \ll 1$, $B(z) = T_k(\frac{\lambda}{4})[\cos\beta z + \sin\beta|z| - 1]$. The contribution by this component of current, shown shaded in Fig. 9 when $\alpha = 0$, is seen to be quite small. Similarly, when $\beta h < 1$,

$$B(z) = T_k(h)\,\frac{k^2h^2}{2}\left[(1 - \frac{z^2}{h^2}) - (1 - \frac{|z|}{h})\right]$$

. This is the very small difference between triangular and parabolic distributions when required to have the same value at $z = 0$. Since $|I(0)|$ increases rapidly relative to $|I(z)|$ along the antenna when α is made larger, the range of βh over which the contribution by $B(z)$ in (59a) is negligible expands with increasing α . If $B(z)$ is neglected in (59a) the approximate distribution is simply

$$I(z) \doteq I(0)\,\frac{\sin k(h-|z|)}{\sin kh} \tag{60}$$

where $I(0)$ is given in (59d).

When (60) is substituted in (41) the vector potential itself cannot be obtained in closed form. However, the derivatives required in (45) may be expressed as follows [27]:

$$B_\theta(\vec{r}) = \frac{j\mu I(0)}{4\pi\rho}\left[e^{-jkR_{1h}} + e^{-jkR_{2h}} - 2\cos kh\, e^{-jkr}\right] \tag{61}$$

$$E_\rho(\vec{r}) = \frac{j\omega\mu I(0)}{4\pi k\rho}\left[\frac{z-h}{R_{1h}}e^{-jkR_{1h}} + \frac{z+h}{R_{2h}}e^{-jkR_{2h}} - \frac{2z}{r}\cos kh\, e^{-jkr}\right] \tag{62}$$

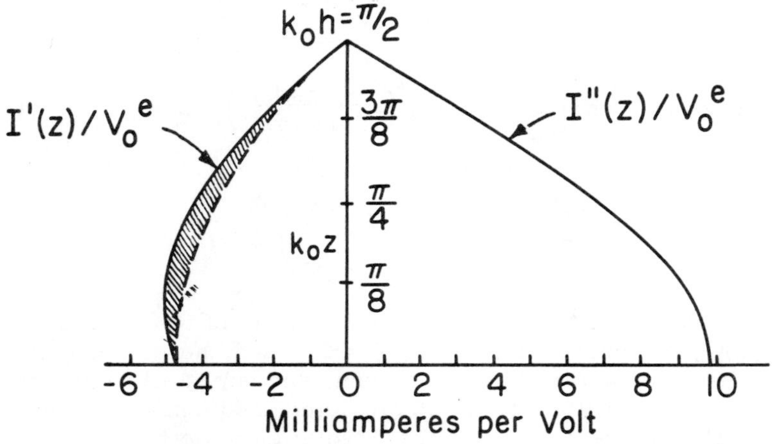

Figure 9. Current distribution along a half-wave dipole. The broken curve is $I_0' \cos k_0 z$.

$$E_z(\vec{r}) = \frac{-j\omega\mu I(0)}{4\pi k}\left[\frac{e^{-jkR_{1h}}}{R_{1h}} + \frac{e^{-jkR_{2h}}}{R_{2h}} - \frac{2}{r}\cos kh\, e^{-jkr}\right] \quad (63)$$

where

$$R_{1h} = \sqrt{(z-h)^2 + \rho^2}\ , \quad R_{2h} = \sqrt{(z+h)^2 + \rho^2}\ , \quad r = \sqrt{z^2 + \rho^2}\ . \quad (64)$$

For the part of the current represented by (60) these expressions are accurate and give the complete electromagnetic field within distances of the cylindrical antenna comparable with the radius a. Since all distances are measured from the axis rather than the surface of the cylinder, these expressions have no meaning for $\rho < a$. They are useful particularly for determining the near field of antennas with $\beta h \leq \pi/2$.

If (61)-(63) are multiplied by $e^{j\omega t}$, the real part is the instantaneous electromagnetic field. However, the formulas so obtained permit no simple physical interpretation other than that the ends and center of the antenna may be regarded as the origins of complicated outward-traveling disturbances. A somewhat simpler picture may be obtained for the half-wave dipole in spheroidal coordinates and for the electrically short antenna in spherical coordinates.

3. THE HALF-WAVE DIPOLE; SPHEROIDAL COORDINATES*. When $\beta h = \pi/2$ the normalized distribution of current in (60) is

$$\frac{I(z)}{I(0)} = \frac{\cos\beta z \cosh\alpha(h-|z|)}{\cosh\alpha h} + j\,\frac{\sin\beta|z|\sinh\alpha(h-|z|)}{\cosh\alpha h}\ . \quad (65)$$

The associated distribution of charge per unit length is obtained

$$q(z) = \operatorname{Re} q(z) + j \operatorname{Im} q(z) = \frac{j}{\omega}\frac{dI(z)}{dz} \quad (66a)$$

where in normalized form,

$$\operatorname{Re}\left[\frac{c\,q(z)}{I(0)}\right] = \frac{\beta\cos\beta z\sinh\alpha(h-|z|) - \alpha\sin\beta|z|\cosh\alpha(h-|z|)}{\beta\cosh\alpha h} \quad (66b)$$

$$\operatorname{Im}\left[\frac{c\,q(z)}{I(0)}\right] = -\left[\frac{\sin\beta|z|\cosh\alpha(h-|z|) + \alpha\cos\beta z\sinh\alpha(h-|z|)}{\beta\cosh\alpha h}\right]. \quad (66c)$$

The real and imaginary parts of $I(z)/I(0)$ and $c\,q(z)/I(0)$ are shown in Fig. 10 for $\alpha h = 0,\ 0.1,\ 0.5,\ 1.0$, and $\pi/2$; c is the velocity of light.

Let the spheroidal coordinates k_h, k_e, and Φ be introduced where

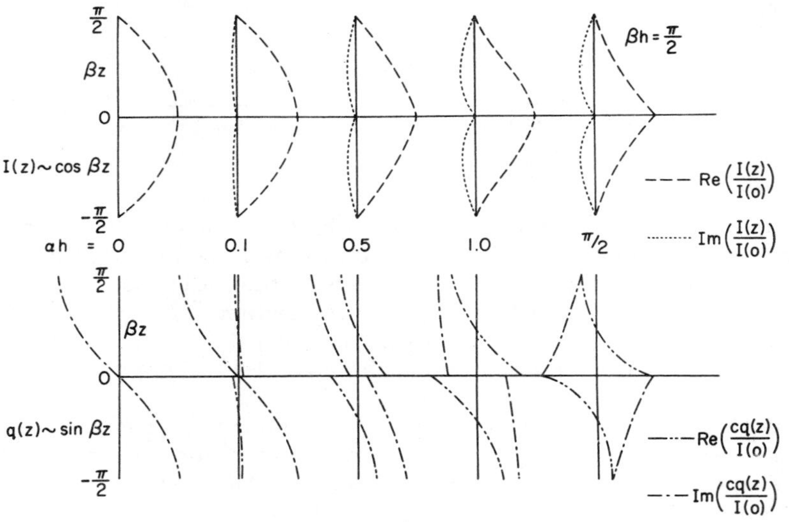

Figure 10. Normalized current and charge in antenna in dissipative medium. (Approximate Theory)

$k_e = a_e/h$ is the reciprocal of the eccentricity of a spheroid with semi-major axis a_e and with its foci at the ends of the antenna, $k_h = a_h/h$ is the corresponding quantity for an orthogonal hyperboloid of two sheets, and Φ is the azimuthal angle. These coordinates are related to the cylindrical coordinates by

$$\rho = h\sqrt{(k_e^2 - 1)(1 - k_h^2)} \qquad z = hk_h k_e$$

they are illustrated in Fig. 11. Note that $1 \leqq k_e \leqq \infty$, $-1 \leqq k_h \leqq 1$. The spheroidal components of the electromagnetic field that correspond to the cylindrical components (61)-(63) are quite complicated when $\alpha \neq 0$. It is convenient to express the instantaneous value of each component as the sum of three terms as follows:

$$B_\Phi(\vec{r}, t) = \sum_{i=1}^{3} B_{\Phi i}(\vec{r}, t) , \quad E_e(\vec{r}, t) = \sum_{i=1}^{3} E_{ei}(\vec{r}, t) ,$$

$$E_h(\vec{r}, t) = \sum_{i=1}^{3} E_{hi}(\vec{r}, t) , \qquad (67)$$

$$B_{\Phi 1}(\vec{r},t) = -\mu A_1 \left[\frac{\cos(\pi k_h/2)\ \sin(\omega t - \pi k_e/2)}{\sqrt{(k_e^2 - 1)(1 - k_h^2)}} \right] \tag{68a}$$

$$E_{e1}(\vec{r},t) = -\zeta_\alpha A_1 \left[\frac{\cos(\pi k_h/2)\ \sin(\omega t + \varphi - \pi k_e/2)}{\sqrt{(k_e^2 - k_h^2)(1 - k_h^2)}} \right] \tag{68b}$$

$$E_{h1}(\vec{r},t) = \zeta_\alpha A_1 \left[\frac{\sin(\pi k_h/2)\ \cos(\omega t + \varphi - \pi k_e/2)}{\sqrt{(k_e^2 - k_h^2)(k_e^2 - 1)}} \right] \tag{68c}$$

$$A_1 = \frac{I(0)}{2\pi h} \cosh\left(\frac{\pi\alpha k_h}{2\beta}\right) \exp\left(-\frac{\pi\alpha k_e}{2\beta}\right) \quad ; \tag{68d}$$

$$B_{\Phi 2}(\vec{r},t) = -\mu A_2 \frac{\sin(\pi k_h/2)\cos(\omega t - \pi k_e/2)}{\sqrt{(k_e^2 - 1)(1 - k_h^2)}} \tag{69a}$$

$$E_{e2}(\vec{r},t) = -\zeta_\alpha A_2 \frac{\sin(\pi k_h/2)\cos(\omega t + \varphi - \pi k_e/2)}{\sqrt{(k_e^2 - k_h^2)(1 - k_h^2)}} \tag{69b}$$

$$E_{h2}(\vec{r},t) = \zeta_\alpha A_2 \frac{\cos(\pi k_h/2)\sin(\omega t + \varphi - \pi k_e/2)}{\sqrt{(k_e^2 - k_h^2)(k_e^2 - 1)}} \tag{69c}$$

$$A_2 = \frac{I(0)}{2\pi h} \sin h\left(\frac{\pi\alpha k_h}{2\beta}\right) \exp\left(-\frac{\pi\alpha k_e}{2\beta}\right) \quad ; \tag{69d}$$

$$B_{\Phi 3}(\vec{r},t) = \mu A_3 \frac{\cos\left(\omega t - \frac{1}{2}\pi\sqrt{k_e^2 + k_h^2 - 1}\right)}{\sqrt{(k_e^2 - 1)(1 - k_h^2)}} \tag{70a}$$

$$E_{e3}(\vec{r},t) = \zeta_\alpha A_3 \frac{k_e \cos\left(\omega t + \varphi - \frac{1}{2}\pi\sqrt{k_e^2 + k_h^2 - 1}\right)}{\sqrt{(k_e^2 + k_h^2 - 1)(k_e^2 - k_h^2)(1 - k_h^2)}} \tag{70b}$$

$$E_{h3}(\vec{r}, t) = \zeta_\alpha A_3 \frac{k_h \cos\left(\omega t + \varphi - \frac{1}{2}\pi\sqrt{k_e^2 + k_h^2 - 1}\right)}{\sqrt{(k_e^2 + k_h^2 - 1)(k_e^2 - k_h^2)(k_e^2 - 1)}} \tag{70c}$$

$$A_3 = \frac{I(0)}{2\pi h} \sinh\left(\frac{\pi\alpha}{2\beta}\right) \exp - \left(\frac{\pi\alpha\sqrt{k_e^2 + k_h^2 - 1}}{2\beta}\right). \tag{70d}$$

Note that $\beta h = \pi/2$, $\varphi = \tan^{-1}(\alpha/\beta)$, $\zeta_\alpha = \omega\mu/\sqrt{\alpha^2 + \beta^2}$.

The third part of the field as given in (70a)-(70d) may be expressed in the spherical coordinates r, Θ, and Φ in the following equivalent form:

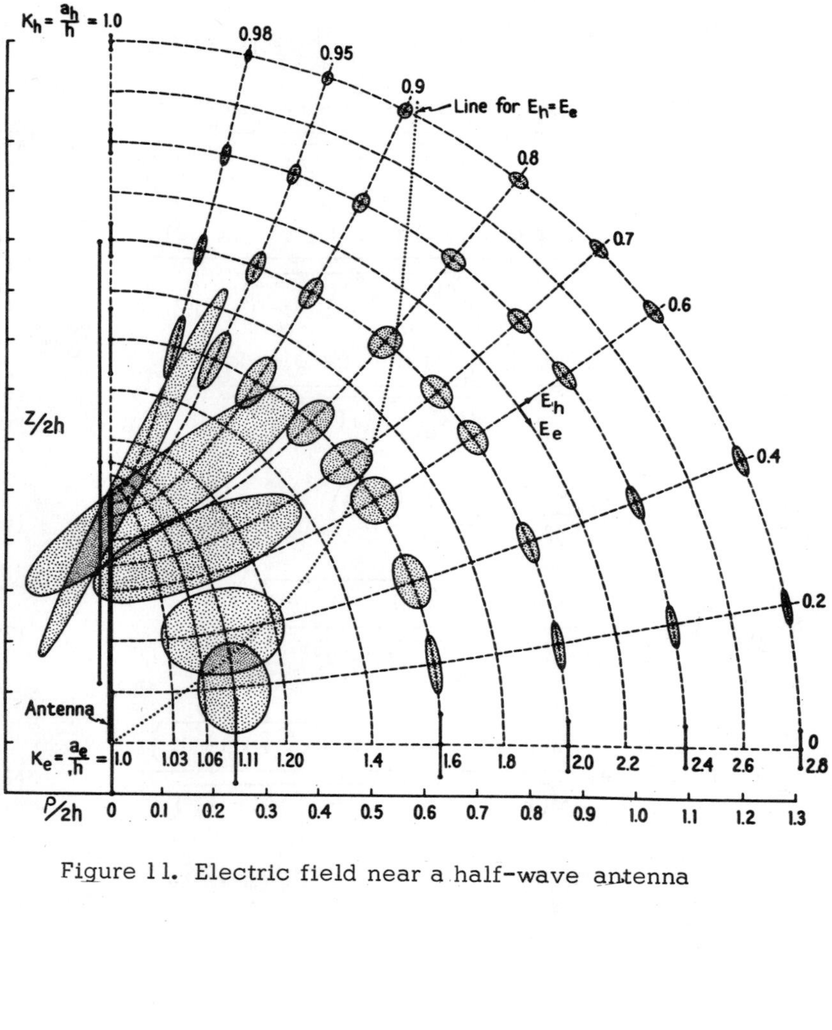

Figure 11. Electric field near a half-wave antenna

$$B_{\Phi 3}(\vec{r},t) = \frac{\mu I(0)}{2\pi} \frac{\cos(\omega t - \beta r)}{r \sin\Theta} \sinh\left(\frac{\pi\alpha}{2\beta}\right) \exp(-\alpha r) \qquad (71a)$$

$$E_{\Theta 3}(\vec{r},t) = \frac{\zeta_\alpha I(0)}{2\pi} \frac{\cos(\omega t + \varphi - \beta r)}{r \sin\Theta} \sinh\left(\frac{\pi\alpha}{2\beta}\right) \exp(-\alpha r) \qquad (71b)$$

$$E_{r3}(\vec{r},t) = 0 \quad . \qquad (71c)$$

These rather elaborate expressions for the electromagnetic field reduce to a simple and readily interpreted form when the attenuation of the medium is rather small. Specifically, if the following inequality is satisfied:

$$\alpha/\beta < \alpha h \ll 1 \qquad (72)$$

the entire electromagnetic field of the half-wave dipole is well approximated by the first terms (68a)-(68c) in the sums in (67) with $\varphi \doteq 0$ and with

$$A_1 \doteq \frac{I(0)}{2\pi h} \exp\left(-\frac{\pi\alpha k_e}{2\beta}\right) = \frac{I(0)}{2\pi h} \exp(-\alpha a_e) \quad . \qquad (73)$$

Except for the addition of the exponential term in the amplitude (73), the field given by (68a)-(68c) with $\varphi = 0$ is like that for the same antenna in air. The components $B_\Phi(\vec{r},t)$ and $E_e(\vec{r},t)$ are in phase with each other and both are a quarter period out of phase with $E_h(\vec{r},t)$. The surfaces of constant phase are the spheroids k_e = constant and these expand outward in such a manner that the end point of the semi-major axis travels with the velocity c . The electric field at any point is elliptically polarized as shown in Fig. 11. The components $B_\Phi(\vec{r},t)$ and $E_e(\vec{r},t)$ decrease in amplitude with distance from the antenna in a manner that approaches $1/r$ at great distances; the component $E_h(\vec{r},t)$, on the other hand, decreases in a manner that approaches $1/r^2$. The entire field is exponentially attenuated in amplitude with the semi-major axis $a_e = hk_e$ as the variable. The instantaneous value of the outwardly directed component $S_h(\vec{r},t)$ of the Poynting vector associated with the electromagnetic field that satisfies (72) is

$$S_h(r,t) = \frac{\zeta_e I^2(0)}{4\pi^2 h^2} \frac{\cos^2(\pi k_h/2)\exp(-\pi\alpha k_e/\beta)}{(1-k_h^2)\sqrt{(k_e^2 - k_h^2)(k_e^2 - 1)}} \sin^2(\omega t - \pi k_e/2) \qquad (74)$$

where $\zeta_e = \omega\mu/\beta$. The time-average power transferred across a spheroidal surface with semi-major axis $a_e = hk_e$ is

$$\overline{T}_e = \tfrac{1}{2} I^2(0) R_0^e e^{-2\alpha a_e} \tag{75}$$

where $R_0^e = 73.1$ ohms. Since terms of the order of magnitude αh have been neglected, the exponential in (75) reduces to unity when a_e approaches h, and (75) reduces to the value for air. The difference

$$T_{e1} - T_{e2} = \tfrac{1}{2} I^2(0) R_0^e [e^{-2\alpha a_{e1}} - e^{-2\alpha a_{e2}}] , \tag{76}$$

where a_{e1} and a_{e2} are the semi-major axes of two spheroids with $a_{e2} > a_{e1}$, is the power dissipated in heating the slightly conducting medium in the volume between the two surfaces. As pointed out in conjunction with (57) and (58) a better approximation of the correct power when the approximate distribution of current (60) with $\beta h = \pi/2$ is used is obtained with the value of $I(0)$ given by (58) instead of the correct value given by (32). Alternatively, the correct power is obtained if $I(0)$ is taken from (32) and the correct input resistant R_0 is substituted in (76) for the radiation resistance R_0^e.

When α is not sufficiently small to satisfy (72) with $\beta h = \pi/2$ the complete expressions (67) - (70d) must be used for the electromagnetic field. These cannot be combined to give a simple picture of outward traveling surfaces of constant phase at all points outside the half-wave dipole. It is not even convenient to combine the first and second parts of the field into a spheroidal wave and treat the third part in the forms (71a)-(71c) as a spherical wave originating at the center since components of both the second and third parts become infinite along the z axis and only their sum is finite. However, if a relatively small region in the vicinity of the antenna is excluded, the complete field can be approximated by spheroidal waves similar to those which obtain when the attenuation constant is small. In effect, the spherical wave originating at the center of the antenna must be approximated by a spheroidal wave. It is readily verified that if the quantity

$$d = 1 - \sqrt{1 - (1 - k_h^2)/k_e^2} \tag{77}$$

is small enough so that it may be neglected completely, the third part of the field given by (70a)-(70d) may be approximated by

$$B_{\Phi 3}(\vec{r}, t) \doteq \mu A_3 \frac{\cos(\omega t - \pi k_e/2)}{\sqrt{(k_e^2 - 1)(1 - k_h^2)}} \tag{78a}$$

$$E_{e3}(\vec{r}, t) \doteq \zeta_\alpha A_3 \frac{\cos(\omega t + \varphi - \pi k_e/2)}{\sqrt{(k_e^2 - k_h^2)(1 - k_h^2)}} \tag{78b}$$

$$E_{h3}(\vec{r}, t) \doteq \zeta_\alpha A_3 \frac{k_h \cos(\omega t + \varphi - \pi k_e/2)}{k_e \sqrt{(k_e^2 - k_h^2)(k_e^2 - 1)}} \tag{78c}$$

$$A_3 = \frac{I(0)}{2\pi h} \sinh\left(\frac{\pi\alpha}{2\beta}\right) \exp\left(-\frac{\pi\alpha k_e}{2\beta}\right) . \tag{78d}$$

It is to be noted that over a considerable range near the z axis k_h is very near one so that $d \doteq 0$. In the vicinity of the equatorial plane where k_h is very small, the excluded range is determined by the magnitude of k_e; it is indicated in Fig. 12. Specifically, for example, $d \le 0.1$ when $(1 - k_h^2)/k_e^2 \le 0.19$.

With the approximate expressions (78a)-(78d) and (68a)-(69d) the following combinations may be made:

$$B_{\Phi 2}(\vec{r}, t) + B_{\Phi 3}(\vec{r}, t) = -\frac{\mu I(0)}{2\pi h} \frac{D_2 \cos(\omega t - \pi k_e/2)}{\sqrt{(k_e^2 - 1)(1 - k_h^2)}} \exp\left(-\frac{\pi\alpha k_e}{2\beta}\right) \tag{79a}$$

$$E_{e2}(\vec{r}, t) + E_{e3}(\vec{r}, t) = -\frac{\zeta_\alpha I(0)}{2\pi h} \frac{D_2 \cos(\omega t + \varphi - \pi k_e/2)}{\sqrt{(k_e^2 - k_h^2)(1 - k_h^2)}} \exp\left(-\frac{\pi\alpha k_e}{2\beta}\right) \tag{79b}$$

$$E_{h1}(\vec{r}, t) + E_{h3}(\vec{r}, t) = \frac{\zeta_\alpha I(0)}{2\pi h} \frac{F_1 \cos(\omega t + \varphi - \pi k_e/2)}{\sqrt{(k_e^2 - k_h^2)(k_e^2 - 1)}} \exp\left(-\frac{\pi\alpha k_e}{2\beta}\right) \tag{79c}$$

where

$$D_2 = \sinh\left(\frac{\pi\alpha k_h}{2\beta}\right) \sin\left(\frac{\pi k_h}{2}\right) - \sinh\left(\frac{\pi\alpha}{2\beta}\right) \tag{79d}$$

$$F_1 = \cosh\left(\frac{\pi\alpha k_h}{2\beta}\right) \sin\left(\frac{\pi k_h}{2}\right) + \frac{\alpha k_h}{k_e} \sinh\left(\frac{\pi\alpha}{2\beta}\right). \tag{79e}$$

With the additional notation,

$$D_1 = \cosh\left(\frac{\pi\alpha k_h}{2\beta}\right) \cos\left(\frac{\pi k_h}{2}\right) \tag{80a}$$

$$F_2 = \sinh\left(\frac{\pi\alpha k_h}{2\beta}\right) \cos\left(\frac{\pi k_h}{2}\right) \tag{80b}$$

the complete field may be obtained by combining (79a) and (79b) respectively with (68a) and (68b), and (79c) with (69c). The results are

$$B_{\Phi}(\vec{r}, t) = -\frac{\mu I(0)}{2\pi h} \frac{D \sin(\omega t + \Delta - \pi k_e/2)}{\sqrt{(k_e^2 - 1)(1 - k_h^2)}} \exp\left(-\frac{\pi \alpha k_e}{2\beta}\right) \tag{81a}$$

$$E_e(\vec{r}, t) = -\frac{\zeta_\alpha I(0)}{2\pi h} \frac{D \sin(\omega t + \varphi + \Delta - \pi k_e/2)}{\sqrt{(k_e^2 - k_h^2)(1 - k_h^2)}} \exp\left(-\frac{\pi \alpha k_e}{2\beta}\right) \tag{81b}$$

$$E_h(\vec{r}, t) = \frac{\zeta_\alpha I(0)}{2\pi h} \frac{F \cos(\omega t + \varphi + \psi - \pi k_e/2)}{\sqrt{(k_e^2 - k_h^2)(k_e^2 - 1)}} \exp\left(-\frac{\pi \alpha k_e}{2\beta}\right) \tag{81c}$$

where

$$D = \sqrt{D_1^2 + D_2^2}\ , \qquad \Delta = \tan^{-1}(D_2/D_1) \tag{82a}$$

and

$$F = \sqrt{F_1^2 + F_2^2}\ , \qquad \psi = -\tan^{-1}(F_2/F_1)\ . \tag{82b}$$

The formulas (81a)-(81c) for the spheroidal components of the field of a half-wave dipole ($\beta h = \pi/2$) in a dissipative medium without restriction on the conductivity are substantially like the formulas for the same antenna in a medium that is only slightly conducting. However, the formulas for the unrestricted medium are not useful in a region near the antenna where the approximation $d \doteq 0$ is not a good

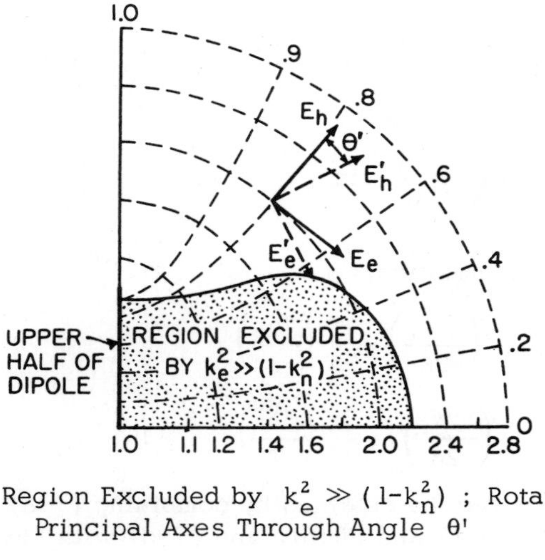

Figure 12. Region Excluded by $k_e^2 \gg (1-k_n^2)$; Rotation of Principal Axes Through Angle θ'

approximation. In addition, they are more complicated owing to the appearance of the different phases Δ and ψ in the expressions for the mutually perpendicular components $E_e(\vec{r}, t)$ and $E_h(\vec{r}, t)$ of the electric field.

The time-average component of the Poynting vector perpendicular to the spheroidal surfaces k_e = constant is

$$\bar{S}_h(r) = \frac{I^2(0)}{8\pi^2 h^2} \frac{D^2 \cos\varphi \exp(-\pi\alpha k_e/\beta)}{(1-k_h^2)\sqrt{(k_e^2 - k_h^2)(k_e^2 - 1)}} . \tag{83}$$

The total time-average power transferred across a spheroidal surface for which $k_e \geq 2.2$ is

$$\bar{T}_e = \frac{\zeta_e I^2(0) \exp(-\pi\alpha k_e/\beta)}{4\pi(1+\alpha^2/\beta^2)} \int_{-1}^{1} \frac{D^2}{1-k_h^2}\, dk_h \tag{84}$$

where $\zeta_e = \omega\mu/\beta$. Owing to the complicated form of D as a function of k_h , the integral in (84) has not been evaluated.

The general formulas (81a)-(81c) indicate that the electromagnetic field of a half-wave dipole in an arbitrary dissipative medium may be interpreted in terms of expanding spheroidal surfaces except very near the antenna where more complicated conditions exist. These surfaces expand with foci at the ends of the antenna and with an outward phase velocity along the z axis that is given by

$$v_p = \omega/\beta \tag{85}$$

where β is the real part of the complex propagation constant k as defined in (19). However, although the phase of $B_\Phi(\vec{r}, t)$, $E_e(\vec{r}, t)$, or $E_h(\vec{r}, t)$ remains constant** as each spheroid moves out along a hyperbola defined by a particular value of k_h , the actual phases at different points along such a spheroid are not the same. That is, the expanding spheroids are surfaces of constant phase, but the constant value on each spheroid is a function of k_h . Thus, respectively, for $B_\Phi(\vec{r}, t)$, $E_e(\vec{r}, t)$, and $E_h(\vec{r}, t)$ the phases, $(\omega t + \Delta - \pi k_e/2)$, $(\omega t + \varphi + \Delta - \pi k_e/2)$, and $(\omega t + \varphi + \psi - \pi k_e/2)$ remain constant** as t and k_e increase together. At each point on a given spheroid k_e = constant, the phase of $E_e(\vec{r}, t)$ differs from that of $B_\Phi(\vec{r}, t)$ by the constant angle $\varphi = \tan^{-1}(\alpha/\beta)$. The phases of the two mutually perpendicular components of the electric field differ by the angle $(\Delta - \psi)$ which is a function of k_h .

In a medium that is dissipationless or has very low attenuation, the electric field is elliptically polarized with principal axes tangent and perpendicular to the spheroidal surfaces of constant phase as shown in Fig. 12. In the dissipative medium with α unrestricted, the principal axes of the ellipses described by the electric vector are rotated from these tangents and perpendiculars by an angle θ' that is a function of k_h. The polarization ellipses for the electric field and their angle of inclination with respect to the direction of $E_h(\vec{r}, t)$ may be determined if the time is eliminated between the expressions for $E_e(\vec{r}, t)$ and $E_h(\vec{r}, t)$ as given in (81b) and (81c). Let these formulas be expressed as follows:

$$E_e(\vec{r}, t) = E_e \sin(\Omega + \Delta) \tag{86}$$

$$E_h(\vec{r}, t) = E_h \cos(\Omega + \psi) \tag{87}$$

where

$$E_e = -\frac{\zeta_\alpha I(0)}{2\pi h} \frac{D \exp(-\pi\alpha k_e/2\beta)}{\sqrt{(k_e^2 - k_h^2)(1 - k_h^2)}} \tag{88}$$

$$E_h = \frac{\zeta_\alpha I(0)}{2\pi h} \frac{F \exp(-\pi\alpha k_e/2\beta)}{\sqrt{(k_e^2 - k_h^2)(k_e^2 - 1)}} \tag{89}$$

and

$$\Omega = (\omega t + \varphi - \pi k_e/2) \ . \tag{90}$$

If (86) and (87) are solved for $\sin\Omega$ and $\cos\Omega$, and these quantities are then squared and added to equal one, the following equation is obtained

$$\frac{E_h^2(\vec{r}, t)}{E_h^2} + \frac{E_e^2(\vec{r}, t)}{E_e^2} + \frac{2E_h(\vec{r}, t)E_e(\vec{r}, t)}{E_h E_e} \sin(\psi - \Delta) = \cos^2(\psi - \Delta) \ . \tag{91}$$

This is the equation of an ellipse that has its principal axes rotated with respect to the directions of E_h and E_e. Let the direction of E'_h be rotated from E_h by an angle θ' as shown in Fig. 12. The direction of E'_e is then rotated by the same angle with respect to E_e. The new components E'_h and E'_e are related to the old ones by the formulas

$$E_h = E'_h \cos\theta' - E'_e \sin\theta' \tag{92a}$$

$$E_e = E'_h \sin\theta' + E'_e \cos\theta' \ . \tag{92b}$$

If the angle θ' is chosen so that

$$\tan 2\theta' = \frac{2E_h E_e}{E_e^2 - E_h^2} \sin(\psi - \Delta) \ , \tag{93}$$

the new equation is

$$\left[\frac{E'_h(r,t)}{E'_h}\right]^2 + \left[\frac{E'_e(r,t)}{E'_e}\right]^2 = \cos^2(\psi-\Delta) \qquad (94)$$

where

$$\left(\frac{1}{E'_h}\right)^2 = \frac{\cos^2\theta'}{E_h^2} + \frac{2\sin(\psi-\Delta)\sin\theta'\cos\theta'}{E_h E_e} + \frac{\sin^2\theta'}{E_e^2} \qquad (95a)$$

$$\left(\frac{1}{E'_e}\right)^2 = \frac{\sin^2\theta'}{E_h^2} + \frac{2\sin(\psi-\Delta)\sin\theta'\cos\theta'}{E_h E_e} + \frac{\cos^2\theta'}{E_e^2}\,. \qquad (95b)$$

The equation (94) is that of an ellipse with semi-principal axes $E'_h\cos(\psi-\Delta)$ and $E'_e\cos(6-\Delta)$. Note that when $\psi = \Delta$, as in a dissipationless medium, $\theta' = 0$, $E'_h = E_h$, $E'_e = E_e$. It can be argued from symmetry or determined directly from the formulas, that $\theta' = 0$ when $k_h = 0, 1$; it follows that the electric field is still linearly polarized parallel to the antenna both along the z axis and in the equatorial plane just as when immersed in air. The polarization ellipses corresponding to those in Fig. 11 are shown in Fig. 13 for $\beta h = \pi/2$ and $\alpha h = 0.1,\ 0.5,\ 1.0$ and $\pi/2$.

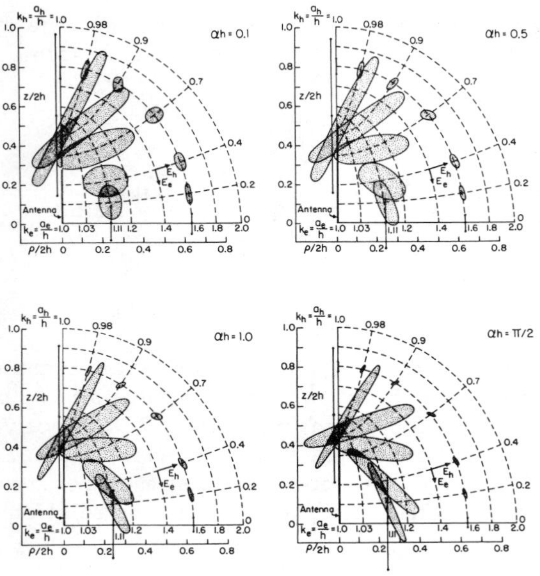

Fig. 13. Electric field near a half-wave antenna in a disspative medium; $k = \beta - j\alpha$, $\beta h = \pi/2$.

4. THE ELECTRICALLY SHORT ANTENNA. As pointed out following (59a)-(59d), the approximate distribution of current (60) in the form

$$I(z) = I(0)(1 - |z|/h) \tag{96}$$

for the electrically short antenna ($\beta h \leq 0.3$, $\alpha h \leq 0.3$) is a particularly good approximation since the omitted term, $B(z) = T_k(h)\frac{k^2h^2}{2}[(1 - \frac{z^2}{h^2}) - (1 - \frac{|z|}{h})]$ is very small. The input current is to be determined from the more accurate formula (34). Since (96) is a special case of (60) with kh small in its real and imaginary parts, it follows that the rigorous expressions (61)-(63) for the electromagnetic field of the distribution (60) apply. They may be converted into a more common but also slightly more restricted form by a series expansion in powers of the small quantity kh and the quantity h/r, which must also be assumed small. The distance $r = \sqrt{\rho^2+z^2}$ is measured from the center of the dipole to the point where the field is calculated. The approximations include

$$R_{1h} \doteq r - h\cos\Theta + (h\sin\Theta)^2/2r \tag{97a}$$

$$R_{2h} \doteq r + h\cos\Theta + (h\sin\Theta)^2/2r \tag{97b}$$

$$\cos kh \doteq 1 - k^2h^2/2 \quad . \tag{97c}$$

With these approximations the complete electromagnetic field in the spherical coordinates r, Θ, Φ has the familiar form

$$B_\Phi(r) \doteq \frac{j\mu I(0)h}{4\pi}\left[\frac{k}{r} - \frac{j}{r^2}\right]e^{-jkr}\sin\Theta \tag{98a}$$

$$E_\Theta(r) \doteq \frac{j\omega\mu I(0)h}{4\pi k}\left[\frac{k}{r} - \frac{j}{r^2} - \frac{1}{kr^3}\right]e^{-jkr}\sin\Theta \tag{98b}$$

$$E_r(r) \doteq \frac{\omega\mu I(0)h}{4\pi k}\left[\frac{2}{r^2} - \frac{j2}{kr^3}\right]e^{-jkr}\cos\Theta \tag{98c}$$

Note that $\omega\mu/k = \sqrt{\mu/\xi} = \zeta$. In this derivation terms of the order of magnitude $|kh|^4$ and h^3/r^3 and higher powers have been neglected. This means that the field given in (97a)-(97c) is not valid in the immediate vicinity of the antenna as are the more general expressions (61)-(63). If desired, the above formulas may be expressed in terms of the equivalent electric moment p_z with the relation

$$j\omega p_z = \int_{-h}^{h} I(z)dz = I(0)h \quad . \tag{99}$$

For a short dipole in air, $k = k_0$ is real; $\omega\mu/k = \zeta_0$. The instantaneous field is obtained from the real parts of (98a)-(98c) when expressed in polar form and multiplied by $e^{j\omega t}$. Specifically,

$$B_\Phi(\vec{r}, t) = \frac{\mu_0 I(0) h}{4\pi} \frac{\sqrt{1 + k_0^2 r^2}}{r^2} \cos(\omega t - k_0 r + \tan^{-1} k_0 r) \sin\Theta \qquad (100a)$$

$$E_\Theta(\vec{r}, t) = \frac{\zeta_0 I(0) h}{4\pi} \frac{\sqrt{1 - k_0^2 r^2 + k_0^4 r^4}}{k_0 r^3} \cos[\omega t - k_0 r + \tan^{-1}(k_0 r - 1/k_0 r)] \sin\Theta \qquad (100b)$$

$$E_r(\vec{r}, t) = \frac{\zeta_0 I(0) h}{2\pi} \frac{\sqrt{1 + k_0^2 r^2}}{k_0 r^3} \cos(\omega t - k_0 r + \cot^{-1} k_0 r) \cos\Theta . \qquad (100c)$$

These expressions do not in general permit the simple interpretation of spherical surfaces of constant phase that travel radially outward with a definite phase velocity as is true in terms of spheroidal waves of the half-wave dipole in air. Each component may be so interpreted, but the phase velocities of all three components are different until $k_0 r$ becomes sufficiently great in the radiation zone so that $k_0^2 r^2 \gg 1$, $\tan^{-1} k_0 r \doteq \pi/2$, $\cot^{-1} k_0 r \doteq 0$. The radiation-zone field is

$$B^r_\Phi(\vec{r}, t) = E^r_\Theta(\vec{r}, t)/c = \frac{\mu_0 I(0) k_0 h}{4\pi r} \sin(\omega t - k_0 r) \sin\Theta \qquad (101a)$$

$$E^r_r(\vec{r}, t) = \frac{\zeta_0 I(0) k_0 h}{2\pi r^2} \cos(\omega t - k_0 r) \cos\Theta \doteq 0 . \qquad (101b)$$

These formulas represent a true spherical wave. All components expand with the same phase velocity c; $B^r_\Phi(\vec{r}, t)$ and $E^r_\Theta(\vec{r}, t)$ are in phase with each other and a quarter period out of phase with $E^r_r(\vec{r}, t)$. $B^r_\Phi(\vec{r}, t)$ and $E^r_\Theta(\vec{r}, t)$ decrease as $1/r$; $E^r_r(\vec{r}, t)$ decreases as $1/r^2$ so that when r is large this component is insignificant as indicated in (101b).

The radial component of the complex Poynting vector for the field in (100a)-(100c) is

$$S_r(\vec{r}) = \frac{|I(0)|^2 k_0^2 h^2 \zeta_0}{32\pi^2} \left[\frac{1}{r^2} - \frac{j}{k_0^3 r^5} \right] \sin^2\Theta , \qquad (102)$$

and the total time-average power radiated is

$$\bar{T}_e = \mathrm{Re} \int_0^{2\pi} d\Phi \int_0^{2\pi} S_r(r) r^2 \sin\Theta d\Theta = \tfrac{1}{2} I^2(0) R_0^e \qquad (103)$$

where the radiation resistance is

$$R_0{}^e = \frac{\zeta_0 k_0^2 h^2}{6\pi} = 20\, k_0^2 h^2 \text{ ohms} . \tag{104}$$

Since the approximate current (96) was used to determine the power radiated instead of the more accurate record (34), $R_0{}^e$ in (104) is only an approximation of the actual input resistance obtained from (35). The more accurate value has as its leading term,

$$R_0(k_0) = \frac{\zeta_0 k_0^2 h^2}{6\pi} \frac{\psi_{dr}}{\Omega - 3} \tag{105}$$

where $\psi_{dr} = 2(\ln\frac{h}{a} - 1)$ and $\Omega = 2\ln(2h/a)$. When $\Omega = 10$, $h/a \doteq 75$, the ratio $\psi_{dr}/(\Omega-3) = 0.95$, so that (104) is in error by about 5%. The error decreases as h/a increases.

When the medium is dissipative with $k = \beta - j\alpha$, the components of the field may be expressed as follows:

$$B_\Phi(\vec{r}) = \frac{\mu I(0) h}{4\pi}\left[\frac{j\beta}{r} + \frac{\alpha}{r} + \frac{1}{r^2}\right] e^{-\alpha r} e^{-j\beta r} \sin\Theta \tag{106a}$$

$$E_\Theta(\vec{r}) = \frac{\omega\mu I(0) h}{4\pi}\left[j\left(\frac{1}{r} + \frac{\alpha}{(\beta^2+\alpha^2)r^2} - \frac{\beta^2-\alpha^2}{(\beta^2+\alpha^2)^2 r^3}\right) + \frac{\beta}{(\beta^2+\alpha^2)r^2} + \frac{2\alpha\beta}{(\beta^2+\alpha^2)^2 r^3}\right] e^{-\alpha r} e^{-j\beta r} \sin\Theta \tag{106b}$$

$$E_r(\vec{r}) = \frac{\omega\mu I(0) h}{2\pi}\left[\frac{\beta}{(\beta^2+\alpha^2)r^2} + \frac{2\alpha\beta}{(\beta^2+\alpha^2)^2 r^3} + j\left(\frac{\alpha}{(\beta^2+\alpha^2)r^2} - \frac{\beta^2-\alpha^2}{(\beta^2+\alpha^2)^2 r^3}\right)\right] e^{-\alpha r} e^{-j\beta r} \cos\Theta \tag{106c}$$

The real part of the complex Poynting vector is

$$\operatorname{Re} S_r(r) = \frac{|I(0)|^2 \beta^2 h^2 \zeta_e}{32\pi^2 r^2}\left(1 + \frac{\alpha}{\beta} L\right) e^{-2\alpha r} \tag{107}$$

where

$$L = \frac{2}{(1+\alpha^2/\beta^2)\beta r} + \frac{4\alpha\beta}{(1+\alpha^2/\beta^2)^2\beta^2 r^2} + \frac{2}{(1+\alpha^2/\beta^2)^2\beta^3 r^3} \tag{108}$$

and where $\zeta_e = \omega\mu/\beta$. The total time-average power transferred outward across a spherical surface of radius r is the integral of (107) over the surface of the sphere. The result is

$$\bar{T}_e = \frac{|I(0)|^2\beta^2h^2\zeta_e}{12\pi}\left(1 + \frac{\alpha}{\beta}L\right)e^{-2\alpha r} . \qquad (109)$$

As in the case of (103) this formula is an approximation that is quite good only for extremely thin antennas. It may be corrected to apply to antennas of somewhat greater thickness by multiplying (109) by the factor $\psi_{dr}/(\Omega-3)$. It is important to note that (109) cannot be used to determine the radiation resistance of the short antenna in a dissipative medium since it is not possible to reduce the spherical surface across which the power T_e is transferred to an envelope that encloses only the antenna and no part of the medium. The smallest spherical surface that contains the antenna has the radius $r = h$, but, since in the transformation from cylindrical to spherical coordinates, terms of the order of magnitude $(h/r)^3$ have been neglected in comparison with unity, (109) is meaningful only when $r > h$. Since a sphere of radius $r > h$ contains a significant part of the dissipative medium, the power transferred across its surface is not the total power radiated from the dipole. Note in particular that the limit $r = 0$ is meaningless.

The actual power supplied to the antenna may be obtained from the driving-point admittance $Y_0(k)$ in (34) in the form $T_e = \frac{1}{2}V_0^{e2}G_0(k) = \frac{1}{2}|I(0)|^2 R_0(k)$. Since the complete expressions for $G_0(k)$ and $B_0(k)$ are rather long, it will serve for purposes of illustration to consider the two special cases $\alpha^2 \ll \beta^2$ and $\alpha = \beta$, for which the formulas are much simpler. The resistance $R_0(k)$ is given by

$$R_0(k) = \frac{G_0(k)}{G_0^2(k) + B_0^2(k)} . \qquad (110)$$

When $\alpha^2 \ll \beta^2$, $G_0^2(k) \ll B_0^2(k)$ so that

$$R_0(k) \doteq \frac{G_0(k)}{B_0(k)} = \frac{\zeta_e\beta^2h^2\psi_{dr}}{6\pi(\Omega-3)}\left[1 + \frac{6\alpha(\Omega-3)}{\beta^2h}\right] \qquad (111)$$

if only the leading terms are retained. When $\alpha = \beta$, $G_0^2(k) \gg B_0^2(k)$, so that from (40)

$$R_0(k) \doteq \frac{1}{G_0(k)} = \frac{\zeta_e\psi_{dr}}{4\pi}\frac{1}{\beta h} . \qquad (112)$$

The power per unit input current, P_r , that is dissipated within a sphere of radius $r > h$ is defined as follows in terms of the power $\bar{T}_e$ supplied to the antenna and the power $\bar{T}_{er}$ transferred outward to the region beyond the sphere:

$$P_r = \frac{2(\bar{T}_e - \bar{T}_{er})}{|I(0)|^2} = R_0(k) - \frac{\beta^2 h^2 \zeta_e \psi_{dr}}{6\pi(\Omega-3)} (1 + \frac{\alpha}{\beta} L) e^{-2\alpha r} . \quad (113)$$

When $\alpha^2 \ll \beta^2$ this becomes

$$P_r = \frac{\zeta_e \beta^2 h^2 \psi_{dr}}{6\pi(\Omega-3)} \frac{\alpha}{\beta} \left[\frac{6(\Omega-3)}{\beta h} - L e^{-2\alpha r} \right] \quad (114a)$$

where

$$L = \frac{z}{\beta r} + \frac{z}{\beta^3 r^3} . \quad (114b)$$

When $\alpha = \beta$,

$$P_r = \frac{\zeta_e \psi_{dr}}{4\pi} \left[\frac{1}{\beta h} - \frac{\beta^2 h^2}{3(\Omega-3)} (1 + L) e^{-2\beta r} \right] \quad (115a)$$

where

$$L = \left(\frac{1}{\beta r} + \frac{1}{\beta^2 r^2} + \frac{1}{2\beta^3 r^3} \right) . \quad (115b)$$

It is instructive to consider a numerical example. Let the power dissipated within the radian sphere $\beta r = 1$ be determined for an antenna with $\beta h = 0.3$ and $h/a \doteq 75$. When $\alpha^2 \ll \beta^2$, $e^{-2\alpha r} = e^{-2\alpha/\beta} \doteq 1 - 2\alpha/\beta$; $L \doteq 4$. With these values, the power supplied to the antenna per unit current is

$$2\bar{T}_e / |I(0)|^2 = R_0(k) = 1.71(1 + 140 \alpha/\beta) \text{ watts/amp}^2 ; \quad (116a)$$

the power transferred beyond the radian sphere per unit current is

$$2\bar{T}_{er} / |I(0)|^2 = 1.71(1 + 2\alpha/\beta) \text{ watts/amp}^2 ; \quad (116b)$$

and the power dissipated as heat in the medium within the radian sphere is

$$P_r = 236 \alpha/\beta \text{ watts/amp}^2 . \quad (116c)$$

When $\alpha = \beta$, the corresponding values are

$$2\bar{T}_e / |I(0)|^2 = R_0(k) = 1990.5 \text{ watts/amp}^2 \quad (117a)$$

$$2\bar{T}_{er} / |I(0)|^2 = 0.81 \text{ watts/amp}^2 \quad (117b)$$

$$P_r = 1989.7 \text{ watts/amp}^2 . \quad (117c)$$

From these numerical results it is clear that when α/β is as small as 10^{-3} or smaller, 90% or more of the power supplied to the antenna is transferred beyond the radian sphere. When α/β is no greater than 0.1, only about 8% is dissipated outside; 92% is used to heat the medium inside the radian sphere. When $\alpha = \beta$ virtually all of the power is dissipated as heat within the radian sphere. The fraction transferred beyond it is only about 0.04%. Note that when $\alpha = \beta$ the input susceptance of the antenna is small, so that virtually the entire impedance is resistive. The antenna effectively does not radiate, but acts like a pair of electrodes with very small surface area—hence the rather high resistance.

CONCLUSION

The general problem of a cylindrical antenna immersed in a dissipative medium has been formulated in a manner that permits the determination not only of the distribution of current and the admittance, but also of the electromagnetic field. The analytical procedure is approximate but quantitatively sufficiently accurate to be of practical value. It may be extended to treat coupled antennas in a dissipative medium.

NOTES

*Much of the work in this section was carried out originally by Mr. S. T. Yu.

**This is strictly true for $B_\Phi(\vec{r}, t)$ and $E_e(\vec{r}, t)$, since k_e does not occur in the phase term Δ. It is not actually true for $E_h(\vec{r}, t)$ owing to the occurrence of k_e in the term $(k_h/k_e)\sinh(\pi\alpha/2\beta)$ in F_1 which contributes to the phase in ψ. However, this term is small, except quite near the ends of the antenna, so that the general pictures is not altered significantly.

REFERENCES

1. C.T. Tai, "Radiation of a Hertzian Dipole Immersed in a Dissipative Medium," Cruft Laboratory Technical Report No. 21, Harvard University (October 10, 1947).

2. H.B. Keller and J.B. Keller have also studied this problem in J. Appl. Phys., 20, 393 (April 1949).

3. R.K. Moore, "Theory of Radio Communication Between Submerged Submarines," Thesis, Cornell University (June, 1951).

4. J.R. Wait, "The Radiation Fields of a Horizontal Dipole in a Semi-infinite Dissipative Medium," J. Appl. Phys., 24, 958 (1953).

5. J. R. Wait and L. L. Campbell, "Fields of Dipoles in a Semi-infinite Conducting Medium," J. Geophys. Research, 58, 21 and 167 (1953).

6. A. Baños, Jr., and J. P. Wesley, "The Horizontal Electric Dipole in a Conducting Half-space," Part I(1953), Part II(1954), University of California Marine Physics Laboratory, Scripps Inst. Oceanog. (unpublished)

7. C. T. Tai, "On Radiation and Radiating Systems in the Presence of a Dissipative Medium," Cruft Laboratory Technical Report No. 77, Harvard University (May 10, 1949).

8. R. King and D. Middleton, "The Cylindrical Antenna: Current and Impedance," Quart. Appl. Math., 3, 302 (1946).

9. M. S. Macrakis, "Cylindrical Antenna Immersed in a Dissipative Medium (Input Impedance)," Cruft Laboratory Technical Report No. 256, Harvard University (April, 1957).

10. C. W. Harrison, Jr., "Calculation of the Impedance of a Cylindrical Antenna in an Ionized Medium of Low Attenuation Factor by Means of Tables of the Exponential Integral for Complex Arguments, "Sandia Corporation Technical Memorandum (1959). (unpublished)

11. C. W. Harrison, Jr., and D. H. Denton, Jr., "Impedance of a Dipole in an Ionized Medium," I and II, Sandia Corporation Technical Memorandum (1959). (unpublished)

12. R. King and C. W. Harrison, Jr., "Half-wave Cylindrical Antenna in a Dissipative Medium: Current and Impedance," J. Research Natl. Bur. Standards, 64D, 365 (July-August, 1960).

13. R. King, C. W. Harrison, Jr., and David H. Denton, Jr., "The Electrically Short Antenna as a Probe for Measuring Electron Densities and Collision Frequencies in an Ionized Region," J. Research Natl. Bur. Standards (to be published).

14. R. King, "Linear Arrays: Currents, Impedances, and Fields," Trans. IRE, AP-7, S440 (December, 1959).

15. T. T. Wu and R. W. P. King, "Driving Point and Input Admittance of Linear Antennas," J. Appl. Phys., 30, 74 (1959).

16. R. W. P. King, Theory of Linear Antennas, Ch. II, Sec. 10, Harvard University Press (1956); also, R. W. P. King, Transmission-Line Theory, pp. 405-411, 430-437 McGraw-Hill (1955).

17. L. V. King, "On the Radiation Field of a Perfectly Conducting Base-insulated Cylindrical Antenna over a Perfectly Conducting Plane Earth, and the Calculation of Radiation Resistance and Reactance," Trans. Roy. Soc. (London), [A] 236, 381 (1937).

18. E. Hallen, "Theoretical Investigations into Transmitting and Receiving Antennae," Nova Acta Regiae Soc. Sci. Upsaliensis [4], 11, 1(1938).

19. R. W. P. King, Theory of Linear Antennas, Ch. II, McGraw-Hill (1956).

20. J. E. Storer, "Variational Solution to the Problem of the Symmetrical Antenna," Cruft Laboratory Technical Report No. 101(1951); see also R. W. P. King, Theory of Linear Antennas, Ch. II, Sec. 39, Harvard University Press (1956).

21. C. T. Tai, "A Variational Solution to the Problem of Cylindrical Antennas," Technical Report No. 12, SRI Project No. 188, Stanford Research Institute (August, 1950).

22. R. H. Duncan and F. A. Hinchey, "Cylindrical Antenna Theory," J. Research Natl. Bur. Standards, 64D, 569 (September-October, 1960).

23. T. T. Wu, "Theory of the Dipole Antenna and the Two-Wire Line," Cruft Laboratory Technical Report No. 318, Harvard University (March 10, 1960). To be published in Jour. Math. Phys.

24. J. G. Beaton and T. T. Wu, "Input Impedances of Center-Driven Dipole Antennas," Cruft Laboratory Technical Report No. 327 (August 25, 1960).

25. R. Mack and E. Mack, "Tables of E(h, z), C(h, z), S(h, z)," Cruft Laboratory Technical Report No. 331, Harvard University (November 1960).

26. R. W. P. King, Electromagnetic Engineering, Appendix 2, pp. 510-518, McGraw-Hill (1945).

27. The integration and differentiation are carried out in detail in R. W. P. King, Theory of Linear Antennas, pp. 523-528, Harvard University Press (1956).

Supported in part by Contract Nonr-1866(32) and the Sandia Corporation.

JAMES R. WAIT

The Propagation of Electromagnetic Waves Along the Earth's Surface

I. INTRODUCTION. The manner in which electromagnetic waves propagate over the surface of the earth is a subject of great practical importance. With the current enthusiasm to explore the ionosphere and the exosphere, the lower boundary (i. e., the earth's surface) has been often overlooked in recent times. Actually, for certain applications at low radio frequencies and short ranges it is permissible to neglect the presence of the ionosphere. In fact, for ranges as great as 500 km, the direct or ground wave may dominate the sky- or ionospherically reflected-wave. Furthermore, with the use of pulse-type transmissions such as used in the Loran C navigation systems, the ground wave may be distinguished from the sky wave for distances as great as 2000 km.

The increased use of electronic navigation systems of both c-w and pulse types has generated a need for a better understanding of ground wave propagation. It is the purpose of the present paper to review some of the recent theoretical progress on this problem. To place the subject in its proper historical perspective one should really return to the beginning of the century when first-class physicists of the day had turned their attention to electromagnetic boundary value problems. The contributions of Lord Rayleigh, Debye, Mie, Lorenz, Poincaré, March and Sommerfeld were particularly noteworthy. The significance of this early work, which is often overlooked or ignored, has been emphasized by Logan[1] in a recent publication. Later activity dealing specifically with ground wave propagation is outlined in a comprehensive monograph by Bremmer [2] who himself has made some very significant contributions. Great strides in the subject have also been made by workers in the U. S. S. R. An excellent summary of this work is contained in a recent review paper by Feinberg [3].

In the present paper we shall present a reasonably self-contained account of some recent work dealing with propagation over an inhomogeneous earth. While the material is based primarily on the author's earlier published and unpublished work, he will be the first to admit that equivalent results have probably appeared elsewhere. The approach adopted here is non-rigorous in the sense that details of a purely mathematical nature are not described.

2. RADIATION FROM AN ELECTRIC DIPOLE OVER A FLAT STRATIFIED GROUND. The ground is considered to be suitably represented by a number of parallel layers each with a thickness h, conductivity σ, dielectric constant ϵ and permeability μ. A subscript n is added to these quantities to denote the n-th layer from the surface. The bottom or N-th layer is taken to be of infinite thickness and is therefore equivalent to a semi-infinite region. The region above the ground (i. e., the air) is assumed to be a semi-infinite insulating space with dielectric constant ϵ_0 and permeability μ_0. The source of the electromagnetic fields is an electric dipole of infinitesimal length ds which carries a current equal to the real part of $I \exp(i\omega t)$. The dipole is situated in the insulating space at a height h above the ground plane.

It is now convenient to introduce a cylindrical coordinate system (ρ, φ, z) such that the ground plane coincides with the plane $z = 0$ and the source dipole is located along the z axis. The situation is illustrated in Fig. 1.

In this particular problem it is found that the fields may be derived from a Hertz vector which has only a z component. This scalar quantity is denoted Π and the field components may be derived from it by carrying out the following operations.

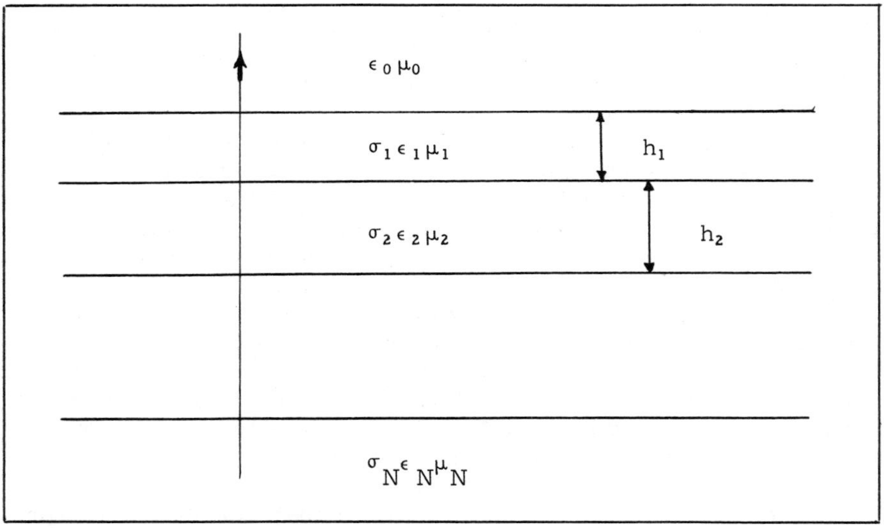

Figure 1. Vertical electric dipole over a stratified earth

$$E_\rho = \frac{\partial^2 \Pi}{\partial\rho\partial z} , \tag{1}$$

$$E_z = \left(-\gamma^2 + \frac{\partial^2}{\partial z^2}\right) \Pi \tag{2}$$

and

$$H_\varphi = \left(- \frac{\gamma^2}{i\mu\omega}\right) \frac{\partial \Pi}{\partial \rho} \tag{3}$$

where $\gamma^2 = i\sigma\mu\omega - \epsilon\mu\omega^2$. The remaining field components, E_φ , H_ρ, and H_z are identically zero. Everywhere, except right at the source, Π satisfies the wave equation

$$(\nabla^2 - \gamma^2)\Pi = 0 \tag{4}$$

where

$$\nabla^2 = \frac{1}{\rho}\frac{\partial}{\partial\rho}\rho\frac{\partial}{\partial\rho} + \frac{\partial^2}{\partial z^2} . \tag{5}$$

A subscript n is again added to these quantities when specific reference is made to the n-th layer. Suitable solutions of equation (4) have the form

$$\exp(\pm uz) J_0(\lambda\rho)$$

where $u = (\lambda^2 + \gamma^2)^{\frac{1}{2}}$ and $J_0(\lambda\rho)$ is the Bessel function of order zero and argument $\lambda\rho$. It is readily verified that this elementary function satisfies equation (4) for any value of the separation constant λ . For the present purpose, the following superposition of these elementary solutions is used.

$$\Pi_n = \int_0^\infty [A_n(\lambda) e^{u_n z} + B_n(\lambda) e^{-u_n z}] J_0(\lambda\rho) d\lambda \tag{6}$$

where

$$u_n = (\lambda^2 + \gamma_n^2)^{\frac{1}{2}} . \tag{7}$$

The quantities $A_n(\lambda)$ and $B_n(\lambda)$ are (unknown) functions of the integration variable which lies along the real axis of the complex λ-plane. The first objective is to determine the specific form of $A_n(\lambda)$ and $B_n(\lambda)$ in terms of the properties of the layers.

Now the direct or primary fields of the dipole in the insulating layer can be derived from

$$\Pi_0 = \Pi_p = c_0 e^{-\gamma_0 R_0}/R_0 \tag{8}$$

where $R_0 = [(z-h)^2 + \rho^2]^{\frac{1}{2}}$ and $c_0 = I\,ds/(4\pi i\omega\epsilon_0)$. Using the well-known integral representation

$$e^{-\gamma_0 R_0}/R_0 = \int_0^\infty \lambda u_0^{-1} e^{-|z-h|u_0} J_0(\lambda\rho) d\lambda \tag{9}$$

it follows that

$$A_0(\lambda) = c_0 \lambda u_0^{-1} \exp(-u_0 h) \quad . \tag{10}$$

Since only outgoing waves can be allowed in the bottom (semi-infinite) region it follows that

$$B_N(\lambda) = 0 \quad .$$

For an N layered ground, as shown in Fig. 1, there are now $2N$ unknown coefficients A_n and B_n which are to be determined. Fortunately, since the E_ρ and H_φ field components are to be continuous at the N interfaces, $2N$ linear equations in A_n and B_n are obtained. (This in turn requires that the quantities $\partial\Pi/\partial z$ and $\gamma^2 \Pi/\mu$ are continuous at the interfaces.)

At this stage of the analysis much of the algebra becomes very tedious so details are omitted. The final result, for the insulating space, is found to be

$$\Pi_0 = \Pi_p + c_0 \int_0^\infty \lambda u_0^{-1} R(\lambda) \exp[-u_0(h+z)] J_0(\lambda\rho)\, d\lambda \tag{11}$$

where

$$R(\lambda) = u_0 \lambda^{-1} \exp(u_0 h) B_0(\lambda) = \frac{K_0 - Z_1}{K_0 + Z_1} \tag{12}$$

$$Z_1 = K_1 \frac{Z_2 + K_1 \tanh u_1 h_1}{K_1 + Z_2 \tanh u_1 h_1} \tag{13}$$

$$Z_2 = K_2 \frac{Z_3 + K_2 \tanh u_2 h_2}{K_2 + Z_3 \tanh u_2 h_2} \tag{14}$$

and so on, until

$$Z_{N-1} = K_{N-1} \frac{K_N + K_{N-1} \tanh u_{N-1} h_{N-1}}{K_{N-1} + K_N \tanh u_{N-1} h_{N-1}} \tag{15}$$

and $Z_N = K_N$. In the above, the K_n's have the nature of wave impedances and they are defined by

$$K_n = u_n (\sigma_n + i\omega\epsilon_n)^{-1}$$

for $n = 0, 1, 2, \ldots N-1, N$.

The formal solution of the problem is thus completely specified. Unfortunately, in its present form, it is not usable. The remaining task is to evaluate the integrals. In the general case this appears to be an almost hopeless task, although with the use of high-speed computers it may be feasible to numerically evaluate the integrals. Here, an attempt is made to find relatively simple asymptotic forms of the solution which are valid for ground wave propagation.

3. ASYMPTOTIC FORMS OF THE SOLUTIONS FOR A STRATIFIED GROUND. A special case of the above is when the lower half-space (i. e., $z < 0$) is homogeneous and $\mu_1 = \mu_0$. The structure of the solution is greatly simplified; in fact, the factor $R(\lambda)$ is now given by

$$R(\lambda) = \frac{\gamma_1^2 u_0 - \gamma_0^2 u_1}{\gamma_1^2 u_0 + \gamma_0^2 u_1} \tag{16}$$

which is obtained from equation (12) as a limiting case when $h_1 \to \infty$.

The resulting integrals for this half-space problem have been discussed by a great many authors over a period of 50 years. The complications and resulting controversy arise from the fact that branch points occur at $\lambda = \pm - i\gamma_0$, $\pm - i\gamma_1$ and poles occur at $\lambda = \pm \lambda_p$ where λ_p is a solution of $\gamma_1^2 u_0 + \gamma_0^2 u_1 = 0$. Since in cases of most physical interest $|\gamma_1^2| \gg |\gamma_0^2|$, the pole at λ_p is very near the branch point at $-i\gamma_0$. This fact has been the source of much confusion on the subject. No attempt is made here to describe the various approaches to this over-worked problem. The usual steps in the treatment of the integral are itemized as follows:

i) Replace the contour from 0 to ∞ by one from $-\infty$ to $+\infty$ along the real axis.

ii) Close the contour by an (infinite) semi-circle in the upper half-plane.

iii) Indent the contour around the branch points.

A simplifying feature of the problem is that the contribution of the integration from the branch point at $-i\gamma_1$ is negligible since the real part of γ_1 is very large. Essentially this is equivalent to replacing u_1 by γ_1 everywhere. Thus for the homogeneous half-space, the integral form of the solution could have been written

$$\Pi_0 \cong c_0\left[\frac{e^{-\gamma_0 R_0}}{R_0} + \frac{e^{-\gamma_0 R_1}}{R_1} - 2P\right] \tag{17}$$

where

$$P = \int_0^\infty \frac{\gamma_0 \lambda \Delta e^{-u_0(z+h)}}{(u_0 + \gamma_0 \Delta_1) u_0} J_0(\lambda\rho)\, d\lambda \tag{18}$$

and where

$$\Delta = \frac{\gamma_0}{\gamma_1} \quad \text{and} \quad R_1 = [(z+h)^2 + \rho^2]^{\frac{1}{2}} .$$

The latter integral is in a form which can be evaluated by the modified saddle-point method of Van der Waerden [4] in a relatively straightforward manner. This leads to

$$P \cong i(\pi p_1)^{\frac{1}{2}} e^{-\bar{p}_1} \operatorname{erfc}(i\bar{p}_1^{\frac{1}{2}}) e^{-\gamma_0 R_1}/R_1 \tag{19}$$

and

$$p_1 = -\gamma_0 R_1 \Delta_1^2/2 = -ikR_1 \Delta_1^2/2 \tag{20}$$

and

$$\bar{p}_1 = -[1 - \sin\Phi + \Delta_1 \cos\Phi + (\Delta_1^2/2)\sin\Phi]\,\gamma_0 R_1$$

where

$$\Phi = \arc\tan\left(\frac{\rho}{z+h}\right) . \tag{21}$$

$\mathrm{Erfc}(i\bar{p}_1^{\frac{1}{2}})$ is the complement of the error function of argument $i\bar{p}_1^{\frac{1}{2}}$. This result is valid subject to $|\Delta_1^2| \ll 1$ and $|\gamma_0 \rho| \gg 1$. Furthermore, if $(z+h) \ll \rho$, which is the usual case,

$$\bar{p}_1 \cong p_1 \left[1 + \frac{z+h}{\Delta_1 R_1}\right]^2 . \tag{22}$$

The result for the homogeneous half-space given in this form agrees with the formula derived by Sommerfeld in his 1926 paper [5].

It was shown by Norton [6] in 1936 that some improvement could be obtained if the numerical distance p_1 in Sommerfeld's formula was defined in a slightly different manner. This change is equivalent to letting Δ_1 assume the value

$$\Delta_1 = \frac{\gamma_0}{\gamma_1}\left[1 - \frac{\gamma_0^2}{\gamma_1^2}\sin^2\Phi\right]^{\frac{1}{2}} \tag{23}$$

Alternatively we could have replaced u_1 in the original integral solution by $(\gamma_1^2 - \gamma_0^2 \sin^2\Phi)^{\frac{1}{2}}$ instead of γ_1.

Since $|\gamma_1^2| \gg |\gamma_0^2|$ the factor in square brackets in equation (23) is very near unity, the resultant modification is usually small. The retention of the square bracket term is usually justified by the fact that the exact form of the Fresnel reflection coefficient is recovered when the asymptotic form of the solution is examined for $|p_1| \gg 1$.

In the case of the stratified conducting medium, the solution proceeds in a very similar fashion. The essential idea is that the u_n's in the exact integral formula for Π_0 may be approximated in the manner

$$u_n \cong (\gamma_n^2 - \gamma_0^2 \sin^2\Phi)^{\frac{1}{2}} = (\gamma_n^2 + k^2 \sin^2\Phi)^{\frac{1}{2}} \tag{24}$$

for $n = 1, 2, \ldots N$. Consequently, the branch-cut integrations around $\lambda = -i\gamma_n$ $(n = 1, 2, \ldots N)$ are neglected.

The final result for the stratified half-space can then be expressed in the form

$$\Pi_0 \cong c_0\left[\frac{e^{-ikR_0}}{R_0} + \frac{e^{-ikR_1}}{R_1} - 2P\right] \tag{25}$$

where

$$P = \left(\frac{p}{w}\right)^{\frac{1}{2}}[1 - F(w)]\,\frac{e^{-ikR_1}}{R_1} \tag{26}$$

where

$$F(w) = 1 - i(\pi w)^{\frac{1}{2}} \operatorname{erfc}(i w^{\frac{1}{2}}) e^{-w} ,$$

$$w = p\left(1 + \frac{z+h}{\Delta R_1}\right)^2 , \quad \Delta = \Delta_1 Q^2 \tag{27}$$

and $p = p_1 Q^2$. The factor Q is a correction factor which reduces to unity when the lower half-space becomes homogeneous. It is given by

$$Q = \frac{\bar{Z}_2 + \bar{K}_1 \tanh[(\gamma_1^2 + k^2 \sin^2 \Phi)^{\frac{1}{2}} h_1]}{\bar{K}_1 + \bar{Z}_2 \tanh[(\gamma_1^2 + k^2 \sin^2 \Phi)^{\frac{1}{2}} h_1]} \tag{28}$$

where

$$\bar{K}_1 = \frac{(\gamma_1^2 + k^2 \sin^2 \Phi)^{\frac{1}{2}}}{\sigma_1 + i\epsilon_1 \omega} \tag{29}$$

and

$$\bar{Z}_2 = \bar{K}_2 \frac{\bar{Z}_3 + \bar{K}_2 \tanh[(\gamma_2^2 + k^2 \sin^2 \Phi)^{\frac{1}{2}} h_2]}{\bar{K}_2 + \bar{Z}_3 \tanh[(\gamma_2^2 + k^2 \sin^2 \Phi)^{\frac{1}{2}} h_2]} \tag{30}$$

with

$$\bar{K}_2 = \frac{(\gamma_2^2 + k^2 \sin^2 \Phi)^{\frac{1}{2}}}{\sigma_2 + i\epsilon_2 \omega} .$$

The process is continued until

$$\bar{Z}_{N-1} = \frac{\bar{K}_N + \bar{K}_{N-1} \tanh[(\gamma_{N-1}^2 + k^2 \sin^2 \Phi)^{\frac{1}{2}} h_{N-1}]}{\bar{K}_{N-1} + \bar{K}_N \tanh[(\gamma_{N-1}^2 + k^2 \sin^2 \Phi)^{\frac{1}{2}} h_{N-1}]} \tag{31}$$

In the case of a two-layer ground where the permeabilities μ_1 and μ_2 are both equal to μ_0 , it is seen that

$$Q = \frac{(\gamma_1^2 + k^2 \sin^2 \Phi)^{\frac{1}{2}} + (\gamma_2^2 + k^2 \sin^2 \Phi)^{\frac{1}{2}} \tanh[(\gamma_1^2 + k^2 \sin^2 \Phi)^{\frac{1}{2}} h_1]}{(\gamma_2^2 + k^2 \sin^2 \Phi)^{\frac{1}{2}} + (\gamma_1^2 + k^2 \sin^2 \Phi)^{\frac{1}{2}} \tanh[(\gamma_1^2 + k^2 \sin^2 \Phi)^{\frac{1}{2}} h_1]} \tag{32}$$

Furthermore, if $|\gamma_1|$ and $|\gamma_2| \gg k \sin \Phi$, this simplifies to

$$Q = \frac{\gamma_1 + \gamma_2 \tanh \gamma_1 h_1}{\gamma_2 + \gamma_1 \tanh \gamma_1 h_1} . \tag{33}$$

When displacement currents in the ground are negligible, such that $\sigma_1 \gg \epsilon_1 \omega$ and $\sigma_2 \gg \epsilon_2 \omega$, it is seen that

$$\gamma_1 h_1 \cong V e^{i\pi/4}$$

where

$$V = (\sigma_1 \mu_0 \omega)^{\frac{1}{2}} h_1$$

and

$$\frac{\gamma_1}{\gamma_2} = \left(\frac{\sigma_1}{\sigma_2}\right)^{\frac{1}{2}} .$$

For this rather idealized case the amplitude and the phase of Q are shown plotted in Fig. 2a and Fig. 2b as a function of V for various values of the ratio $(\sigma_1/\sigma_2)^{\frac{1}{2}}$. It is immediately evident that the argument q may range from $+45°$ to $-45°$ depending on the thickness of the upper layer and the value of the conductivity ratio. Noting that $p = p_1 Q^2$ it is seen that the argument of p ranges from $+90°$ to $-90°$. In the case of a homogeneous ground the argument of p was always in the range $0°$ to $-90°$.

To discuss the manner in which the field varies with distance, it is convenient to consider first the case where the observer and the source are both on the surface of the ground (i. e., $z = h = 0$). Then the z component of the Hertz vector is given by

$$\Pi_0 = 2c_0 (e^{-ik\rho}/\rho) F(p) \tag{34}$$

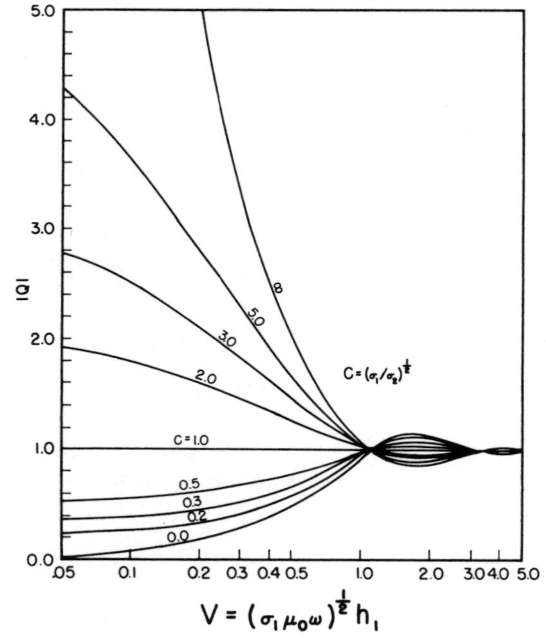

Figure 2a. Amplitude of the correction factor Q for a two-layer ground

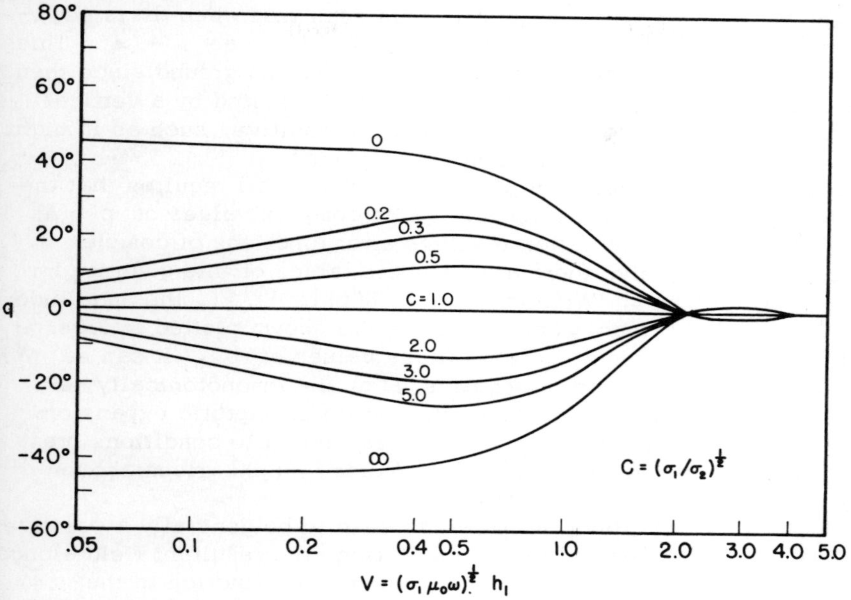

Figure 2b. Phase of correction factor Q for a two-layer ground.

where

$$F(p) = 1 - i(\pi p)^{\frac{1}{2}} e^{-p} \operatorname{erfc}(ip^{\frac{1}{2}}) \tag{35}$$

and $p = -ik\rho\,\Delta^2/2$. The corresponding expression for the vertical electric field is

$$E_{0z} = 2k^2 c_0 (e^{-ik\rho}/\rho) F(p) \tag{36}$$

subject, of course, to $k\rho \gg 1$. The function $F(p)$ can be regarded as the correction to the field of a dipole on the surface of a perfectly conducting plane for if $p \to 0$, $F(p) \to 1$.

The nature of the attenuation function $F(p)$ depends rather critically on the complex value of p . For example, if $p = |p| e^{ib}$, it is not difficult to show that

$$F(p) \cong -\frac{1}{2p} - \frac{1 \cdot 3}{(2p)^2} - \frac{3 \cdot 5}{(2p)^3} - \frac{1 \cdot 3 \cdot 5 \cdot 7}{(2p)^4} - \cdots \tag{37}$$

for $|p| \gg 1$, and $-2\pi < b < 0$, while

$$F(p) \cong -2i(\pi p)^{\frac{1}{2}} e^{-p} - \frac{1}{2p} - \frac{1 \cdot 3}{(2p)^2} - \frac{1 \cdot 3 \cdot 5}{(2p)^3} - \cdots \tag{38}$$

for $|p| \gg 1$ and $2\pi > b > 0$. It is thus seen that when b is negative, the vertical electric field E_z varies as $1/\rho^2$ as $\rho \to \infty$. This is the state of affairs for a homogeneous conducting ground since then b is in the range from 0 to $\pi/2$ for the waves excited by a vertical electric dipole. On the other hand, if b is positive, such as it might be for a stratified ground, E_z can vary as $1/\rho^{\frac{1}{2}}$.

To examine the distance dependence in any detail requires that the function $F(p)$ be computed for a range of complex values of p. As can be seen, this computation involves error functions of complex argument. Fortunately, there are adequate tables of this quantity for all interesting values. Writing $F(p) = |F(p)|e^{-i\Phi(p)}$, the amplitude $|F(p)|$ and phase (lag) $\Phi(p)$ functions are shown plotted in Figs. 3a and 3b as a function of p for various values of b. It can be seen that when b is zero or negative $F(p)$ is a monotonically decreasing function of $|p|$ as suggested by its asymptotic expansion. On the other hand, if b is positive corresponding to conditions present in certain stratified media, the amplitude $|F(p)|$ rises above unity for certain intermediate values of $|p|$.

The phase (lag) function $\Phi(p)$ is seen to be generally a positive function. Thus for vertical dipole excitation, the resultant field along the surface is always a "slow" wave in contra-distinction to the Zenneck wave which is a "fast" wave.

To illustrate the behavior of the field when the source dipole and the observer are both raised to heights h and z, respectively, it is desirable to consider the asymptotic or far-field situation where $|p|$ or $|w| \gg 1$. The solution may then be written in the following form

$$\Pi_0 \cong \psi_a + \psi_b + \epsilon\psi_s$$

where $\epsilon = 0$ for arg $w < 0$ and $\epsilon = 1$ for arg $w > 0$, and where the three partial fields are given by

$$\psi_a/c_0 \cong \frac{e^{-ikR_0}}{R_0} + \frac{C-\Delta}{C+\Delta}\,\frac{e^{-ikR_1}}{R_1} \tag{39}$$

$$\psi_b/c_0 \cong -\left\{\frac{1}{p(1+C/\Delta)^3} + \frac{1\cdot 3}{2p^2(1+C/\Delta)^5} + \frac{1\cdot 3\cdot 5}{4p^3(1+C/\Delta)^7} + \cdots\right\}\frac{e^{-ikR_1}}{R_1} \tag{40}$$

and

$$\frac{\psi_s}{c_0} \cong -\frac{2\Delta}{\Delta+C}\,2i(\pi w)^{\frac{1}{2}}\,e^{-w}\,\frac{e^{-ikR_1}}{R_1} \tag{41}$$

where

$$C = \cos\Phi = \frac{h+z}{R_1}\,.$$

The contribution ψ_a can be described as a "space wave" since it is composed of a primary influence e^{-ikR_0}/R_0 and a specularly reflected

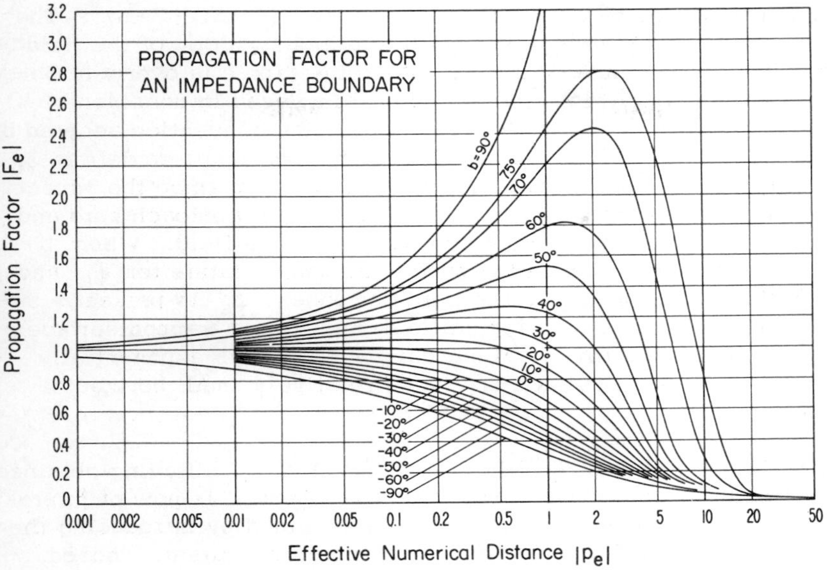

Figure 3a

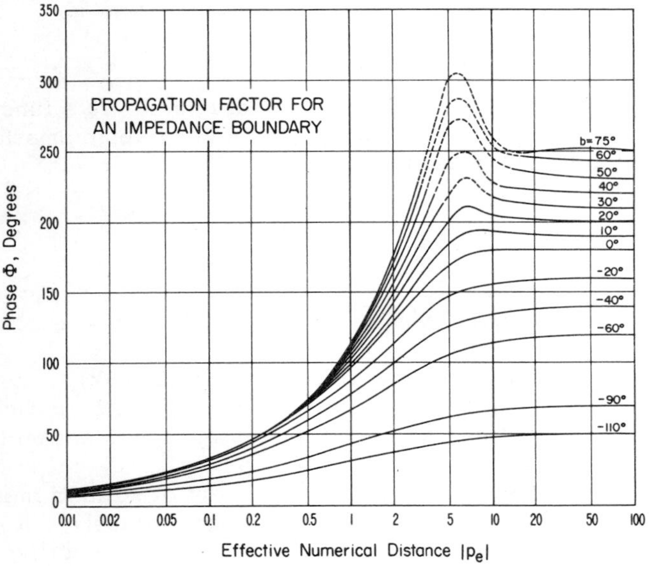

Figure 3b

component modified by a reflection coefficient $(C-\Delta)/(C+\Delta)$. The term ψ_b when added to ψ_a is the complete description of the field for $b < 0$. This includes the case where the dipole is over a homogeneous half-space which is the problem discussed in considerable detail by Sommerfeld and Norton. Following the convention adopted by the second author, it would seem to be very appropriate to define ψ_b as the Norton Surface Wave. This is a logical step since the "space wave" vanishes as the antenna heights z and h approach zero and, if $b < 0$, ψ_b is then the sole contribution to the field. When $b > 0$, there is no reason to change the suggested nomenclature for ψ_a and ψ_b. In this case, however, the third component ψ_s is present. Because of its properties it is logical to define it as a trapped surface wave. It propagates like a cylindrical wave, decays exponentially with height above the surface and has a relatively small horizontal attenuation.

4. A NOTE ON THE SURFACE IMPEDANCE CONCEPT. Having obtained a useful solution to a rather complicated problem, it is now of interest to see if a more compact treatment can be obtained by introducing the approximations into the boundary conditions at the outset. Indeed, this is the case, for we see that equation (17) satisfies the boundary condition

$$E_\rho = -ZH_\varphi \tag{42}$$

on the plane $z = 0$, where

$$Z = \eta_0 \Delta . \tag{43}$$

In the exact solution of the problem, Δ, of course, is a function of λ, the integration variable. However, as a good approximation Δ can be replaced by the quantity

$$\Delta = \Delta_1 Q^2 \tag{44}$$

where

$$\Delta_1 = \frac{\gamma_0 \mu_1}{\gamma_1 \mu_0} \left[1 - \frac{\gamma_0^2}{\gamma_1^2} \sin^2 \Phi\right]^{\frac{1}{2}}$$

and Q is the correction factor defined by equation (32).

The quantity Z, which is proportional to Δ, is by definition the ratio of the tangential fields for a plane wave incident on the surface $z = 0$ at an angle Φ.

It is also of interest to note that the concept of surface impedance may be applied to the case of a uniformly rough surface[7]. A model which yields a simple, yet meaningful, result is a conducting plane with a (uniform) distribution of hemi-spherical bosses of finite conductivity[8]. In the cases where the bosses are electrically small, it was shown that the effective value of Δ, for near grazing incidence, is

$$\Delta \cong i3kv(1 - \frac{\Gamma^*}{2}) \qquad (45a)$$

where v is the volume of the bosses per unit area and Γ^* is a complex factor which accounts for the ohmic and magnetic losses. For highly conducting non-magnetic bosses

$$\Gamma^* \cong 1 + \frac{3}{2}(i-1)\frac{\delta}{a} \cong 1 \qquad (45b)$$

where δ is the skin depth of the boss material and a is the radius of the boss. Consequently, as can be seen from the relation $p = -ik\Delta^2/2$, the argument b of the numerical distance is near +90°. Thus a trapped surface wave is excited by a vertical dipole over such a surface.

5. THE HEIGHT-GAIN FUNCTIONS. For some applications it is of interest to know how the field varies with height z above the surface of the ground. The ratio G(z) of the vertical electric field at height z to the vertical electric field at the ground is often called the height-gain function. For $h = 0$ and $k\rho \gg 1$, it is given by

$$G(z) = [1 - i(\pi\rho)^{\frac{1}{2}} e^{-w} \operatorname{erfc}(iw^{\frac{1}{2}})]/F(p) \qquad (46)$$

where

$$w = p\left(1 + \frac{z}{\Delta R_1}\right)^2 \cong p\left(1 + \frac{z}{\Delta\rho}\right)^2 . \qquad (47)$$

This result follows directly from equation (27). For small heights, it is of interest to develop G(z) in a power series in z. For example

$$G(z) = G(0) + z\left(\frac{dG}{dz}\right)_{z=0} + \frac{z^2}{2}\left(\frac{d^2G}{dz^2}\right)_{z=0} + \cdots \qquad (48)$$

Now

$$\frac{dG}{dz} = [-(\frac{p}{w})^{\frac{1}{2}} + i(\pi p)^{\frac{1}{2}} e^{-w} \operatorname{erfc}(iw^{\frac{1}{2}})]\frac{dw}{dz}\,\frac{1}{F(p)} \qquad (49)$$

and

$$\frac{dw}{dz} = 2p\left(1 + \frac{z}{\Delta\rho}\right)\frac{1}{\Delta\rho} . \qquad (50)$$

Therefore

$$\left(\frac{dG}{dz}\right)_{z=0} = ik\Delta \qquad (51)$$

and, to a first order in z,

$$G(z) \cong (1 + ik\Delta z) . \qquad (52)$$

The generation of higher-order terms using this method is cumbersome, and it is really better to return to the original integral for Π_0 given by

$$\Pi_0(z) = 2c_0 \int_0^\infty \frac{\lambda J_0(\lambda\rho)}{u + ik\Delta} e^{-uz} d\lambda \qquad (53)$$

where $h = 0$. Expanding the exponential, this is rewritten

$$\Pi_0(z) = 2c_0 \int_0^\infty [1 - uz + u^2z^2/2 - \cdots] \frac{\lambda J_0(\lambda\rho)}{u + ik\Delta} d\lambda \qquad (54)$$

$$= 2[\Pi_0(0) + ik\Delta\Pi_0(0) + \frac{z^2}{2}\left(\frac{\partial^2 \Pi_0(z)}{\partial z^2}\right)_{z=0} + \cdots] \qquad (55)$$

Now since $\Pi_0(z)$ satisfies the wave equation, $\partial^2/\partial z^2$ can be replaced by

$$-\frac{1}{\rho}\frac{1}{\partial\rho}\rho\frac{\partial}{\partial\rho} - k^2 \qquad (56)$$

and thus

$$\Pi(z) \cong [1 + ik\Delta z - \frac{z^2}{2}\left(k^2 + \frac{1}{\rho}\frac{\partial}{\partial\rho}\rho\frac{\partial}{\partial\rho}\right) + \cdots]\,\Pi(0) \qquad (57)$$

In the case $-2\pi < b < 0$ and it is not difficult to show that the third term is negligible if $k\rho \gg 1$ and $\rho^2 \gg z^2$.

6. CORRESPONDING SOLUTION FOR THE MAGNETIC DIPOLE. The solution for the vertical magnetic dipole located at height h above the surface of an N-layered half-space is almost identical to the previous results for a vertical electric dipole. In fact, the solution for magnetic dipole excitation may be obtained by making the following well-known transformations

$$\sigma + i\omega\epsilon \to i\mu\omega$$

$$i\mu\omega \to \sigma + i\epsilon\omega$$

$$\vec{E} \to \vec{H}$$

$$\vec{H} \to -\vec{E}$$

These follow immediately from the nearly symmetrical form of Maxwell's equations. In the case of a homogeneous earth, the numerical distance which occurs so consistently in the theory now has the form

$$p' = -ikR_1(\Delta_1')^2/2 \qquad (58)$$

where

$$\Delta_1' = \frac{\gamma_0 \epsilon_1}{\gamma_1 \epsilon_0} [1 - \frac{\gamma_0^2}{\gamma_1^2} \sin^2 \Phi]^{\frac{1}{2}} \tag{59}$$

On comparing this with equation (23) we see that $\Delta_1' \cong \frac{1}{\Delta_1}$ when $|\gamma_1^2| \gg |\gamma_0^2|$. Thus the numerical distance p' is usually a very large number since $\Delta_1 \ll 1$. This means that only the leading term of the asymptotic expansions in inverse powers of p' need be retained.

While the radiation fields of a vertical magnetic dipole over a multilayer conducting half-space may be readily computed using the previous results, it should be mentioned that an exact solution exists for a special problem. The specific situation is when the magnetic dipole is located in the plane interface between two homogeneous media. As we will see this leads to integrals which can be expressed in simple closed form.

The magnetic dipole or small wire loop of area δA is situated at the origin of a cylindrical coordinate system (ρ, φ, z) with the axis of the loop oriented in the z direction. The loop is assumed to carry a constant current I. The formal solution (in terms of integrals) was given by Sommerfeld, but as mentioned it can also be obtained as a special case of the previous analysis for the electric dipole. For $h = 0$ and $\mu_1 = \mu_0$, the fields can be obtained from

$$E_\varphi = \frac{\partial F}{\partial \rho}, \quad i\mu\omega H_z = (-\gamma^2 + \frac{\partial^2}{\partial z^2}) F, \quad i\mu\omega H_\rho = \frac{\partial^2 F}{\partial \rho \partial z} \tag{60}$$

where

$$F_0 = \frac{I\delta A i\mu_0 \omega}{2\pi} \int_0^\infty \frac{\lambda J_0(\lambda\rho) \exp(-u_0 z)}{u_1 + u_0} d\lambda \tag{61}$$

and

$$F_1 = \frac{I\delta A i\mu_0 \omega}{2\pi} \int_0^\infty \frac{\lambda J_0(\lambda\rho) \exp(+u_1 z)}{u_1 + u_0} d\lambda \tag{62}$$

when the subscript 0 pertains to $z > 0$, whereas the subscript 1 pertains to $z < 0$. As before

$$u_0 = (\lambda^2 + \gamma_0^2)^{\frac{1}{2}} \quad \text{and} \quad u_1 = (\lambda^2 + \gamma_1^2)^{\frac{1}{2}}$$

When $z = 0$ the integrals F_0 and F_1 become identical and they are now designated F, where

$$F = \frac{I\delta A i\mu_0 \omega}{2\pi} \int_0^\infty \frac{J_0(\lambda\rho)}{u_1 + u_0} d\lambda \tag{63}$$

On multiplying numerator and denominator by $u_1 - u_0$, this becomes

$$F = \frac{i\mu_0 \omega I \delta A}{2\pi(\gamma_1^2 - \gamma_0^2)} \left[\int_0^\infty \lambda u_1 J_0(\lambda\rho) d\lambda - \int_0^\infty \lambda u_0 J_0(\lambda\rho) d\lambda \right] \tag{64}$$

It is now noted that

$$\int_0^\infty \lambda u_1 J_0(\lambda\rho) d\lambda = \left[\frac{\partial^2}{\partial z^2} \int_0^\infty \frac{\lambda J_0(\lambda\rho)}{u_1} e^{-u_1 z} d\lambda \right]_{z=0}$$

$$= \left[\frac{\partial^2}{\partial z^2} \frac{\exp[-\gamma_1(\rho^2 + z^2)^{\frac{1}{2}}]}{(\rho^2 + z^2)^{\frac{1}{2}}} \right]_{z=0}$$

$$= -\frac{1}{\rho^3}(1 + \gamma_1\rho) e^{-\gamma_1\rho} \ . \tag{65}$$

Thus

$$F = \frac{-I\mu_0 \omega I \delta A}{2\pi(\gamma_1^2 - \gamma_0^2)\rho^3} [(1 + \gamma_1\rho) e^{-\gamma_1\rho} - (1 + \gamma_0\rho) e^{-\gamma_0\rho}] \tag{66}$$

The fields in the interface are then found to be

$$E_\varphi = \frac{-i\mu_0 \omega I \delta A}{2\pi(\gamma_1^2 - \gamma_0^2)\rho^4} [(3 + 3\gamma_0\rho + \gamma_0^2\rho^2) e^{-\gamma_0\rho} - (3 + 3\gamma_1\rho + \gamma_1^2\rho^2) e^{-\gamma_1\rho}] \tag{67}$$

and

$$H_z = \frac{I \delta A}{2\pi(\gamma_1^2 - \gamma_0^2)\rho^4} [(9 + 9\gamma_1\rho + 4\gamma_1^2\rho^2 + \gamma_1^3\rho^3) e^{-\gamma_1\rho} - (9 + 9\gamma_0\rho + 4\gamma_0^2\rho^2 + \gamma_0^3\rho^3) e^{-\gamma_0\rho}] \tag{68}$$

These are exact expressions and they are valid at all distances from the source. Unfortunately, it is not possible to express H_ρ in such simple form.

It may be noted that if $\text{Re}\gamma_1\rho \gg 1$, and $|\gamma_0\rho| = k\rho \gg 1$, it is possible to write

$$E_\varphi \cong \frac{-i\mu_0 \omega I \delta A}{2\pi\rho^2} \left(\frac{\gamma_0^2}{\gamma_1^2 - \gamma_0^2} \right) e^{-\gamma_0\rho} \cong \eta_0 H_z \tag{69}$$

where $\eta_0 = i\mu_0\omega/\gamma_0 \cong 120\pi$. Some numerical values based on equation (68) are available in the literature [9].

7. RADIATION FROM A DIPOLE OVER A SPHERICALLY STRATIFIED GROUND. In previous sections the earth's curvature has been neglected. In most applications to field strength computations, it is

necessary to consider the influence of sphericity. In this section the theory of propagation over a spherical earth with concentric stratifications is developed.

The method of solution is a direct extension of Watson's method[10,11]. He treated the (radially oriented) dipole in the presence of a homogeneous sphere. To simplify the analysis, the surface impedance concept is exploited.

The source of the field is considered to be an electric dipole oriented in the radial direction to the spherical earth of radius a. Choosing a spherical coordinate system (r, θ, φ), the surface of the earth is then defined by $r = a$, and the dipole is located at $r = b$ and $\theta = 0$. It is understood that $b > a$. Due to the spherical nature of the problem and because of the azimuthal symmetry, the fields can be derived from a Hertz vector, which has only a radial component U. Thus for $r > a$

$$E_r = \left(k^2 + \frac{\partial^2}{\partial r^2}\right)(rU) \tag{70}$$

$$E_\theta = \frac{1}{r}\,\frac{\partial^2}{\partial r \partial \theta}\,(rU) \tag{71}$$

$$H_\varphi = -i\epsilon\omega\,\frac{\partial U}{\partial \theta} \tag{72}$$

and

$$E_\varphi = H_r = H_\theta = 0\ . \tag{73}$$

The function of U satisfies

$$(\nabla^2 + k^2)U = 0 \tag{74}$$

in the exterior region $r > a$ except right at the source dipole. In the immediate vicinity of the source, U must have the following singularity

$$U \to -\frac{c_0}{bR}\,e^{-ikR}$$

where $R = (r^2 + b^2 - 2br\cos\theta)^{\frac{1}{2}}$ and $c_0 = -I\,ds/4\pi i\epsilon\omega$. This condition is readily verified by noting that the primary fields of the dipole are obtained when the operations are carried out.

The total field U is now written as the sum of two parts, $U_e + U_s$, where U_e has the proper singularity as $R \to 0$, and U_s remains finite. U_s is now expressed as a superposition of suitable solutions of the homogeneous wave equation. These have the form

$$h_n^{(2)}(kr)\,P_n(\cos\theta)$$

where $h_n^{(2)}(kr)$ is a spherical Hankel function of the second kind, which assures outgoing waves at infinity, and $P_n(\cos\theta)$ is a Legendre polynomial. The index n takes integral values. Now, making use of the known fact that exp(−ikR)/R can be expressed as an expansion in spherical functions, it readily follows that a suitable expansion for U_e is given by

$$U_e = \frac{ikc_0}{2} \sum_{n=0}^{\infty} (2n+1) h_n^{(1)}(kr) h_n^{(2)}(kb) P_n(\cos\theta) \quad \text{for } r < b , \tag{75}$$

and

$$U_e = \frac{ikc_0}{2} \sum_{n=0}^{\infty} (2n+1) h_n^{(2)}(kr) h_n^{(1)}(kb) P_n(\cos\theta) \quad \text{for } r > b , \tag{76}$$

where $h_n^{(1)}(kr)$ is the spherical Hankel function of the first kind.[1] A corresponding expansion for U_s is

$$U_s = \frac{ikc_0}{2} \sum_{n=0}^{\infty} (2n+1) A_n h_n^{(2)}(kr) P_n(\cos\theta) \tag{77}$$

where A_n is an unknown coefficient.

Having U_e and U_s expressed in this form enables the boundary conditions to be applied in a straightforward manner. The important simplification to the solution is that we impose the single boundary condition

$$E_\theta = -Z H_\varphi \quad \text{at } r = a . \tag{78}$$

This can be rewritten

$$\frac{1}{r} \frac{\partial}{\partial r} rU = Z i \epsilon \omega U . \tag{79}$$

In other words, it is assumed that the influence of the earth can be described adequately by its surface impedance Z . In this problem, Z is taken to be equal to the ratio of the tangential electric and magnetic fields for a vertically polarized plane wave at grazing incidence on a plane stratified earth.

By application of equation (79), it readily follows that

$$A_n = - \frac{h_n^{(1)}(ka)}{h_n^{(2)}(ka)} \left[\frac{\frac{d}{dx} \log x h_n^{(1)}(x) - i\Delta}{\frac{d}{dx} \log x h_n^{(2)}(x) - i\Delta} \right] h_n^{(2)}(kb) \tag{80}$$

where $\Delta = \epsilon \omega Z/k = Z/\eta$. The total field is then of the form

$$U = \sum_{n=0}^{\infty} (2n+1) f(n) P_n(\cos\theta) \tag{81}$$

where f(n) is a known function.

The expansions of the field as developed are not particularly useful in the radio problem since an enormous number of terms would be required in the summations over n . Instead, following the ideas of Watson and others, the summation is transformed into the following contour integral

$$U = i \int_{C_1+C_2} \frac{n\,dn}{\cos n\pi} f(n - \frac{1}{2}) P_{n-\frac{1}{2}}[\cos(\pi-\theta)] \qquad (82)$$

where n is now regarded as a continuous variable. The contour $C_1 + C_2$ encloses the real axis as illustrated in Fig. 4. Noting that the poles of the integrand are located at $n = \frac{1}{2}, \frac{3}{2}, \frac{5}{2}, \ldots$ etc., it can be readily verified by the theorem of residues that this integral is equivalent to equation (81).

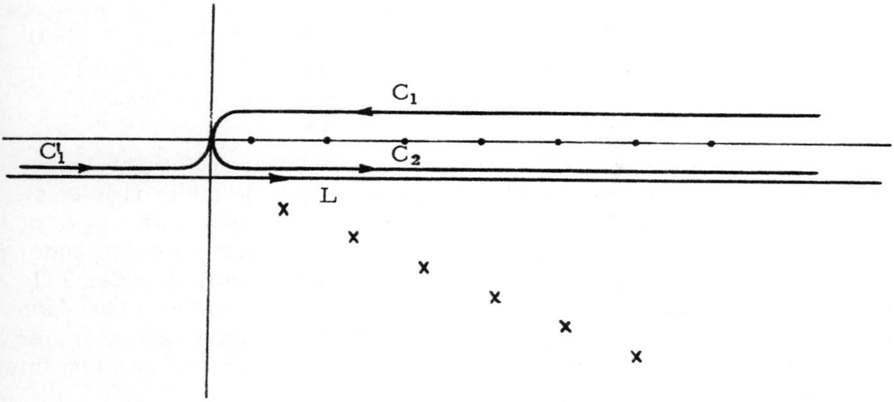

Figure 4. The contour in the complex n plane showing the location of the real and complex poles

Now since $f(n-\frac{1}{2})$ is an even function of n , the part of the contour C_1 above the real axis can be replaced by the contour C_1' which is located just below the negative real axis. The contour $C_1' + C_2$ is now entirely equivalent to L , a straight line running along just below the real axis. Replacing $n - \frac{1}{2}$ by ν the contour integral representation for U takes the fom

$$U = -i \int_{L} \frac{(\nu+1/2)}{\sin \nu\pi} f(\nu) P_{\nu}[\cos(\pi-\theta)]\,d\nu \qquad (83)$$

The next step in the analysis is to close L by an infinite semi-circle in the negative half-plane. The contribution from this portion of the contour vanishes as the radius of the semi-circle approaches infinity. The value of the integral for U along the contour L is now equal to the sum of the residues of the poles of the integrand in the lower half-plane.

The poles are located at the points $\nu = \nu_s$ which are solutions of

$$M(\nu) = 0$$

where

$$M(\nu) = \frac{d}{dx} \log x\, h_\nu^{(2)}(x) - i\Delta \tag{84}$$

with $x = ka$. It follows then that U is proportional to

$$\sum_s \frac{(\nu_s + 1/2)\, h_{\nu_s}^{(2)}(kb)\, h_{\nu_s}^{(2)}(kr)\, P_{\nu_s}[\cos(\pi-\theta)]}{\sin(\pi\nu_s) \left[\frac{\partial M(\nu)}{\partial \nu}\right]_{\nu=\nu_s} [h_{\nu_s}^{(2)}(ka)]^2} \tag{85}$$

where the summation extends over the complex poles ν_s . The location of these poles in the complex plane is one of the major problems in radio propagation. The difficulty stems from the fact that ν_s is of the same order of magnitude as ka . Thus, care must be exercised in approximating the spherical Hankel functions since their order and argument are not appreciately different. Watson and others [12a] have shown that in this region the spherical Hankel functions may be represented by Hankel functions of order 1/3 . For the present problem this amounts to using the result

$$x h_{\nu-\frac{1}{2}}^{(2)}(x) \cong e^{-i\pi/6} (-2\tau/3)^{\frac{1}{2}} x^{1/6} H_{1/3}^{(2)}[(1/3)(-2\tau)^{3/2}] \tag{86}$$

where $\nu = x + x^{1/3}\tau$. This relation is often called the Hankel approximation. Apparently it was first used by Lorenz (1890) [12b]. The root-determining equation can thus be well approximated by

$$\delta\, e^{i\pi/3} \frac{H_{2/3}^{(2)}[(1/3)(-2\tau_s)^{3/2}]}{H_{1/3}^{(2)}[(1/3)(-2\tau_s)^{3/2}]} = -(-2\tau_s)^{-\frac{1}{2}} \tag{87}$$

where

$$\delta = -i \frac{\eta}{(ka)^{1/3} Z} \quad \text{and} \quad \tau_s = \frac{\nu_s - ka}{(ka)^{1/3}} .$$

This equation is valid for $(ka) \gg 1$ and for the important roots (i.e., those leading to small attenuation).

Equation (85) for U can now be considerably simplified; the Legendre function can be replaced by the leading term in its asymptotic expansion, and $h_\nu^{(2)}(kb)$ and $h_\nu^{(2)}(kr)$ are replaced by their Hankel approximations. This results in

$$U = 2U_0(2\pi X)^{\frac{1}{2}} e^{-i\pi/4} \sum_s \frac{f_s(h_1) f_s(h_2) e^{-i\tau_s X}}{2\tau_s - 1/\delta^2} \tag{88}$$

where

$$f_s(h_i) = \left[\frac{X_i^2 - 2\tau_s}{-2\tau_s}\right]^{\frac{1}{2}} \frac{H_{1/3}^{(2)}[\frac{1}{3}(X_i^2 - 2\tau_s)^{3/2}]}{H_{1/3}^{(2)}[\frac{1}{3}(-2\tau_s)^{3/2}]} \tag{89}$$

$$U_0 = \frac{Ids\, e^{-ika\theta}}{4\pi i \epsilon \omega a(\theta \sin\theta)^{\frac{1}{2}}} \tag{90}$$

$$h_1 = r-a\ , \quad h_2 = b-a\ , \quad X = (ka)^{1/3}\theta$$

and

$$X_i = (ka)^{1/3}(2h_i/a)^{1/2} \quad \text{for } i = 1, 2\ .$$

The preceding equations are identical in form to those obtained by van der Pol and Bremmer [13] for the homogeneous earth. Their results are obtained as a special case by letting

$$Z = \eta_0 \Delta \tag{91}$$

with $\Delta = \frac{\gamma_0}{\gamma_1}\left(1 - \frac{\gamma_0^2}{\gamma_1^2}\right)^{\frac{1}{2}}$, where $\gamma_0 = ik$ and where γ_1 is the propagation constant of the homogeneous ground.

The residue series formula given by equation (88) has also been obtained by Fock [14]. Despite the fact that the notation is very different, his final results are very similar. There are a number of reasons why Fock's notation is to be preferred. The main advantage is that it does away with the awkward Hankel functions of order one-third. In their place Airy integrals are used. Now, Fock's solution may be written (for a time dependence $\exp(i\omega t)$) as follows

$$U = U_0 V(x, y_1, y_2, q) \tag{92}$$

where

$$V = -e^{-i\pi/4} 2(\pi x)^{\frac{1}{2}} \sum_s \frac{e^{-ixt_s}}{1-t_s/q^2} \frac{w_1(t_s-y_1)}{w_1(t_s)} \frac{w_1(t_s-y_2)}{w_1(t_s)} \tag{93}$$

where

$$y_1 = \left(\frac{2}{ka}\right)^{\frac{1}{3}} kh_1 \quad \text{and} \quad y_2 = \left(\frac{2}{ka}\right)^{\frac{1}{3}} kh_2$$

$$x = (ka/2)^{\frac{1}{3}}\theta \ , \quad q = -i(ka/2)^{\frac{1}{3}}\Delta$$

and $w_1(t)$ is an Airy integral. The roots t_s are solutions of the equation

$$w_1'(t) - q\,w_1(t) = 0 \tag{94}$$

where the prime indicates a derivative with respect to t . Since

$$w_1(t) = -e^{-i\pi/4}(-\pi/3t)^{\frac{1}{2}} H^{(2)}_{1/3}[(2/3)(-t)^{3/2}] \tag{95}$$

it is not difficult to see that equation (93) is <u>identical</u> to equation (88). Furthermore, the root-determining equations (94) and (87) are also equivalent to one another. The Airy integral function $w_1(t)$ is defined by a contour integral as follows

$$w_1(t) = \frac{1}{\pi^{\frac{1}{2}}} \int_{\Gamma_1} \exp(st - s^3/3)\,ds \tag{96}$$

where Γ_1 may be taken as a straight line segment from $\infty e^{i\pi 2/3}$ to the origin and out along the real axis to ∞ . The associated Airy function $w_2(t)$ also occurs frequently and it is defined by

$$w_2(t) = \frac{1}{\pi^{\frac{1}{2}}} \int_{\Gamma_2} \exp(st - s^3/3)\,ds \ , \tag{97}$$

where Γ_2 is the straight line segment from $\infty e^{-i2\pi/3}$ to the origin and out along the real axis to ∞ [2].

For certain applications it is desirable to express V as a contour integral in the complex t plane. This has the form

$$V = e^{i\pi/4} \left(\frac{x}{\pi}\right)^{\frac{1}{2}} \int_{\Gamma_2} e^{ixt} F(t, y_1, y_2, q)\,dt \tag{98}$$

where

$$F = \tfrac{1}{2} w_1(t-y_2)[w_2(t-y_1) + B(t)\,w_1(t-y_1)] \tag{99}$$

where

$$B(t) = - \left[\frac{w_2'(t) - q\, w_2(t)}{w_1'(t) - q\, w_1(t)} \right] \quad (100)$$

When the contour is closed by a circular arc (of infinite radius) in the lower half-plane it is possible to verify that the $-2\pi i$ times the sum of the residues at the poles $t = t_s$ leads back to equation (93). To demonstrate the equivalence, use is made of the fact that $w_1(t)$ and $w_2(t)$ satisfy the (Airy) differential equation

$$w''(t) - t\,w(t) = 0 \quad (101)$$

and that

$$w_1'(t_s) - q\, w_1(t_s) = 0 \,. \quad (102)$$

The form of equation (98) is particularly suitable for deriving approximate forms which are useful in special cases.

8. MODIFIED FLAT EARTH FORMULA. The residue series formula given by equation (88) enables field strength calculations to be carried out. In fact, there are many curves available in the literature which are based on this van der Pol-Bremmer theory. However, at short distances and in some cases at low frequencies, the residue series formula becomes quite poorly convergent. A new type of expansion has recently been developed in which the first term corresponds to the radiation of a dipole over a plane (stratified) earth [15], [16]. Succeeding terms are then proportional to inverse powers of ka .

The first step is to re-express U in the form of a contour integral or inverse Laplace transform as follows

$$\frac{iU(q)}{2g^{\frac{1}{2}}\, U_0} = \frac{1}{2\pi i} \int_{c - i\infty}^{c + i\infty} \frac{\pi^{\frac{1}{2}} f(p, h_1)\, f(p, h_2)\, e^{pg}}{1 + e^{i\pi/3}\, p^{\frac{1}{2}} A(p)}\, dp \quad (103)$$

where c is some small positive constant

$$g = iX/(2\delta^2) \,, \quad (104)$$

$$A(p) = \frac{H^{(2)}_{2/3}\left(\frac{p^{3/2}}{3\delta^3}\right)}{H^{(2)}_{1/3}\left(\frac{p^{3/2}}{3\delta^3}\right)} \quad (105)$$

and

$$f(p, h_i) = \left[\frac{X_i^2 + (p/\delta^2)}{(p/\delta^2)} \right]^{\frac{1}{2}} \frac{H_{1/3}^{(2)}\left[\frac{1}{3}(X_i^2 + (p/\delta^2))^{3/2}\right]}{H_{1/3}^{(2)}\left[\frac{1}{3}(p/\delta^2)^{3/2}\right]} . \quad (106)$$

It can be noted that the poles p_s of the integrand are determined by the solution of

$$H_{1/3}^{(2)}\left(\frac{p_s^{3/2}}{3\delta^3}\right) + e^{i\pi/3} p_s^{\frac{1}{2}} H_{2/3}^{(2)}\left(\frac{p_s^{3/2}}{3\delta^3}\right) = 0 . \quad (107)$$

If p_s is replaced by $2\delta^2 \tau_s e^{i\pi}$, this equation is identical to equation (87). It can be verified that the sum of the residues evaluated at the poles p_s leads back to equation (88).

The procedure is now to expand the integrand in powers of $1/p$. Each term is then a fairly simple inverse Laplace transform. Inverting each of these can be carried out if certain results from the operational calculus are employed. The details of this rather tedious process are given elsewhere [16]. The final formula is given as follows

$$\frac{U}{2U_0} = W \cong G \{F(p) - \frac{\delta^3}{2}[1 - i(\pi p)^{\frac{1}{2}} - (1+2p) F(p)]$$
$$+ \delta^6 [1 - i(\pi p)^{\frac{1}{2}}(1-p) - 2p + \frac{5}{6}p^2 + (\frac{p^2}{2} - 1) F(p)]$$
$$+ \text{terms in } \delta^9 , \delta^{12} , \text{etc.}\} \quad (108)$$

where

$$F(p) = 1 - i(\pi p)^{\frac{1}{2}} \operatorname{erfc}(i p^{\frac{1}{2}}) e^{-p} , \quad \delta^3 = \frac{i}{ka\Delta^3} , \quad (109)$$

and

$$G \cong (1 + ikh_1\Delta)(1 + ikh_2\Delta) . \quad (110)$$

This series formula is valid for relatively small heights such that kh_1^2 and $kh_2^2 \ll 2a\theta$.

At distances from the antenna greater than a few wavelengths, the quantity U is proportional to the vertical component of the actual electric field. On the other hand, $2U_0$ is proportional to the field of an identical source over a flat perfectly conducting earth. The field strength E, in millivolts per meter, at a distance d_{km} in kilometers, is then given by

$$E = \frac{300}{d_{km}} |W| \quad (111)$$

for a dipole whose strength is such that it would radiate one kilowatt over a perfectly conducting ground.

9. SOME NUMERICAL RESULTS. The function W for the case of ground-based terminals ($h_1 = h_2 = 0$) may be expressed by the residue series formula

$$W = (2\pi X)^{\frac{1}{2}} e^{-i\pi/4} \sum_s \frac{e^{-i\tau_s X}}{2\tau_s - 1/\delta^2} \tag{112}$$

where

$$X = (ka)^{\frac{1}{3}} d/a$$

in terms of the great circle distance, d , and the radius of the earth, a . τ_s are the roots of equation (87) and

$$\delta \cong e^{-i3\pi/4} \left(\frac{\sigma}{\epsilon_0 \omega}\right)^{\frac{1}{2}} (ka)^{-\frac{1}{3}}$$

where σ is the conductivity of the ground. The preceding form for δ is valid at low frequencies where the displacement currents in the ground are small compared to the conduction currents (i. e., $\epsilon\omega \ll \sigma$).

Numerical values of the amplitude and phase of W are given in Tables 1 and 2 for $\sigma = 4$, 10^{-2} and 10^{-3} mhos/m and six different values of the distance d . These results were obtained on SEAC (the National Bureau of Standards electronic automatic computer) by Dr. H. H. Howe. There are several gaps in the tables where it was not possible to devise a convenient program. In these particular calculations a was taken to be 4/3 times the actual earth radius to allow for standard atmospheric refraction [17], [18].

At the shorter distances (i. e., 60. 6 km) the residue series formula quoted above was very poorly convergent and as many as 1000 terms were required to secure convergence at frequencies less than 200 c/s. A good check on the calculations in this distance was afforded by the use of equation (108) which is highly convergent for short distances. These numerical values of W have been used in the preparation of some fairly detailed field strength- and phase- vs. distance curves [19].

Using a different machine program very extensive values of W (or its equivalent) have been recently obtained by Johler and colleagues [20].

10. MIXED-PATH GROUND WAVE PROPAGATION OVER A FLAT EARTH. In many cases, the assumption of a homogeneous or a concentrically stratified earth is adequate for the computation of ground wave field strengths. There may be situations, however, where the propagation path passes over land-sea boundaries. Clearly, in such a situation the assumed constancy of the electrical properties along this path is seriously violated. However, since coast-lines are relatively abrupt it is desirable to adopt a model in which the properties change at a

TABLE 1. Amplitude of W

Frequency	Distance (miles)					
	37.7	75.3	150.6	377	753	1,506
kc	$\sigma = 4$					
0.2	1.00060	--------	0.99407	0.97581	0.93220	0.81890
0.5	.99900	--------	.99047	.96176	.89458	.72915
1.0	.99850	--------	.98641	.94614	.85400	.64030
2.0	.99779	0.99334	.98069	.92445	.79981	.53391
5.0	.99638	.98931	.96939	.88286	.70267	.37563
10.0	.99478	.98478	.95680	.83827	.60807	.25677
20.0	.99252	.97839	.93925	.77923	.49714	.15426
50.0	.98802	.96582	.90541	.67493	.33772	.06105
100.0	.98296	.95183	.86886	.57555	.22340	.02377
200.0	.97578	.93237	.81996	.46216	.12951	.00714
500.0	.96130	.89459	.73171	.30572	.04907	.00089
	$\sigma = 10^{-2}$					
0.2	1.00060	0.99873	0.99401	0.97582	0.93223	0.81899
0.5	-------	--------	.99040	.96179	.89468	.72946
1.0	-------	--------	.98634	.94620	.85425	.64104
2.0	.99843	.99333	.98062	.92461	.80044	.53554
5.0	.99914	.98927	.96930	.88333	.70458	.37952
10.0	.99532	--------	.95652	.83914	.61196	.26304
20.0	.99252	.97783	.93797	.77999	.50364	.16225
50.0	.98508	.95997	.89577	.66732	.34198	.06646
100.0	.96884	.92669	.82821	.53124	.20598	.02256
200.0	.92053	.83428	.66792	.30708	.06808	.00243
500.0	-------	--------	-------	-------	-------	.00000
	$\sigma = 10^{-3}$					
0.2	1.00060	0.99873	0.99434	0.97583	0.93228	0.81916
0.5	-------	.99732	.99062	.96182	.89485	.73010
1.0	.99936	.99572	.98650	.94625	.85465	.64246
2.0	.99838	.99324	.98056	.92458	.80121	.53834
5.0	.99653	.98866	.96837	.88212	.70525	.38440
10.0	.99365	.98207	.95224	.83247	.60808	.26627
20.0	.98687	.96739	.92012	.75019	.47724	.15362
50.0	.95220	.89869	.79018	.50525	.21268	.02962
100.0	-------	--------	-------	-------	-------	-------
200.0	-------	--------	-------	-------	.00901	.00000
500.0	-------	.02701	.00912	.00069	.00001	.00000
	Distance (kilometers)					
	60.6	121	242	606	1,211	2,420

TABLE 2. Phase of W (in degrees). (The values are all negative)

Frequency	Distance (miles)					
	37.7	75.3	150.6	377	753	1,506
kc	$\sigma = 4$					
0.2	0.050	----	0.364	1.431	4.021	11.111
0.5	.079	----	.579	2.267	6.323	17.222
1.0	.112	----	.825	3.209	8.883	23.829
2.0	.162	0.429	1.178	4.541	12.445	32.717
5.0	.273	.704	1.898	7.183	19.319	49.020
10.0	.414	1.036	2.738	10.160	26.792	65.744
20.0	.641	1.546	3.978	14.377	36.939	87.334
50.0	1.190	2.693	6.616	22.793	55.986	126.041
100.0	1.965	4.205	9.879	32.423	76.410	166.527
200.0	3.341	6.740	15.031	46.466	104.711	222.115
500.0	7.052	13.162	27.188	76.567	162.995	335.992
	$\sigma = 10^{-2}$					
0.2	0.087	0.193	0.437	1.546	4.184	11.347
0.5	----	----	.761	2.555	6.735	17.823
1.0	----	----	1.189	3.787	9.714	25.054
2.0	.536	.943	1.907	5.701	14.121	35.229
5.0	1.232	1.989	3.721	10.104	23.590	55.601
10.0	2.241	----	6.389	16.047	35.511	79.551
20.0	4.284	6.695	11.298	26.273	54.866	116.592
50.0	10.277	15.572	24.990	53.082	102.976	205.783
100.0	20.107	29.943	46.675	93.804	173.888	335.889
200.0	39.462	57.839	87.843	168.225	300.818	207.051
500.0	----	----	----	----	----	250.022
	$\sigma = 10^{-3}$					
0.2	0.169	0.309	0.613	1.808	4.558	11.883
0.5	----	.640	1.184	3.212	7.674	19.189
1.0	.729	1.151	2.024	5.103	11.603	27.839
2.0	1.361	2.112	3.562	8.343	17.937	40.945
5.0	3.256	4.913	7.886	16.749	33.306	70.570
10.0	6.369	9.455	14.690	29.420	55.301	110.389
20.0	12.533	18.377	27.897	53.146	95.179	181.992
50.0	30.804	44.539	65.916	118.842	202.064	9.181
100.0	----	----	----	----	----	----
200.0	----	----	----	----	65.632	9.896
500.0	----	192.925	220.429	320.516	146.157	159.609
	Distance (kilometers)					
	60.6	121	242	606	1,211	2,420

discrete number of points along the path.

The method employed [21] here is not really rigorous but the final formulae appear to be identical with those obtained from more involved derivations [22]. For a start the earth is considered to be flat and defined by the plane $z = 0$ in a simple cartesian coordinate system. The (air) region above the earth corresponds to positive values of z. The earth medium to the left of the boundary line, defined by $y = 0$, $z = 0$, is characterized by a surface impedance Z. The earth medium to the right of the boundary is characterized by a surface impedance Z_1. The situation is illustrated in Fig. 5. Short dipole antennas are located at A and B which are assumed to be located on the x axis. These dipole antennas are oriented normal to the surface (i. e., they point in the z direction).

It is now assumed that a current I_a applied at the terminals of the antennas would produce electric and magnetic fields $\vec{E}_a$ and $\vec{H}_a$ for the case when the earth media on <u>both</u> sides of the boundary were characterized by a surface impedance Z. The mutual impedance for this case is denoted z_{ab}. Now, when the surface impedance is Z for $x < 0$ and Z_1 for $x > 0$ as shown in Fig. 5, the fields of antenna A, with the <u>same</u> current I_a, become $\vec{E}'_a$ and $\vec{H}'_a$, and the mutual impedance becomes z'_{ab}. In a similar fashion, a current I_b applied at the terminals of antenna B result in fields $\vec{E}_b$ and $\vec{H}_b$ when the whole plane is characterized by a surface impedance Z.

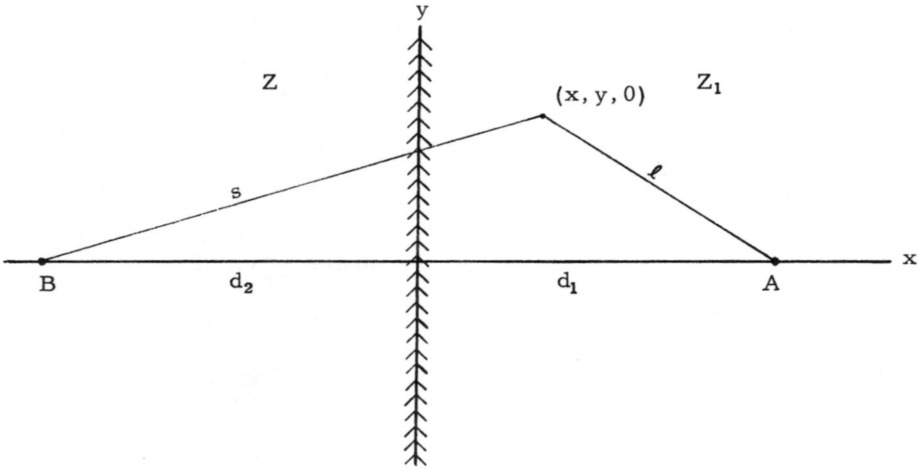

Figure 5. The plan view of the two-section flat earth. The coordinates of A are $(d_1, 0, 0)$ and the coordinates of B are $(-d_2, 0, 0)$. Also note that

$$AB = d = d_1 + d_2 .$$

It now follows from Ballantine's "Corollary I" [23], or from the work of Monteath [24], that

$$z'_{ab} - z_{ab} = \frac{1}{I_a I_b} \iint_S [\vec{E}_b \times \vec{H'}_a - \vec{E'}_a \times \vec{H}_b]_z \, dxdy \ , \qquad (113)$$

where the integration extends over the whole ground plane S. The subscript z indicates that the z or normal component of the vector products is taken. The above integral expression is really a formulation of the problem, and as such it cannot be used directly since the primed field quantities which are unknown enter into the integrand. A perturbation treatment can be used, however, which gives useful results for mixed-path ground wave propagation.

First, it should be noted that $E_x = -ZH_y$ and $E_y = ZH_x$ at $z = 0$ for the whole ground plane, while

$$E'_x = -Z_1 H'_y \ , \quad E'_y = Z_1 H'_y \quad \text{for } x > 0 \ , \quad z = 0 \ , \qquad (114a)$$

and

$$E'_x = -ZH'_y \ , \quad E'_y = ZH'_y \quad \text{for } x < 0 \ , \quad z = 0 \ . \qquad (114b)$$

Equation (113) may now be rewritten

$$I_a I_b \, \Delta z_m = (Z - Z_1) \iint_{S_0} (\vec{H'}_{at} \cdot \vec{H}_{bt}) \, dxdy \qquad (115)$$

where $\Delta z_m = z'_{ab} - z_{ab}$ is the change of the mutual impedance, from a two-section to a one-section path. The vector quantity $\vec{H'}_{at}$ is the tangential magnetic field of antenna A over the two-section ground plane while $\vec{H}_{bt}$ is the tangential magnetic field of antenna B over the one-section ground plane. The integration now extends over the surface S_0 to the right of the boundary line (i.e., $x > 0$).

Letting the short dipole antenna at B have an effective height h_b, the tangential magnetic field at P, a distance s from B is given by

$$\vec{H}_{bt} \cong \frac{ik I_b h_b}{2\pi s} e^{-iks} \left(1 + \frac{1}{iks}\right) F(s, Z) (\vec{i}_s \times \vec{i}_z) \qquad (116)$$

where

$$F(s, Z) = 1 - i(\pi p)^{\frac{1}{2}} e^{-p} \operatorname{erfc}(i p^{\frac{1}{2}}) \qquad (117)$$

and

$$p = -(iks/2)(Z/\eta_0)^2 \ . \qquad (118)$$

$\vec{i}_s$ and $\vec{i}_z$ are unit vectors in the directions of increasing s and z, respectively. Equation (116) follows directly from the results presented in Section 3.

The tangential magnetic field $\vec{H'}_{at}$ at a distance ℓ from antenna A, of effective height h_a, is now written in the form

$$\vec{H}'_{at} = \frac{ikI_a h_a}{2\pi\ell} e^{-ik\ell}\left(1 + \frac{1}{ik\ell}\right) F'(\ell, Z, Z_1)\,(\vec{i}_\ell \times \vec{i}_z) \qquad (119)$$

where $\vec{i}_\ell$ is a unit vector in the direction of increasing ℓ and where $F'(\ell, Z, Z_1)$ is some function of ℓ, Z, and Z_1. It can be expected that F' is slowly varying compared with $\exp(-ik\ell)$.

The mutual impedance formula can now be written

$$\Delta z_m = (Z_1 - Z)\frac{k^2 h_a h_b}{4\pi^2} \iint_{S_0} \frac{e^{-ik(\ell+s)}}{\ell s}\left(1 + \frac{1}{iks}\right)\left(1 + \frac{1}{ik\ell}\right) \qquad (120)$$

$$\times F(s, Z)\,F'(\ell, Z, Z_1)(\cos\delta)\,dx\,dy$$

where δ is the angle subtended by $\vec{i}_s$ and $\vec{i}_\ell$. The major contribution to the integrand occurs when the phase of the exponential term is nearly constant, since the other factors are relatively slowly varying. The exponent is expanded in a power series in y^2 as follows

$$\ell + s \cong d_2 + d_1 + \frac{y^2}{2}\left[\frac{1}{d_2 + x} + \frac{1}{d_1 - x}\right] \quad \text{for } d_1 > x > 0 \qquad (121a)$$

$$\cong d_2 - d_1 + 2x + \frac{y^2}{2}\left[\frac{1}{d_2 + x} + \frac{1}{x - d_1}\right] \quad \text{for } x > d_1 \qquad (121b)$$

where terms in y^4, y^6, etc., are neglected. A further approximation is to replace $1 + (1/iks)$ and $1 + (1/ik\ell)$ by unity in the integrand. This is justified if A and B are not near the boundary (i.e., $k\ell$ and ks are assumed to be much greater than unity over the most important range of the integration).

The integral can be written in the approximate form

$$\Delta z_m = \frac{(Z_1 - Z)k^2 h_a h_b}{4\pi^2} e^{-ikd} \int_0^{d_1} \frac{F(d_2 + x, Z)\,F'(d_1 - x, Z, Z_1)}{(d_2 + x)(d_1 - x)}$$

$$\times \left[\int_{-\infty}^{+\infty} e^{-i\alpha^2 y^2}\,dy\right] dx \qquad (122)$$

where $\alpha^2 = \dfrac{kd}{2(d_2 + x)(d_1 - x)}$. The integration over x extends only from 0 to d_1, because the contribution from the integrand for $x > d_1$ is negligible due to the presence of the rapidly varying function $\exp(-2ikx)$. The integration with respect to y is now simple and the square bracket term is replaced by $(\pi/i)^{\frac{1}{2}}/\alpha$. It should be noted that if $d_1 < 0$, corresponding to A on the same side of the boundary as B, Δz_m would be zero to the extent of the stationary phase approximation.

As the final step in the derivation, it is noted that

$$z_{ab} = \frac{h_a h_b i \mu_0 \omega}{2\pi d} e^{-ikd} F(d, Z) \tag{123}$$

and

$$z'_{ab} = \frac{h_a h_b i \mu_0 \omega}{2\pi d} e^{-ikd} F'(d, Z, Z_1) \tag{124}$$

provided $kd \gg 1$. Thus,

$$F'(d, Z, Z_1) \cong F(d, Z) - i\epsilon_0 \omega (Z_1 - Z) \left(\frac{d}{2\pi ik}\right)^{\frac{1}{2}} \int_0^{d_1} \frac{F(d_2 + x, Z) F'(d_1 - x, Z, Z_1)}{(d_2 + x)^{\frac{1}{2}} (d_1 - x)^{\frac{1}{2}}} dx \tag{125a}$$

for $d_1 > 0$, and

$$F'(d, Z, Z_1) \cong F(d, Z) \text{ for } d_1 < 0 . \tag{125b}$$

This is still an integral equation for the unknown attenuation function F' . However, in view of equation (125b) it follows that $F'(d_1 - x, Z, Z_1)$ where it occurs in the integrand of equation (125a) may be replaced by $F(d_1 - x, Z_1)$. After a change of variable, the final expression for $F'(d, Z, Z_1)$ can be written in convenient form

$$F' = F(p_0) - i(p_0/\pi)^{\frac{1}{2}} (1 - K^{\frac{1}{2}}) \int_0^{p_1} \frac{F(p) F(p_0 - Kp)}{[p(p_0 - Kp)]^{\frac{1}{2}}} dp \tag{126}$$

where

$$F(p) = 1 - i(\pi p) e^{-p} \operatorname{erfc}(ip^{\frac{1}{2}}) , \tag{127}$$

$$p_0 = -(ikd/2)(Z/\eta_0)^2 , \tag{128}$$

$$p_1 = -(ikd_1/2)(Z_1/\eta_0)^2 = p_0 V/K , \tag{129}$$

$$K = (Z/Z_1)^2 \text{ and } V = \frac{d_1}{d_1 + d_2} = \frac{d_1}{d} \tag{130}$$

It is remarkable that the above expression for F' for a two-section path is given in terms of the attenuation function F characterizing propagation between A and B over a one-section path. It should be noted that p_0 is the "numerical distance" appropriate for a one-section path from A to B over the plane with surface impedance Z , whereas p_1 is the numerical distance appropriate for a one-section path from the point B to the boundary at $(x = 0)$ over a plane with surface impedance Z_1 .

Apparently the integral given on the right-hand side is not expressible in closed form since the integrand involves the products of error functions. Fortunately, $F(p)$ and $F(p_0 - Kp)$ are slowly varying functions of p so that the integral readily yields to a numerical treatment. Some numerical results for various two-section paths are available [21], [25].

In certain limiting cases, the integral over p can be evaluated in an approximate manner. For example, when $p_0(1-V)$ and p_1 are small compared with unity, the power series expansions for the functions $F(p)$ and $F(p_0 - Kp)$ can be used over the whole range of the integration. These have the form

$$F(p) = 1 - i(\pi p)^{\frac{1}{2}} - 2p + i\pi^{\frac{1}{2}} p^{3/2} + \cdots \tag{131}$$

so that

$$\begin{aligned} F' = F(p_0) &+ 2i(p_0/\pi)^{\frac{1}{2}}(1-K^{-\frac{1}{2}}) \tan^{-1}\left(\frac{V}{1-V}\right) \\ &- 2p_0(1-K^{\frac{1}{2}})\left[\frac{1}{K}(1-\sqrt{1-V}) + \left(\frac{V}{K}\right)^{\frac{1}{2}}\right] \end{aligned} \tag{132}$$

+ terms in $p_0^{3/2}$, p_0^2, etc.

Another limiting case is when $d_1 \ll d$ so that as a first approximation

$$\frac{F(p)}{p^{\frac{1}{2}}} \cong \frac{F(p_0)}{p_0^{\frac{1}{2}}} \tag{133}$$

which when combined with the series expansion for $F(p)$ leads readily to the result

$$\frac{F'}{F(p_0)} \cong 1 - \frac{2i(1-K^{\frac{1}{2}})}{\pi^{\frac{1}{2}}}\left[p_1^{\frac{1}{2}} - \frac{i\pi^{\frac{1}{2}}p_1}{2} - \frac{2p_1^{3/2}}{3} + \frac{i\pi^{\frac{1}{2}}p_1^2}{4} + \frac{4p_1^{5/2}}{15} - \cdots\right] \tag{134}$$

As mentioned above, the final results obtained are valid only when both antennas A and B are at least several wavelengths from the boundary line separating the two sections of the path. It is desirable to investigate the field relatively near the boundary without resorting to a stationary phase method to evaluate the double surface integral. Again, it is admitted that the analysis is not rigorous since certain approximations are justified mainly on physical grounds.

The starting point is the double integral representation for the mutual impedance increment Δz_m in the form given by equation (120). Now, since it is assumed that $d_1 \ll d_2$, it can be anticipated that the important contribution to the surface integration is confined to the region where x and y are also small compared with d_2. As a consequence, it is permissible to employ the following approximations

$$F(s, Z) \cong F(d_2, Z) \cong F(d, Z)$$

$$F'(\ell, Z, Z_1) \cong 1 \quad (\text{subject to } |p_1| \ll 1)$$

$$1/s \cong 1/d_2 \quad , \quad \cos\delta \cong \frac{x-d_1}{\ell} \quad ,$$

and

$$k(s+\ell) \cong k(d_2+x+\ell) \quad .$$

In other words, the boundary is in the Fraunhofer field of the source at A .

The integral formula for the mutual impedance now becomes

$$\Delta z_m \cong (Z_1-Z)\frac{k^2 h_a h_b}{4\pi^2 d_2} e^{-ikd_2} F(d_2, Z)$$

$$\times \int_{x=0}^{+\infty} e^{-ikx} \int_{y=-\infty}^{+\infty} \frac{e^{-ik\ell}}{\ell} \frac{(x-d_1)}{\ell} (1+\frac{1}{ik\ell}) dxdy \ , \qquad (135)$$

where $\ell \cong [(x-d_1)^2 + y^2]^{\frac{1}{2}}$.

The y integrations can now be carried out by noting that

$$\int_0^{\infty} \frac{e^{-ik\ell}}{\ell} dy = -\frac{\pi i}{2} H_0^{(2)}[k|x-d_1|] \qquad (136)$$

while the x integrations are effected by using the result that

$$\int_0^{\infty} e^{-ikx} \frac{d}{dx} H_0^{(2)}[k|x-d_1|] dx$$

$$= -(1-ikd_1) H_0^{(2)}(kd_1) + kd_1 H_1^{(2)}(kd_1) \quad \text{for } d_1 > 0 \qquad (137)$$

$$= -(1-ikd_1) H_0^{(2)}(-kd_1) - kd_1 H_1^{(2)}(-kd_1) \quad \text{for } d_1 < 0 \ . \qquad (138)$$

$H_0^{(2)}$ and $H_1^{(2)}$ are the Hankel functions of order zero and one, respectively.

Using the above results it is not difficult to show that

$$\frac{F'}{F} \cong 1 + (q/2) e^{i3\pi/4}[(1-i\alpha) H_0^{(2)}(\alpha) - \alpha H_1^{(2)}(\alpha)] e^{i\alpha} \qquad (139)$$

for $\alpha = kd_1 > 0$, and

$$\frac{F'}{F} \cong 1 + (q/2) e^{i3\pi/4} e^{-i\alpha}[(1+i\alpha) H_0^{(2)}(\alpha) - \alpha H_1^{(2)}(\alpha)] \qquad (140)$$

for $\alpha = -kd_1 > 0$, where

$$q = \frac{Z - Z_1}{\eta_0} e^{-i\pi/4} \ .$$

In the case of a two-section path where each section is homogeneous

$$Z_1 \cong (i\mu_0\omega/\sigma_1)^{\frac{1}{2}} \quad \text{if} \quad \sigma_1 \gg \epsilon_1\omega \ , \tag{141}$$

and

$$Z \cong (i\mu_0\omega/\sigma)^{\frac{1}{2}} \quad \text{if} \quad \sigma \gg \epsilon\,\omega \ , \tag{142}$$

so that

$$q \cong |q| \cong 0.0075(1 - \sqrt{\sigma/\sigma_1})(f_{mc}/\sigma)^{\frac{1}{2}}$$

where f_{mc} is the frequency in megacycles per second. It is seen that q is a measure of the conductivity contrast between the two media and it is a positive or negative real number when displacement currents in the ground can be neglected.

Equations (139) and (140) are expected to be valid quite close to and on either side of the boundary of separation. Because of the approximate boundary conditions which are used, however, the results are not valid very near and at the boundary itself. It is believed that the results are applicable only when α is somewhat greater than $|Z/\eta_0|$ or $|Z_1/\eta|$ which is usually small compared with unity. Further modification of the theory to remove this restriction would require a more precise description of how the two sections of the path are joined up.

When the distance of B from the boundary becomes large compared with the wavelength it is permissible to employ the asymptotic developments for the Hankel functions. Thus, for $\alpha \gg 1$,

$$\frac{F'}{F} \cong 1 + iq\left(\frac{2\alpha}{\pi}\right)^{\frac{1}{2}}\left[1 + i\frac{3}{8\alpha} - \frac{5}{128\,\alpha^2} + \cdots\right] \tag{143}$$

when $d_1 > 0$, and

$$\frac{F'}{F} \cong 1 - \frac{q}{2}\left(\frac{1}{2\pi\alpha}\right)^{\frac{1}{2}} e^{-2i\alpha}\left[1 - \frac{i}{8\alpha} + \cdots\right] \tag{144}$$

when $d_1 < 0$.

It is significant that the right-hand side of equation (143), when the square-bracketed term is replaced by unity, is in agreement with the first two terms of the series development given by equation (134). [Any closer correspondence is not expected since here p_1 has been assumed very small.] As expected, this shows that the stationary phase approximation limits the validity of the results to $\alpha \gg 1$.

It is also rather interesting to note that the stationary phase development would yield a value of unity for the right-hand side of equation (144). The departure from unity can be interpreted as a wave reflected from the boundary. It forms, with the incident wave, a standing wave pattern which is damped as B recedes from the boundary (toward A). Since q is a small number in most practical cases this results in only a small perturbation.

11. MIXED-PATH PROPAGATION OVER A SPHERICAL EARTH

In the preceding analysis it was assumed that the earth was flat. The propagation of vertically polarized waves along a two-section path on a spherical earth is treated here. The initial formulation is almost identical to that used in the flat-earth case.

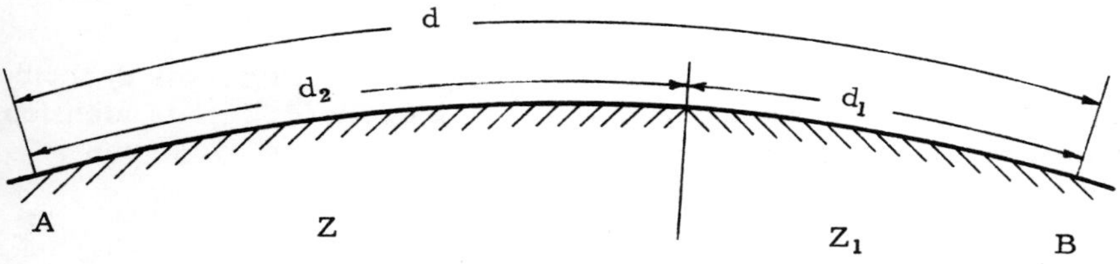

Figure 6

The mutual impedance between two vertical dipoles A and B on the two-section earth shown in Fig. 6 is again denoted z'_{ab}. The mutual impedance for the single-section path when the surface impedance is Z is denoted z_{ab}. We now define attenuation functions W' and W as follows

$$z'_{ab} = \frac{h_a h_b i\mu_0\omega}{2\pi d} e^{-ikd} W'(d, Z, Z_1) \tag{145}$$

and

$$z_{ab} = \frac{h_a h_b i\mu_0\omega}{2\pi d} e^{-ikd} W(d, Z) \tag{146}$$

where d is the great circle distance between A and B measured along the earth's surface.

Using the same method as for the flat-earth case above, the following explicit expression for W' can be obtained:

$$W'(d, Z, Z_1) \cong W(d, Z) - \left(\frac{ikd}{2\pi}\right)^{\frac{1}{2}} \frac{Z_1 - Z}{\eta_0} \int_0^{d_1} \frac{W(d-\alpha, Z)\, W(\alpha, Z_1)}{[\alpha(d-\alpha)]^{\frac{1}{2}}} d\alpha \tag{147}$$

The integration variable α ranges from B to the boundary line. The result given here is an approximation which is not valid near the boundary line since it utilizes a stationary phase method to reduce the surface integration to a line integration from 0 to d_1. Furthermore, the wave reflected from the boundary is neglected. As shown in Section 10, this latter effect is very small when $|Z_1|$ and $|Z|$ are small compared with η_0.

The attentuation function $W(d, Z)$ is obtained readily from the theory of Section 7. It is given by the series

$$W(d,Z) \cong \left(\frac{2\pi d}{a}\right)^{\frac{1}{2}} e^{-i\pi/4}(ka)^{1/6} \sum_s \frac{\exp[-i\tau_s(ka)^{1/3}d/a]}{2\tau_s - (1/\delta^2)} \tag{148}$$

where $\delta = -i(ka)^{-1/3}(\eta_0/Z)$ and τ_s are the complex roots described in Section 7. The corresponding expansion for $W(\alpha, Z_1)$ is identical in form to the above, but now d and δ are replaced by α and δ_1 where

$$\delta_1 = -i(ka)^{-1/3}(\eta_0/Z_1) .$$

By making use of these expansions, the integration in equation (147) can be easily carried out to yield

$$W'(d,Z,Z_1) \cong W(d,Z) + (2\pi ikd)^{\frac{1}{2}} \frac{Z_1 - Z}{\eta_0} \sum_{s=0}^{\infty} \sum_{q=0}^{\infty} \frac{\exp[-i\tau_s(ka)^{1/3}d/a]}{(2\tau_s - 1/\delta^2)} \frac{\{\exp[i(\tau_s - \tau_s^1)\frac{d_1}{a}(ka)^{1/3}] - 1\}}{(2\tau_q^1 - 1/\delta_1^2)(\tau_s - \tau_q^1)} \tag{149}$$

The coefficients τ_s are solutions of equation (87) while τ_q^1 are solutions of

$$\delta_1 e^{-i\pi/3} \frac{H_{2/3}^{(2)}[(1/3)(-2\tau_q^1)^{3/2}]}{H_{1/3}^{(2)}[(1/3)(-2\tau_q^1)^{3/2}]} = -(-2\tau_q^1)^{-\frac{1}{2}} \tag{150}$$

This double summation converges quite poorly in the many cases of practical interest. However, when the distances d_1 and d_2 are both large only a few terms are needed. An alternative series formula can be developed which is useful at short distances, but the analytical form of the coefficients is quite complicated.

In view of the fact that extensive numerical data for the W functions are available, it is really better to evaluate the integral by a numerical method. However, to convert the integral to a form suitable for numerical integration, it is desirable to change the variable of integration to remove the singularity at $\alpha = 0$. Thus, letting $\alpha = x^2$, it follows that

$$W' = W + 2(p_0/\pi)^{\frac{1}{2}} \left[\frac{1-K^{\frac{1}{2}}}{K^{\frac{1}{2}}}\right] e^{-i\pi/2} \int_0^{d_1^{\frac{1}{2}}} \frac{W(d-x^2, Z)\, W(x^2, Z_1)}{(d-x^2)^{\frac{1}{2}}}\, dx \tag{151}$$

where $K = (Z/Z_1)^2$ and $p_0 = -(ikd/2)(Z/\eta_0)^2$. This integral formula has proved to be quite useful.

12. SOME GRAPHICAL RESULTS FOR ONE- AND TWO-SECTION PATHS. To illustrate the application of the theory, a two-section path is considered. When one section becomes of zero length, the results correspond to a homogeneous spherical earth. The following values of the parameters are adopted.

$\sigma = 10^{-2}$ mhos/m corresponding to land,
$\sigma_1 = 4$ mhos/m corresponding to sea, and
$a = 4/3$ times the earth's radius.

In Fig. 7 the amplitude of W' is shown plotted as a function of distance d for frequencies of 10, 20, 50, 100 and 200 kc. Two values of d_1/d are indicated on the curves, namely 0 corresponding to an all-land path and 0.8 corresponding to an 80% sea path. For the lower frequencies, the curves are almost indistinguishable and the shape of W' is determined primarily by diffraction by the earth's curvature. The phase lag φ' (i.e., $\varphi' = -\arg W'$) is shown plotted in Figs. 8a to 8e as a function of d for the same frequencies. The values of d_1/d , which indicate the ratio of the length of the sea path to the length of the total path, are 0, 0.2, 0.4, 0.6, 0.8 and 1.0.

The preceding analysis has been discussed in relation to the mutual impedance between two dipole antennas at A or B . It is probably desirable to express the results in terms of the vertical electric field E at B (or A) for a standard source at A (or B). For example

$$E = E_0 W' = E_0 |W'| e^{-i\varphi'} \tag{152}$$

where

$$E_0 = \frac{160.5}{d}\left[1 - \frac{1}{(kd)^2} - \frac{i}{kd}\right] e^{-ikd} = |E_0| e^{-i\Phi_0} e^{-ikd}. \tag{153}$$

The "near field" E_0 is chosen such that the radiation component is 0.10 volt/m at d = 1 mile = 1605 meters. The amplitude E_0 and the phase Φ_0 are shown plotted in Figs. 9a and 9b, respectively, for frequencies of 10, 20, 50, 100 and 200 kc. It should be noted that $|E_0| \cong 160.5/d$ and $\Phi_0 \cong 1/kd$ when $kd \gg 1$. Actually E_0 is the

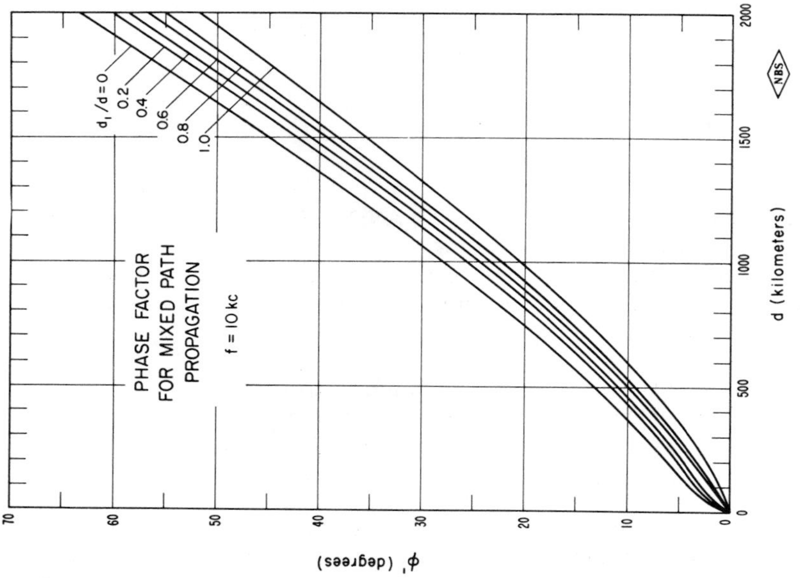

Figure 8a

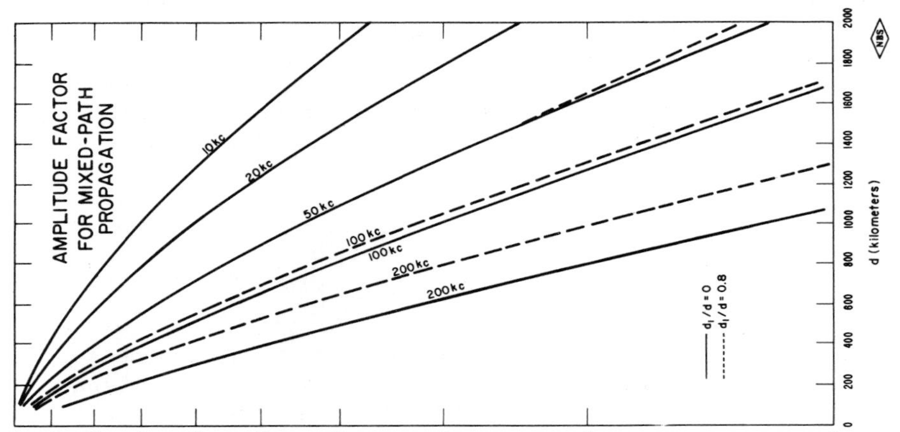

Figure 7

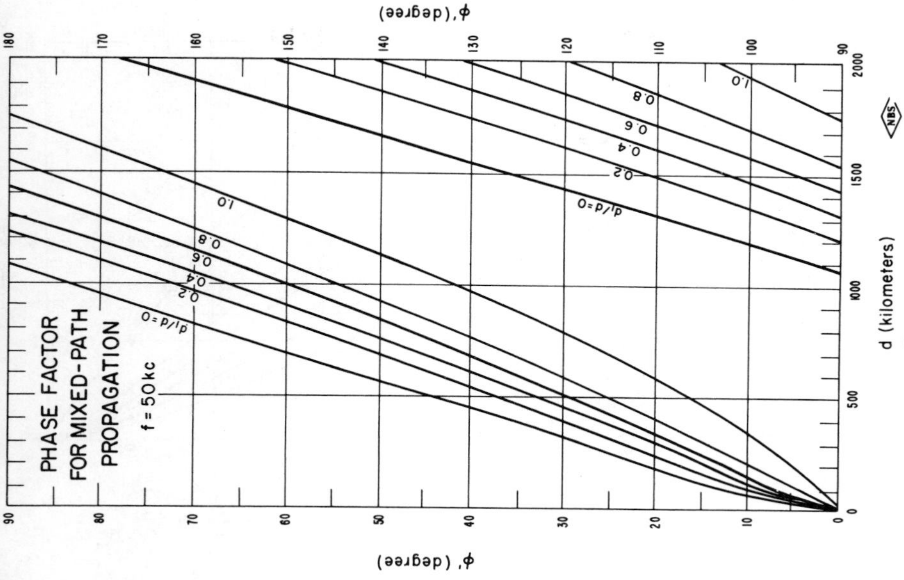

Figure 8c

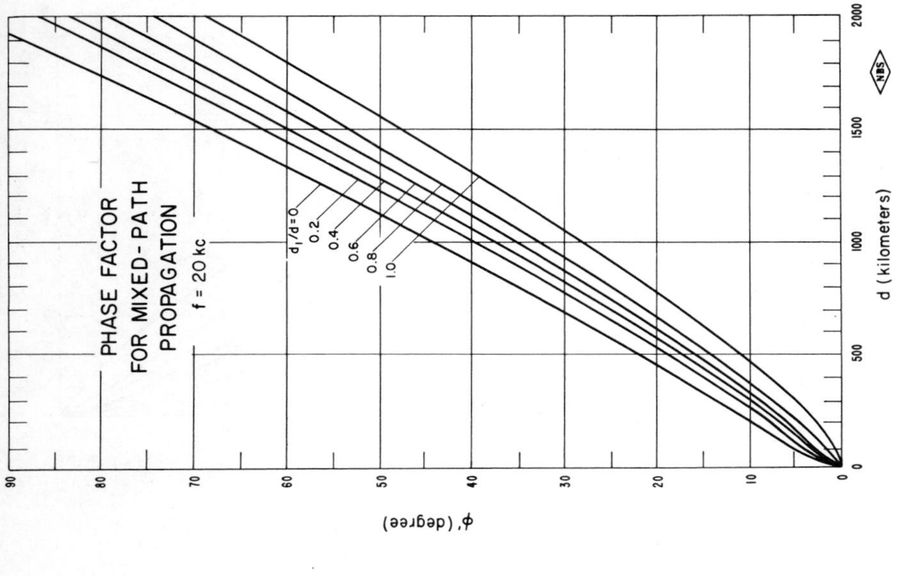

Figure 8b

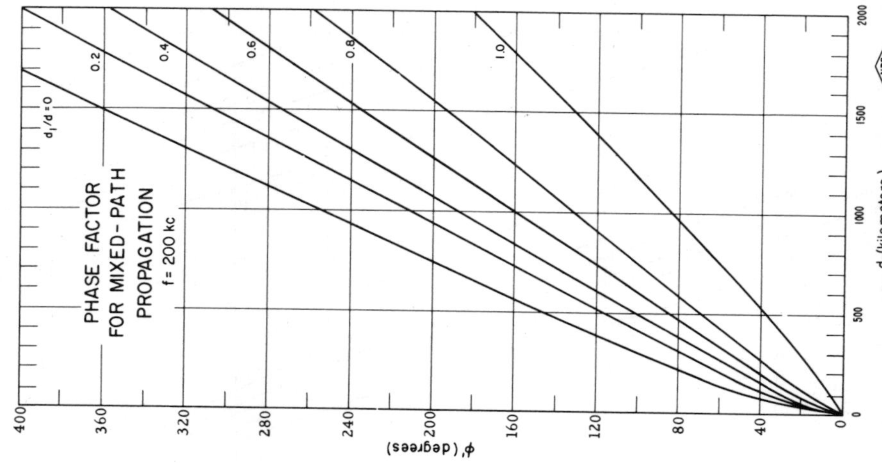
PHASE FACTOR
FOR MIXED-PATH
PROPAGATION
f = 200 kc
$d_1/d = 0$
0.2
0.4
0.6
0.8
1.0
φ' (degrees)
d (kilometers)
0
40
80
120
160
200
240
280
320
360
400
500
1000
1500
2000

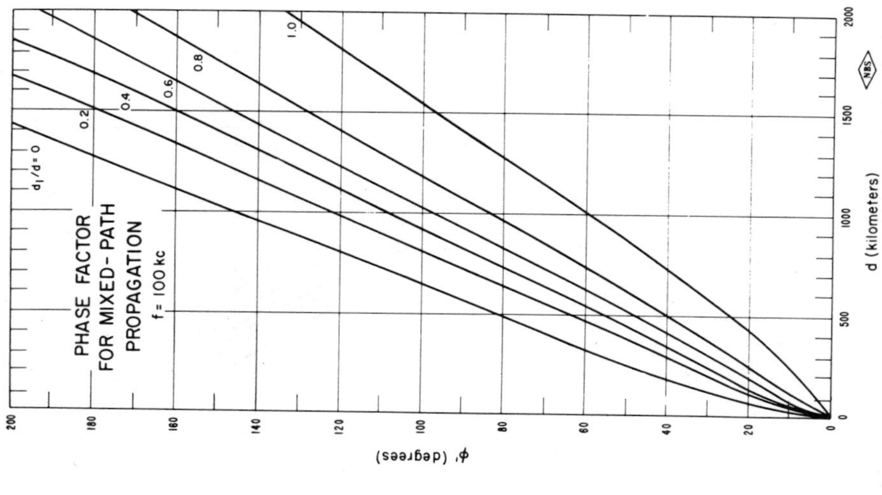
PHASE FACTOR
FOR MIXED-PATH
PROPAGATION
f = 100 kc
$d_1/d = 0$
0.2
0.4
0.6
0.8
1.0
φ' (degrees)
d (kilometers)
0
20
40
60
80
100
120
140
160
180
200
500
1000
1500
2000

Figure 8d

total field of the source on a flat perfectly conducting earth. To a good first approximation the total field E over a mixed path on a spherical earth is obtained by multiplying the near field E_0 by the attentuation function W' as indicated above.

To provide an illustration of the applicability of the numerical results, the total phase correction $\Phi(= \Phi_0 + \varphi')$ at 100 kc, is shown in Fig. 10 for the case of a transmitter on land, a distance d_2 from the coast. The plotted curves show how Φ varies with $d(= d_1 + d_2)$ for various values of d_2. As the receiver moves away from the transmitter, the rate of increase of the phase is characteristic of propagation over land. As the coast line is crossed at $d = d_2$, the phase lag is reduced somewhat and eventually continues to increase at a much slower rate as the receiver moves out to sea. This abrupt reduction of the rate of increase of phase lag is known as a "recovery effect" and has been verified experimentally [26].

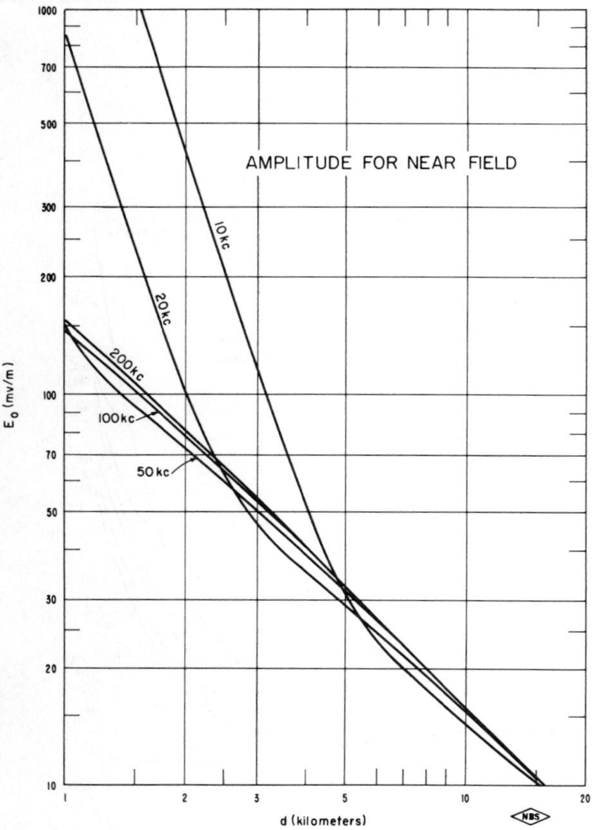

Figure 9a

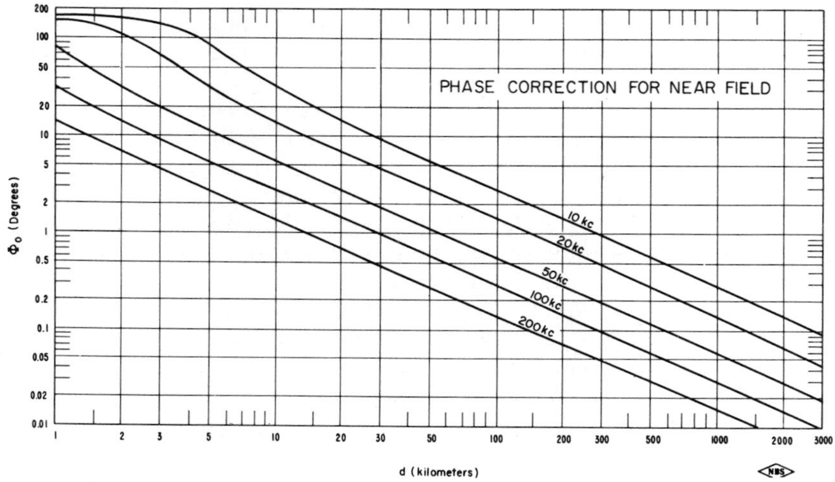

Figure 9b

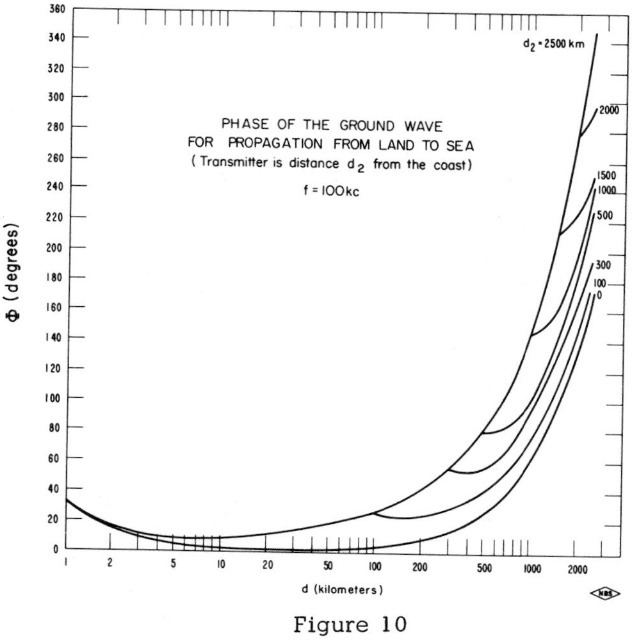

Figure 10

13. PROPAGATION OVER A THREE-SECTION PATH. The methods used for treating propagation over a two-section path can be readily extended to three-section or multi-section paths. The only limitation is one of complexity. For this reason it is doubtful if computations for paths with more than three sections are justified. However, a path consisting of three sections is representative of a number of practical situations such as when the propagation is all over sea water except for an intervening island or peninsula. This case will be discussed here.

The three sections of the path are assumed to have surface impedances Z, Z_2, and Z_1 as illustrated in Fig. 11.

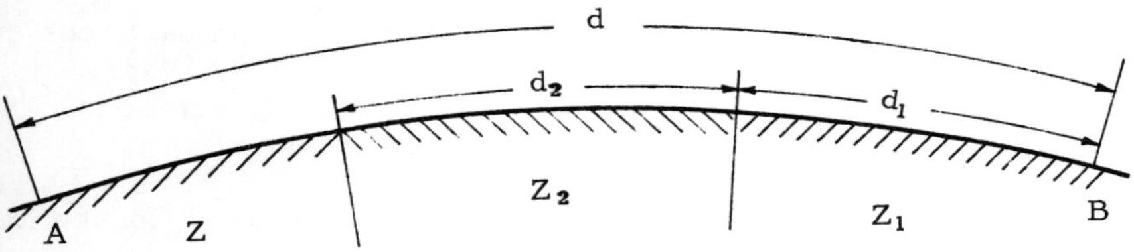

Figure 11

The (great-circle) separation between the dipoles is again denoted by d. The (great-circle) distances d_1 and d_2 are the lengths of two segments of surface impedance Z_1 and Z_2, respectively.

Using the method described above, it is not difficult to show that

$$W'(d, Z, Z_2, Z_1) = W(d, Z) - \left(\frac{ikd}{2\pi}\right)^{\frac{1}{2}} \frac{Z_1 - Z}{\eta_0} \int_0^{\infty} \frac{W(d-\alpha, Z) W(a, Z_1)}{[\alpha(d-\alpha)]^{\frac{1}{2}}} d\alpha$$

$$- \left(\frac{ikd}{2\pi}\right)^{\frac{1}{2}} \frac{Z_2 - Z}{\eta_0} \int_{d_1}^{d_1+d_2} \frac{W(d-\alpha, Z) W'(\alpha, Z_1, Z_2)}{[\alpha(d-\alpha)]^{\frac{1}{2}}} d\alpha \qquad (154)$$

where $W(d, Z)$ is the attentuation factor characteristic of propagation from A to B over a spherical surface of constant impedance Z. $W(d-\alpha, Z)$ and $W(\alpha, Z_1)$ are also attentuation functions for propagation over sections of the surface whose impedances are Z and Z_1, respectively. $W'(\alpha, Z_1, Z_2)$, on the other hand, is the appropriate two-section attenuation function for propagation from B to the point α on the middle section. It follows from equation (147) that

$$W'(\alpha, Z_1, Z_2) = W(\alpha, Z_1) - \left(\frac{ik\alpha}{2\pi}\right)^{\frac{1}{2}} \frac{Z_2 - Z_1}{\eta_0} \int_0^{\alpha - d_1} \frac{W(\alpha-\alpha', Z_1) W(\alpha', Z_2)}{[(\alpha-\alpha')\alpha']^{\frac{1}{2}}} d\alpha' \qquad (155)$$

The above integral formulae for a three-section path are approximations since the surface integrations have been approximated by line integrations. Consequently, A or B should not be near the boundaries of separation between the sections.

14. A SHORT BIBLIOGRAPHY ON GROUND WAVE PROPAGATION

H. Bremmer, "Applications of operational calculus to ground-wave propagation, particularly for long waves," IRE Trans. PGAP, vol. AP-6, p. 267; 1958. (VLF Symposium paper.)

H. Bremmer, "Propagation of electromagnetic waves," Handbuch der Physik, vol. 16, p. 423; 1958.

T. L. Eckersley, "Refraction of electric waves," Radio Review, vol. 1, p. 421, 1920.

E. Feinberg, "On the propagation of radio waves along an imperfect surface," Jour. of Phys., U.S.S.R., vol. 10, p. 410; 1946.

- a. W. P. Frantz, "A precision multi-purpose radio navigation system, Part I, Characteristics and applications;"
- b. W. Dean, "Part II, Propagation characteristics;"
- c. R. L. Frank, "Part III, Instrumentation," IRE National Convention Record; 1957.

K. Furutsu, "Propagation of electromagnetic waves over a flat earth across a boundary separating different media and coastal refraction," Jour. of the Radio Res. Labs., Japan, vol. 2, p. 1; 1955.

G. Grunberg, "Theory of coastal refraction of electromagnetic waves," Jour. of Phys., U.S.S.R., vol. 6, p. 185; 1942.

G. Grunberg, "Suggestions for a theory of coastal refraction," Physical Rev., vol. 63, p. 185; 1943.

J. R. Johler, W. J. Keller and L. C. Walters, "Phase of the low radio-frequency ground wave, "NBS Circular No. 573; 1956.

J. R. Johler, "Propagation of the radiofrequency ground-wave transient over a finitely conducting plane earth," Geof. Pura e Appl. (Milan), vol. 37, p. 116; 1957.

J. R. Johler, "Transient radio frequency ground waves over the surface of a finitely conducting plane earth," J. Research NBS, vol. 60, p. 281; 1958.

J. R. Johler and L. C. Walters, "Propagation of a ground-wave pulse around a finitely conducting spherical earth from a damped sinusoidal source current," IRE Trans., PGAP, vol. AP-7, p. 1; 1959.

J. Keilson and R. V. Row, "Transfer of transient electromagnetic waves into a lossy medium," J. Appl. Phys., vol. 30, p. 1595; 1959.

Martin B. Kraichman, "Basic experimental studies of the magnetic field from electromagnetic sources immersed in a semi-infinite conducting medium," J. Research NBS, vol. 64D, p. 21; January 1960. (VLF Symposium paper.)

B. R. Levy and J. B. Keller, "Propagation of electromagnetic pulses around the earth," IRE Trans. PGAP, vol. AP-6, p. 56; 1958.

G. Millington, "Ground-wave propagation over an inhomogeneous smooth earth," Proc. IEE, Paper No. 794R, vol. 96, Part III, p. 53; 1949.

K. A. Norton, "The calculation of the ground wave field intensity," Proc. IRE, vol. 29, p. 723; 1941.

K. A. Norton, "System loss in radio wave propagation," J. Research NBS, vol. 63D, p. 53; 1959.

B. G. Pressey, G. E. Ashwell and C. S. Fowler, "The measurement of the phase velocity of ground-wave propagation at low frequencies over a land path," Proc. IEE, Paper No. 1438R, vol. 100, Part III, p. 73; 1953.

B. G. Pressey, G. E. Ashwell and C. S. Fowler, "Change of phase with distance of a low-frequency ground wave propagated across a coast-line," Proc. IEE, Paper No. 2082R, vol. 103B, p. 527; July, 1956.

B. G. Pressey and G. E. Ashwell, "The deviation of low-frequency ground waves at a coast-line," Proc. IEE, Paper No. 2083R, vol. 103B, p. 535; July, 1956.

B. G. Pressey, G. E. Ashwell and R. Roberts, "Further studies of the deviation of low- and medium-frequency ground waves at a coast-line," Proc. IEE, Paper No. 3018E, vol. 106B, No. 30, p. 548; November, 1959.

T. B. A. Senior, "Radio propagation over a discontinuity in the earth's electrical properties - II, Coastal refraction," Proc. IEE, Monograph No. 201R, vol. 104C, p. 139; October, 1956.

R. L. Smith-Rose, "A study of radio direction-finding," Radio Research Board Special Report No. 5 (H. M. Stationery Office; 1927).

A. N. Sommerfeld, "Uber die Ausbreitung der Wellen in der drachtlosen Telegraphie," Ann. Physik, vol. 81, p. 1135; 1926.

G. M. Stanley, "Layered-earth propagation in the vicinity of Point Barrow, Alaska," J. Research NBS, vol. 64D, p. 95; 1960. (VLF Symposium paper.)

J. R. Wait and H. H. Howe, "Amplitude and phase curves for ground-wave propagation in the band 200 cycles per second to 500 kilocycles," NBS Circular No. 574; 1956.

J. R. Wait, "Low frequency radiation from a horizontal antenna over a spherical earth," Can. Jour. Phys., vol. 34, p. 586; 1956.

J. R. Wait, "Mixed-path ground wave propagation: 1. Short distances," J. Research NBS, vol. 57, p. 1; 1956.

J. R. Wait, "Amplitude and phase of the low-frequency ground wave near a coastline," J. Research NBS, vol. 58, p. 237; 1957.

J. R. Wait, "The transient behaviour of the electromagnetic ground wave over a spherical earth," IRE Trans. PGAP, vol. AP-5, p. 198; 1957.

J. R. Wait, "Propagation of a pulse across a coastline," Proc. IRE, vol. 45, p. 1550; 1957.

J. R. Wait, "Transient fields of a vertical dipole over homogeneous curved ground," Can. J. Research, vol. 34, p. 116; 1957.

J. R. Wait, "A note on the propagation of the transient ground wave," Can. J. Phys., vol. 35, p. 1146; 1957.

J. R. Wait and James Householder, "Mixed-path ground-wave propagation: 2. Larger distances," J. Research NBS, vol. 59, p. 19; 1957. (A similar solution has been given recently by Y. K. Kalinin and E. L. Feinberg, Radiotechnika i Electronika, vol. 3; September, 1958.)

J. R. Wait, "On the theory of propagation of electromagnetic waves along a curved surface," Can. J. Phys., vol. 36, p. 9; 1958.

FOOTNOTES

[1] The spherical Hankel functions are defined as follows:

$$h_n^{(1)}(x) = -i(-1)^n x^n \left(\frac{d}{xdx}\right)^n \left(\frac{e^{ix}}{x}\right) \quad \text{and} \quad h_n^{(2)}(x) = i(-1)^n x^n \left(\frac{d}{xdx}\right)^n \left(\frac{e^{-ix}}{x}\right)$$

[2] Since Fock employs an $e^{-i\omega t}$ time factor, his definitions of $w_1(t)$ and $w_2(t)$ correspond to our definitions of $w_2(t)$ and $w_1(t)$, respectively.

REFERENCES

1. N.A. Logan, "General Research in Diffraction Theory," vols. I-II; 1959, Lockheed Missiles and Space Division, Sunnyvale, Calif.
2. H. Bremmer, "Terrestrial Radio Waves," Elsevier Publishing Co., New York and Amsterdam; 1949. See also, by the same author, "Propagation of electromagnetic waves," Handbuch der Physik, vol. 16, pp. 423-639; 1958.
3. E. L. Feinberg, "Propagation of radio waves along an inhomogeneous surface," Nuovo Cimento, Supplemento Al vol. XI, Series X, pp. 60-91; 1959.
4. B. L. Van der Waerden, "On the method of saddle points," App. Sci. Res., vol. 32, pp. 33-45; 1950.
5. A. N. Sommerfeld, "Uber die Ausbreitung der Wellen in der drahtlosen Telegraphie," Ann. Physik, vol. 81, pp. 1135-1170; 1926.
6. K.A. Norton, "The propagation of radio waves over the surface of the earth and in the upper atmosphere," Proc. IRE, vol. 24, pp. 1367-1387; 1936, and vol. 25, pp. 1203-1236; 1937.
7. Y. P. Lysanov, "On the scattering of electromagnetic waves from a rough surface," Doklady Akad. Nauk. (U. S. S. R.), vol. 87, pp. 719-722; 1952.
8. J. R. Wait, "Guiding of electromagnetic waves by uniformly rough surfaces," IRE Trans. PGAP, vol. AP-7, pp. S154-162; December 1959.

9. J. R. Wait, "Mutual coupling of loops lying on the ground," Geophysics, vol. 19, No. 2, pp. 290-296; April, 1954.
10. G. N. Watson, "The diffraction of radio waves by the earth," Proc. Roy. Soc., vol. A95, pp. 83-99; October 1918.
11. G. N. Watson, "The transmission of electric waves around the earth," Proc. Roy. Soc., vol. A95, pp. 546-563; July 1919.
12a. R. E. Langer, "On the connection formulas and the solutions of the wave equation," Phys. Rev., vol. 51, p. 669; 1937.
12b. L. V. Lorenz, Lysbevoegelsen i og uden for en plane Lysbølger belyst Kugle Vid. Selsk, Skr. (6), 6, p. 403; 1890.
13. B. van der Pol and H. Bremmer, "The diffraction of electromagnetic waves from an electrical point source round a finitely conducting sphere," Phil. Mag. ser. 7, vol. 24, pp. 141-176; July, 1937.
14. V. A. Fock, "Diffraction of radio waves around the earth's surface," J. Phys., U. S. S. R., vol. 9, pp. 256-266; April 1945.
15. H. Bremmer, "Applications of operational calculus to ground wave propagation, particularly for long waves," IRE Trans., vol. AP-6, No. 3, pp. 267-272; July, 1958.
16. J. R. Wait, "Radiation from a vertical antenna over a curved stratified ground," J. Research NBS, vol. 56, No. 4, pp. 237-244; April, 1956.
17. W. E. Miller, "Effective earth's radius for radio wave propagation beyond the horizon," Jour. App. Phys., vol. 22, pp. 55-62; January 1952.
18. J. R. Wait, "Radio wave propagation in an inhomogeneous atmosphere," NBS Technical Note No. 24; September 10, 1959.
19. J. R. Wait and H. H. Howe, "Amplitude and phase curves for ground-wave propagation in the band 200 cycles per second to 500 kilocycles," NBS Circular No. 574; May 1956.
20. J. R. Johler, L. C. Walters and C. M. Lilley, "Amplitude and phase of the low- and very-low radiofrequency ground wave," NBS Technical Note. No. 60; June 1, 1960.
21. J. R. Wait, "Mixed-path ground wave propagation, I. Short distances," J. Research NBS, vol. 57, No. 1, pp. 1-15; July, 1956.
22. See bibliography.
23. S. Ballantine, "Reciprocity in electromagnetic, acoustical and inter-connected systems," Proc. IRE, vol. 17, p. 929; 1929.
24. G. D. Monteath, "Application of the compensation theorem to certain radiation and propagation problems," Monograph No. 3, The Institution of Electrical Engineers (London); 1951.
25. Z. Godzinski, "The theory of ground-wave propagation over an inhomogeneous earth," Proc. I. E. E., vol. 105C, p. 448; April 1958.
26. B. G. Pressey, G. E. Ashwell, and C. S. Fowler, "Change of phase with distance of a low-frequency ground wave propagated across a coast-line," Proc. IEE, Paper No. 2082R, vol. 103B, p. 527; July, 1956.

ACKNOWLEDGMENTS

This paper was written while the author was on a visit to the Laboratory of Electromagnetic Theory, Technical University of Denmark, Copenhagen, Denmark. During this time some support was extended by the Air Force Cambridge Research Laboratories under Contract CSO and A 58-40, dated March 31, 1958.

I would like to thank Mrs. Eileen Brackett for her extensive help in preparing this paper and Mr. Kenneth Spies for his critical reading of the manuscript.

SAMUEL N. KARP

Far Field Amplitudes and Inverse Diffraction Theory

1. SUMMARY. In electromagnetic and acoustic diffraction problems the behavior of the plane wave far field scattering amplitude is of crucial importance, both theoretically and practically. In the present paper we present some new properties of this function for plane wave excitation, in the case of two dimensional scattering and with special reference to the <u>inverse</u> diffraction problem.

The function in question, which will be defined analytically below, is a continuous analogue of a scattering matrix. For a given scatterer and frequency, it depends on two variables, the angle of incidence θ_0 of the plane wave, and the angle of observation θ of the far diffracted field at infinity. We call it $f(\theta, \theta_0)$. In the first part of the analysis, [section 3] we consider determinants formed from the values of this function. We deduce necessary and sufficient geometrical conditions (as to the geometry of the scatterer) for the vanishing of such determinants, under specific hypotheses as to the boundary conditions being fulfilled. These conditions show that for an acoustically <u>soft</u> obstacle no third order determinant formed by using three different angles can vanish, and we conjecture the same result for all odd order determinants. Even order determinants can vanish.

In the second part of the analysis [section 4] we discuss the case where $f(\theta, \theta_0) = f(\theta - \theta_0)$ in the case of a soft obstacle. Such an amplitude arises when the scatterer is a circle, as is well known. We show that this is the <u>only</u> possible cause. This is an explicitly solvable problem in the exact Inverse Diffraction Theory.

The analysis of sections 3 and 4 is preceded [section 2] by a statement of definitions and known results, and the proof of a basic lemma.

2. DEFINITIONS AND PRELIMINARY LEMMAS. Let a plane wave $\phi(r, \theta; \theta_0) \equiv \exp ikr \cos(\theta - \theta_0)$, travelling in the direction θ_0, be incident on a scatterer S, contained within some circle of radius a,

say, whose center is the origin of both polar and cartesian coordinates. Then the total field, produced by the interaction of the incident and diffracted fields, is denoted by $u(r, \theta; \theta_0)$, obeys the Helmholtz* equation $\Delta u + k^2 u = 0$, and can be written in the form

$$u(r, \theta; \theta_0) \equiv \phi(r, \theta; \theta_0) + v(r, \theta; \theta_0) \tag{1}$$

where $v(r, \theta; \theta_0)$ is the diffracted field, which must be regular outside S and be an outgoing wave function. We can write

$$u(r, \theta; \theta_0) = \exp ikr \cos(\theta-\theta_0) - \frac{i}{4} \oint [H_0(k\overline{PQ}) \frac{\partial V}{\partial n_Q} - V(Q) \frac{\partial H_0}{\partial n_Q}(k\overline{PQ})] \, dS_Q, \tag{2}$$

where Q denotes a point on S , P an observation point, $\overline{PQ}$ their distance, $\partial/\partial n$ the outward normal derivative, and $H_0(kr)$ is the Hankel function of the <u>first</u> kind. (Here a time dependence $\exp(-i\omega t)$ has been assumed and then suppressed.] If we let $r \to \infty$ then we have the asymptotic formula

$$v \to \widetilde{H}_0(kr) f(\theta, \theta_0) \; ; \; \widetilde{H}_0 \equiv \sqrt{\frac{2}{\pi kr}} \, e^{i(kr - \frac{\pi}{4})} , \tag{3}$$

and this <u>defines</u> the far field amplitude function $f(\theta, \theta_0)$. Comparison with (2) shows that

$$f(\theta, \theta_0) = -\frac{i}{4} \oint [e^{-ikr_Q \cos(\theta-\theta_0)} \frac{\partial V}{\partial n}(Q; \theta_0) - V(Q; \theta_0) \frac{\partial}{\partial n} e^{-ikr_Q \cos(\theta-\theta_0)}] \, dS \tag{4}$$

The function $f(\theta, \theta_0)$ has the following well known properties:

$$f(\theta, \theta_0) = f(\theta_0 + \pi, \theta + \pi) , \tag{5}$$

$$\frac{1}{2\pi} \int_0^{2\pi} |f(\theta, \theta_0)|^2 \, d\theta = -\mathrm{Re}\, f(\theta, \theta_0) . \tag{6}$$

Equation (5) expresses reciprocity and may be obtained as a limiting form of the reciprocity theorem for Green's function. Equation (6) is the well known forward amplitude theorem, often quoted or proved in the literature. The results stated so far are well known. A more general result will now be given in the form of a lemma, based on definitions which will be used in the rest of the paper.

Lemma: Let

$$u_i \equiv u(r,\theta;\theta_i) \qquad \phi_i \equiv \exp ik(x\cos\theta_i + y\sin\theta_i)$$
$$f_i \equiv f(\theta,\theta_i) \qquad u_i = \phi_i + v_i \tag{7a}$$
$$v_i \equiv v(\theta,\theta_i)$$

and let $\{A_i\}$ be n complex numbers, and let

$$U \equiv \sum_1^n A_i u_i \ , \quad V \equiv \sum A_i v_i \ , \quad \Phi \equiv \sum A_i \phi_i \ , \quad F \equiv \sum A_i f_i \ ,$$
$$f_{ij} \equiv f(\theta_i, \theta_j) \ , \quad F_i \equiv \sum A_j f_{ij} \ . \tag{7b}$$

Then

$$\operatorname{Im} \oint_S V \frac{\partial V^*}{\partial n} dS = 2 \sum_i \sum_j A_i^* A_j (f_{ij} + f_{ji}^*) \equiv -\frac{2}{\pi} \int_0^{2\pi} |F|^2 d\theta \ , \tag{7c}$$

if it is assumed that on S we have, for all i, the boundary condition

$$d(S) u_i + \lambda(S) \frac{\partial u_i}{\partial n} = 0 \ ; \quad \operatorname{Im} \lambda(S)/d(S) = 0 \ , \tag{7d}$$

or, more generally, if the boundary conditions are such that

$$\operatorname{Im} \oint_S U \frac{\partial U^*}{\partial n} dS = 0 \text{ for arbitrary } \{A_i\} \ .$$

Proof: Under the given hypotheses we have $\operatorname{Im} \oint U \frac{\partial U^*}{\partial n} dS = 0$, while it is easily checked that $\operatorname{Im} \oint \frac{\partial \Phi^*}{\partial n} dS = 0$, since Φ is regular in the interior of S. Thus

$$0 = \operatorname{Im} \oint_S U \frac{\partial U^*}{\partial n} dS = \operatorname{Im} \left[\oint \left(V \frac{\partial \Phi^*}{\partial n} + \Phi^* \frac{\partial V}{\partial n} \right) dS + \oint V \frac{\partial V^*}{\partial n} dS \right] . \tag{7e}$$

We have**, by definition of f_{ij}, and use of (4)

$$f_{ij} = \frac{1}{4i} \oint \left(\frac{\phi_i^* \partial v_j}{\partial n} - \frac{\partial \phi_i^* v_j}{\partial n} \right) dS \ .$$

Therefore

$$4i \sum A_i^* F_i \equiv 4i \sum\sum A_i^* A_j f_{ij} = \oint \left(\Phi^* \frac{\partial V}{\partial n} - V \frac{\partial \Phi^*}{\partial n} \right) dS \ .$$

If we take the imaginary part of the last expression we find precisely the first half of (7c), in virtue of (7e). Now using the fact that for large r, $v_i \to \tilde{H}_0(kr) f_i$ and hence $V \to \tilde{H}_0(kr) F$, and using the fact that

$$\text{Im} \oint_S V \frac{\partial V^*}{\partial n} dS = \text{Im} \oint_{S_\infty} V \frac{\partial V^*}{\partial n} dS ,$$

where S_∞ is a circle at ∞, we can easily verify that the second equation in (7c) is correct. Q. E. D.

3. Equation (4) shows that $f(\theta, \theta_0)$ is an analytic function of θ. Thus it is uniquely determined by its values on any dense set. The problem of inverse diffraction is to determine S given $f(\theta, \theta_0)$, for a fixed k. It is of interest to consider the case when θ_0 is fixed or also, the case of variable θ, θ_0. The program to be followed would be to use f to determine v and hence u, and then to find the locus on which u obeys the boundary conditions. This is obviously difficult in general. In the present paper we prove some simple results which relate f and S under special circumstances. The present section is concerned with properties which arise from a consideration of determinants formed from $f(\theta, \theta_0)$, i.e. $\det(f_{ij})$. We treat the boundary conditions $u = 0$, $\partial u/\partial n = 0$ in this paper. The main results will now be listed.

Case a). Soft obstacles, boundary condition $u_i = 0$. We prove the following theorems.

Theorem Ia. If $\det(f_{ij}) = 0$, where $\{\theta_i\} = \theta_1, \theta_2, \cdots, \theta_n$ are n different angles modulo 2π, and if no subdeterminant vanishes, then there exist n nonvanishing constants $\{A_m\}$ such that the necessary and sufficient condition for (x, y) to be on S is that

$$\sum_1^n A_m \exp ik(x \cos \theta_m + y \sin \theta_m) = 0 . \tag{8a}$$

The A_m are subdeterminants of $\det(f_{ij})$. If S contains a closed curve then the wave number k is an eigenvalue for the interior of that curve. Equation (8a) can be interpreted to mean that S lies on an arc of an interference pattern.

Theorem IIa. No third order determinant of the above kind can vanish, since (8a) is impossible on a real arc for $n = 3$. The latter assertion, to be proved below, means that three plane waves can't interfere on an arc.

Theorem IIIa. For any integer n such that there is no real arc along which (8a) holds, $\det(f_{ij})$ cannot vanish under the circumstances described in the hypothesis of Theorem Ia.

Theorem IVa. If n is even it is always possible to find a real S on which (8a) is fulfilled. (For example (8a) is fulfilled along any segment of any node of any eigenfunction of a square membrane for which k is an eigenvalue, as is easily seen. It is well known that some of these nodes are curved. See [1] p. 314 for examples.)

> Conjecture. If n is odd it is impossible to find a real arc along which (8a) is satisfied.

If the above conjecture can be proved, then Theorem IIIa implies that no odd order determinant of f_{ij} can ever vanish, if no subdeterminants vanish.

Case b). Hard obstacle, boundary condition $\partial u_i/\partial n = 0$. We have the following results.

Theorem Ib. Theorem Ia is valid if we replace (8a) by

$$\sum_m A_m \frac{\partial}{\partial n} [\exp ik(x \cos \theta_m + y \sin \theta_m)] = 0 . \tag{8b}$$

On the other hand, Theorem IIa is not valid when this substitution is made, although Theorem IIIa is. This follows from the fact that a sum of three plane waves can be easily constructed so as to satisfy (8b) on any segment of the x axis. Probably the conjecture stated above is incorrect for a hard obstacle.

Case c). Reactive or capacitive obstacle. The boundary condition is $d(S) \frac{\partial u}{\partial n} + \lambda(S) u = 0$ with $d(S)/\lambda(S)$ real. One can derive a differential equation for the obstacle but the discussion is beyond the scope of the present paper.

Some additional results arise in the course of the proofs of the above assertions. We find, under the hypotheses of Ia or Ib,

$$\sum A_m f(\theta, \theta_m) = 0 \qquad \text{for all } \theta , \tag{9}$$

$$\sum A_m V(r, \theta; \theta_m) = 0 \qquad \text{for all } \theta , \tag{10}$$

$$\sum A_m f(\theta_m + \pi , \theta + \pi) = 0 \qquad \text{for all } \theta . \tag{11}$$

The last equation follows from reciprocity and it expresses a forced relation between the scattered field in certain characteristic directions when the direction of excitation, $\theta+\pi$, is arbitrary. The well known evenness or oddness of the scattered far field produced by a conducting strip is an example of (11) for $n = 2$. Other*** geometries possessing this property for the case of $u = 0$, are any combination of parallel, vertical, zero thickness conductors of any size, placed any number of half wave lengths apart, when $\theta_1 = 0$, $\theta_2 = \pi$. In the case $\partial u/\partial n = 0$, these segments can be closed by horizontal segments placed arbitrarily. Thus we obtain the case of a rectangle, for example. Another case of interest here is the case of a finite or infinite grating of rectangular grooves of depth = 1/2 wave length, cut out of the conducting half space $x \geq 0$; provided we are in Case b), equation (10) shows that the incident wave plus the usual reflected wave, that is, $e^{ikx} + e^{-ikx}$, satisfies all conditions. There is no diffracted field. This is easily verified a posteriori.

It should be noted that equations (9) and (10) are deduced from the determinantal condition and lead to our main results. But, of course, (9) and (10) also follow from the main results. In fact, if (8a) or (8b) are satisfied, then application of the boundary conditions to $\sum_m A_m V(r, \theta; \theta_m) \equiv F$ proves (10) if the uniqueness theorem is applied to the radiating wave function F. Equation (9) is the asymptotic form of equation (10).

We now proceed to prove the results already stated. Consider the function V defined in equation (7b). It is an outgoing wave function regular in the exterior of the obstacle S, and by (7d) we have, on S

$$d(S)\sum_i A_i u_i + \lambda(S)\sum_i A_i \frac{\partial u_i}{\partial n} = 0 . \tag{12}$$

Now, by the definitions in (7b) $U = \Phi + V$. Consequently, on S,

$$d(S)\Phi + \lambda(S)\frac{\partial \Phi}{\partial n} = -\left\{d(S)V + \lambda(S)\frac{\partial V}{\partial n}\right\} . \tag{13}$$

[For a hard obstacle $d(S) = 0$. For a soft obstacle $\lambda(S) = 0$.] Now suppose $\det(f_{ij}) = 0$, and no subdeterminant vanishes. Then we set

$$A_j = \text{cofactor of } f_{1j} \neq 0 , \tag{14}$$

and we easily deduce that the double sum in (7c) vanishes. Hence the function F vanishes. This is equation (9). Since F is the leading term in the expansion of V for large r, we deduce from Rellich's Lemma that V vanishes identically for this choice of $\{A_j\}$, which proves equation (10). This implies that the right-hand side of (13) vanishes identically. If the left-hand side of (13) is specialized to the case of soft (hard) obstacles, Theorem Ia(Ib) follows (cf. (8a) and (8b)]. Notice that when condition (7d) is used and not specialized, then we get a differential equation for S from the vanishing of the left side of (13), using $\partial y/\partial n = dx/dS$. The converses of

Theorems Ia and Ib follow from the fact that if (8a) or (8b) is assumed, and none of the A_i is zero, then the left-hand side of (13) vanishes. Hence so does the right side. Hence $\text{Im} \oint V \frac{\partial V}{\partial n} dS = 0$. Hence $F \equiv 0$. Hence, using $F = \sum A_i f(\theta, \theta_i)$, we deduce equation (9), of which equation (10) is an easy consequence. If we set $\theta = \theta_j$ in (9), we have n homogeneous equations for $j = 1, \ldots n$. Since none of the A_i vanish it follows that $\det(f_{ij}) = 0$, and no subdeterminant is zero. As to equation (11), it follows from (9) by reciprocity.

We proceed to Theorem IIa. Let S be a real arc along which (8a) holds.

Let $\gamma_m(S) \equiv \frac{dx}{dS} \cos \theta_m + \frac{dy}{dS} \sin \theta_m$, and let $\dot{\gamma}_m \equiv d\gamma_m/dS$. Construct two additional linear equations for the A_m by differentiating (8a) twice with respect to arc length. Then it is readily verified that the determinant of the coefficients is a multiple of

$$\begin{vmatrix} 1 & 1 & 1 \\ \gamma_1 & \gamma_2 & \gamma_3 \\ \gamma_1^2 & \gamma_2^2 & \gamma_3^2 \end{vmatrix} + \sqrt{-1} \begin{vmatrix} 1 & 1 & 1 \\ \gamma_1 & \gamma_2 & \gamma_3 \\ \dot{\gamma}_1 & \dot{\gamma}_2 & \dot{\gamma}_3 \end{vmatrix} .$$

The first term is a Vandermonde determinant. Its vanishing shows that two of the γ's must be equal. Since this must be true on a continuum of S , it follows that the corresponding pair of angles are equal modulo 2π , contrary to hypothesis. Hence, there is no real arc on which (8a) is satisfied nontrivially for $n = 3$. But if $\det(f_{ij}) = 0$ for $n = 3$, for the case of a real obstacle, then (8a) must be satisfied. This contradiction proves IIa. Unfortunately, this seems too complicated a method for higher values of n .

Theorem IIIa is now obvious, since it is the negation of Theorem Ia.

Theorem IVa has been explained adequately, if briefly, and so have the conjecture and the related remarks in re case b).

4. THE CIRCLE THEOREM: $f(\theta, \theta_0) = f(\theta - \theta_0)$. The purpose of the present section is to prove the following theorem: If the far field amplitude $f(\theta, \theta_0)$ has the form $f(\theta - \theta_0)$, and if the boundary value problem giving rise to it is to find a function $v(r, \theta; \theta_0)$ such that

$$v \equiv e^{ikr\cos(\theta-\theta_0)} + v(r, \theta; \theta_0) = 0 \qquad (15)$$

on the scatterer S , and if

$$v \underset{r\to\infty}{\rightarrow} \widetilde{H}_0^{(1)}(kr) f(\theta-\theta_0) , \qquad (16)$$

then S is a circle.

Proof: Let the coordinates be chosen so that the smallest circle, say C , which encloses the scatterer has the equation $r = a$. Then v is regular outside $r = a$, and we can write v in the form

$$v = \sum_{-\infty}^{\infty} v_n(\theta_0) \frac{H_n^{(1)}(kr)}{H_n^{(1)}(ka)} e^{in\theta} , \quad r \geqq a , \tag{17}$$

where

$$v(a, \theta; \theta_0) = \sum_{-\infty}^{\infty} v_n(\theta_0) e^{in\theta}$$

and the function v is sufficiently regular so that for large r

$$v \to \widetilde{H}_0(kr) \sum_{-\infty}^{\infty} \frac{v_n(\theta_0)}{H_n^{(1)}(ka)} e^{\frac{in\pi}{2}} e^{in\theta} , \tag{18}$$

Comparison with (16) shows that $v_n(\theta_0)$ has the form $c_n \exp(-in\theta_0)$. Therefore we have

$$v(r, \theta; \theta_0) = \sum_{-\infty}^{\infty} c_n \frac{H_n^{(1)}(kr)}{H_n^{(1)}(ka)} e^{in(\theta-\theta_0)} . \tag{19}$$

Hence, using the polar coordinate expansion for a plane wave we have

$$u(r, \theta; \theta_0) = \sum_{-\infty}^{\infty} i^n J_n(kr) e^{in(\theta-\theta_0)} + \sum_{-\infty}^{\infty} c_n \frac{H_n^{(1)}(kr)}{H_n^{(1)}(ka)} e^{in(\theta-\theta_0)}$$

or

$$u(r, \theta; \theta_0) = \sum_{-\infty}^{\infty} \left[i^n J_n(kr) + c_n \frac{H_n^{(1)}(kr)}{H_n^{(1)}(ka)} \right] e^{in(\theta-\theta_0)} . \tag{20}$$

Now let $r \to a$. The circle $r = a$ touches the body S at some point at which $\theta = \beta$, say. Hence

$$u(a, \beta; \theta_0) = \sum_{-\infty}^{\infty} \{[i^n J_n(ka) + c_n] e^{in\beta}\} e^{-in\theta_0} = 0 . \tag{21}$$

Although θ is fixed at the value β , equation (21) holds for all θ_0 ; hence it follows that

$$c_n = -i^n J_n(ka) . \tag{22}$$

But this implies that u vanishes for $r = a$ and all θ. Therefore a solution is the circle $r = a$. Now, we have seen that

$$u \equiv \sum_{-\infty}^{\infty} i^n [J_n(kr) - \frac{J_n(ka)}{H_n^{(1)}(ka)} H_n^{(1)}(kr)] e^{in(\theta-\theta_0)} \tag{23}$$

vanishes everywhere on the circle $r = a$. However, the same proof also indicates that if u vanishes at any other point, at which $r = b \neq a$, then u vanishes on the entire circle $r = b$. We shall next prove that the function u as given by (23) cannot vanish on two concentric circles. This will prove that all points of S lie on the circle $r = a$.

To prove that if $u(a, \theta-\theta_0) \equiv 0$ then $u(b, \theta-\theta_0) \not\equiv 0$ unless $a = b$, we define

$$Z_n(kr) \equiv \text{Re}\,[J_n(kr) - \frac{J_n(ka)}{H_n(ka)} H_n(kr)] . \tag{24}$$

Then, as remarked in the previous paragraph, $u(a, \theta-\theta_0) \equiv 0$ implies $Z_n(ka) = 0$, and $u(b, \theta-\theta_0) \equiv 0$ implies $Z_n(kb) = 0$. These relations hold for all values of n. Now define

$$F_n(kr, \theta) = Z_n(kr) \sin n\theta . \tag{25}$$

Then $F_n(r, \theta)$ vanishes on the "rectangle" $B_n[r = a, r = b, \theta = 0, \theta = \frac{\pi}{r}]$. Hence k is an eigenvalue for B_n. Now recall that k is fixed. Recall also that the lowest eigenvalue of a membrane can be made arbitrarily large by decreasing the area. But the area of the rectangle B_n tends to zero with increasing n. Hence F_n cannot vanish on B_n for all values of n. Since $\sin n\theta$ <u>does</u> vanish on $\theta = 0$, $\theta = \frac{\pi}{n}$, it follows that if $Z_n(ka) = 0$ for all n, $Z_n(kb) \neq 0$ for all n, unless $b = a$. This result of course implies that $u(r, \theta-\theta_0)$ cannot vanish on two different circles, as was to be shown.

We have proved that all points of the conductor S lie on a single circle $r = a$. To complete the proof that the conductor is a circle we have to show that all points of the circle $r = a$ are covered by the conductor, i. e. show that S is closed.

Assume, to the contrary, that there is a gap on the circle $r = a$. Observe that the known estimates of Bessel and Hankel functions for large order and fixed argument show that the series

$$\sum_{-\infty}^{\infty} i^n [J_n(kr) - \frac{J_n(ka)}{H_n^{(1)}(ka)} H_n^{(1)}(kr)] e^{in(\theta-\theta_0)}$$

converges uniformly and absolutely for all r other than $r = 0$, and defines a regular wave function. This shows that the series provides the regular continuation of u into the region $r < a$. The existence of a gap in the conductor S therefore allows u to be continued into the interior of the circle and inexorably leads to a singularity at the origin where there is no conductor. This only can be avoided by excluding the origin, i. e. by the absence of a gap in the conductor. Hence the conductor S which can only lie on the circle $r = a$, is closed, and this completes the proof.

It should be noted that this section presents an example of arguments proving the uniqueness of the inverse problem of diffraction in a particular case. The general case deserves study.

NOTES

* $k = \omega/c$ where ω is the frequency of the assumed monochromatic wave and c is the velocity of propagation.

** Note that i indicates an integer when used as a subscript, while otherwise i means $\sqrt{-1}$.

*** See ref [2] where some of these results are derived for the case of $n = 2$.

BIBLIOGRAPHY

1. Rayleigh, The Theory of Sound. N. Y. Dover Publications, vol. I, p. 314.

2. S. N. Karp and J. Radlow, On resonance in infinite gratings of cylinders, N. Y. U. Inst. Math. Sci. Div. EM Res. Report no. EM-90 April 1956. See also IRE Trans. PGAP, AP-4, pp. 654-660, 1956.

BERNARD FRIEDMAN

Propagation in a Non-homogeneous Medium

This paper is written to present some problems concerning the expansion of arbitrary functions in terms of the eigenfunctions of non-self adjoint differential operators. These problems arise in the consideration of propagation in a non-homogeneous medium which is such that Maxwell's equations can be solved by separation of variables.

We begin with Maxwell's equations for a monochromatic field (time factor $e^{-i\omega t}$) as follows:

$$\begin{aligned} \nabla\times\vec{E} &= i\omega\vec{B} \\ \nabla\times\vec{H} &= -i\omega\vec{D} \end{aligned} \qquad . \tag{1}$$

We have $\vec{B} = \mu\vec{H}$ and $\vec{D} = \epsilon\vec{E}$ where we shall assume the magnetic permeability μ is a constant independent of position but that the electric permittivity ϵ is a tensor depending on position. Under certain conditions on ϵ it is possible to obtain a decomposition of an arbitrary electromagnetic field satisfying (1) into the sum of two fields: one, corresponding to a transverse electric field and the other to a transverse magnetic field. This decomposition is a generalization of a result of Bromwich [1].

Consider Maxwell's equations written in orthogonal curvilinear coordinates ξ_1, ξ_2, ξ_3 with the distance element given by

$$ds^2 = h_1^2 d\xi_1^2 + h_2^2 d\xi_2^2 + h_3^2 d\xi_3^2 \quad .$$

We assume that at every point of space the dielectric tensor ϵ has its principal axes in the direction of the ξ_1, ξ_2, ξ_3 coordinates with components ϵ_1, ϵ_2 and ϵ_3. The components of $\vec{E}$ and $\vec{H}$ along the ξ_j coordinate ($j = 1, 2, 3$) will be denoted by E_j, H_j, respectively. A solution of (1) such that $E_3 = 0$ or $H_3 = 0$ will be called a <u>transverse electric</u> or <u>transverse magnetic field</u>, respectively. We obtain the following theorem:

Theorem I: A solution of (1) can be expressed as the sum of a transverse electric and a transverse magnetic field if, and only if,

a) the ratio h_1/h_2 is independent of ξ_3 ,

b) after replacing ξ_3 by $\xi_3' = f(\xi_3)$ we have $h_3'=1$

c) $\epsilon_1 = \epsilon_2$.

Conditions a) and b) were given previously by Bromwich. Condition c), which essentially requires the medium to have the properties of a uniaxial crystal, seems to be new. The proof of the theorem is similar to that given by Bromwich and will be omitted.

If conditions a), b), and c) are satisfied, then there exist two scalar functions ψ_1 and ψ_2 which will respectively determine the transverse electric field $\vec{E}^{(1)}$, $\vec{H}^{(1)}$ and the transverse magnetic fields $\vec{E}^{(2)}$, $\vec{H}^{(2)}$ as follows:

For the transverse field we have

$$h_1 H_1^{(1)} = \frac{\partial^2 \psi_1}{\partial \xi_1 \partial \xi_3} \qquad h_2 E_1^{(1)} = i\omega\mu \frac{\partial \psi_1}{\partial \xi_2}$$

$$h_2 H_2^{(1)} = \frac{\partial^2 \psi_1}{\partial \xi_2 \partial \xi_3} \qquad h_1 E_2^{(1)} = -i\omega\mu \frac{\partial \psi_1}{\partial \xi_1}$$

$$H_3^{(1)} = k_1^2 \phi_1 + \frac{\partial^2 \psi_1}{\partial \xi_3^2} \qquad E_3^{(1)} = 0$$

Here $k_1^2 = \omega^2 \epsilon_1 \mu$ and ψ_1 satisfies the equation

$$\frac{\partial^2 \psi_1}{\partial \xi_3^2} + \frac{1}{h_1 h_2}\left[\frac{\partial}{\partial \xi_1}\left(\frac{h_2}{h_1}\frac{\partial \psi_1}{\partial \xi_1}\right) + \frac{\partial}{\partial \xi_2}\left(\frac{h_1}{h_2}\frac{\partial \psi_1}{\partial \xi_2}\right)\right] + k_1^2 \psi_1 = 0 \quad (3)$$

For the transverse magnetic field we have

$$h_1 E_1 = \frac{\partial}{\partial \xi_1}\left(\frac{1}{\epsilon_1}\frac{\partial(\epsilon_1 \psi_1)}{\partial \xi_3}\right) \qquad h_2 H_1 = -i\omega \frac{\partial(\epsilon_1 \psi_2)}{\partial \xi_2}$$

$$h_2 E_2 = \frac{\partial}{\partial \xi_2}\left(\frac{1}{\epsilon_1}\frac{\partial(\epsilon_1 \psi_2)}{\partial \xi_3}\right) \qquad h_1 H_2 = i\omega \frac{\partial(\epsilon_1 \psi_2)}{\partial \xi_1}$$

$$E_3 = k_1^2 \psi_2 + \frac{\partial^2 \psi_2}{\partial \xi_3^2} \qquad H_3 = 0$$

Here ψ_2 satisfies the equation (4)

$$\frac{\partial}{\partial \xi_3}\left(\frac{1}{\epsilon_1}\frac{\partial(\epsilon_1 \psi_2)}{\partial \xi_3}\right) + \frac{1}{\epsilon_3 h_1 h_2}\left[\frac{\partial}{\partial \xi_1}\left(\frac{h_2}{h_1}\frac{\partial(\epsilon_1 \psi_2)}{\partial \xi_1}\right) + \frac{\partial}{\partial \xi_2}\left(\frac{h_1}{h_2}\frac{\partial(\epsilon_1 \psi_2)}{\partial \xi_2}\right)\right] + k_1^2 \psi_2 = 0$$

The problem of solving Maxwell's equations has thus been reduced to the problem of solving the two elliptic partial differential equations (3) and (4). It can be shown that the restrictions on the coordinate system implied by Theorem I, namely that $h_3 = 1$ and h_1/h_2 be independent of ξ_3, imply that the coordinate system is either Euclidean or cylindrical along the ξ_3-axis with a constant cross section, or spherical polars. In each of these coordinate systems, if ϵ_1 is independent of ξ_1 and ξ_2 we may solve both (3) and (4) by separation of variables.

Henceforth we will restrict ourselves to the case of spherical coordinates. We put $\xi_1 = \theta$, $\xi_2 = \phi$, $\xi_3 = r$, then $h_1 = r$, $h_2 = r \sin\theta$ and $h_3 = 1$. Note the conditions of Theorem I are satisfied. Put $\psi_1 = r^2 u$ and equation (3) becomes

$$\frac{\partial^2 u}{\partial r^2} + \frac{2}{r}\frac{\partial u}{\partial r} + \frac{1}{r^2}\Omega u + k^2 u = 0 \tag{5}$$

where

$$\Omega u = \frac{1}{\sin\theta}\left[\frac{\partial}{\partial\theta}\left(\sin\theta\frac{\partial u}{\partial\theta}\right) + \frac{1}{\sin\theta}\frac{\partial^2 u}{\partial\phi^2}\right]$$

and where k^2 may be a function of r.

The customary way of using separation of variables to solve (5) is to assume that u can be expanded into a series of spherical harmonics

$$u = \Sigma\, v_n(r) Y_n(\theta, \phi) \tag{6}$$

where

$$\Omega Y_n = \lambda_n Y_n .$$

Thus Y_n is an eigenfunction of Ω corresponding to the eigenvalue λ_n. The coefficients v_n in (6) are the solutions of

$$v''_n + \frac{2}{r}v'_n + (k^2 - \frac{\lambda_n}{r^2})v = 0 \tag{7}$$

satisfying the prescribed boundary conditions for the problem to be solved.

This method of solution was found to be inefficient in discussing the propagation of radio waves around the earth because the series (6) converged too slowly. It can be shown that, for the frequencies used in radio propagation, from $10^4 - 10^8$ terms of (6) must be taken in order that the terms stop oscillating and begin converging to zero. The summation of such a series was clearly impractical before the time of the electronic computer and may be impractical even now.

In 1918, G. N. Watson [2] showed that the series (6) could be written as a contour integral. After evaluating this integral by residues, he obtained a rapidly convergent series for the field produced by a dipole above the earth.

In 1951, Marcuvitz [3] and Friedman [4], in independent papers, pointed out that the residue series Watson obtained was an illustration of the method of "alternative representations" for the solution of the wave equation in spherical coordinates. In a later paper Friedman [5] discussed this method in the abstract framework of tensor products of Hilbert spaces.

With the method of alternative representations the solution of (5) is written in the form

$$u = \Sigma w_n(r) Z_n(\theta, \phi) \tag{8}$$

where $w_n(r)$ are solutions of an equation similar to (7), namely

$$w'' + \frac{2}{r} w' + (k^2 - \frac{\lambda}{r^2}) w = 0 \tag{9}$$

and $Z_n(\theta, \phi)$ are again solutions of

$$\Omega Z = \lambda Z \ . \tag{10}$$

The series (6) was obtained by taking Z as an eigenfunction of Ω, λ as the corresponding eigenvalue, and then solving (9) for that value of λ. The series (8), however, is obtained by taking w as the eigenfunction of (9), λ as the corresponding eigenvalue, and then solving (10) for that value of λ. In order to obtain the series (8), it is necessary to prove the completeness of the eigenfunctions defined by (9) and it is this question of completeness which we shall discuss.

For a precise formulation of the question at issue, consider a differential equation

$$y'' + (\lambda + q(x)) y = 0 \ , \qquad 0 \leq x < \infty \tag{11}$$

where $q(x)$ is positive, of class C^2, and approaches infinity as x approaches infinity. It is known that there exist two linearly independent solutions of (11), $y_1(x, \lambda)$ and $y_2(x, \lambda)$, such that at infinity $y_1(x, \lambda)$ behaves like $q(x)^{-1/4} \exp[i \int q^{1/2} dx]$ and $y_2(x, \lambda)$ behaves like $q(x)^{-1/4} \exp[-i \int q^{1/2} dx]$. Values of λ for which

$$y_1(0, \lambda) = 0$$

will be called eigenvalues of equation (11) and the corresponding solutions $y_1(x, \lambda)$ will be called eigenfunctions of (11). Note that, formally,

$$\int_0^\infty y_1(x, \lambda_n) y_1(x, \lambda_m) dx = 0$$

if $\lambda_n \neq \lambda_m$.

The question of completeness is this: for what class of functions $f(x)$ does the formal expansion

$$\Sigma \alpha_n y_1(x, \lambda_n) \quad ,$$

where the sum is over all eigenfunctions of (11) and where

$$\alpha_n = \frac{\int_0^\infty f(x) y_1(x, \lambda_n)\, dx}{\int_0^\infty y_1(x, \lambda_n)^2\, dx} \quad ,$$

converge to $f(x)$? In this general formulation, very little is known. It is not even known whether eigenfunctions exist and, if they do exist, whether there are an infinite number of them.

A few things can be stated in the three special cases where $q(x) = x$, x^2 , or e^{2x} . In these cases the solution of (11) can be expressed explicitly in terms of Airy functions, Weber functions, and Bessel functions, respectively. Our knowledge of these special functions is so extensive that we can show there exist an infinite number of eigenvalues and we can exhibit the eigenfunctions. However, the question of what classes of functions can be represented by these eigenfunctions is still open.

We shall consider these special cases in detail. First, suppose $q(x) = x$. The eigenfunctions are solutions of

$$y'' + (x+\lambda) y = 0 \tag{12}$$

such that $y(0) = 0$ and

$$y(x) \sim x^{-1/4} \exp(\tfrac{2}{3} i x^{3/2})$$

asymptotically at infinity. This is not a classical Sturm-Liouville problem because of the peculiar boundary condition at infinity. If we put

$$L = -\frac{d^2}{dx^2} - x \quad ,$$

equation (12) may be written

$$Ly = \lambda y \; . \tag{13}$$

The domain of L is the set of functions $y(x) \in C^2$, which are such that y and Ly are in L^2 and $y(0) = 0$. Because infinity is a limit-point boundary point for the differential equation, the operator L is self-adjoint. The classical Sturm-Liouville eigenfunction would be a solution of (13) in the domain of L . No such solution exists;

thus, the discrete spectrum of L is empty. In fact, the spectrum of L is continuous and extends from $-\infty$ to ∞. A function in the domain of L can be represented by an integral [6] whose kernel contains solutions of (13). These solutions of (13) satisfy $y(0) = 0$ but they are real functions which do not satisfy the asymptotic condition

$$y(x) \sim x^{-1/4} \exp(\tfrac{2}{3} i x^{3/2})$$

at infinity; consequently, the indicated expansion is not the one in which we are interested.

Instead of the operator L, consider the operator

$$L_1 = -\frac{d^2}{dx^2} + x$$

with the same domain as L. This operator has a purely discrete spectrum [7] with real positive eigenvalues μ_n satisfying the equation

$$J_{1/3}(\tfrac{2}{3}\mu^{3/2}) + J_{-1/3}(\tfrac{2}{3}\mu^{3/2}) = 0 .$$

The normalized eigenfunctions are

$$\psi_n(x) = \frac{-\sqrt{3}\,\psi_0(x, \mu_n)}{\pi\lambda_n\{J_{2/3}(\tfrac{2}{3}\mu^{3/2}) - J_{-2/3}(\tfrac{2}{3}\mu^{3/2})\}}$$

where, for $x < \mu$,

$$\psi_0(x, \mu) = \frac{\pi}{\sqrt{3}} (\mu-x)^{1/2}[J_{1/3}\{\tfrac{2}{3}(\mu-x)^{3/2}\} + J_{-1/3}\{\tfrac{2}{3}(\mu-x)^{3/2}\}] .$$

By the classical Sturm-Liouville theory as explained in Titchmarsh's book on Eigenfunction Expansions, a function $f(\xi)$ in the domain of L_1 can be expanded as follows:

$$f(\xi) = \Sigma a_n \psi_n(\xi) \tag{14}$$

where

$$a_n = \int_0^\infty f(\eta)\psi_n(\eta)d\eta . \tag{15}$$

From (14) and (15) we shall obtain the desired eigenfunction expansion for the operator L. Note that for large values of ξ

$$\psi_n(\xi) \sim c_n(\xi-\mu)^{-1/4}\exp\{-\tfrac{2}{3}(\xi-\mu)^{3/2}\}$$

where c_n is a normalization constant. Put

$$\xi = x e^{-\pi i/3} ,$$

$$\psi_n(x e^{-\pi i/3}) = \phi_n(x) ,$$

$$\mu e^{-2\pi i/3} = \lambda ;$$

then for large values of x

$$\phi_n(x) \sim c_n e^{\pi i/12}(x+\lambda_n)^{-1/4} \exp\{i\tfrac{2}{3}(x+\lambda_n)^{3/2}\} \tag{16}$$

and the operator L_1 becomes a constant multiple of the operator L. The result of these transformations is that there exists complex numbers $\lambda_n = \mu_n e^{-2\pi i/3}$ such that the solution $\phi_n(x)$ of the equation

$$\phi''_n + (x+\lambda_n)\phi_n = 0$$

satisfies both the condition $\phi_n(0) = 0$ and from (16) the desired asymptotic condition. These functions $\phi_n(x)$ are the eigenfunctions we have been looking for because they are the ones that come up naturally in the solution of propagation problems.

The expansion problem is now this: for what class of functions $g(x)$ does the expansion

$$g(x) = \Sigma \alpha_n \phi_n(x) \tag{17}$$

where

$$\alpha_n = e^{-\pi i/3} \int_0^\infty g(x)\phi_n(x)\,dx ,$$

converge? Almost nothing is known about this problem. What is known is given by the following theorem.

Theorem II. Let $g(x)$ be analytic in a region of the complex x-plane containing the sector

$$0 \leq \arg x \leq \pi/3 . \tag{18}$$

Suppose that $g(x) = O[\exp(-x^\beta)]$, where $\beta > \frac{1}{2}$, in the sector (18). Let $xg(x)$ and $g''(x)$ belong to $\mathscr{L}_2$ along the ray $\arg x = \pi/3$. Suppose that $g(0) = 0$ and that

$$\alpha_n = O[\exp(-n^\gamma)] \tag{19}$$

where $\gamma > 1/3$. Then the expansion (17) will converge to $g(x)$ for all x in the sector defined by (18).

Proof: We note first that, from the equation satisfied by μ_n, it is easy to show that $\mu_n = O(n^{2/3})$; consequently $\lambda_n = O(n^{2/3})$. Using the binomial theorem on $(\lambda_n + x)^{3/2}$ and the fact that $\lambda_n^{3/2} = -\mu_n^{3/2}$, a real number, we find that, for large values of n ,

$$\phi_n(x) \sim \beta_n \lambda_n^{-1/4} \exp(i \lambda_n^{1/2} x)$$

where β_n is a bounded sequence. Therefore

$$\phi_n(x) = O[\exp n^{\gamma'}] \tag{20}$$

for $\gamma' > 1/3$.

Put $x = \xi e^{\pi i/3}$ and $g(\xi e^{\pi i/3}) = f(\xi)$. Because of the hypotheses on $g(x)$, the function $f(\xi)$ satisfies the conditions for the convergence of the expansion (14) with

$$a_n = \int_0^\infty f(\xi)\psi_n(\xi)\,d\xi \ . \tag{21}$$

From (16) it is easy to see that, for large x ,

$$\phi_n(x) = O[\exp x^{\beta'}]$$

for $\beta' > 1/2$. Because of the hypothesis about the behavior of $g(x)$ at infinity, we find that $a_n = \alpha_n$; therefore, the series

$$\Sigma\, \alpha_n \phi_n(x) \tag{22}$$

converges to $g(x)$ on the ray $\arg x = \pi/3$. From (19) and (20), by picking γ' such that $1/3 < \gamma' < \gamma$, we find that the series (22) converges uniformly in the sector (18). Finally, analytic continuation enables us to conclude the proof of Theorem II.

Similar methods can be used in the case $q(x) = x^2$. Starting with the well-known expansion into Hermite functions and using a sector of opening $\pi/4$, we may obtain results similar to those of Theorem II. Comparable results have been obtained by S. M. Shah[8].

The case $q(x) = e^{2x}$ is the most interesting because it is the one that occurs in considering propagation around a sphere. To see this, make the substitutions $r = e^x$, $w = r^{-1/2}y$ in equation (9). We obtain the equation

$$y'' + (k_2 e^{2x} - \lambda + 1/4)y = 0 \ .$$

The condition that w be zero on the surface of the sphere $r = 1$ implies y is zero for $x = 0$. Thus, we have the expansion problem for the kind of differential operator discussed previously.

Some recent work [9] on this problem seems to indicate unexpected difficulties due to the complicated asymptotic behavior of the Bessel functions. The theorem obtained is not the desired one because the differential equation had to be so modified that the eigenvalue parameter appears in a nonlinear fashion. The report [9, p. 36] also gives an example of a function for which the eigenfunction series diverges. The proof of divergence seems wrong because a factor $(\sin \pi \nu_n)^{-1}$ is omitted from the estimate of $H_{\nu_n}(x)$ [9, p. 41 top]. Since ν_n is complex, this factor goes to zero as $\nu_n \to \infty$ and thus destroys the proof.

The preceding discussion has shown how little is known about the expansion of functions in terms of the eigenfunctions of a non-self adjoint differential operator. With the theory of self-adjoint differential well nigh complete, the time is ripe for a new attack on non-self adjoint problems. For such an attack, new methods will have to be developed which in turn may help to understand better the self-adjoint problems.

BIBLIOGRAPHY

1. T. S. Brownwich, Philosophical Magazine 38 (1919), 144.
2. G. N. Watson, Roy. Soc. of London, Proc., Series A, 95(1918), 83.
3. N. Marcuvitz, Comm. in Pure and Appl. Math., 4(1951), 263.
4. B. Friedman, Comm. in Pure and Appl. Math. 4(1951), 317.
5. B. Friedman, Proc. of Conf. on Diff. Eq., Univ. of Maryland, 1955, 209-226.
6. E. C. Titchmarsh, Eigenfunction Expansions, Oxford, section 4.13, p. 80-81.
7. E. C. Titchmarsh, ibid., p. 80.
8. S. N. Shah, Jour. Lon. Math. Soc., 27(1952), 58.
9. E. Pflumn, N. Y. U. Inst. of Math. Sci., Div. of E. M. Res., Report No. BR-35.

~~~~~~~~~~~

The research on this paper was supported in part by ONR under Contract NONR 222(60).
~~~~~~~~~~~

GEORG GOUBAU

Some Characteristics of Electromagnetic Wave Beams

The following discussion is limited to "coherent" electromagnetic wave beams. This means, to beams which have well-defined surfaces of uniform phase for every frequency within the transmitted frequency spectrum. There is some confusion about the meaning of the term "coherent" since it is frequently associated with interference. The phenomena of interference, however, is also dependent on the frequency spectrum. This fact has caused misunderstandings in discussions on light-MASERS or LASERS which, at present, are hybrid sources in that they emit coherent and incoherent light.

The difference between a coherent beam as it is radiated by a high gain microwave antenna, and an incoherent beam such as the beam of a search light, is particularly apparent if the beams are focused. The maximum power density in the focal plane of an incoherent beam is determined by the radiation <u>density</u> at the surface of the source. In the case of a coherent beam the power density in the focal plane is only limited by the <u>total</u> power of the source. This fact is of particular interest in regard to the LASERS because it should be possible to concentrate the total power within a focal area of a few wavelengths in diameter, and thus to obtain electromagnetic energy densities which are many orders in magnitude greater than the densities ever achieved before with microwaves. We shall return to the focusing problem again, after we have formulated a general expression for a coherent wave beam.

We consider a wave field which propagates in the z-direction of a cylindrical coordinate system ρ, φ, z . Let the source be located somewhere in the half space $z<0$. The field can be derived from two scalar potentials Φ and Ψ which satisfy the wave equation

$$\underline{H} = \nabla \times (\Phi \cdot \underline{e}_z) \; ; \; \underline{E} = \nabla \times (\Psi \cdot \underline{e}_z) \; ; \; (\Delta + k^2)\,\Phi, \Psi = 0 \qquad (1)$$

$\underline{e}_z$ is the unit vector in the z-direction; Φ describes E-waves (TM-waves) having a longitudinal E-component; and Ψ yields H-waves

TE-waves) having a longitudinal H-component. The E- and H-waves can be combined to hybrid waves which are symmetrical in E and H. Thus, the entire field can be constructed of partial solutions of azimuthal periodicity $m = 0, 1, 2, \cdots$ with the components

$$E_\rho = E^{\pm}_{\rho m} \cos(m\varphi + \alpha_m) \qquad H_\rho = \mp \sqrt{\tfrac{\varepsilon}{\mu}}\, E^{\pm}_{\rho m} \sin(m\varphi + \alpha_m)$$

$$E_\varphi = E^{\pm}_{\varphi m} \sin(m\varphi + \alpha_m) \qquad H_\rho = \pm \sqrt{\tfrac{\varepsilon}{\mu}}\, E^{\pm}_{\varphi m} \cos(m\varphi + \alpha_m) \quad (2a)$$

$$E_z = E^{\pm}_{zm} \cos(m\varphi + \alpha_m) \qquad H_z = \mp \sqrt{\tfrac{\varepsilon}{\mu}}\, E^{\pm}_{zm} \sin(m\varphi + \alpha_m)$$

with

$$E^{\pm}_{\rho m} = \tfrac{1}{2}\int_0^\infty f^{\pm}_m(\gamma)\{(k \pm h) J_{m+1}(\gamma\rho) + (k \mp h) J_{m-1}(\gamma\rho)\} e^{-jhz} \gamma\, d\gamma$$

$$E^{\pm}_{\varphi m} = \tfrac{1}{2}\int_0^\infty f^{\pm}_m(\gamma)\{(k \pm h) J_{m+1}(\gamma\rho) - (k \mp h) J_{m-1}(\gamma\rho)\} e^{-jhz} \gamma\, d\gamma \quad (2b)$$

$$E^{\pm}_{zm} = j\int_0^\infty f^{\pm}_m(\gamma\rho)\, e^{-jhz}\, \gamma^2 d\gamma$$

The two signs refer to the two alternatives for combining E- and H-waves to symmetrical hybrid waves. $f^{+}_m(\gamma)$ and $f^{-}_m(\gamma)$ are arbitrary functions of the real variable γ, subject to the condition that the integrals in (2b) and the integrals over the first derivatives of the integrants with respect to ρ and z exist. They represent the amplitude spectra of the elementary cylindrical waves which form the beam. The propagation constant h and the parameter γ are connected by the relation $\gamma^2 + h^2 = k^2$ where k is the plane wave propagation constant J_{m-1}, J_m and J_{m+1} are Bessel-functions of the order m-1, m and m+1 respectively.

For each $m > 0$ there are <u>four</u> independent solutions, two with $\alpha_m = 0$ and two with $\alpha_m = \pi/2$. For $m = 0$ there are only <u>two</u> independent solutions since the fields derived from f_0^+ and f_0^- are linearly dependent. Therefore only one function f_0 needs to be considered.

The elementary waves are propagating waves in the range $0 < \gamma < k$ and evanescent waves in the range $k < \gamma < \infty$. For $z > 0$ and at large distances r from the point $z = \rho = 0$ the field transforms into the far-field which decreases with $1/r$. The radiation characteristic for E_φ and E_ϑ is given by

$$\Theta^{\pm}_m(\vartheta) = \cos\vartheta\, f^{\pm}_m(k \sin\vartheta) \quad (3)$$

where ϑ is the angle between the r- and z-directions. Obviously only the range $0 < \gamma < k$ contributes to the far-field since the evanescent waves decrease exponentially with z. If the radiation characteristic is known $f_m^{\pm}(\gamma)$ can be determined within the range $0<\gamma<k$. The field in the entire half-space, but without the reactive portion which is formed by the evanescent waves, is then given by (1b) and (1a).

For the following considerations we assume that the source of the beam is so far removed in the $(-z)$-direction that evanescent waves are negligible. If $f_m^{\pm}(\gamma)$ is a real function then, as evidenced by (1b), the corresponding transverse field components within any two planes $z=+z_0$ and $z=-z_0$ are conjugate complex. The wave beam arriving from the $(-z)$-direction converges toward the $z=0$ plane, and after passing this plane continues as a diverging beam in the $(+z)$-direction. The field in the vicinity of the plane $z = 0$, the focal plane of the beam exhibits interesting features which are presently under study. One of these features is, for instance, that the real part of the Pointing-vector which is normal to the plane $z = 0$ can reverse its direction within certain areas of this plane. Since the real Pointing-vector has no divergence, some of the power flux lines must turn around and, because of the symmetry of the field with respect to the plane $z = 0$, form closed loops.

An interesting question which can be formulated by an integral equation is the following: what amplitude functions $f_m^{\pm}(\gamma)$ for a given beam power yield maximum power flux through a prescribed area around the center of the focal plane? Though this problem has not yet been solved it can be shown that more than 90% of the energy can be focused within a circle of one wave length radius.

In the following we consider reiterative wave beams. This means beams which can be repeated over and over again simply by reconstituting the cross-sectional phase distribution at uniform intervals. Such beams are of particular interest with regard to a new transmission device which has been named "Beam Waveguide".

As already mentioned, the fields in any two planes $z=-z_0$ and $z=+z_0$ are conjugate complex if $f_m^{\pm}(\gamma)$ are real functions and evanescent waves are disregarded. Therefore, if a phase transformation could be performed within the plane $z = +z_0$ which converts the phase distribution at this plane into the phase distribution at the plane $z = -z_0$ the beam would be repeated. In other words, the field distributions within the space ranges $-z_0 < z < +z_0$ and $+z_0 < z < 3z_0$ would become the same. It is obvious that this transformation could be made at regular intervals of $2z_0$ and thus a guided propagation of the beam along the phase shifting structure achieved. It is very questionable whether such phase transformations are physically realizable for every beam with real $f(\gamma)$, particularly since the required phase transformations are in general different for the ρ- and φ-components of the field. However there are beams, for which this phase transformation is indeed feasible, and this even with very simple means. Such beams are characterized by a γ-spectrum substantially limited to values of $\gamma \ll k$. In other words, the functions $f_m^{\pm}(\gamma)$ have appreciable values only within a range $0 < \gamma < \gamma_c$ where $\gamma_c \ll k$. In this case h in the amplitude terms of the transverse field components can be replaced by k , and in the phase terms by $h = k - \frac{\gamma^2}{2k}$. The latter approximation limits the z_0-range, in that $(\gamma^2/2k)^4 k z_0$ must be small compared to π . The transverse field components which are of primary interest, have then equal distribution and are given by a Hankel transformation of the amplitude function $f_m^{\pm}(\gamma)$ multiplied by the phase factor $e^{j(\gamma^2/2k)z}$:

$$E_{\rho m}^{\pm} = \pm E_{\varphi m}^{\pm} = k e^{-jkz} \int_0^{\infty} f_m^{\pm}(\gamma) J_{m\pm 1}(\gamma\rho) e^{j(\gamma^2/2k)z} \gamma \, d\gamma \qquad (4)$$

$f_m^{\pm}(\gamma)$ can be developed into a system of orthogonal functions

$$f_m^{\pm}(\gamma) = \sum_{n=0}^{\infty} a_{n,m}^{\pm} f_{n,m}(\gamma) \quad \text{with} \int_0^{\infty} f_{i,m}(\gamma) f_{k,m}(\gamma)\gamma\, d\gamma = \begin{cases} c_{im} & \text{for } i = k \\ 0 & \text{for } i \neq k \end{cases} . \qquad (5a)$$

Thus any beam can be thought to be composed of elementary beams which are derived from the amplitude functions $f_{n,m}(\gamma)$.

Forthcoming deductions will demonstrate that the orthogonal functions best adopted to our problem are the following:

$$f_m^{\pm}(\gamma) = \left(\frac{\gamma}{\gamma_0}\right)^{m\pm 1} L_{n,\, m\pm 1}\left(\frac{\gamma^2}{\gamma_0^2}\right) e^{-\frac{1}{2}\gamma^2/\gamma_0^2} \qquad (5b)$$

where $L_{n,m\pm 1}$ are the generalized Laguerre polynomials and γ_0 is an arbitrary constant. The Hankel transformation of (4) can be readily performed and one obtains for the fields of the elementary beams

$$E_{\rho n,m}^{\pm} e^{jkz} = \pm E_{\varphi n,m}^{\pm} e^{jkz} = A_{n,m}^{\pm} \frac{u^{m\pm 1}}{(1+v^2)^{\frac{1}{2}(m\pm 1+1)}} L_{n,\, m\pm 1}\left(\frac{u^2}{1+v^2}\right) e^{-\frac{u^2}{1+v^2}} \cdot e^{j} \qquad (6a)$$

with

$$\psi = (2n + m\pm 1+1) \arc\tan v - \frac{1}{2}\frac{u^2 v}{1+v^2}\rho^2$$

$$u = \gamma_0 \rho \ , \quad v = \frac{\gamma_0^2}{k} z \ , \quad A_{n,m} = (-1)^n \gamma_0^2 k \qquad (6b)$$

For $m = 0$ only the upper signs are valid. The elementary beams or "beam modes" are orthogonal with respect to power. This means, the total power of a beam comprising several beam modes is the sum of the powers of the individual beams. The field of every mode decreases exponentially in the radial direction. The radial extension, however, increases with the order of the Laguerre polynomials. The mode system is mathematically a complete system in that any given transverse field distribution in a plane z = constant can be developed in the mode functions. However, this development has physical meaning only if the amplitude function $f_m^{\pm}(\gamma)$ of the given field has appreciable magnitude only within the range $0 < \gamma < \gamma_c$ where $\gamma_c \ll k$. The same condition applies to the physical reality of individual modes. Modes which do not satisfy this condition are inconsistent with Maxwell's equations. There, physical reality therefore depends on γ_0/k which must be sufficiently small, and on the order n, m of the Laguerre polynomial.

Each beam mode (6a) has a plane phase surface at $z = 0$. The phase distribution (6b) in any other plane $z \neq 0$ is composed of two parts:

$$\psi_1 = (2n + m \pm 1 + 1)\arctan\left(\frac{\gamma_0^2}{k} z\right) \tag{7a}$$

is independent of ρ but dependent on the order n, m of the Laguerre Polynomials.

$$\psi_2 = -\frac{1}{2}\frac{\frac{\gamma_0^2}{k} z}{1 + \left(\frac{\gamma_0^2}{k} z\right)^2}\gamma_0^2 \rho^2 = -\alpha\rho^2 \tag{7b}$$

is dependent on ρ but independent of n, m. If a phase transformation is performed at the plane $z = z_0$ by a factor $e^{-j2\psi_2}$, the field distribution of each mode at $z = -z_0$ is re-established at the plane $z = +z_0$.

A phase transformation of this kind is physically realizable, though not over the entire plane $z = z_0$ but over any desired finite area. The effects of the cross-sectional limitation of the phase transformation shall be discussed later. First we disregard this limitation. The factor α (see 7b) of the ρ^2-proportional phase transformation depends on the parameter γ_0 which characterizes the mode system. Conversely, if α is given, the mode system is determined which is iterated by this transformation.

Although every single beam mode is iterated by the same phase transformation (7b), wave beams composed of several modes are not iterated because the independent phase shift ψ_1 (7a) is different for every mode. A system of equally spaced identical phase transformers guides such a beam, i.e., prevents the energy from spreading out, but the field distribution is not repeated from interval to interval. The conditions are similar to those in ordinary waveguides where a field consisting of several modes is guided with continuously varying cross-sectional field distribution.

Since the phase transformation cannot be performed over an infinitely extended plane, we are particularly interested in a mode system which has the highest energy concentration or smallest field extension at the location of the phase transformers. It can be expected that such a mode system will be less affected by the finite diameter of the phase transformers than any other mode system of larger field extension. If the spacing $2z_0$ of the phase transformers is given, the only variable in the mode system is the parameter γ_0 . It can easily be shown that the optimum value of γ_0 is

$$\gamma_0 = \sqrt{k/z_0} \tag{8a}$$

and the corresponding phase transformation

$$-2\psi_2 = \frac{k}{2z_0}\rho^2 \quad . \tag{8b}$$

The case of maximum energy concentration is illustrated in Fig. 1 which shows envelope curves of constant power flux for the mode $m = 1$, $n = 0$, $(-)$. For this mode is:

$$|E^-_{\rho 0,1}| = |E^-_{\rho 0,1}| = \frac{1}{\sqrt{2}} e^{-\frac{k^2}{2z_0}\rho^2/(1+(z/z_0)^2)} \tag{9}$$

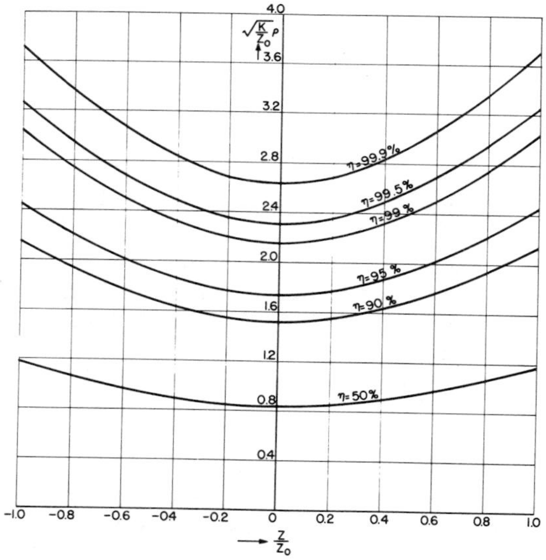

Figure 1

The field has a Gaussian distribution and expands along the path $z = 0$ to $z = z_0$ by a factor $\sqrt{2}$. As an example, we consider a beam at a frequency of 35000 mc/sec whose phase is adjusted at intervals of 10m (z_0 = 5m) the diameter of the beam for 90% energy flux varies from 25cm ($z = 0$) to 35.4 cm($z = z_0$) , for 99% from 35.6 cm to 50.4 cm, for 99.9% from 43.6 cm to 61.6 cm. The corresponding $f^-_{01}(\gamma)$ is in this example

$$f^-_{0,1}(\gamma) = e^{-\frac{1}{2}(\gamma^2/\gamma_0^2)} . \tag{10}$$

For $\gamma > 5\gamma_0$ the amplitude function is less than $e^{-12.5} = 5 \times 10^{-6}$ and γ^2/k^2 in the range $0 < \gamma < 5\gamma_0$ is less than 7×10^{-3} . The assumptions that led to the simplified beam equations are in this case well justified.

The ρ^2-proportional phase transformation for the iteration of wave beams resulted from the special choice of orthogonal functions in the series expansion of $f(\gamma)$. Of course, there are phase transformations of higher order in ρ conceivable which also would iterate wave beams. For instance, if we consider the combination of any two modes of the above mode system, then this combination as a unit is not iterated by a ρ^2-proportional phase transformation because of the difference in the mode dependent phase shift ψ_1 (Eq. 7a). However, there exists a phase transformation which would iterate the combination, though it would be a complicated function of ρ . The question whether such a transformation would also lead to a reasonable system of orthogonal functions has not yet been investigated.

Although the field of the beam modes, particularly the lowest one, decreases rapidly in the radial direction, some distortion will be introduced if the phases are corrected only within a finite area. The energy outside this area can be considered lost, since the uncorrected field diverges and is radiated into space. The beam mode system which has been derived with the assumption of unlimited phase correction will be modified in two respects: 1) The field functions will depend on the dimensions of the phase transforming devices, and 2) There will be an attenuation factor which is caused by the loss of energy bypassing the phase transformers. This attenuation factor does not include any absorption or reflection losses which may occur in actual phase transforming structures.

In the following, the assumption is made that the phase transformation is performed within a circle of radius R ;, while the area outside this circle is covered with an ideal absorber which prevents the field from being reflected or transmitted into the succeeding space section. The modes of this system are characterized by the condition that the field distributions in successive phase correction plane $z = (\pm 2i-1) z_0$ and $z = (\pm 2i-1) z_0$ are the same, except for a complex constant whose absolute value determines the loss caused by the finite area of phase correction.

We assume that the field at $z = z_0$ after being subjected to the phase transformation is known. Since according to (4) $E^{\pm}_{\rho m}(\rho, z_0)$ can be considered as the Hankel transform of

$f^{\pm}_m(\gamma) e^{-j\frac{\gamma^2}{2k} z_0}$, $f^{\pm}_m(\gamma)$ is obtained with the inverse transformation

$$f^{\pm}_m(\gamma) = \frac{1}{k} e^{-jkz_0(1-(\gamma^2/2k^2))} \int_0^R E^{\pm}_{\rho m}(\rho, -z_0) J_{m\pm 1}(\gamma\rho)\rho\, d\rho \qquad (11)$$

The integration is only extended from O to R instead of infinity because $E^{\pm}_m(\rho_1 - z_0)$ is limited to this range by the absorbing screen. The $f^{\pm}_m(\gamma)$ obtained with (11) can be used to express with (4) the field at $z = +z_0$ by the field at $z = -z_0$. The integration over γ can be performed and one obtains

$$E^{\pm}_{\rho m}(\rho, +z_0) = \frac{jk}{2z_0} e^{-2jkz_0} \int_0^R E^{\pm}_{\rho m}(\eta_1 - z_0) \cdot J_{m\pm 1}\left(\frac{k}{2z_0}\eta\rho\right) \cdot e^{-j\frac{k}{4z_0}(\eta^2+\rho^2)} \eta\, d\eta \qquad (12)$$

The absorbing screen allows only passage of the field within the range $0 < \rho < R$. This portion of the field is somewhat modified because of the boundary conditions at the screen. However, since we consider apertures of many wave lengths in diameter the modification is limited to a narrow zone along the rim $\rho = R$. It is minimized if the phase transformation is adopted to maximum field concentration. This means to minimum field intensity near the rim. If the aperture is sufficiently large, the overall modification of the field distribution is practically negligible.

The iteration condition requires the optimum phase transformed field at $z = +z_0$ to be the same as the field at $-z_0$, except for a complex factor p . Thus

$$E^{\pm}_{\rho m}(\rho, +z_0) e^{j\frac{k}{2z_0}\rho^2} = p\, E^{\pm}_{\rho m}(\rho_1 - z_0) . \qquad (13)$$

Substituting $E^{\pm}_{\rho m}(\rho_1 + z_0)$ in the right-hand side of (12) leads to the homogeneous integral equation of the second kind

$$F^{\pm}_m(x) = q\int_0^a F^{\pm}_m(\xi) J_{m\pm 1}(x\cdot\xi)\xi\, d\xi \qquad (14a)$$

where

$$x = \sqrt{\frac{k}{2z_0}}\rho , \quad a = \sqrt{\frac{k}{2z_0}} R , \quad F^{\pm}_m(x) = E^{\pm}_{\rho m}(\rho_1 - z_0) e^{-j\frac{k}{4z_0}\rho^2} \qquad (14b)$$

The eigenfunctions $F_m^{(+)}(x)$ and $F_m^{(-)}(x)$ are real and each form a complete orthogonal system. Together they determine the orthogonal system for the transverse field vector. They characterize the modes of the system with cross-sectional beam limitation. The eigenvalues q are greater than one. $1/q = p$ represents the attenuation of the field between two successive phase corrections. Any beam of arbitrary cross-sectional field distribution can be considered as the superposition of these modes. If such a beam is passed through a large number of phase transformers, the "higher modes" which correspond to the higher eigenvalues are gradually damped out until only the lowest mode remains.

If "a" approaches infinity, the modes transform into the unlimited beam modes. The eigenvalues become ± 1, since there is no beam limitation and, therefore, no diffraction loss.

If the phase corrections at $z = (\pm 2i+1)z$ are thought to be performed in two equal steps, then $F_m^{(\pm)}(x)$ represents the field distribution in between these two steps. Since $F_m^{(\pm)}(x)$ is real, the field in the middle planes of the phase transformers has uniform phase.

For every order v of the Bessel function, there are two values of m : $m = v-1$ and $m = v+1$, and therefore, two identical sets of eigenfunctions—one for $f_{v-1}^{+}(\gamma)$ and one for $f_{v+1}^{-}(\gamma)$. Both can be combined to two sets of linearly polarized vector fields with the corresponding field vectors perpendicular to each other. Since the solution for $v = 0$ is also linearly polarized, we may consider the entire mode system as being composed of two linearly polarized sets.

The integral equation (14) can be solved in the following manner: The kernel can be expanded into a series of the eigenfunctions $f_{n,m}^{\pm}$ of the unlimited case $(a = \infty)$. An approximate solution is then obtained by replacing the actual kernel by the first N terms of this series. This approximated equation can be solved rigorously by expanding $F_m(x)$ also into the mode functions of the unlimited system. Applying the orthogonality relations between the $f_{n,m}^{\pm}$ one obtains a system of N linear homogeneous equations for the expansion coefficients. The condition that the determinant of this system must be zero yields an algebraic equation for the eigenvalues.

The following results pertain to the mode system $m = 1, (-)$.

Figure 2 shows curves for the first eigenvalue as a function of $F_1^{-}(x)$ calculated with a desk calculator using the above-described series expansion with $n = 1,3$ and 5 (curves I to III). Curve IV has been obtained with an IBM computer using a power series expansion. The ordinate is given in a db scale and refers to p^2 which determines the diffraction loss caused by the finite aperture. Figure 3 is a plot of eigenfunctions for $a = 1.8$, 2.0, 2.2 and 2.4, as obtained with the computer.

The diffraction loss of a beam at a frequency of 35,000 Mc/sec,

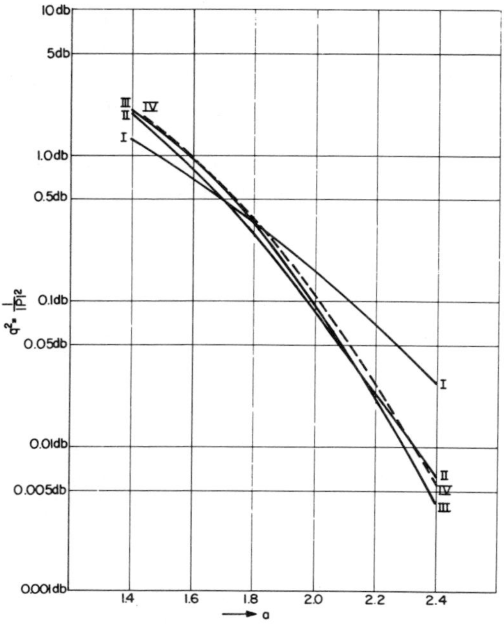

Figure 2

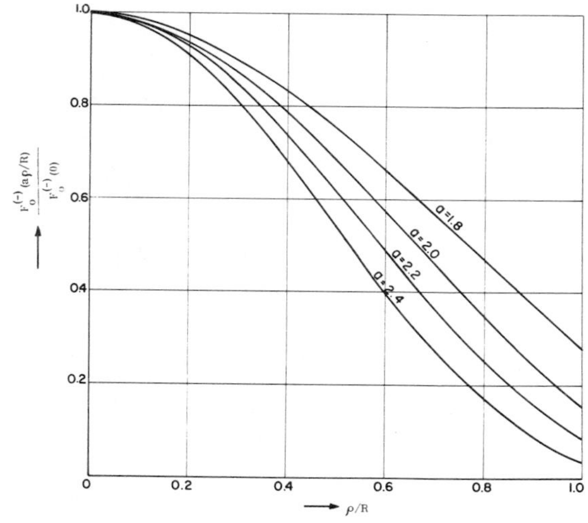

Figure 3

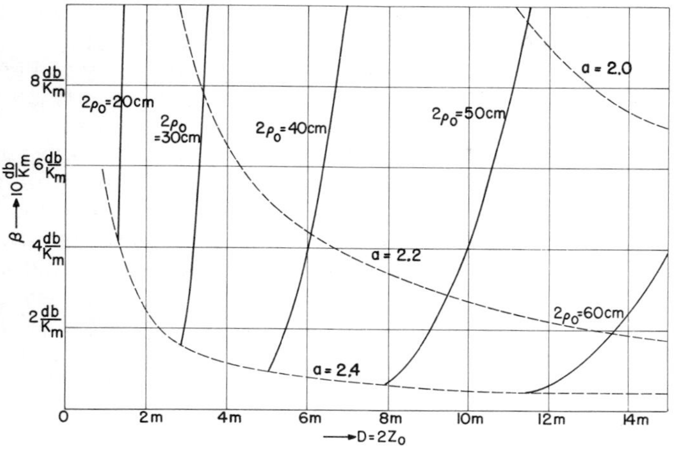

Figure 4

guided by an array of phase transformers over a distance of 1 km is shown in Figure 4. Each curve refers to a certain diameter of the beam measured at the locations of phase transformation. The loss is very small as long as $a > 2.4$ and increases rapidly with decreasing a, i.e., with increasing z_0. For a given loss, the spacing increases more rapidly than the beam diameter.

The presented theory on reiterative wave beams has been developed by Dr. Schwering and myself. Dr. Schwering extended this theory to beams with regular symmetry. The functions which characterize the beam modes in this case are Hermite polynomials instead of Laguerre polynomials. The iteration loss for a square aperture is somewhat greater than that of a circular aperture of equal area.

Several statements in this short presentation remain unproved. The complete theory including proofs, will be contained in the May issue of the IRE-PGAP-Transactions. Perhaps, more convincing than mathematical proofs in problems of this kind, are experimental results. Such results are shown in Figure 5. They have been obtained by Mr. Beyer and Mr. Mink, graduate students of Prof. Scheibe of the Electrical Engineering Department of this University.

The iteration loss was measured with a resonator consisting of a plane and a parabolic reflector. The location of these reflectors with respect to the coordinate system used in the theoretical development is the following: The plane reflector which is large enough to effect no limitation on the beam, is placed at $z = 0$. The other reflector which limits the beam diameter is placed at $z = +z_0$. The curvature is designed to perform optimum phase transformation for the reflected beam. The focal length is in this case equal to the reflector spacing. The loss determined from resonance measurements "a" was varied by varying z . using reflectors of appropriate focal length. The points are measured values. The curve is the computed curve of Figure 2. Considering the fact that the diameter of the beam is only 20 wave-lengths and there is an uncertainty in the theory because of the omission of rim-effects, the agreement between theory and experiment is very good. If the measured points are used for defining an effective diameter of the reflector, this diameter differs from the actual diameter by less than 0.4 wave-lengths. Our own experimental results are quite similar, though they are less accurate. For this reason and also for the reason that the measurements by Dr. Scheibe and his associates are perhaps less biased than ours, I asked Prof. Scheibe for the permission to use their results. I would like to take the opportunity to thank him for his cooperation.

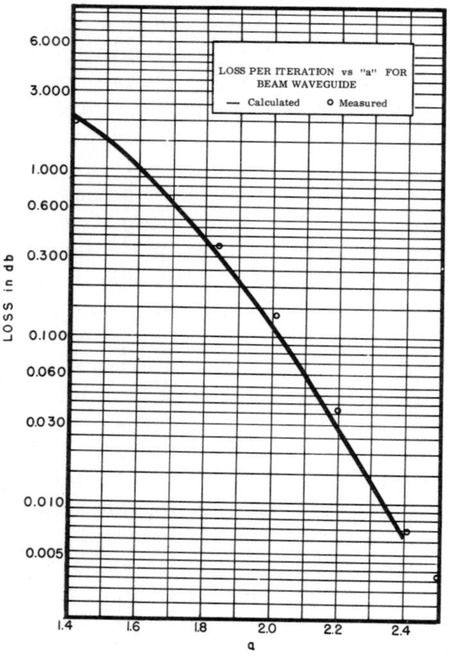

Figure 5

B. NOBLE

Integral Equation Perturbation Methods in Low-frequency Diffraction

1. INTRODUCTION. The idea that approximate low-frequency solutions of the steady-state wave equation can be obtained from the solutions of the corresponding static problems goes back to Rayleigh [34]. The title of his original paper published in 1897 might well have been the subject of one of the lectures at this symposium.

Since about 1950 there has been a revival of interest in this subject, with the aim of obtaining systematic series expansions valid for small values of the wave-number k . Rayleigh obtained only the first terms in the expansions for the problems which he considered. An extension of Rayleigh's method to give further terms for certain three-dimensional scattering problems have been given by Stevenson [38]. Neither Rayleigh nor Stevenson use integral equations.

My own interest in the integral equation approach originated from the work of Bouwkamp [6] who extended and corrected the low-frequency expansions obtained by earlier authors for diffraction by a strip of finite width. Various other writers have considered particular problems by means of particular integral equations. The present paper is intended as a contribution towards the basic theory underlying the use of integral equations for obtaining approximate solutions in low-frequency scattering problems. Specific applications to illustrate this theory are also included. It would seem that many of the ideas are implicit in the work of Schwinger and his co-workers during the war and others since that time, but little attempt has been made in the literature to approach the problem from a systematic and reasonably general point of view.

2. INTEGRAL EQUATION FORMULATIONS. The fundamental tool used when formulating scattering problems in terms of integral equations is Green's theorem (e.g. [31], p. 806]:

$$\int_A \left\{ G(\underline{r}, \underline{r}') \frac{\partial u(\underline{r})}{\partial N} - u(\underline{r}) \frac{\partial G(\underline{r}, \underline{r}')}{\partial N} \right\} dA = \begin{cases} u(\underline{r}'), & \underline{r}' \text{ inside } V, \\ 0, & \underline{r}' \text{ outside } V, \end{cases} \tag{1}$$

where the integration is taken over a surface A with surface element dA . The surface encloses a volume V . The vector $\underline{r}$ refers to a point on the surface of V , and $\underline{r}'$ refers to any point in space not on the surface. The normal derivative $\partial/\partial N$ is taken in a direction outwards from the volume. The Green's function $G(\underline{r}, \underline{r}')$ satisfies the equation

$$\nabla^2 G(\underline{r}, \underline{r}') + k^2 G(\underline{r}, \underline{r}') = -\delta(\underline{r}-\underline{r}') \tag{2}$$

in free space.

The total wave function $u_t(\underline{r})$ in a diffraction problem is represented as the sum of incident and scattered waves:

$$u_t(\underline{r}) = u_i(\underline{r}) + u_s(\underline{r}) \ .$$

Each wave function satisfies the scalar wave equation in regions where no sources are present:

$$\nabla^2 u(\underline{r}) + k^2 u(\underline{r}) = 0 \ .$$

For simplicity we treat only the scalar case in this paper. The general electromagnetic problem in three dimensions would involve dyadic Green's functions instead of scalar Green's functions ([19], [24], [31] Chap. 13).

We apply Green's theorem to the scattered wave in the region between the surface of the body and a surface at a large distance from the body. This latter surface can be taken, for example, as a sphere or cylinder of large radius in the three and two dimensional cases, respectively. If this radius tends to infinity the integrals over the surface at infinity tend to zero since both u_s and G satisfy the radiation condition at infinity. Hence (1) gives

$$u_s(\underline{r}') = \int_B \left\{ u_s(\underline{r}) \frac{\partial G(\underline{r}, \underline{r}')}{\partial n} - G(\underline{r}, \underline{r}') \frac{\partial u_s(\underline{r})}{\partial n} \right\} dA \ , \tag{3}$$

where $\underline{r}'$ is any point outside the body, the integration is carried out over the surface B of the body, and $\partial/\partial n = -\partial/\partial N$ denotes integration outwards from the surface of the body.

The incident wave function u_i and the Green's function are both defined inside the volume occupied by the body and neither function possesses singularities in this region. Hence (1) can be applied to u_i in the volume occupied by the body and this gives

$$0 = \int_B \left\{ u_i(\underline{r}) \frac{\partial G(\underline{r}, \underline{r}')}{\partial n} - G(\underline{r}, \underline{r}') \frac{\partial u_i(\underline{r})}{\partial n} \right\} dA \tag{4}$$

where $\underline{r}'$ refers to any point outside the body. On adding (3) and (4) we obtain

$$u_s(\underline{r}') = \int_B \left\{ u_t(\underline{r}) \frac{\partial G(\underline{r}, \underline{r}')}{\partial n} - G(\underline{r}, \underline{r}') \frac{\partial u_t(\underline{r})}{\partial n} \right\} dA \ . \tag{5}$$

Consider first of all the problem of scattering by a body on the surface of which $u_t = 0$, i. e. $u_s = -u_i$. If in (5) we let the point $\underline{r}'$ tend to a point on the surface of the body we obtain immediately the integral equation

$$\int_B G(\underline{r}, \underline{r}') \frac{\partial u_t(\underline{r})}{\partial n} dA = u_i(\underline{r}') \ , \qquad (\underline{r}' \text{ on } B) \ . \tag{6}$$

This is a singular integral equation of the first kind for the unknown function $\partial u_t/\partial n$.

A different integral equation for the same problem can be obtained in the following way. Define

$$U(\underline{r}') = \int_B G(\underline{r}, \underline{r}') f(\underline{r}) dA \ ,$$

where $\underline{r}'$ denotes a point outside B . Consider the derivative of U taken in the direction of a line normal to the surface B in the outward direction from B . Let $\partial U/\partial n'$ denote the limiting value of this derivative as $\underline{r}'$ tends to a point on the surface B . Then

$$\frac{\partial U(\underline{r}')}{\partial n'} = -\tfrac{1}{2} f(\underline{r}') + \int_B \frac{\partial G(\underline{r}, \underline{r}')}{\partial n'} f(\underline{r}) dA \ . \tag{7}$$

This is a generalization of a result which is well-known in the theory of potential (e.g. [18], p. 164). If we take the derivative of (5) along an outward normal and let $\underline{r}'$ tend to a point on the body, in a similar way, we find, on using (7) and remembering that $u_t = 0$,

$$\tfrac{1}{2} \frac{\partial u_t(\underline{r}')}{\partial n'} + \int_B \frac{\partial G(\underline{r}, \underline{r}')}{\partial n'} \frac{\partial u_t(\underline{r})}{\partial n} dA = \frac{\partial u_i(\underline{r}')}{\partial n'} , \quad (\underline{r}' \text{ on } B) . \tag{8}$$

This is an integral equation of the second kind with a non-singular kernel for the unknown function $\partial u_t/\partial n$.

Consider next the problem of scattering by a body on which $\partial u_t/\partial n = 0$ on the surface of the body. Consider the integral

$$V(\underline{r}') = \int_B \frac{\partial G(\underline{r}, \underline{r}')}{\partial n} g(\underline{r}) dA \ .$$

If $\underline{r}'$ tends to a point on the body from the outside of B then (cf. [18], p. 169)

$$V(\underline{r}') = \tfrac{1}{2} g(\underline{r}') + \int_B \frac{\partial G(\underline{r}, \underline{r}')}{\partial n} g(\underline{r}) dA \ . \tag{9}$$

If now in (5) we use the boundary condition $\partial u_t/\partial n = 0$ and let $\underline{r}'$ tend to a point on B we find

$$\tfrac{1}{2} u_t(\underline{r}') - \int_B \frac{\partial G(\underline{r}, \underline{r}')}{\partial n} u_t(\underline{r})\, dA = u_i(\underline{r}') \quad , \quad (\underline{r}' \text{ on } B) . \tag{10}$$

This is an integral equation of the second kind with a non-singular kernel for the unknown function u_t . Alternatively, set $\partial u_t/\partial n = 0$ in (5) and take the derivative of the resulting equation along a line normal to B . If $\underline{r}'$ tends to a point on B , since $\partial u_s/\partial n' = -\partial u_i/\partial n'$ on B , we obtain the integral equation

$$\frac{\partial}{\partial n'} \int_B \frac{\partial G(\underline{r}, \underline{r}')}{\partial n} u_t(\underline{r})\, dA = - \frac{\partial u_i(\underline{r}')}{\partial n'} , \quad (\underline{r}' \text{ on } B) . \tag{11}$$

We have obtained two integral equations (6) and (8) for the condition $u_t = 0$ on the obstacle and two integral equations (10) and (11) for the condition $\partial u_t/\partial n = 0$. Equations (6) and (11) are Fredholm integral equations of the first kind with singular kernel. Equations (8) and (10) are Fredholm integral equations of the second kind with non-singular kernel. Most of the applications of integral equations to solve specific problems in diffraction theory have used forms (6) and (11). Most investigations of existence theorems have used forms (8) and (10) (e.g. [20]). Millar [30] has used an equation related to (10) for a specific problem.

3. INTEGRAL EQUATION PERTURBATION METHODS. In terms of linear operators the basic principles underlying perturbation methods can be formulated in the following way. We wish to solve a problem

$$\mathscr{L} f = g \tag{12}$$

where $\mathscr{L}$ is a linear operator, g is a known function and f is an unknown function which it is required to find. In cases where it is impracticable to invert $\mathscr{L}$ explicitly it is often possible to split the operator $\mathscr{L}$ into the sum of two parts $\mathscr{L}_0$ and $\mathscr{L}_1$ such that

(i) $\mathscr{L}_0$ is the dominant part of $\mathscr{L}$.
(ii) $\mathscr{L}_0$ can be inverted explicitly.

Then (12) can be written

$$\mathscr{L}_0 f + \mathscr{L}_1 f = g .$$

On applying the operator $\mathscr{L}_0^{-1}$ to each side we find

$$f + \mathscr{L}_0^{-1} \mathscr{L}_1 f = \mathscr{L}_0^{-1} g .$$

If condition (i) is satisfied then this equation may be suitable for application of a perturbation procedure. The abstract operator formalism has been carried further by Professor Marcuvitz in another paper in this symposium. It should be emphasized that although it is often theoretically possible to carry out the above procedure it is usually difficult to carry it through explicitly in concrete applications. From one point of view, the present paper illustrates some of the factors involved in performing the perturbation procedure explicitly when dealing with integral equation formulations of specific low-frequency scattering problems.

Before considering the methods to be used in connection with the integral equations of Section 2, we derive a result which will be useful later. Suppose that $F(\underline{r})$ is the solution of the integral equation

$$\int_B K(|\underline{r}-\underline{r}'|)F(\underline{r})\,dA = 1 , \quad (\underline{r}' \text{ in } B) , \tag{13}$$

and we wish to deduce a solution of the equation

$$\int_B \{C + K(|\underline{r}-\underline{r}'|)\}f(\underline{r})\,dA = 1 , \quad (\underline{r}' \text{ in } B) . \tag{14}$$

This equation can be rewritten in the form

$$\int_B K(|\underline{r}-\underline{r}'|)f(\underline{r})\,dA = 1 - C\int_B f(\underline{r})\,dA , \tag{15}$$

where the term on the right is a constant, though the value of the integral is so far unknown. From (13), by linearity, the solution of (15) is

$$f(\underline{r}) = \{1 - C\int_B f(\underline{r})\,dA\}F(\underline{r}) . \tag{16}$$

On integrating this expression over the surface B and rearranging we find

$$\int_B f(\underline{r})\,dA = \int_B F(\underline{r})\,dA/\{1 + C\int_B F(\underline{r})\,dA\} .$$

Substitution in (16) gives the following solution of (14):

$$f(\underline{r}) = \frac{F(\underline{r})}{1 + C\int_B F(\underline{r})\,dA} \tag{17}$$

A straightforward extension of the above method can be used to solve the integral equation

$$\int_B \{K(|\underline{r}-\underline{r}'|) + \sum_{i=1}^{n} \phi_i(\underline{r})\psi_i(\underline{r}')\}f(\underline{r})\,dA = g(\underline{r}'), \quad (\underline{r}' \text{ in } B) , \tag{18a}$$

if the solutions of the following integral equations are known:

$$\int_B K(|\underline{r}-\underline{r}'|)F_0(\underline{r})\,dA = g(\underline{r}') , \quad (\underline{r}' \text{ in } B) ,$$

$$\int_B K(|\underline{r}-\underline{r}'|)F_i(\underline{r})\,dA = \psi_i(\underline{r}') , \quad i = 1 \text{ to } n , \quad (\underline{r}' \text{ in } B) . \tag{18b}$$

When the kernel of an integral equation depends on a small parameter k it is often convenient to expand all functions as power series in k. As an example consider the equation

$$\int_B K(\underline{r},\underline{r}')f(\underline{r})\,dA = g(\underline{r}') , \quad (\underline{r}' \text{ in } B) , \tag{19}$$

and assume that the following expansions are valid for small k:

$$K = K_0 + kK_1 + k^2K_2 + \cdots \tag{20a}$$

$$f = f_0 + kf_1 + k^2f_2 + \cdots \tag{20b}$$

$$g = g_0 + kg_1 + k^2g_2 + \cdots \tag{20c}$$

The functions K_i, f_i, g_i may themselves be functions of k. If we insert these in (19), multiply out, and equate powers of k we readily find

$$\int_B K_0 f_0\,dA = g_0 , \qquad (\underline{r}' \text{ in } B) , \tag{21a}$$

$$\int_B K_0 f_1\,dA = g_1 - \int_B K_1 f_0\,dA , \qquad (\underline{r}' \text{ in } B) , \tag{21b}$$

$$\int_B K_0 f_2\,dA = g_2 - \int_B (K_1 f_1 + K_2 f_0)\,dA , \qquad (\underline{r}' \text{ in } B) , \text{ etc.} \tag{21c}$$

The integral operator with kernel K_0 obviously corresponds to the part $\mathscr{L}_0$ of the linear operator $\mathscr{L}$ introduced at the beginning of this section. For the procedure to be useful in practice the following three conditions must be satisfied (compare conditions (i) and (ii) at the beginning of this section):

(a) K_0 is the principal part of K.

(b) The following integral equation can be solved

$$\int_B K_0(\underline{r},\underline{r}')F(\underline{r})\,dA = G(\underline{r}') , \quad (\underline{r}' \text{ in } B) . \tag{22}$$

(This is the only integral equation that needs to be solved.)

(c) The functions $f_0, f_1, \ldots$ which appear in integrals on the right of (21b, c) must be such that these integrals can be evaluated and the resulting integral equations solved in reasonably simple terms.

The Green's functions which occur in the integral equations of Section 2 are given in Table I, together with the appropriate Green's function for Laplace's equation

Table I: Summary of Green's functions $G(\underline{r}, \underline{r}')$

	Steady-state wave equation $\nabla^2 G + k^2 G = -\delta(\underline{r}-\underline{r}')$	Laplace's equation $\nabla^2 G = -\delta(\underline{r}-\underline{r}')$
3 - dimensions	$\dfrac{\exp(ik\|\underline{r}-\underline{r}'\|)}{4\pi\|\underline{r}-\underline{r}'\|}$	$\dfrac{1}{4\pi\|\underline{r}-\underline{r}'\|}$
2 - dimensions	$\frac{1}{4} i H_0^{(1)}(k\|\underline{r}-\underline{r}'\|)$	$-\frac{1}{2\pi}\log\|\underline{r}-\underline{r}'\|$

Because of the form of the three-dimensional Green's function for the steady-state wave equation which tends to the Green's function for Laplace's equation as the wave-number k tends to zero, the most obvious procedure for three-dimensional problems is to proceed as in equations (20)-(21) above. However we can do slightly better than this. Consider the integral equation

$$\int_B \frac{\exp(ik|\underline{r}-\underline{r}'|)}{4\pi|\underline{r}-\underline{r}'|} f(\underline{r})\,dA = g(\underline{r}') \quad , \quad (\underline{r}' \text{ in } B) .$$

Set

$$\frac{\exp(ik|\underline{r}-\underline{r}'|)}{4\pi|\underline{r}-\underline{r}'|} = K_0(|\underline{r}-\underline{r}'|) - \frac{k^2}{8\pi}|\underline{r}-\underline{r}'| + O(k^3) \quad , \tag{23}$$

where

$$K_0(|\underline{r}-\underline{r}'|) = \frac{1}{4\pi|\underline{r}-\underline{r}'|} + \frac{ik}{4\pi} .$$

We expand f, g as in (20b, c) and assume that F, ϕ_0, ϕ_1 are the solutions of the following static problems

$$\int_B \frac{1}{4\pi|\underline{r}-\underline{r}'|} F(\underline{r})\,dA = 1 \, , \qquad (\underline{r}' \text{ in } B) \, , \tag{24a}$$

$$\int_B \frac{1}{4\pi|\underline{r}-\underline{r}'|} \phi_s(\underline{r})\,dA = g_s(\underline{r}') \, , \quad s = 0, 1, \; (\underline{r}' \text{ in } B) . \tag{24b}$$

On applying a generalization of (17) to (21a, b), remembering that the integral involving K_1 on the right of (21b) is zero, we find

$$f_0(\underline{r}) + kf_1(\underline{r}) = \phi_0(\underline{r}) + k\phi_1(\underline{r}) - \frac{ik\int_B\{\phi_0(\underline{r})+k\phi_1(\underline{r})\}dA\ F(\underline{r})}{4\pi + ik\int_B F(\underline{r})dA} . \quad (25)$$

Strictly speaking this result is correct only to terms in order k :

$$f_0(\underline{r}) + kf_1(\underline{r}) \approx \phi_0(\underline{r}) + k\{\phi_1(\underline{r}) - \frac{i}{4\pi}\int_B \phi_0(\underline{r})dA\ F(\underline{r})\} .$$

This approximation could have been obtained directly from a power-series expansion of the kernel, choosing $K_0 = 1/(4\pi|\underline{r}-\underline{r}'|)$, $K_1 = ik/4\pi$, in (20a), (21a, b). The more general procedure does provide parts of the coefficients of higher-order terms and the method does save labor when finding the exact coefficients for higher-order terms.

In the two-dimensional case the Green's function for the steady-state wave equation does not tend to the Green's function for Laplace's equation as the wave-number k tends to zero because of the presence of terms involving $\log k$ in the Hankel function. Consider the integral equation

$$\int_B \frac{1}{4} iH_0^{(1)}(k|\underline{r}-\underline{r}'|)f(\underline{r})dA = g(\underline{r}') , \quad (\underline{r}' \text{ in } B) . \quad (26)$$

We have

$$\frac{1}{4}iH_0^{(1)}(k|\underline{r}-\underline{r}'|) = -\frac{1}{2\pi}\{K_0(|\underline{r}-\underline{r}'|) + k^2K_2(|\underline{r}-\underline{r}'|) + k^4K_4(|\underline{r}-\underline{r}'|)+\cdots\}$$

where $K_0(|\underline{r}-\underline{r}'|) = q + \log|\underline{r}-\underline{r}'|$

$$K_{2n}(|\underline{r}-\underline{r}'|) = \frac{(-1)^n|\underline{r}-\underline{r}'|^{2n}}{2^{2n}(n!)^2}\{q-1-\frac{1}{2} - \ldots - \frac{1}{n} + \log|\underline{r}-\underline{r}'|\} , \quad (27)$$

with $q = C + \log\frac{1}{2}k - \frac{1}{2}\pi i$, $C = 0.5772\ldots$ (Euler's constant). For clarity we consider in detail only the term of zero order in the solution of (26), with $g_0(\underline{r}') = 1$. Then we need to solve

$$-\frac{1}{2\pi}\int_B (q + \log|\underline{r}-\underline{r}'|)f_0(\underline{r})dA = 1 , \quad (\underline{r}' \text{ in } B) . \quad (28)$$

Suppose that $F(\underline{r})$ is the solution of

$$-\frac{1}{2\pi}\int_B \log|\underline{r}-\underline{r}'|F(\underline{r})dA = 1 , \quad (\underline{r}' \text{ in } B) . \quad (29)$$

Then from (17) the solution of (28) is

$$f_0(\underline{r}) = \frac{2\pi F(\underline{r})}{2\pi - q\int_B F(\underline{r})dA} . \tag{30}$$

From the general theory it is seen that this result can be generalized to obtain the complete solution as a series in powers of k^2 and inverse powers of the parameter

$$p' = C + \log\frac{1}{2}k - \frac{1}{2}\pi i - \{2\pi/\int_B F(\underline{r})dA\} . \tag{31}$$

It is well known that the solution for diffraction by a strip can be expanded as a series in powers of k^2 and inverse powers of the parameter

$$p = C + \log\frac{1}{4}kb - \frac{1}{2}\pi i , \tag{32}$$

where the strip has width $2b$ and $u_t = 0$ on the strip. We can derive (32) from (31) since for a strip (29) becomes, on remembering that $F(r)$ is the same on both sides of the strip,

$$-\frac{1}{\pi}\int_{-b}^{b} \log|x-\xi|F(\xi)d\xi = 1 , \quad (-b \le x \le b) , \tag{33}$$

with solution ([24], p. 143):

$$F(\xi) = \frac{1}{(b^2-\xi^2)^{\frac{1}{2}}\log(2/b)} , \quad 2\int_{-b}^{b} F(\xi)d\xi = \frac{2\pi}{\log(2/b)} . \tag{34}$$

On substituting this result in (31) we see that p' reduces to p given in (32).

Equation (34) illustrates a point which is of some interest, namely that the solution of (33) tends to infinity as b tends to 2. This means that for $b = 2$ the equation (33) has no solution. In fact, the corresponding homogeneous equation

$$\int_{-2}^{2} \log|x-\xi|F(\xi)d\xi = 0 , \quad (-2 \le x \le 2) ,$$

has the solution $F(\xi) = C(4-\xi^2)^{-\frac{1}{2}}$, an example of the Fredholm alternative. It has been pointed out to me by Dr. M. A. Jaswon of Imperial College that this result can be generalized to the case of the obstacle of general shape. If we consider an integral equation of form (29) for a two-dimensional object of any shape and alter the scale so that all dimensions are altered by a factor σ then for one value of σ the integral equation will not possess a solution. From the present point of view, if the scale is altered by σ a factor $\log \sigma$

is added to the kernel so that the new integral equation has a solution of the form (30) with $q = \log \sigma$. As σ goes from 0 to ∞, $\log \sigma$ goes from $-\infty$ to ∞. Provided the integral in (30) is non-zero there is always some value of σ which will reduce the denominator of (30) to zero. For this value of σ the original equation will have no solution. Physically this phenomenon is connected with the occurrence of logarithmic potentials at infinity in two-dimensional problems, which means that the zero level of potential is not uniquely defined, independently of scale factors.

4. DIFFRACTION BY AN ELLIPTIC CYLINDER. When the shape of the obstacle is such that the appropriate boundary-value problem for Laplace's equation can be solved by separation of variables then a solution for the diffraction problem, suitable for small values of the wave-number k, can be obtained by perturbation of the static solution in a comparatively straightforward way. The fundamental reason for this is the following. If we formulate a boundary-value problem in terms of an integral equation

$$\int_B K(\underline{r}, \underline{r}')f(\underline{r})\,dA = g(\underline{r}') \quad , \quad (\underline{r}' \text{ in } B) , \tag{35}$$

and if the original boundary-value problem can be solved by separation of variables, then the kernel $K(\underline{r}, \underline{r}')$ can be expanded in a series of orthogonal functions

$$K(\underline{r}, \underline{r}') = \sum_{n=1}^{\infty} \alpha_n \phi_n(r)\phi_n(\underline{r}') ,$$

where

$$\int_B \phi_m(\underline{r})\phi_n(\underline{r})\omega(\underline{r})\,dA = \begin{cases} 1, & (m = n) \\ 0, & (m \neq n) \end{cases} .$$

Hence if we write

$$g(\underline{r}') = \sum_{n=1}^{\infty} g_n\phi_n(\underline{r}') \quad , \quad f(\underline{r}) = \omega(\underline{r}) \sum_{n=1}^{\infty}{}' f_n\phi_n(\underline{r}) ,$$

we immediately find from (35) that

$$f_n = g_n/\alpha_n \quad , \quad n = 1, 2, \ldots ,$$

and this gives the solution of the integral equation. The procedure is in fact the Hilbert-Schmidt method for the solution of integral equations ([28], Chapter II).

We illustrate the method by considering diffraction by an elliptic cylinder. The geometry is defined by the coordinate transformation

$$x = b \cosh \mu \cos \theta , \quad y = b \sinh \mu \sin \theta ,$$

where the foci of the ellipses are at the points $(\pm b, 0)$. It can be shown that the expansion for $\log|\underline{r}-\underline{r}'|$ in terms of these coordinates is given, for $\mu' > \mu$, by

$$\log|\underline{r}-\underline{r}'| = \mu' + \log \tfrac{1}{2}b - 2\sum_{n=1}^{\infty} \frac{1}{n} e^{-n\mu'} (\cosh \mu \cos n\theta \cos n\theta' + \sinh n\mu \sin n\theta \sin n\theta'). \tag{36}$$

If we consider an elliptic cylinder defined by $\mu = \text{const.}$, $0 \le \theta \le 2\pi$, then the surface element of length is given by

$$ds = b(\cosh^2 \mu - \cos^2 \theta)^{\frac{1}{2}} d\theta . \tag{37}$$

This can be obtained, for example, from [39], p. 54 equation (103) with the identification $\xi \equiv \cosh \mu$, $\eta = \cos \theta$, $ds = h_2 d\eta$, using p. 48(71). Similarly from p. 49 equation (78) of the same reference we have $\partial/\partial n = h_1^{-1}\partial/\partial \xi$, and from p. 54(103) we find

$$\frac{\partial}{\partial n} = \frac{1}{b(\cosh^2 \mu - \cos^2 \theta)^{\frac{1}{2}}} \frac{\partial}{\partial \mu} . \tag{38}$$

On combining (37) and (38) we find that

$$\frac{\partial f}{\partial n} ds \equiv \frac{\partial f}{\partial \mu} d\theta \tag{39}$$

For two-dimensional scattering by an elliptic cylinder on which $u_t = 0$ the integral equation (6) becomes

$$\int_0^{2\pi} G(\theta, \theta') f(\theta) d\theta = g(\theta') , \quad (0 \le \theta' \le 2\pi) , \tag{40}$$

where $f(\theta) \equiv \partial u_t(\underline{r})/\partial \mu$, $g(\theta') \equiv u_i(\underline{r}')$,

$$G(\theta, \theta') \equiv \frac{1}{4} i H_0^{(1)}(k|\underline{r}-\underline{r}'|) .$$

We examine in detail only the terms to order k for a plane wave incident on the cylinder from a direction making an angle Θ with the positive x-axis,

$$u_i = e^{-ik(x \cos \Theta + y \sin \Theta)} \equiv g(\theta') . \tag{41}$$

On expanding as in Section 3 equation (40) gives

$$-\frac{1}{2\pi}\int_0^{2\pi}(q+\ln|\underline{r}-\underline{r}'|)\{f_0(\theta)+kf_1(\theta)\}d\theta = g_0(\theta')+kg_1(\theta'), \quad (0\le\theta'\le 2\pi), \tag{42}$$

where, if the obstacle is specified by $\mu = M$, say, $\log|\underline{r}-\underline{r}'|$ is given by (36) with $\mu = \mu' = M$. We have set

$$f(\theta) = \partial u_t(\underline{r})/\partial\mu = f_0(\theta)+kf_1(\theta)+O(k^2) . \tag{43}$$

Also

$$g_0(\theta') = 1 , \tag{44a}$$

$$g_1(\theta') = -i(\cosh M\cos\theta'\cos\Theta+\sinh M\sin\theta'\sin\Theta) . \tag{44b}$$

We note first of all that the solution of the integral equation

$$-\frac{1}{2\pi}\int_0^{2\pi}(q+\log|\underline{r}-\underline{r}'|)F(\theta)d\theta = \alpha_0+\sum_{n=1}^{\infty}(\alpha_n\cos n\theta'+\beta_n\sin n\theta') \tag{45}$$

is given by

$$F(\theta) = -\frac{\alpha_0}{p''}+\sum_{n=1}^{\infty} n e^{nM}\left\{\frac{\alpha_n\cos n\theta}{\cosh nM}+\frac{\beta_n\sin n\theta}{\sinh nM}\right\} \tag{46}$$

where

$$p'' = C+\log\frac{1}{4}kbe^{M}-\frac{1}{2}\pi i . \tag{47}$$

For the special case of the strip $M=0$ and p'' reduces to p defined in (32). On comparing (41), (42), (43), (44) we see that

$$f_0(\theta) = -\frac{1}{p''}, \tag{48a}$$

$$f_1(\theta) = -ie^{M}(\cos\Theta\cos\theta+\sin\Theta\sin\theta) . \tag{48b}$$

Consider next the integral equation (8). On using (38), (39) and introducing approximations as in the derivation of (42) we find that, to the first order in k, equation (8) gives

$$\frac{1}{2}f_s(\theta')-\frac{1}{2\pi}\int_0^{2\pi}\frac{\partial\log|\underline{r}-\underline{r}'|}{\partial\mu'}f_s(\theta)d\theta = h_s(\theta'), \quad s=0,1, (0\le\theta'\le 2\pi), \tag{49}$$

where the $f_s(\theta)$ are defined as in (43) and

$$h(\theta') = \partial u_i(\underline{r}')/\partial\mu' = h_0(\theta')+kh_1(\theta')+O(k^2) ,$$

$$h_0(\theta') = 0 \ , \tag{50a}$$

$$h_1(\theta') = -i(\sinh M \cos\theta' \cos\Theta + \cosh M \sin\theta' \sin\Theta) \ . \tag{50b}$$

In differentiating (36) with respect to $\mu = \mu' = M$ we obtain

$$\begin{aligned} \frac{\partial \log|\underline{r}-\underline{r}'|}{\partial\mu'} &= 1 + \sum_{n=1}^{\infty} \{\cos n(\theta-\theta') + e^{-2nM}\cos n(\theta+\theta')\} \\ &= \frac{1}{2} + \pi \sum_{n=-\infty}^{\infty} \delta(\theta-\theta' - 2n\pi) + \sum_{n=1}^{\infty} e^{-2nM}\cos n(\theta+\theta') \ , \end{aligned} \tag{51}$$

where we have replaced the sum over cosines by the well-known equivalent sum in terms of Dirac δ-functions (see, for example, [25], p. 68):

$$\sum_{n=1}^{\infty} \cos n\chi = -\frac{1}{2} + \pi \sum_{n=-\infty}^{\infty} \delta(\chi - 2n\pi) \ . \tag{52}$$

If we insert (51) in (49), the δ-function sum would give a term $-\frac{1}{2}f(\theta')$, but this has already been taken into account from a different point of view by formula (7). We therefore ignore the contribution from the δ-function, and (49) becomes

$$\tfrac{1}{2} f_s(\theta') - \frac{1}{2\pi}\int_0^{2\pi} \{\tfrac{1}{2} + \sum_{n=1}^{\infty} e^{-2nM}\cos n(\theta+\theta')\} f_s(\theta)\,d\theta = h_s(\theta') \ ,$$

$$s = 0, 1, \qquad (0 \le \theta' \le 2\pi) \ . \tag{53}$$

It is easily shown that the homogeneous equation possesses the non-zero solution $f_s(\theta')$ = constant. Hence on using the previous method of solution in conjunction with (50) we find

$$f_0(\theta) = C_0 \ , \tag{54a}$$

$$f_1(\theta) = C_1 - ie^{M}(\cos\Theta\cos\theta + \sin\Theta\sin\theta) \ , \tag{54b}$$

where C_0, C_1 are undetermined constants. These constants must presumably be determined by substituting into the other integral equation (42). On comparing (48) and (54) it is seen that we must obtain the same solution as before.

For two-dimensional diffraction by an elliptic cylinder on which $\partial u_t/\partial n = 0$, equation (10) gives, on proceeding as in the derivation of (42) and (49),

$$\tfrac{1}{2} f_s(\theta') + \frac{1}{2\pi}\int_0^{2\pi} \frac{\partial \log|\underline{r}-\underline{r}'|}{\partial\mu} f_s(\theta)\,d\theta = g_s(\theta') \ , \tag{55}$$

where $s = 0, 1$, $(0 \le \theta \le \pi)$. The $f_s(\theta')$ are derived from the expansion

$$f(\theta') = u_t(\underline{r}') = f_0(\theta') + k f_1(\theta') + O(k^2) , \tag{56}$$

and the $g_s(\theta')$ are defined as in (44). From (36)

$$\frac{\partial \log |\underline{r}-\underline{r}'|}{\partial \mu} = -2\sum_{n=1}^{\infty} e^{-n\mu'}(\sinh n\mu \cos n\theta \cos n\theta' + \cosh n\mu \cos n\theta \cos n\theta') . \tag{57}$$

If we set $\mu = \mu' = M$ and use (52) we obtain

$$\frac{\partial \log|\underline{r}-\underline{r}'|}{\partial \mu} = -\pi \sum_{n=-\infty}^{\infty} \delta(\theta-\theta'-2n\pi) + \tfrac{1}{2} + \sum_{n=1}^{\infty} e^{-nM} \cos n(\theta+\theta')$$

As before, when this is inserted in (55) we ignore the effect of the δ-functions since this was included when we used (9). Hence (55) becomes

$$\tfrac{1}{2}f_s(\theta') + \frac{1}{2\pi}\int_0^{2\pi} \{\tfrac{1}{2} + \sum_{n=1}^{\infty} e^{-nM} \cos n(\theta+\theta')\} f_s(\theta)\,d\theta = g_s(\theta') ,$$

$$s = 0, 1, \quad (0 \le \theta' \le 2\pi) . \tag{58}$$

From (44),

$$f_0(\theta) = 1 , \tag{59a}$$

$$f_1(\theta) = -ie^{M}(\cos\Theta \cos\theta + \sin\Theta \sin\theta) . \tag{59b}$$

We finally consider the equations for f_0 and f_1 derived from (11). By using (57) we see that these equations can be written

$$-\frac{1}{\pi}\sum_{n=1}^{\infty} n e^{-nM}\{\sinh nM \cos n\theta' \int_0^{2\pi} f_s(\theta) \cos n\theta\, d\theta$$
$$+ \cosh nM \sin n\theta' \int_0^{2\pi} f_s(\theta) \sin n\theta\, d\theta\} = -h_s(\theta') , \tag{60}$$

$$s = 0, 1, \quad (0 \le \theta' \le 2\pi) ,$$

where the $h_s(\theta')$ have been defined in (50), and the orders of summation and integration have been interchanged to avoid any difficulties in connection with a divergent kernel. We see that the homogeneous equation has the solution f_s = const. Hence

$$f_0(\theta) = D_0 ,$$

$$f_1(\theta) = D_1 - ie^{M}(\cos\Theta \cos\theta + \sin\Theta \sin\theta) ,$$

where D_0, D_1 are unknown constants which can be determined by substituting into the other integral equation (58). These results agree with (59).

One interesting feature of these investigations is that although (42) and (60) (derived from (6) and (11) in Section 2) are singular integral equations of the first kind, whereas (49) and (55) (derived from (8) and (10)) are non-singular equations of the second-kind, it is equations (42) and (55) which have unique solutions. For the obstacle of general shape it would seem that it is simpler to use the integral equations with unique solutions, namely those derived from (6) and (10) in Section 2.

When the ellipse $\mu = M$ collapses into a strip ($M = 0$) it is seen that (49) and (55) degenerate. On using (52) in the limiting form of (53) as M tends to zero we find for the strip on which $u_t=0$:

$$\left(\frac{\partial u_t}{\partial y}\right)_{y=+0} + \left(\frac{\partial u_t}{\partial y}\right)_{y=-0} = 2\left(\frac{\partial u_i}{\partial y}\right)_{y=0} .$$

Similarly for the strip on which $\partial u_t/\partial y = 0$ the integral equation (55) degenerates to give the result

$$(u_t)_{y=+0} + (u_t)_{y=-0} = 2(u_i)_{y=0} .$$

For the strip on which $\partial u_t/\partial y = 0$ we are forced to use a form of integral equation, namely (60) derived from (11), which does not have a unique solution. In this case it is well-known that edge-conditions must be invoked to produce a unique solution.

The series in the integrands of (53) and (58) can be summed in closed form:

$$\frac{1}{2} + \sum_{n=1}^{\infty} e^{-2nM} \cos n(\theta+\theta') = \frac{\frac{1}{2}\tanh M}{1 - \varepsilon^2 \cos^2 \frac{1}{2}(\theta+\theta')} ,$$

where $\varepsilon = 1/\cosh M$ is the eccentricity of the ellipse. This kernel is of a form which is well-known in connection with the potential problem inside an ellipse (see, for example, [28], p. 27(8)]. The above expansion of the closed form of the kernel, which has been derived here from separation of variables, is precisely the expansion obtained by contour integration in [28], p. 29.

When solving diffraction problems involving strips, the expansion

$$\log 2|\cos\theta - \cos\theta'| = -2\sum_{n=1}^{\infty} \frac{1}{n} \cos n\theta \cos n\theta'$$

is usually quoted as a result for which no explanation is required. The present approach provides a logical derivation for this result, namely it is the special case $\mu = \mu' = 0$ of the expansion in elliptic coordinates of the Green's function for Laplace's equation (see (36)).

In considering the perturbation procedure we have limited ourselves to a discussion of the lowest-order terms. Obviously a considerable amount of work will be involved if it is desired to obtain higher-order terms but the calculations are completely systematic and straightforward as illustrated by various authors for the case of the strip, e.g. Millar [29]. In these calculations and in the direct generalizations for elliptic cylinders it is possible to predict the analytical forms of the results. The only unknowns are the coefficients of the various terms. The determination of these coefficients can be reduced to a purely numerical routine. There is no reason why an automatic computer should not be programmed to perform the laborious algebra which is necessary if the calculations are carried out by a human being.

Although we have devoted considerable attention to the elliptic cylinder, it is necessary to keep a sense of proportion about this particular application. The wave equation can be separated in elliptic coordinates. If low-frequency results are required the easiest procedure may well be to derive them directly from the Mathieu-function expansions as in [7], [17]. The justification for dealing with the elliptic cylinder in such detail is that it illustrates in a comparatively simple form the problems which are involved in the integral equation perturbation method when Laplace's equation can be solved by separation-of-variables. Since Laplace's equation can be separated in many more coordinate systems than the steady-state wave equation, the potentialities of the method are obvious, although they do not seem to have been exploited in the literature.

5. DIFFRACTION BY A CIRCULAR DISK. A large number of methods exist for solving potential problems involving a circular disk. Each of these can be used as the basis of a perturbation method for low-frequency diffraction by a circular disk. We shall describe a method of approach which is mathematically interesting and illustrates the general theory of Section 3 from a point of view which is quite different from that adopted in Section 4.

We consider diffraction by a disk of radius a lying in $z = 0$, $0 \leq \rho \leq a$, in cylindrical coordinates (ρ, θ, z), with an incident wave which is decomposed into its various Fourier components in θ. Without going into detail we state that if $\partial u_t/\partial z = 0$ on the disk, the scattered wave can be written

$$u_s = \pm \int_0^\infty A(t) J_n(\rho t) e^{-\gamma |z|} dt \tag{61}$$

where the upper sign holds for $z \geq 0$, and the lower for $z \leq 0$. The values $n = 0, 1, 2, \ldots$ apply to the successive Fourier components of the waves in the coordinate θ, and

$$\gamma = (t^2-k^2)^{\frac{1}{2}} \text{ for } t \geq k, \quad -i(k^2-t^2)^{\frac{1}{2}} \text{ for } t \leq k . \tag{62}$$

The boundary conditions on $z = 0$ are that u_s is continuous on $z = 0$, $\rho > a$, and $\partial u_s/\partial z = -\partial u_i/\partial z$ which is known, on $z = 0$, $\rho < a$. If these are applied to (61) the following dual integral equations are obtained for the unknown function $A(t)$:

$$\int_0^\infty \gamma A(t) J_n(\rho t)\,dt = f(\rho), \qquad (0 \le \rho < a), \tag{63a}$$

$$\int_0^\infty A(t) J_n(\rho t)\,dt = 0, \qquad (\rho > a). \tag{63b}$$

The function $f(\rho)$ in (63a) is known.

In order to reduce the above dual integral equations to a Fredholm integral equation suitable for small k we first of all solve the following system

$$\int_0^\infty t^\alpha A(t) J_\nu(\rho t)\,dt = f(\rho), \qquad (0 \le \rho < 1), \tag{64a}$$

$$\int_0^\infty A(t) J_\nu(\rho t)\,dt = 0, \qquad (\rho > 1), \tag{64b}$$

where for simplicity we now take the radius a to be unity. Also α, ν are general parameters. There is no additional difficulty in performing the analysis in general terms and this illustrates more clearly the structure of the manipulations. We shall use Sonine's first finite integral ([41], p. 373):

$$J_{\nu+\xi+1}(z) = \frac{z^{\xi+1}}{2^\xi \Gamma(\xi+1)} \int_0^{\frac{1}{2}\pi} J_\nu(z \sin\theta) \sin^{\nu+1}\theta \cos^{2\xi+1}\theta \, d\theta .$$

This is valid for $\nu > -1$, $\xi > -1$. In this integral we set $z = xt$, $\rho = x \sin\theta$, and this gives

$$t^{-\xi-1} J_{\nu+\xi+1}(xt) = \frac{x^{-\xi-\nu-1}}{2^\xi \Gamma(\xi+1)} \int_0^x J_\nu(\rho t) \rho^{\nu+1} (x^2-\rho^2)^\xi d\rho . \tag{65}$$

Multiply both sides of (64a) by

$$x^{-\xi-\nu-1}\, 2^{-\xi} \{\Gamma(\xi+1)\}^{-1} \rho^{\nu+1} (x^2-\rho^2)^\xi$$

and integrate with respect to ρ from 0 to x. Interchange orders of integration on the left-hand side and use (65). This gives

$$\int_0^\infty t^{\alpha-\xi-1} A(t) J_{\nu+\xi+1}(xt)\,dt = \frac{x^{-\xi-\nu-1}}{2^\xi \Gamma(\xi+1)} \int_0^x f(\rho) \rho^{\nu+1} (x^2-\rho^2)^\xi d\rho . \tag{66}$$

This is valid for $0 < x < 1$, $\xi > -1$, $\nu > -1$.

Another formula due to Sonine is ([41], p. 417):

$$t^{-\eta-1}J_{\nu-\eta-1}(xt) = \frac{x^{\nu-\eta-1}}{2^{\eta}\Gamma(\eta+1)}\int_0^{\infty} J_{\nu}\{t(s^2+x^2)^{\frac{1}{2}}\}(s^2+x^2)^{-\frac{1}{2}\nu}s^{2\eta+1}ds .$$

This is valid for $\frac{1}{2}\nu - \frac{1}{4} > \eta > -1$. If we set $s^2+x^2 = \rho^2$ this becomes

$$t^{-\eta-1}J_{\nu-\eta-1}(xt) = \frac{x^{\nu-\eta-1}}{2^{\eta}\Gamma(\eta+1)}\int_x^{\infty} J_{\nu}(\rho t)\rho^{-\nu+1}(\rho^2-x^2)^{\eta}d\rho . \tag{67}$$

Multiply (64b) by

$$x^{\nu-\eta-1}\,2^{-\eta}\{\Gamma(\eta+1)\}^{-1}\rho^{-\nu+1}(\rho^2-x^2)^{\eta}$$

and integrate with respect to ρ from x to infinity. Interchange orders of integration and use (67). We obtain

$$\int_0^{\infty} t^{-\eta-1}A(t)J_{\nu-\eta-1}(xt)\,dt = 0 , \tag{68}$$

valid for $\frac{1}{2}\nu - \frac{1}{4} > \eta > -1$, $-1 < x < \infty$.

So far ξ and η are arbitrary, subject to the limitations given after equations (66), (68). We should like to set

$$\nu+\xi+1 = \nu-\eta-1 , \quad \alpha-\xi-1 = -\eta-1 ,$$

so that the orders of Bessel functions and the powers of t on the left-hand sides of (66), (68) should be identical. On solving these equations we see that this would mean

$$\xi = -1 + \frac{1}{2}\alpha , \quad \eta = -1 - \frac{1}{2}\alpha .$$

Since ξ and η must both be greater than -1 this is impossible. It is possible to overcome this difficulty in the following way. We shall be interested in the case $\alpha = 1$ and this leads us to choose $\xi = -1 + \frac{1}{2}\alpha$, $\eta = -\frac{1}{2}\alpha$. From the conditions following (66), (68) we see that then

$$0 < \alpha < 2 , \quad \nu > \tfrac{1}{2}-\alpha , \tag{69}$$

and (66), (68) become

$$\int_0^{\infty} t^{\frac{1}{2}\alpha}A(t)J_{\nu+\frac{1}{2}\alpha}(xt)\,dt = \frac{x^{-\nu-\frac{1}{2}\alpha}}{2^{-1+\frac{1}{2}\alpha}\Gamma(\frac{1}{2}\alpha)}\int_0^{x} f(\rho)\rho^{\nu+1}(x^2-\rho^2)^{-1+\frac{1}{2}\alpha}d\rho ,$$

$$(0 \le x < 1) , \tag{70}$$

$$\int_0^\infty t^{\frac{1}{2}\alpha-1} A(t) J_{\nu+\frac{1}{2}\alpha-1}(xt)\,dt = 0 , \qquad (x > 1) . \qquad (71)$$

Multiply both sides of (71) by $x^{-\nu-\frac{1}{2}\alpha+1}$ and differentiate with respect to x. Then

$$\int_0^\infty t^{\frac{1}{2}\alpha} A(t) J_{\nu+\frac{1}{2}\alpha}(xt)\,dt = 0 , \qquad (x > 1) . \qquad (72)$$

Equations (70) and (72) have identically the same left-hand sides. This common left-hand side is therefore defined for $0 < x < \infty$ and can be inverted by Hankel's theorem, provided that $\nu+\frac{1}{2}\alpha > -1$, which is satisfied, from (69). Hence

$$A(t) = \frac{(2t)^{1-\frac{1}{2}\alpha}}{\Gamma(\frac{1}{2}\alpha)} \int_0^1 x^{-\nu-\frac{1}{2}\alpha+1} J_{\nu+\frac{1}{2}\alpha}(xt)\,dx \int_0^x f(\rho)\rho^{\nu}(x^2-\rho^2)^{-1+\frac{1}{2}\alpha}\,d\rho . \qquad (73)$$

This solution is identical with that derived originally by a completely different method in [40], p. 339. The above method has points of contact with methods used in [14], [21]. It is closely connected with the "multiplying-factor method" described in [33], Chapter VI.

The above analysis has been included to provide motivation for the methods we use in the remainder of this section. We next reduce the following dual integral equations to a Fredholm integral equation of the second kind:

$$\int_0^\infty t^{\alpha}\{1 + K(t)\}A(t) J_{\nu}(\rho t)\,dt = f(\rho) , \qquad (0 \le \rho < 1) , \qquad (74a)$$

$$\int_0^\infty A(t) J_{\nu}(\rho t)\,dt = 0 , \qquad (\rho > 1) . \qquad (74b)$$

By following the procedure leading to (70), equation (74a) becomes

$$\int_0^\infty t^{\frac{1}{2}\alpha}\{1+K(t)\}A(t) J_{\nu+\frac{1}{2}\alpha}(xt)\,dt = F(x) , \qquad (0 \le x < 1) , \qquad (75)$$

where

$$F(x) = \frac{x^{-\nu-\frac{1}{2}\alpha}}{2^{-1+\frac{1}{2}\alpha}\Gamma(\frac{1}{2}\alpha)} \int_0^x f(\rho)\rho^{\nu+1}(x^2-\rho^2)^{-1+\frac{1}{2}\alpha}\,d\rho . \qquad (76)$$

We introduce the (unknown) function $h(\rho)$ defined by

$$\int_0^\infty A(t) J_{\nu}(\rho t)\,dt = h(\rho) , \qquad (0 \le \rho \le 1) . \qquad (77)$$

From (64b) the left-hand side of this equation is zero for $\rho > 1$ so that Hankel's inversion theorem gives

$$A(t) = t\int_0^1 \rho\, h(\rho) J_\nu(\rho t)\, d\rho \quad . \tag{78}$$

If this is introduced in (75) we obtain

$$w(x) + \int_0^1 \rho h(\rho) L(x, \rho)\, d\rho = F(x) \quad , \quad (0 \le x \le 1) \quad , \tag{79}$$

where

$$L(x, \rho) = \int_0^\infty t^{1+\frac{1}{2}\alpha} K(t) J_{\nu+\frac{1}{2}\alpha}(xt) J_\nu(\rho t)\, dt \quad , \tag{80}$$

$$w(x) = \int_0^\infty t^{1+\frac{1}{2}\alpha} \int_0^1 \rho\, h(\rho) J_\nu(\rho t)\, d\rho\, J_{\nu+\frac{1}{2}\alpha}(xt)\, dt$$

$$= -x^{\nu+\frac{1}{2}\alpha-1} \frac{d}{dx} x^{-\nu-\frac{1}{2}\alpha+1} \int_0^\infty t^{\frac{1}{2}\alpha} \int_0^1 \rho h(\rho) J_\nu(\rho t) d\rho\, J_{\nu+\frac{1}{2}\alpha-1}(xt)\, dt \; .$$

The derivative in this formula is introduced to allow interchange of orders of integration, remembering that $\alpha > 0$. On interchanging and using the Weber-Schafheitlin integral we find

$$w(x) = -\frac{x^{\nu+\frac{1}{2}\alpha-1}\, 2^{\frac{1}{2}\alpha}}{\Gamma(1-\frac{1}{2}\alpha)} \frac{d}{dx} \int_x^1 \frac{\rho^{1-\nu} h(\rho)}{(\rho^2-x^2)^{\frac{1}{2}\alpha}}\, d\rho \quad . \tag{81}$$

This is an Abel-type integral equation which can be inverted by standard methods. On physical grounds it is known that $h(\rho) = 0$ on $\rho = 1$ and we find the result

$$h(\rho) = \frac{\rho^\nu\, 2^{1-\frac{1}{2}\alpha}}{\Gamma(\frac{1}{2}\alpha)} \int_\rho^1 \frac{\xi^{1-\nu-\frac{1}{2}\alpha} w(\xi)}{(\xi^2-\rho^2)^{1-\frac{1}{2}\alpha}}\, d\xi \quad . \tag{82}$$

There are now two methods of procedure.

(i) to find an integral equation for $w(x)$ we substitute (82) in (79) and interchange orders of integration. This gives, on remembering that

$$\int_0^1 \left\{ \int_\rho^1 d\xi \right\} d\rho = \int_0^1 \left\{ \int_0^\xi d\rho \right\} d\xi \quad ,$$

and evaluating the inner integral by (65),

$$w(x) + \int_0^1 \xi\, w(\xi) M(x, \xi)\, d\xi = F(x) \quad , \qquad (0 \le x < 1) \quad , \tag{83}$$

where $$M(x, \xi) = \int_0^\infty t\, K(t)\, J_{\nu+\frac{1}{2}\alpha}(xt)\, J_{\nu+\frac{1}{2}\alpha}(\xi t)\, dt \;. \tag{84}$$

This integral equation has been derived by different methods in [11], [32].

(ii) To find an integral equation for $h(\rho)$ we can invert (79) by (82), regarding the integral in (79) as known. This gives

$$h(r) + \int_0^1 \rho\, h(\rho)\, N(r, \rho)\, d\rho = \frac{r^\nu 2^{1-\frac{1}{2}\alpha}}{\Gamma(\frac{1}{2}\alpha)} \int_r^1 \frac{\xi^{1-\nu-\frac{1}{2}\alpha} F(\xi)}{(\xi^2 - r^2)^{1-\frac{1}{2}\alpha}}\, d\xi \;, \tag{85}$$

where

$$N(r, \rho) = \frac{r^\nu 2^{1-\frac{1}{2}\alpha}}{\Gamma(\frac{1}{2}\alpha)} \int_r^1 \frac{\xi^{1-\nu-\frac{1}{2}\alpha}}{(\xi^2 - r^2)^{1-\frac{1}{2}\alpha}} \int_0^\infty t^{1+\frac{1}{2}\alpha} K(t) J_{\nu+\frac{1}{2}\alpha}(\xi t)\, J_\nu(\rho t)\, dt\, d\xi \;.$$

I have not been able to reduce this kernel to a more elegant form, but the result is included because the method is relevant to an alternative procedure given below.

We now apply the integral equation (83) to the diffraction problem formulated in (63). In comparing (63), (74), and (83) we see that the object is to choose $K(t)$ so that the integral part of the Fredholm equation (83) is as small as possible. For small k this indicates that we choose

$$K(t) = \{(t^2 - k^2)^{\frac{1}{2}} - t\}/t \;. \tag{86}$$

Equation (84) then becomes

$$M(x, \xi) = \int_0^\infty \{(t^2 - k^2)^{\frac{1}{2}} - t\} J_{\nu+\frac{1}{2}\alpha}(xt)\, J_{\nu+\frac{1}{2}\alpha}(\xi t)\, dt \;. \tag{87}$$

This integral can be simplified in the following way. We work in the complex plane $s = \sigma + i\tau$. Suppose that $x > \xi$. We write

$$J_\mu(xs) J_\mu(\xi s) = \tfrac{1}{2}\{H_\mu^{(1)}(xs) J_\mu(\xi s) + H_\mu^{(2)}(xs) J_\mu(\xi s)\}$$

where the first and second terms on the right tend to zero in upper and lower half-planes respectively. Suppose that δ, ε are small real constants and R is a large real constant. Integrate

$$\{(s^2 - k^2)^{\frac{1}{2}} - s\} H_\mu^{(1)}(xs)\, J_\mu(\xi s)$$

round a contour consisting of $s = \delta$ to $k - \varepsilon$, the semicircle of radius ε above $s = k$, $s = k + \varepsilon$ to R, the quarter-circle $s = R \exp i\Theta$, $0 \le \Theta \le \frac{1}{2}\pi$, the imaginary axis iR to $i\delta$, and the quarter-circle $\delta \exp i\theta$, $\frac{1}{2}\pi \ge \theta \ge 0$. There are no singularities within this contour so that the integral is zero. If we let δ, ε tend to zero and R tend so that the integral is zero. If we let δ, ε tend to zero and R tend to infinity the contributions from the corresponding areas tend to zero. Hence

$$\int_0^k \{i(k^2-\sigma^2)^{\frac{1}{2}}-\sigma\}H_\mu^{(1)}(x\sigma)J_\mu(\xi\sigma)d\sigma + \int_k^\infty \{(\sigma^2-k^2)^{\frac{1}{2}}-\sigma\}H_\mu^{(1)}(x\sigma)J_\mu(\xi\sigma)d\sigma$$
$$+ i\int_\infty^0 \{i(\tau^2+k^2)^{\frac{1}{2}}-i\tau\}H_\mu^{(1)}(ix\tau)J_\mu(i\xi\tau)d\tau = 0 . \quad (88)$$

Integration over a similar contour in the lower right-hand quadrant passing under the branch-point at $s = k$ gives

$$\int_0^k \{i(k^2-\sigma^2)^{\frac{1}{2}}-\sigma\}H_\mu^{(2)}(x\sigma)J_\mu(\xi\sigma)d\sigma + \int_k^\infty \{(\sigma^2-k^2)^{\frac{1}{2}}-\sigma\}H_\mu^{(2)}(x\sigma)J_\mu(\xi\sigma)d\sigma$$
$$-\int_\infty^0 \{-i(\tau^2+k^2)^{\frac{1}{2}}+i\tau\}H_\mu^{(2)}(-ix\tau)J_\mu(-i\xi\tau)d\tau = 0 . \quad (89)$$

But

$$H_\mu^{(1)}(ix\tau)J_\mu(i\xi\tau) = -i(2/\pi)K_\mu(x\tau)I_\mu(\xi\tau) = -H_\mu(-ix\tau)J_\mu(-i\xi\tau) .$$

Hence on adding (88) and (89) we find, for $x > \xi$,

$$\int_k^\infty \{(t^2-k^2)^{\frac{1}{2}}-t\}J_\mu(xt)J_\mu(\xi t)dt$$
$$= \int_0^k tJ_\mu(xt)J_\mu(\xi t)dt + \int_0^k (k^2-\sigma^2)^{\frac{1}{2}}Y_\mu(xt)J_\mu(\xi t)dt .$$

Then (87) gives, on remembering (62),

$$M(x,\xi) = -i\int_0^k (k^2-t^2)\ H^{(1)}_{\nu+\frac{1}{2}\alpha}(xt)J_{\nu+\frac{1}{2}\alpha}(\xi t)dt , \quad (x \geq \xi) . \quad (90)$$

This is now in a form which is convenient for small k. The final result is that the diffraction problem represented by the dual integral equations (63) has been reduced to the Fredholm integral equation of the second kind (83) with kernel (90). The function $F(x)$ is defined in (76) and $\alpha = 1$, $\nu = n$. The special case $\nu = n = 0$ has been discovered by a completely different method by Professor Magnus [26].

We next use a related procedure to reduce the original dual integral equations (63) to a different Fredholm integral equation. The discussion in terms of general parameters is not so straightforward as in the method we have just described, so we shall consider the specific equations

$$\int_0^\infty (t^2-k^2)^{\frac{1}{2}}A(t)J_0(\rho t)dt = f(\rho) , \quad (0 \leq \rho < 1) , \quad (91a)$$

$$\int_0^\infty A(t)\,J_0(\rho t)\,dt = 0 \,, \qquad (\rho > 1) \,. \tag{91b}$$

Instead of (65) derived from Sonine's first finite integral we shall use a result derived from Sonine's second finite integral ([41], p. 376(1)):

$$\int_0^{\frac{1}{2}\pi} J_\mu(z\sin\theta)\,J_\nu(Z\cos\theta)\sin^{\mu+1}\theta\cos^{\nu+1}\theta\,d\theta = z^\mu Z^\nu \frac{J_{\mu+\nu+1}\{(Z^2+z^2)^{\frac{1}{2}}\}}{(Z^2+z^2)^{\frac{1}{2}(\mu+\nu+1)}} \,, \tag{92}$$

valid for $\mu > -1$, $\nu > -1$. In this equation we set $\mu = 0$, $\nu = -\frac{1}{2}$, $z = xt$, $Z = ixk$, $\rho = x\sin\theta$. We find

$$\int_0^x \rho\, J_0(\rho t)\frac{\cosh k(x^2-\rho^2)^{\frac{1}{2}}}{(x^2-\rho^2)^{\frac{1}{2}}}\,d\rho = \frac{\sin x(t^2-k^2)^{\frac{1}{2}}}{(t^2-k^2)^{\frac{1}{2}}} \,. \tag{93}$$

If this is applied to (91a) in exactly the same way as (65) was applied to (64a) we find

$$\int_k^\infty \sin\{x(t^2-k^2)^{\frac{1}{2}}\}A(t)\,dt + \int_0^k \sin\{x(t^2-k^2)^{\frac{1}{2}}\}A(t)\,dt = G(x) \,, \qquad (0 \le x \le 1) \,, \tag{94}$$

where

$$G(x) = \int_0^x \rho\, f(\rho)\frac{\cosh\{k(x^2-\rho^2)^{\frac{1}{2}}\}}{(x^2-\rho^2)^{\frac{1}{2}}}\,d\rho \,. \tag{95}$$

Following our previous procedure in connection with (75) we introduce

$$h(\rho) = \int_0^\infty A(t)\,J_0(\rho t)\,dt \,. \tag{96}$$

From this equation and (91b), using Hankel's inversion theorem,

$$A(t) = t\int_0^1 \rho\, h(\rho)\,J_0(\rho t)\,d\rho \,. \tag{97}$$

If this is inserted in (94) we obtain

$$W(x) + \int_0^1 \rho\, h(\rho)\,R(x,\rho)\,d\rho = G(x) \,, \qquad (0 \le x < 1) \,, \tag{98}$$

where

$$R(x,\rho) = \int_0^k t\sin x(t^2-k^2)^{\frac{1}{2}} J_0(\rho t)\,dt \,, \tag{99}$$

$$= i\frac{x}{\rho}\frac{d}{d\rho}\frac{\sin k(\rho^2-x^2)^{\frac{1}{2}}}{(\rho^2-x^2)^{\frac{1}{2}}} \tag{100}$$

$$W(x) = \int_k^\infty t \sin x(t^2-k^2)^{\frac{1}{2}} \int_0^1 \rho\, h(\rho) J_0(\rho t)\, d\rho\, dt$$

$$= -\frac{d}{dx} \int_0^1 \rho\, h(\rho) \int_k^\infty t J_0(\rho t) \frac{\cos x(t^2-k^2)^{\frac{1}{2}}}{(t^2-k^2)^{\frac{1}{2}}} dt\, d\rho$$

$$= -\frac{d}{dx} \int_x^1 \rho\, h(\rho) \frac{\cos k(\rho^2-x^2)^{\frac{1}{2}}}{(p^2-x^2)^{\frac{1}{2}}} d\rho \ , \qquad (101)$$

where we have used [41], p. 415(1). Note the similarity between (79), (81) and (98), (101). Equation (101) can be inverted by use of the Laplace transform or operational methods (see, for example, [16], Appendix A) to give, since we know on physical grounds that $h(1) = 0$,

$$h(\rho) = \frac{2}{\pi} \int_\rho^1 W(\xi) \frac{\cosh k(\xi^2-\rho^2)^{\frac{1}{2}}}{(\xi^2-\rho^2)^{\frac{1}{2}}} d\xi \ , \quad (0 \le \rho \le 1) \ . \qquad (102)$$

At this point there are two methods of procedure, as in the previous analysis:

(i)' We can obtain an integral equation for $W(x)$ by substituting for $h(\rho)$ from (102) in (98). On interchanging orders of integration we find

$$W(x) + \int_0^1 W(\xi) S(x, \xi)\, d\xi = G(x) \ , \quad (0 \le x \le 1) \ , \qquad (103)$$

where

$$S(x, \xi) = \frac{2}{\pi} \int_0^\xi \rho \frac{\cos k(\xi^2-\rho^2)^{\frac{1}{2}}}{(\xi^2-\rho^2)^{\frac{1}{2}}} R(x, \rho)\, d\rho \ . \qquad (104)$$

On substituting from (99) we find that the integral in ρ can be evaluated by means of (93)

$$S(x, \xi) = \frac{2}{\pi} \int_0^k t \sin x(t^2-k^2)^{\frac{1}{2}} \frac{\sin \xi(t^2-k^2)^{\frac{1}{2}}}{(t^2-k^2)^{\frac{1}{2}}} dt \ . \qquad (105)$$

This is reduced to an elementary integral by the substitution $k^2-t^2 = u^2$, remembering that $(t^2-k^2)^{\frac{1}{2}} = -i(k^2-t^2)^{\frac{1}{2}}$ from (62). We find

$$S(x, \xi) = \frac{i}{\pi} \left\{ \frac{\sinh k(x-\xi)}{x-\xi} - \frac{\sinh k(x+\xi)}{x+\xi} \right\} \ . \qquad (106)$$

(ii)' Alternatively we can obtain an integral equation for $h(\rho)$ by using (102) to eliminate $W(x)$ from (98). This gives

$$h(r) + \int_0^1 h(\rho) T(r, \rho)\, d\rho = U(r) \ , \quad (0 \le r \le 1) \qquad (107)$$

where

$$U(r) = \frac{2}{\pi} \int_r^1 G(\xi) \frac{\cosh k(\xi^2-r^2)^{\frac{1}{2}}}{(\xi^2-r^2)^{\frac{1}{2}}} d\xi ,$$

$$T(r,\rho) = \frac{2\rho}{\pi} \int_r^1 \frac{\cosh k(\xi^2-r^2)^{\frac{1}{2}}}{(\xi^2-r^2)^{\frac{1}{2}}} R(\xi,\rho) d\xi . \qquad (108)$$

In this integral we make the substitutions

$$\eta^2 = 1-\rho^2 , \quad y^2 = 1-r^2 , \quad u^2 = 1-\xi^2 ,$$

so that, from (100),

$$\rho R(\xi,\rho) = i \frac{d}{d\rho} \xi \left\{ \frac{\sin k(u^2-\eta^2)^{\frac{1}{2}}}{(u^2-\eta^2)^{\frac{1}{2}}} \right\} .$$

If we replace the bracketed term by the integral representation (93), change orders of integration in the resulting form of (108), evaluate the new inner integral by (93), and differentiate, we find that the resulting integral is identical with (105), and

$$T(r,\rho) = \frac{i}{\pi} \frac{\rho}{\eta} \left\{ \frac{\sinh k(y-\eta)}{y-\eta} - \frac{\sinh k(y+\eta)}{y+\eta} \right\} .$$

On setting

$$h(r) = e(y) , \quad U(r) = V(y) ,$$

we find that (107) becomes

$$e(y) + \int_0^1 e(\eta) S(y,\eta) d\eta = V(y) , \quad (0 \leq y \leq 1) , \qquad (109)$$

where $S(y,\eta)$ is defined in (106). It is remarkable that the kernel in this equation is identical with the kernel in (103).

The integral equation (109) was obtained by D. S. Jones [16]. An earlier treatment is that of Bardeen [2]. See also [1], [37]. Recently integral equations of the forms (103), (109)] have been derived, using similar methods, independently, by Heins and MacCamy [15], Bazer and Brown [4] and Collins [10]. (See also the paper by Professor Heins in this symposium.)

In terms of the theory in Section 3, we have investigated in this section two different splits of integral operators involving kernels derived from the Green's function

$$e^{ikR}/R , \quad \text{where } R = |r-r'| .$$

In the first case we performed a "static" split:

$$e^{ikR}/R = 1/R + (e^{ikR}-1)/R \;.$$

In the second case we performed what D. S. Jones called a "non-radiating" split, corresponding to a standing-wave condition at infinity:

$$e^{ikR}/R = \cos k\,R/R + i\,\sin k\,R/R \;.$$

Professor Marcuvitz tells me that this type of split is well-known in quantum mechanics.

The difficulty in carrying out the perturbation procedure explicitly lies in the inversion of the integral operators corresponding to $1/R$ and $\cos k\,R/R$. We have introduced the following splits in the first of the dual integral equation pair:

$$\int_0^\infty (t^2-k^2)^{\frac{1}{2}}\{\ldots\}dt = \int_0^\infty t\{\ldots\}dt + \int_0^\infty [(t^2-k^2)^{\frac{1}{2}}-t]\{\ldots\}dt \;,$$

$$\int_0^\infty (t^2-k^2)^{\frac{1}{2}}\{\ldots\}dt = \int_k^\infty (t^2-k^2)^{\frac{1}{2}}\{\ldots\}dt + \int_0^k (t^2-k^2)^{\frac{1}{2}}\{\ldots\}dt \;.$$

These correspond to the static and non-radiating splits respectively but from this point of view the basic reason for introducing these splits is that we can solve exactly the dual integral equations involving only the first half of these splits. One interesting feature of this section is the parallelism between the methods used in the static and non-radiating cases. It is also remarkable that it has been possible to reduce the kernels of the Fredholm equations of the second kind to such simple and elegant forms.

6. THE HELMHOLTZ RESONATOR AND RELATED PROBLEMS. As a final set of specific examples we consider some mixed boundary-value problems involving spherical boundaries. Suppose that, using spherical coordinates (r, θ, ϕ) a wave ([31], p. 1466)

$$\begin{aligned} u_i &= \exp ikz = \exp ikr\cos\theta \\ &= \sum_{n=0}^{\infty} (2n+1)\, i^n P_n(\cos\theta)\, j_n(kr) \end{aligned}$$

falls on a Helmholtz resonator specified by a rigid boundary in $r = a$, $\alpha \le \theta \le \pi$ on which $\partial u_t/\partial r = 0$. Since the field is axially symmetrical, general representations for waves inside and outside $r = a$ are:

$$(u_t)_{\text{inside}} = \sum_{n=0}^{\infty} A_n P_n(\cos\theta)\frac{j_n(kr)}{j'_n(ka)} \;, \tag{110}$$

$$(u_s)_{\text{outside}} = \sum_{n=0}^{\infty} B_n P_n(\cos\theta) \frac{h_n(kr)}{h'_n(ka)} . \tag{111}$$

In these equations we have used the spherical Bessel functions:

$$j_n(z) = (\pi/2z)^{\frac{1}{2}} J_{n+\frac{1}{2}}(z) , \quad y_n(z) = (\pi/2z)^{\frac{1}{2}} Y_{n+\frac{1}{2}}(z) ,$$
$$h_n(z) = j_n(z) + i y_n(z) , \quad j'_n(z) = d j_n(z)/dz , \text{ etc.}$$

Since $\partial u_t/\partial r$ is continuous on $r = a$ we find

$$A_n = B_n + (2n+1) i^n j'_n(ka) .$$

The boundary conditions on $r = a$ are

$$\partial u_t/\partial r = 0 , \quad (\alpha \le \theta \le \pi) , \quad u_t \text{ continuous } (0 \le \theta < \alpha) .$$

On applying these to (110), (111), using the Wronskian

$$j_n(z) h'_n(z) - j'_n(z) h_n(z) = i/z^2 ,$$

we find

$$\sum_{n=0}^{\infty} \frac{1}{j'_n(ka) h'_n(ka)} A_n P_n(\cos\theta) = \sum_{n=0}^{\infty} (2n+1) i^n \frac{1}{h'_n(ka)} , \quad (0 \le \theta < \alpha) , \tag{112a}$$

$$\sum_{n=0}^{\infty} A_n P_n(\cos\theta) = 0 , \quad (\alpha \le \theta \le \pi) . \tag{112b}$$

These "dual series" can be reduced to an integral equation by the following method. Let the (unknown) value of the second equation for $0 \le \theta < \alpha$ be denoted by $f(\theta)$. Then

$$B_n = (n+\tfrac{1}{2}) \int_0^{\alpha} f(t) P_n(\cos t) \sin t \, dt .$$

Substitution in (112b) gives the integral equation

$$\sum_{n=0}^{\infty} \frac{(n+\frac{1}{2})}{j'_n(ka) h'_n(ka)} \int_0^{\alpha} f(t) P_n(\cos t) \sin t \, dt \, P_n(\cos\theta) ,$$
$$= \sum_{n=0}^{\infty} (2n+1) i^n \frac{1}{h'_n(ka)} , \quad (0 \le \theta < \alpha) . \tag{113}$$

We examine the behavior of this equation for small k . In this case

$$j_0'(z) \approx -\frac{1}{3} z \ , \qquad h_0'(z) \approx i/z^2 \ ,$$

$$j_n'(z) h_n'(z) \approx \frac{i\, n(n+1)}{(2n+1) z^3} \ .$$

Hence (113) becomes, approximately,

$$-\frac{3}{(ka)^2} \int_0^\alpha f(t) \sin t\, dt + \sum_{n=1}^{\infty} \frac{(2n+1)^2}{n(n+1)} \int_0^\alpha f(t) P_n(\cos t) \sin t\, dt\, P_n(\cos \theta)$$

$$= 2(ka)^{-1} \ , \quad (0 \le \theta < \alpha) \ . \qquad (114)$$

We compare this with the integral equation for the electrostatic charge on a spherical cap lying in $r = a$, $0 \le \theta < \alpha$. Let ϕ denote the potential due to the cap. Then

$$(\phi)_{\text{inside}} = \sum_{n=0}^{\infty} C_n P_n(\cos \theta)(r/a)^n \ ,$$

$$(\phi)_{\text{outside}} = \sum_{n=0}^{\infty} C_n P_n(\cos \theta)(a/r)^{n+1}$$

The boundary conditions on $r = a$ are

$$\phi = 1 \ , \quad (0 \le \theta < \alpha) \ , \quad \partial\phi/\partial r \text{ continuous,} \quad (\alpha \le \theta \le \pi) \ .$$

On following the same steps as in deriving (112), (113) previously we find the integral equation

$$\sum_{n=0}^{\infty} \int_0^\alpha F(t) P_n(\cos t) \sin t\, dt\, P_n(\cos \theta) = G(\theta) \ , \quad (0 \le \theta \le \alpha) \ , \qquad (115)$$

where $F(\theta)$ is the discontinuity in $\partial\phi/\partial r$ across the cap. We have written a general function $G(\theta)$ on the right of this integral equation. In the case of the cap at constant potential $G(\theta) = 2a$. Equation (115) can be solved by transforming the kernel in the following way. We use Mehler's integral representation for the Legendre polynomial ([27], p. 52) which gives

$$\sum_{n=0}^{\infty} P_n(\cos t) P_n(\cos \theta) = \frac{\sqrt{2}}{\pi} \int_0^\theta \frac{1}{(\cos \chi - \cos \theta)^{\frac{1}{2}}} \left\{ \sum_{n=0}^{\infty} \cos(n+\tfrac{1}{2}) \chi\, P_n(\cos t) \right\} d\chi .$$

The sum can be evaluated by a result in [27], p. 53 and we find

$$\sum_{n=0}^{\infty} P_n(\cos t) P_n(\cos \theta) = \frac{1}{\pi} \int_0^{\min \theta, t} \frac{d\chi}{(\cos \chi - \cos \theta)^{\frac{1}{2}} (\cos \chi - \cos t)^{\frac{1}{2}}} \ .$$

If this result is substituted in (115) and orders of integration are interchanged we obtain

$$\frac{1}{\pi}\int_0^{\theta}\frac{S(\chi)\,d\chi}{(\cos\chi-\cos\theta)^{\frac{1}{2}}} = G(\theta)\ , \quad (0 \le \theta < \alpha)\ , \tag{116}$$

where

$$S(\chi) = \int_{\chi}^{\alpha}\frac{F(t)\sin t\,dt}{(\cos\chi-\cos t)^{\frac{1}{2}}}\ . \tag{117}$$

The integral equations (116),(117) are easily reduced to Abel's integral equation. Inversion gives

$$\sin t\,F(t) = -\frac{1}{\pi}\frac{d}{dt}\int_t^{\alpha}\frac{\sin\chi\,S(\chi)\,d\chi}{(\cos t-\cos\chi)^{\frac{1}{2}}}\ , \tag{118}$$

$$S(\chi) = \frac{d}{d\chi}\int_0^{\chi}\frac{\sin\theta\,G(\theta)\,d\theta}{(\cos\theta-\cos\chi)^{\frac{1}{2}}}\ . \tag{119}$$

From (118) we derive the following result which we use later:

$$\int_0^{\alpha}\sin t\,F(t)\,dt = \frac{\sqrt{2}}{\pi}\int_0^{\alpha}\cos\tfrac{1}{2}\chi\,S(\chi)\,d\chi\ . \tag{120}$$

If $G(\theta) = 1$ then (119),(120) give

$$S(\chi) = \sqrt{2}\cos\tfrac{1}{2}\chi\ ,$$

$$\int_0^{\alpha}\sin t\,F(t)\,dt = \frac{1}{\pi}(\alpha+\sin\alpha)\ . \tag{121}$$

We now return to equation (114). We approximate still further by writing the equation in the form

$$-\left\{\frac{3}{(ka)^2}+4\right\}\int_0^{\alpha}f(t)\sin t\,dt + 4\sum_{n=0}^{\infty}\int_0^{\alpha}f(t)\,P_n(\cos t)\sin t\,dt\,P_n(\cos\theta) = 2(ka)^{-1},$$

$$(0 \le \theta < \alpha)\ . \tag{122}$$

This integral equation can be solved by setting $f(t) = C\,F(t)$ where C is a constant which is to be determined and $F(t)$ is the solution of (115) with $G(\theta) = 1$. For then (122) becomes, on using (121),

$$C\left\{-\frac{1}{\pi}\left[\frac{3}{(ka)^2}+4\right](\alpha+\sin\alpha)+4\right\} = 2(ka)^{-1}\ .$$

If ka and α are both small we therefore obtain the approximate result

$$f(t) = \frac{1}{(ka)\{2 - (3\alpha/\pi)(ka)^{-2}\}} F(t) \quad . \tag{123}$$

Resonance occurs when the denominator is zero, i.e.,

$$ka = (3\alpha/2\pi)^{\frac{1}{2}} \tag{124}$$

This result was found by Rayleigh [35]. The present method can be compared with the integral equation-variational method of Levine [23]. The reduction of the problem of the spherical cap to the repeated Volterra integral equations (116), (117) was carried out from a different point of view by Lebedev [22] (see also [12], [8]).

In the above treatment we have confined ourselves to the simplest possible approximation. We have in fact used the approximation (17) derived in general terms in Section 3. Resonance phenomena occur when the denominator of (17) is small. More accurate results can be obtained systematically by the method described in connection with (18a, b). We split (113) into the dominant part represented by the sum in (122), and a series of perturbation terms

$$\sum_{n=0}^{N}\left\{\frac{n+\frac{1}{2}}{j'_n(ka)\,h'_n(ka)} - 4\right\}\int_0^{\alpha} f(t)\,P_n(\cos t)\sin t\,dt\;P_n(\cos\theta) \quad , \tag{125}$$

where N is a suitable integer. In (122) we have included only an approximate form of the first term of this series. Following (18b) we need to solve integral equations of the form (115) with $G(\theta) = P_n(\cos\theta)$. The solution of (115) for general $G(\theta)$ is given in (118), (119) so that the perturbation procedure can be carried out for any value of N in (125) although naturally the complication increases extremely rapidly with N.

Clearly solutions can be obtained for any angle α of the aperture of the resonator so that in the case $\alpha = \pi$ we obtain results for diffraction by a sphere and in the other limit as α tends to zero we obtain results for diffraction by a flat circular disk.

We can use the same method to determine the resonance frequencies of a spherical cavity $0 \le r \le a$ with mixed boundary conditions on $r = a$:

$$u_t = 0 \;,\quad (0 \le \theta < \alpha) \;,\quad \partial u_t/\partial r = 0 \;,\quad (\alpha \le \theta \le \pi) \;. \tag{126}$$

We consider only the lowest axially symmetrical eigenvalue. On using the solution (110) for u_t we find the dual integral equations

$$\sum_{n=0}^{\infty} \frac{j_n(ka)}{j'_n(ka)} A_n P_n(\cos\theta) = 0 \;, \qquad (0 \le \theta < \alpha) \;,$$

$$\sum_{n=0}^{\infty} A_n P_n(\cos\theta) = 0 , \qquad (\alpha \le \theta \le \pi) .$$

By following the procedure used previously, these can be reduced to the singular integral equation

$$\sum_{n=0}^{\infty} (n+\tfrac{1}{2}) \frac{j_n(ka)}{j'_n(ka)} \int_0^{\alpha} f(t) P_n(\cos t) \sin t \, dt \; P_n(\cos\theta) = 0 , \; (0 \le \theta < \alpha) . \qquad (127)$$

This equation is of an unusual type. In general it possesses no solutions, but solutions exist for special values of k and these are the required resonance frequencies. To obtain the lowest eigenvalue we introduce the approximations

$$\tfrac{1}{2} j_0(ka)/j'_0(ka) \approx -3/(2ka) , \; (n+\tfrac{1}{2}) j_n(ka)/j'_n(ka) \approx ka .$$

Then (127) becomes

$$-\left\{\frac{3}{2(ka)^2} + 1\right\} \int_0^{\alpha} f(t) \sin t \, dt + \sum_{n=0}^{\infty} \int_0^{\alpha} f(t) P_n(\cos t) \sin t \, dt \; P_n(\cos\theta) = 0 ,$$

$$(0 \le \theta < \alpha) . \qquad (128)$$

This equation can be solved by setting $f(t) = C\,F(t)$ where $F(t)$ is the solution of (115) with $G(\theta) = 1$. This has been investigated above, and on using (121) equation (128) becomes

$$-\frac{1}{\pi}\left[\frac{3}{2(ka)^2} + 1\right](\alpha + \sin\alpha) + 1 = 0 .$$

This equation gives an approximate value for the smallest eigenvalue k. If α is small we find that

$$ka \approx (3\alpha/\pi)^{\frac{1}{2}} . \qquad (129)$$

On comparing with (124) it is seen that this is greater than that for the open (Helmholtz) resonator by a factor of $\sqrt{2}$. Higher order approximations can be obtained systematically by exactly the same procedure as outlined previously in connection with (125).

The above examples are particularly interesting in that the static approximation is used to give resonance frequencies.

We can similarly obtain perturbation solutions for diffraction by a sphere on which mixed boundary-value conditions are specified. Consider a plane wave of the form specified at the beginning of this section incident on a sphere on which conditions (126) hold. We use the representation (111) and obtain the integral equation

$$\sum_{n=0}^{\infty} (n+\tfrac{1}{2}) \frac{h_n(ka)}{h'_n(ka)} \int_0^{\alpha} f(t)\, P_n(\cos t) \sin t \, dt \, P_n(\cos \theta)$$

$$= \frac{i}{(ka)^2} \sum_{n=0}^{\infty} (2n+1) i^n P_n(\cos\theta) \frac{1}{h'_n(ka)} \ .$$

This can be solved approximately by the methods described above.

Similar methods can be used to investigate the corresponding problems in two dimensions, namely diffraction by a cylinder on which mixed boundary conditions are specified, diffraction by a slotted cylinder, and resonance inside a cylinder with mixed boundary conditions. In the last two cases the lowest resonance frequencies for small angles of the gap differ by a factor of $\sqrt{2}$, as in the three-dimensional problem. In the two-dimensional problems the static integral equation has a kernel

$$\log |\cos \theta - \cos t| \ .$$

The solution of such integral equations by a method due to Schwinger is well-known in waveguide theory. An application to propagation of waves in a slotted cylinder is given in [13].

7. GENERALITIES. It is clear that the success of any integral equation perturbation method depends ultimately on the existence of a convenient inversion formula for the integral equation representing the dominant part of the operator. The aim of Section 4 was to illustrate that if Laplace's equation can be solved by separation-of-variables then the corresponding static integral equations can be solved in a straightforward way. The most obvious systems for which Laplace's equation separates but the wave equation does not, are bipolar, bispherical, and toroidal coordinates. It should therefore be possible to find low-frequency perturbation solutions for scalar and vector diffraction by bodies with shapes defined by these coordinate systems. This does not imply that the most convenient method of solution is to separate variables in the appropriate coordinate system. For instance static problems involving spherical caps can be solved exactly by separation-of-variables in toroidal coordinates but in Section 6 we treated diffraction by a spherical cap as a mixed boundary-value problem and solved the static integral equation directly.

It would seem that the great majority of low-frequency perturbation solutions so far derived satisfy two conditions:

(i) They are based on perturbation of the static approximation.

(ii) The corresponding static problems could be solved by separation of variables even though this may not be the method used in practice to deal with any particular case.

Condition (ii) should be understood in an extended sense. It is assumed to include bodies for which the corresponding static problems can be solved by Kelvin's method of images, or inversion. The following statement of this method from an integral equation point of view does not seem to be widely known (see [36], p. 251). We use cylindrical coordinates (r, θ, z). The Green's function for a potential which varies as $\cos m\theta$ corresponds to the solution of Laplace's equation for a ring source with charge density varying as $\cos m\theta$. This is proportional to

$$\int_0^{2\pi} \frac{\cos m(\theta-\Theta)\, d\theta}{\{d^2 + \{rr'[1-\cos(\theta-\theta')]\}^{\frac{1}{2}}}$$

$$= 2(rr')^{-\frac{1}{2}} Q_{m-\frac{1}{2}}\{1 + (d^2/2rr')\} \cos m(\theta'-\Theta) \quad ,$$

where $Q_{m-\frac{1}{2}}$ is the Legendre function of the second kind and

$$d^2 = (r-r')^2 + (z-z')^2 \quad .$$

The perturbation solution for diffraction by an object defined by a curve $z = f(r)$ in the (r, z) plane therefore depends on solving an integral equation with a kernel of the form

$$Q_{m-\frac{1}{2}}\{1 + (d^2/2rr')\} \quad , \qquad (130)$$

where $z = f(r)$, $z' = f(r')$. We introduce new coordinates (R, Z) related to (r, z) by the equation

$$w = \frac{aW + b}{cW + d} \quad , \qquad (a, b, c, d \text{ real constants}), \qquad (131)$$

where $w = z + ir$, $W = Z + iR$. Then it is found that

$$d^2/(2rr') = D^2/(2RR') \quad ,$$

where

$$D^2 = (R-R')^2 + (Z-Z')^2 \quad .$$

But the integral equation for the static problem for the object defined by the corresponding curve in the (R, Z) plane depends on a kernel

$$Q_{m-\frac{1}{2}}\{1 + (D^2/2RR')\} \quad .$$

It is clear therefore that this integral equation can be reduced to an integral equation with kernel (130) by means of the substitution (131). If one integral equation can be solved, so can the other.

As an example we show that the change of variable which Collins guessed in order to solve the spherical cap problem in [8] can be written down immediately by a deductive procedure. If we invert a spherical cap lying in $r = a$, $0 \leq \theta < \alpha$ into a disk by projection from the pole $r = a$, $\theta = \pi$ onto the plane tangent to the cap at $r = a$, $\theta = 0$ we find that if ρ is the radius of the ring on the plane corresponding to a given value of θ then

$$r = a \tan \tfrac{1}{2} \theta . \tag{132}$$

For the spherical cap $R = a \sin \theta$, $Z = a \cos \theta$ and we find

$$\frac{D^2}{2RR'} = \frac{(\tan\frac{1}{2}\theta - \tan\frac{1}{2}\theta')^2}{2\tan\frac{1}{2}\theta \tan\frac{1}{2}\theta'} = \frac{(r-r')^2}{2rr'} = \frac{d^2}{2rr'} .$$

Hence the substitution (132) reduced the integral equation for a spherical cap to that for a circular disk. Snow [36], Chapter IX shows that problems in bipolar, bispherical and toroidal coordinates can be solved in a similar way. By means of some of the other examples discussed by Snow it should be possible to find perturbation solutions for diffraction by a dumb-bell, or the disk-shaped object formed by rotating the outline of a dumb-bell about its other axis of symmetry.

When considering diffraction by a body formed by rotating a curve about an axis we have decomposed the wave functions into their Fourier components in the angular direction. However a closed form is known for the Green's function for the general static problem for the disk (e.g. [3], p. 466). It may therefore be possible to develop a perturbation series for diffraction of a general incident wave by a disk without having to decompose into Fourier components.

The treatment of the flat circular disk in Section 5 by a "standing-wave" approximation seems to be the only three-dimsnsional example so far discovered which does not depend on perturbation of the static solution. The most powerful method for deriving the "standing-wave" results seems to be the complex-variable procedure of Bazer and Brown [4], Collins [10], Heins and McCamy [15], presented by Professor Heins in another paper in this symposium. These workers seem to agree that it is unlikely that a "standing-wave" integral equation can be obtained by the complex-variable method for any lamina or solid of revolution other than the disk. It seems certain, for instance, that no such integral equation exists for caps though it seems surprising that the method should be so limited, at least from this general point of view. On the other hand the method is applicable to many static problems involving bodies of revolution. Unfortunately it seems that the shapes of bodies that can be dealt with in this way are those which we have already discussed in this section, namely those which fit into a coordinate system in which Laplace's equation is separable or which can be transformed by inversion to fit into such a system. This applies, for example, to the solution by Collins [9] of the integral equations for lenses, derived by the complex-variable method.

The complex variable method has the considerable advantage that it is very easy to formulate many-body problems if the appropriate single-body problems can be formulated by the method. Thus Collins [10] has obtained the system of integral equations for axially symmetrical diffraction by two parallel disks.

It seems possible that a Fredholm equation of the second kind of the D. S. Jones type exists for two-dimensional diffraction by a strip but no one has yet produced an elegant closed form for the kernel of such an equation. The static perturbation dual integral equation method in Sec. 5 can be extended to deal with strip diffraction by choosing $\nu = \pm \frac{1}{2}$ where ν is the order of the Bessel functions in the equations.

We have confined ourselves strictly to a discussion of perturbation methods. It should be mentioned that it is often useful to insert perturbation solutions in variational expressions of the Levine-Schwinger type ([5], [24], [31]). In particular the way in which the perturbation solution has been derived may indicate how the integrals in the variational expression can be evaluated.

8. CONCLUDING REMARKS. This paper has not attempted to present an exhaustive and balanced survey of low-frequency integral-equation perturbation methods. Instead we have tried to illuminate some of the basic principles by discussing three sets of examples in a reasonable amount of detail. Topics which are not directly relevant to these examples have been omitted.

It is comparatively simple to formulate scattering problems in terms of integral equations. It is easy to set up a formal scheme for low-frequency perturbation of the static solution. The difficulties appear when we try to carry out this program in detail for objects of specific shape. The crux of the problem is to obtain a convenient inversion formula for the integral equation selected as the dominant part of the complete operator. Once this is achieved the details of carrying out the perturbation solution often become routine. Most of the integral equations that have been solved can either be reduced to the static integral equations for the disk or strip or they can be solved by means of separation-of-variables solutions of Laplace's equation. However, even if we confine ourselves to the integral equations which can be solved at the moment, there is still considerable scope for investigating low-frequency diffraction by bodies of unusual shape.

9. ACKNOWLEDGMENT. Most of my ideas on diffraction theory in this work germinated during a visit to the Division of Electromagnetic Research, The Institute of Mathematical Sciences, New York University sponsored by the U.S. Air Force Cambridge Research Center under Contract No. AF 19(604) 5238.

REFERENCES

1. N. I. Ahiezer and A. N. Ahiezer, On the diffraction of electromagnetic waves by a circular hole in a plane screen, Dokl. Akad. Nauk. SSSR, 109(1956), 53-56.

2. J. Bardeen, Diffraction of a circularly symmetrical electromagnetic wave by a coaxial disk of infinite conductivity, Phys. Rev. 36 (1930), 1482-1488.

3. H. Bateman, Partial Differential Equations, Camb. Univ. Press (1932).

4. J. Bazer and A. Brown, Diffraction of scalar waves by a circular aperture, Inst. Radio Engrs., Trans. on Antennas and Propagation, Vol. AP-7(1959), 12-20. See also Inst. Math. Sci., New York Univ., Res. Rept. EM-144 (1959).

5. F. E. Borgnis and C. H. Papas, Randwertprobleme der Mikrowellenphysik, Springer-Verlag (1955).

6. C. J. Bouwkamp, Article on Diffraction Theory in Reports on Progress in Physics, The Physical Society, London, 17 (1954), 35-100. See also Inst. Math. Sci., New York Univ., Res. Rept. EM-50 (1953).

7. J. E. Burke and V. Twersky, On the scattering of waves by an elliptic cylinder and by a semi-elliptical protuberance on a ground plane, Electronic Defense Laboratories, Mountain View, Calif., Tech. Mem. No. EDL-M-266(1960).

8. W. D. Collins, Note on the electrified spherical cap, Proc. Camb. Phil. Soc., 55 (1959), 377-379.

9. W. D. Collins, On the solution of some axisymmetric boundary-value problems III, Proc. London Math. Soc. (3) 10(1960), 428-460.

10. W. D. Collins, On the solution of some axisymmetric boundary-value problems V, Quart. J. Mech. and Appl. Math. 14(1961), 101-116.

11. J. C. Cooke, A solution of Tranter's dual integral equations problem, Quart. J. Mech. and Appl. Math., 9(1956), 103-110.

12. E. T. Copson, On the problem of the electrified disk, Proc. Edin. Math. Soc. (3) 8(1947), 14-19.

13. L. O. Goldstone and A. A. Oliner, Leaky wave antennas II, Circular waveguides, Microwave Res. Inst., Polytechnic Inst. of Brooklyn, Res. Rep. R-629-57, PIB-557(1958).

14. A. N. Gordon, Dual integral equations, Journal Lond. Math. Soc. 29(1954), 360-363.

15. A. E. Heins and R. C. MacCamy, On the scattering of waves by a a disk, J. Appl. Math. Phys. (ZAMP) 11(1960), 249-264.

16. D. S. Jones, A new method for calculating scattering with particular reference to the circular disk, Comm. Pure Appl. Math. 9 (1956), 713-746.

17. D. S. Jones and B. Noble, The low-frequency scattering by a perfectly conducting strip, Proc. Camb. Phil. Soc. In the press.

18. O. D. Kellog, Foundations of Potential Theory, Springer, Berlin (1929).

19. R. D. Kodis, An introduction to variational methods in electromagnetic scattering, J. Soc. Industr. Appl. Math. 2(1954), 89-112.

20. W. D. Kupradse, Randwertaufgaben der Schwingungstheorie und Integralgleichungen, (translated from the Russian), Deutscher Verlag (1958).

21. G. Latta, An operational calculus for the Mellin transform, Appl. Math. and Stat. Lab., Stanford Univ. Tech. Rep. No. 44(1955).

22. N. N. Lebedev, Applications of singular integral equations to the problem of the determination of charge on their non-closed surfaces (in Russian), Zhurn. Tekh. Fys. U. S. S. R. 18(1948), 775-784.

23. H. Levine, The wavelength of a spherical resonator with a circular aperture, J. Acoust. Soc. Amer. 23(1951), 307-311.

24. H. Levine and J. Schwinger, On the theory of electromagnetic wave diffraction by an aperture in an infinite plane conducting screen, Comm. Pure Appl. Math. 3(1950), 355-391. (Reprinted in The Theory of Electromagnetic Waves, Interscience (1951.)

25. M. J. Lighthill, Introduction to Fourier Analysis and Generalised Functions, Camb. Univ. Press (1958).

26. W. Magnus, An infinite system of linear equations arising in diffraction theory, Inst. Math. Sci., New York Univ., Res. Rep. EM-80(1955).

27. W. Magnus and F. Oberhettinger, Special Functions of Mathematical Physics, Chelsea (1949).

28. S. G. Mikhlin, Integral Equations (translated from the Russian), Pergamon (1957).

29. R. F. Millar, A note on diffraction by an infinite slit, Can. J. Phys. 38(1960), 38-47.

30. R. F. Millar, Scattering of plane waves by a row of small cylinders, Can. J. Phys., 39(1960), 272-289. See also ibid. 39 (1961), 81-118.

31. P. M. Morse and H. Feshbach, Methods of Theoretical Physics, McGraw-Hill(1953).

32. B. Noble, Certain dual integral equations. J. Math. Phys. 27 (1958), 128-136.

33. B. Noble, The Wiener-Hopf Technique, Pergamon (1958).

34. Lord Rayleigh, On the incidence of aerial and electric waves upon small obstacles in the form of ellipsoids or elliptic cylinders and on the passage of electric waves through a circular aperture in a plane screen, Phil. Mag. 43(1897), 28-52.

35. Lord Rayleigh, The theory of the Helmholtz resonator, Proc. Roy. Soc. A 92(1916), 265-275.

36. C. Snow, Hypergeometric and Legendre functions with applications to the integral equations of potential theory, Nat. Bur. Stand. AMS19(1952).

37. A. Sommerfeld, Die frei schwingende Kolbenmembran, Ann. d. Phys. 42(1942/43), 389-420.

38. A. F. Stevenson, Solution of electromagnetic problems as a power series in the ratio (Dimension of scatterer/wavelength), J. Appl. Phys. 24(1953), 1134-1142 (see also ibid. 1143-1151.)

39. J. A. Stratton, Electromagnetic Theory, McGraw-Hill (1941).

40. E. C. Titchmarsh, Theory of Fourier Integrals, Oxford Univ. Press (1937).

41. G. N. Watson, Bessel Functions, Camb. Univ. Press (1944).

VICTOR TWERSKY

Scattering of Waves by Two Objects

CONTENTS

1. SUMMARY AND INTRODUCTION. This paper develops certain "self-consistent" sets of equations which relate many-body scattering functions, such as "multiple scattering coefficients", to their single-body analogs. We start with surface integral representations of the fields scattered by arbitrary objects, and recast these fields as continuous sets of plane waves multiplied by the required scattering amplitudes. Systems of integral equations relating the scattering amplitudes for many objects to corresponding functions for the isolated objects are obtained from the superposition principle without requiring explicit application of the boundary conditions. Writing the scattering amplitudes as series of elementary angular functions times scattering coefficients (Fourier or Mathieu series) leads directly to the algebraic sets of equations which may be obtained by separations of variables; however, no knowledge of addition theorems is required for the present derivation. In addition, circular function representations are derived for non-separable problems. For arbitrary configurations

of scatterers, series expansions of these equations are obtained by iteration; closed form approximations are given for two small objects.

Returning to the integral equation for the scattering amplitudes, we obtain asymptotic representations for large separations. For arbitrary configurations, the resulting system of differential equations for the multiple scattered amplitudes are developed as an asymptotic series of single-scattered functions; "closed forms" involving differential operators are obtained for two objects.

The literature of scattering by more than one object has been surveyed recently [1], and much of the formalism we will use has been applied previously [2] to related problems. Consequently, discussion and detail will be omitted where feasible. Relevant results of Karp, Karp and Zitron, Millar, Saermark, Burke and Twersky, Twersky, and others will be cited in their appropriate context.

2. ONE SCATTERER The time-independent, two-dimensional problem of the scattering of a plane wave by a cylinder parallel to $\underline{z}$ is specified in the external region by a solution of

$$(\nabla^2+k^2)\psi(\underline{r}) = 0 \; ; \quad \nabla^2 = \partial_x^2 + \partial_y^2 \; , \quad k = 2\pi/\lambda \; , \tag{1}$$

subject to prescribed boundary conditions on the cylinder's surface. With increasing distance from the scaterer, $r \to \infty$, the wave function ψ reduces to a plane wave

$$\psi_i = e^{i\underline{k}\cdot\underline{r}} \, , \quad \underline{k}\cdot\underline{r} = kx\cos\alpha + ky\sin\alpha = kr\cos(\theta-\alpha) \; , \tag{2}$$

and the difference $\psi-\psi_i \equiv u$, which becomes proportional to $e^{ikr}/\sqrt{r}$, is an outgoing cylindrical wave. Thus in

$$\psi(\underline{r},\alpha) = \psi_i(\underline{r},\alpha) + u(\underline{r},\alpha) \; , \tag{3}$$

ψ_i represents the incident plane wave, and u the corresponding scattered wave. The boundary conditions on ψ , and its internal form, are determined by the physical constants of the cylinder; however, these will not be considered explicitly. (In general, for concreteness, we take the origin of coordinates as the center of the circle circumscribing the scatterer; however, we may also use the midpoint of the axis of symmetry, or the midpoint of the longest line through the scatterer.)

2.1. Surface integral representation: We apply Green's theorem to the pair of functions $u(\underline{\rho})$ and $iH_0(k|\underline{r}-\underline{\rho}|)/4$, where H_0 is the Hankel function of the first kind, and $\underline{r}(r,\theta)$ and $\underline{\rho}(\rho,\phi)$ label a field point and a point on the scatterer's surface (see Fig. 1). Integrating over a volume external to the scatterer yields

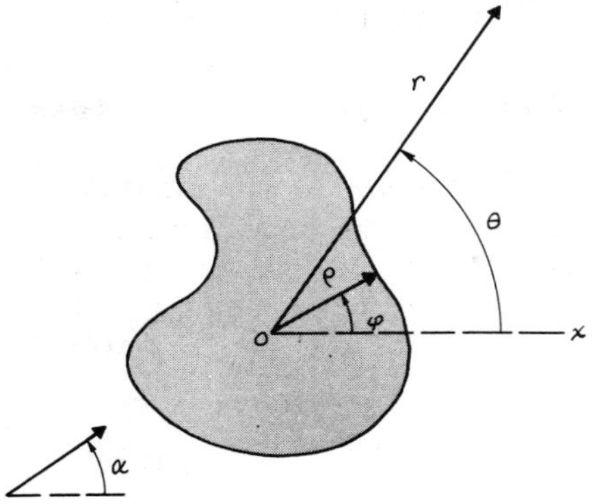

Figure 1. Coordinates for single-body problem

$$u(\underline{r}, \alpha) = (1/4i) \oint [H_0(k|\underline{r}-\underline{\rho}|)\partial_n u(\underline{\rho}, \alpha) - u(\underline{\rho}, \alpha)\partial_n H_0(k|\underline{r}-\underline{\rho}|)]\, dA(\underline{\rho})$$

$$\equiv \{H_0(k|\underline{r}-\underline{\rho}|), u(\underline{\rho}, \alpha)\} \ , \qquad (4)$$

where n is the outward normal. The integral may be taken over any surface inclosing the scatterer and excluding $\underline{r}$.

If $kr \gg 1$, $r \gg \rho$, then

$$H_0(k|\underline{r}-\underline{\rho}|) \sim H(kr)e^{ik\rho\cos(\phi-\theta)} \ , \quad H(kr) \equiv (2/\pi kr)^{\frac{1}{2}} e^{ikr-i\pi/4} \ , \qquad (5)$$

and (4) reduces to the "far-field" form

$$u(\underline{r}) \sim H(kr)g(\theta, \alpha) \ , \qquad (6)$$

$$g(\theta, \alpha) \equiv \{e^{-ik\rho\cos(\phi-\theta)}, u(\underline{\rho}, \alpha)\} \ , \qquad (7)$$

where the integral is over any surface inclosing the scatterer. The "scattering amplitude" $g(\theta, \alpha)$, which we assume to be known, indicates the far field response in the direction θ to plane-wave excitation of direction α .

2.2. Plane-wave representation: If u is known, then (7) gives g on integration. The inverse relation follows on introducing the plane-wave representation of H_0 in (4). In terms of $\underline{r}(x, y)$ and $\underline{\rho}(\xi, \eta)$, we use

$$H_0(k|\underline{r}-\underline{\rho}|) = \frac{1}{\pi}\int_{\gamma+i\infty}^{\pi+\gamma-i\infty} e^{ikr\cos(\theta-\tau)-ik\rho\cos(\phi-\tau)}\,d\tau \;,$$

$$-\pi+\Theta<\gamma<\Theta \;, \quad \tan\Theta = (y-\eta)/(x-\xi) \;, \qquad (8)$$

as obtained by replacing $R\cos\tau$ in the usual Sommerfeld representation [3] by $|\underline{r}-\underline{\rho}|\cos(\Theta-\tau)$; the conditions on γ are equivalent to $r\sin(\theta-\gamma) - \rho\sin(\phi-\gamma) > 0$. Substituting into (4), yields

$$\begin{aligned} u(\underline{r},\alpha) &= \frac{1}{\pi}\int e^{ikr\cos(\theta-\tau)}\{e^{-ik\rho\cos(\phi-\tau)}, u(\rho,\alpha)\}d\tau \\ &= \frac{1}{\pi}\int e^{ikr\cos(\theta-\tau)} g(\tau,\alpha)\,d\tau \;, \end{aligned} \qquad (9)$$

where $-\pi + \Theta_{max} < \gamma < \Theta_{min}$, or equivalently $r\sin(\theta-\gamma) - [\rho\sin(\phi-\gamma)]_{max} > 0$; values of ρ on the scatterer's surface give the greatest range to γ . If we take $\gamma = \theta-\pi/2$, then we require $r > [\rho\cos(\theta-\phi)]_{max}$, i.e., the distance (r) from the "center" of the scatterer to the observation point must be greater than the scatterer's projection on $\underline{r}$; this value of γ suffices for all r and θ , if $r > \rho_{max}$. Thus the scattering amplitude g (introduced to specify the behavior of u at large distances from the object) serves to describe the field at least for all distances $r > \rho_{max}$. In this range, (7) and (9) constitute a pair of "transforms".

The limiting form $u \sim Hg$ (which we obtained from (4)) may also be obtained from (9) by the usual saddle-point procedure [3] for $kr \to \infty$. Thus if we expand $\cos(\theta-\tau)$ and $g(\tau,\alpha)$ of (9) in Taylor series around the saddle point $\tau_0 = \theta + e^{-i\pi/4}\cdot 0$, and treat g as slowly varying, we obtain the "far field" form $u \sim Hg$ as the leading term. This limiting form is correct to $(kr)^{-\frac{1}{2}}$.

A more general asymptotic form may be derived by keeping additional terms of the Taylor series. However, the required result may be obtained directly by exploiting the analogous known [3] Hankel asymptotic representation for H_n :

$$\begin{aligned} i^n H_n(r) &= \frac{1}{\pi}\int e^{ir\cos\tau + i\tau n}\,d\tau \sim H(r)\sum_{m=0} \frac{(1-4n^2)(9-4n^2)\cdots([2m-1]^2-4n^2)}{(i8r)^m m!} \\ &= H(r)\left[1 + \frac{(1-4n^2)}{i8r} + \cdots\right] \;. \end{aligned}$$

Thus, since the Taylor series for $f(\tau)$ around τ_0 may be written symbolically as $f(\tau) = e^{\tau\partial}f(\tau_0)$, $\partial \equiv \partial/\partial\tau_0$, we see by inspection of Hankel's result that

$$I = \frac{1}{\pi}\int e^{ir\cos\tau} f(\tau)\,d\tau \sim H(r)\sum_{m=0} \frac{(1+4\partial^2)(9+4\partial^2)\cdots([2m-1]^2+4\partial^2)}{(i8r)^m m!} f(\tau_0) \;. \qquad (10)$$

(This procedure also suggests obtaining Debye-type asymptotic representations of I based on the "saddle point" of $ir\cos\tau + \tau\partial$.)

Using (10) in (9), subject to whatever restrictions on g this may entail to insure slow variation, yields

$$u \sim H(kr)\left[g + \frac{g+4g^{(2)}}{i8kr} - \frac{9g + 40g^{(2)} + 16g^{(4)}}{128(kr)^2} + \cdots\right] \qquad (11)$$

in terms of the scattering amplitude $g(\theta, \alpha)$ and its θ derivatives. Terms to $(kr)^{-3/2}$ were derived by Karp and Zitron [4] essentially by substituting $H(kr)[g+g_1/kr]$ into the wave equation and solving for g_1 ; they also give the corresponding expansion in terms of plane waves in the neighborhood of r . (There are other ways [5] leading to (11), but that based on (10) appears to be most direct. In a subsequent section, we use (10) for more general scattering situations.)

2.3. Special function representations: We may also obtain general representations for u and g as series of elementary wave functions. Thus [5] outside a circle circumscribing the scatterer, we can apply the addition theorem for cylindrical functions to H_0 in order to represent u as a Hankel-Fourier series. The corresponding Bessel-Fourier series for $e^{-ik\rho\cos(\theta-\phi)}$ yields a Fourier series for g . Similarly for Mathieu functions. Of course such representations are particularly useful when the surface of the scatterer coincides with one or more complete coordinate surfaces of the system, and the boundary conditions are such that the scattering problem is separable. However, they may also be used for general considerations for non-separable scatterers [5, 6].

Alternatively, we may start with series representations of g and use (9) to construct the corresponding series for u . Thus (since the field is single-valued and the scatterer bounded) g has periodicity 2π in both α and θ , and may be expanded as the Fourier series

$$g(\theta, \alpha) = \sum_{n=-\infty}^{\infty} a_n(\alpha) e^{in\theta} = \sum_n \sum_m a_{nm} e^{in\theta + im\alpha} \qquad (12)$$

where the "scattering coefficients" a are assumed to be known. Substituting (12) into (9), we write for $r > \rho_{max}$

$$u = \frac{1}{\pi} \int_{\theta-\frac{\pi}{2}+i\infty}^{\theta+\frac{\pi}{2}-i\infty} e^{ikr\cos(\theta-\tau)} \sum a_n(\alpha) e^{in\tau} d\tau$$

$$= \sum a_n(\alpha) e^{in\theta} \frac{1}{\pi} \int_{-\frac{\pi}{2}+i\infty}^{\frac{\pi}{2}-i\infty} e^{ikr\cos\tau + in\tau} d\tau = \sum a_n(\alpha) i^n H_n(kr) e^{in\theta}$$

where we isolated one of the usual representations [3] for $H_n = H_n^{(1)}$. The series may be regarded as a "mean value form" of the surface integral (4): for $r > \rho_{max}$ (the radius of the circle circumscribing the scatterer), the scattered field appears to originate at $r = 0$. Introducing the asymptotic form $i^n H_n \sim H$ yields $u \sim Hg$ with g as in (12). Additional terms of the asymptotic series for u as in (11) may be obtained [5] by using the Hankel type expansion of H_n.

For circular cylinders we have the simpler series

$$g(\theta, \alpha) = \sum_{n=-\infty}^{\infty} a_n e^{in(\theta-\alpha)} , \quad a_n = a_{-n} . \tag{13}$$

For elliptic cylinders,

$$g(\theta, \alpha) = \sum_{n=0}^{\infty} [a_{e_n} S_{e_n}(\theta) S_{e_n}(\alpha) + a_{o_n} S_{o_n}(\theta) S_{o_n}(\alpha)] , \tag{14}$$

where S_{i_n} (with $i = e$ or o) stands for normalized even or periodic Mathieu functions such that $\int_0^{2\pi} S_{i_n}^2(\theta)\,d\theta = 2\pi$.

2.4. Theorems: The normalization of g was chosen so that for lossless scatterers (e.g., ψ vanishing at the surface) the usual theorem for the forward amplitude reads

$$-\mathrm{Re}\, g(\alpha, \alpha) = \frac{1}{2\pi} \int_0^{2\pi} |g(\theta, \alpha)|^2 d\theta = \frac{k p}{4} , \tag{15}$$

where the middle form is the average of $|g|^2$ over all angles of observation, and p is the total scattering cross section. (This follows from applying Green's theorem to ψ and ψ^* in the external region, and using $\{\psi^*, \psi\} = 0$.) For other angles of observation (using $\{\psi_1^*, \psi_2\} = 0$, where the subscripts indicate fields arising from different angles of incidence),

$$-g(\theta, \alpha) - g^*(\alpha, \theta) = \frac{1}{\pi} \int_0^{2\pi} g^*(\phi, \theta) g(\phi, \alpha) d\phi . \tag{16}$$

In addition, for arbitrary scatterers, the reciprocity principle $\{\psi_1, \psi_2\} = 0$ gives

$$g(\theta, \alpha) = g(\pi + \alpha, \pi + \theta) . \tag{17}$$

Using (12) in (17) yields

$$g(\theta, \alpha) = \Sigma a_n(\pi+\theta) e^{in(\pi+\alpha)} = \Sigma\Sigma a_{nm} e^{im(\pi+\theta)+in(\pi+\alpha)} ,$$

$$a_{nm} = a_{mn}(-1)^{n+m} . \tag{18}$$

Similarly, from (12) and (16),

$$-\Sigma a_n(\alpha) e^{-in\theta} - \Sigma a_m^*(\theta) e^{-im\alpha} = 2\Sigma a_p^*(\theta) a_p(\alpha) \ ,$$

$$- a_n(\alpha) - a_{-n}^*(\pi+\alpha) = 2\Sigma a_p(\alpha) a_{pn}^* \ , \qquad (19)$$

$$- a_{mn} - a_{-n-m}^* = 2\Sigma_p a_{p-m}^* a_{p-n} \ .$$

Special forms of the above follow if the scatterer is symmetrical. Thus if the scatterer is symmetrical to the line β, then

$$g(\theta,\alpha) = g(2\beta-\theta, 2\beta-\alpha) \ , \quad a_n(\alpha) = a_{-n}(2\beta-\alpha) e^{-in2\beta} \ ,$$

$$a_{nm} = a_{-n-m} e^{-i(n+m)2\beta} \ .$$

If the scatterer has inversion symmetry, then $g(\theta,\alpha) = g(\alpha,\theta)$, $a_{nm} = a_{mn}$, etc. In particular, for lossless circular and elliptic cylinders, (16) gives

$$-\mathrm{Re}\, a_{i_n} = |a_{i_n}|^2 \ , \qquad (20)$$

where $i = e$ or o, or is superfluous.

3. ONE SCATTERER, MANY INCIDENT WAVES. If the scatterer is excited by a set of plane waves, say

$$\Psi_i = \Sigma C_n(\alpha_n) e^{ikr\cos(\theta-\alpha_n)} + \int C(\alpha) e^{ikr\cos(\theta-\alpha)} d\alpha$$
$$\equiv \not{\Sigma}\!\!\!\int C(\alpha) e^{ikr\cos(\theta-\alpha)} \qquad (21)$$

(where C is independent of r and θ), then by superposition, the corresponding scattered field may be written

$$U(\underline{r}) = \{H_0(k|\underline{r}-\underline{\rho}|), U(\underline{\rho})\} = \not{\Sigma}\!\!\!\int C(\alpha) u(\underline{r},\alpha) \ , \qquad (22)$$

where u is the known single scattered function. The corresponding scattering amplitude defined by means of

$$U(\underline{r}) \sim H(kr) G(\theta;\alpha) \ , \quad G(\theta;\alpha) = \{e^{-ik\rho\cos(\theta-\phi)}, U(\underline{\rho})\} \qquad (23)$$

is thus

$$G(\theta;\alpha) = \not{\Sigma}\!\!\!\int C(\alpha) g(\theta,\alpha) \ , \qquad (24)$$

as follows directly on substituting (22) into (12) and using (7). The supplementary index α is introduced in G to characterize the set of relevant plane waves.

As for the case of one incident plane wave, we may express G as a Fourier series

$$G(\theta;\alpha) = \Sigma A_n e^{in\theta} . \qquad (25)$$

Using (25) and (12) in (24), it follows that

$$A_n = \oint C(\alpha) a_n(\alpha) . \qquad (26)$$

Scattering and reciprocity theorems for G may be obtained on applying Green's theorem. Thus for lossless scatterers, we use $\{\Psi_i + U)^*, \Psi_i + U\} = 0$ to obtain the analog of (15):

$$-\mathrm{Re}\oint C^*(\alpha) G(\alpha^*;\alpha) = \frac{1}{2\pi}\int_0^{2\pi} |G(\theta;\alpha)|^2 d\theta . \qquad (27)$$

Similarly using $\{(\Psi_i + U)^*_\alpha, (\Psi_i + U)_\beta\} = 0$, where the subscripts α and β indicate different sets of plane waves, yields the analog of (16):

$$-\oint_\alpha C^*(\alpha) G(\alpha^*;\beta) - \oint_\beta C(\beta) G^*(\beta^*;\alpha) = \frac{1}{\pi}\int_0^{2\pi} G^*(\theta;\alpha) G(\theta;\beta) d\theta . \qquad (28)$$

Finally, using $\{(\Psi_i + U)_\alpha, (\Psi_i + U)_\beta\} = 0$ yields the reciprocity relation

$$\oint C(\alpha) G(\pi+\alpha;\beta) = \oint C(\beta) G(\pi+\beta;\alpha) . \qquad (29)$$

Detailed applications of the above to special cases have been given previously [7].

In considering scattering by more than one object, we exploit the above formalism by representing the total field at any one object (say s) as the incident plane wave, plus a superposition of plane waves whose amplitudes involve G_t $(t \neq s)$, plus one cylindrical wave U_s outgoing from its origin [2, 7]. Its "multiple scattered" wave U_s and its "multiple scattered" amplitude G_s may then be written directly in terms of presumably known "single scattered" functions by using (22) and (24).

4. MANY OBJECTS. If a plane wave $\psi_i = e^{ikr\cos(\theta-\alpha)}$ excites a finite number of scatterers in a bounded domain, then the one-scatterer formalism applies to the "compound field" and "compound scattering amplitude" of this compound object. To facilitate reference, we use different symbols:

$$\Psi = \psi_i + \mathcal{U} , \quad \mathcal{U}(\underline{r},\alpha) = \{H_0(k|\underline{r}-\underline{\rho}|), \mathcal{U}(\underline{r},\alpha)\} \qquad (30)$$

$$\mathscr{U} \to H(kr)\, \mathscr{G}(\theta, \alpha) \quad , \quad \mathscr{G}(\theta, \alpha) = \{e^{-ik\rho \cos(\theta-\phi)}, \mathscr{U}(\underline{\rho}, \alpha)\} \quad , \tag{31}$$

where $\underline{r}$ and $\underline{\rho}$ are measured from a convenient origin central to the configuration, and where the surface of integration incloses all objects. Contracting the surface and breaking it up into individual portions inclosing a single object, we write [2]

$$\mathscr{U} = \Sigma V_s \quad , \quad V_s = \{H_0(k|\underline{r}-\underline{\rho}|), \mathscr{U}(\underline{\rho})\}_s = \{H_0(k|\underline{r}-\underline{\rho}|), V_s(\underline{\rho})\} \, , \tag{32}$$

where $\{\}_s$ represents an integration over a surface separating scatterer s from the others, and where $\{\}$ is over any surface inclosing s .

Introducing the "local coordinates" $\underline{r}_s = \underline{r}-\underline{b}_s$, $\underline{\rho}_s = \underline{\rho}-\underline{b}_s$ with origin at $\underline{b}_s(b_s, \beta_s)$ with respect to the central origin of the configuration, we write the primary plane wave excitation at scatterer s as

$$\psi_i = e^{i\underline{k}\cdot\underline{r}} = e^{i\underline{k}\cdot\underline{b}_s + i\underline{k}\cdot\underline{r}_s} = e^{ikb_s\cos(\beta_s-\alpha) + ikr_s\cos(\theta_s-\alpha)} ; \tag{33}$$

see Figure 2. We rewrite (32) as

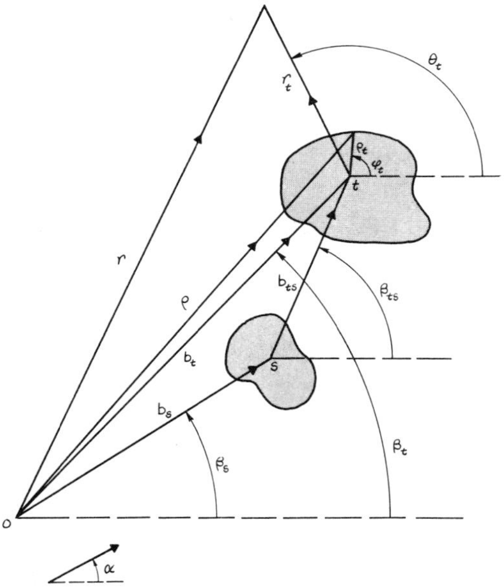

Figure 2. Coordinates for many-body problem

$$\mathcal{U}(r) = \Sigma U_s(\underline{r}-\underline{b}_s)\, e^{i\underline{k}\cdot\underline{b}_s},$$

$$U_s = \{H_0(k|\underline{r}_s-\underline{\rho}_s|),\, U_s(\underline{\rho}_s)\} = \{H_0(k|\underline{r}-\underline{b}_s-\underline{\rho}_s|)\, U_s(\underline{\rho}_s)\} \; . \qquad (34)$$

The phase factor $e^{i\underline{k}\cdot\underline{b}_s}$ (the value of ψ_i at the origin of s) was made explicit to obtain a form U_s which reduces to the single scattered value u_s (of an object at the "phase origin") when the separations between the other scatterers and s become infinite. The wave U_s arises essentially from a source at $\underline{b}_s$, and this provides motivation for the manipulation in (32); see first paper of reference 2 for details.

For $\underline{r}_s = |\underline{r}-\underline{b}_s| \gg r$, we have

$$U_s(\underline{r}_s) \sim H(kr_s)\, \{e^{-ik\rho_s\cos(\theta_s-\phi_s)},\, U_s(\underline{\rho}_s, \alpha)\} \equiv H(kr_s)\, G_s(\theta_s, \alpha) \; , \qquad (35)$$

where G_s , the "multiple scattered amplitude" of scatterer s , reduces to the single scattered function g_s as the others recede to infinity. In addition, if $r \gg b_s$, then $H(kr_s) = H(k|\underline{r}-\underline{b}_s|) \sim H(kr)\, e^{-ikb_s\cos(\theta-\beta_s)}$; similarly $G_s(\theta_s,\alpha) \sim G_s(\theta, \alpha)$. Thus

$$\mathcal{U} = \Sigma\, U_s e^{i\underline{k}\cdot\underline{b}_s} \sim H(kr)\, \Sigma_s e^{i(\underline{k}_\alpha-\underline{k}_\theta)\cdot\underline{b}_s} G_s(\theta, \alpha) \; ;$$

$$\underline{k}_\alpha = \underline{k} \; , \quad \underline{k}_\theta = k\underline{r}/r \; . \qquad (36)$$

Consequently the compound scattering amplitude introduced in (31) equals

$$\mathcal{G}(\theta, \alpha) = \Sigma_s e^{i(\underline{k}_\alpha-\underline{k}_\theta)\cdot\underline{b}_s} G_s(\theta, \alpha) \; , \qquad (37)$$

as, of course also follows from

$$\mathcal{G} = \{e^{-i\underline{k}_\theta\cdot\underline{\rho}},\, \mathcal{U}\} = \Sigma_s \{e^{-i\underline{k}_\theta\cdot(\underline{b}_s+\underline{\rho}_s)},\, e^{i\underline{k}_\alpha\cdot\underline{b}_s} U_s\}$$

$$= \Sigma\, e^{i(\underline{k}_\alpha-\underline{k}_\theta)\cdot\underline{b}_s} \{e^{-i\underline{k}_\theta\cdot\underline{\rho}_s},\, U_s\} \; .$$

$\mathcal{G}$ fulfills the same theorems as g , i.e., (15) to (19) hold with g replaced by $\mathcal{G}$, and a by (say) $\mathcal{A}$.

4.1. Integral equations: We now recast U_s in terms of plane waves. Substituting (8) into U_s of (34) and using G_s defined in (35) yields

$$U_s = \int e^{ikr_s\cos(\theta_s-\tau)}\{e^{-ik\rho_s\cos(\phi_s-\tau)}, U_s(\rho_s, \alpha_s)\} d\tau/\pi$$

$$= \int e^{ikr_s\cos(\theta_s-\tau)} G_s(\tau,\alpha) d\tau/\pi \tag{38}$$

which is completely analogous to (9). The limits on the present integral involve Θ_s . Substituting into (34) (or using (9) in terms of $\mathcal{U}$ and $\mathcal{G}$) yields

$$\mathcal{U}(\underline{r}) = \Sigma_s e^{i\underline{k}\cdot\underline{b}_s} \int e^{i\underline{k}_\tau\cdot\underline{r}_s} G_s(\tau,\alpha) d\tau/\pi$$

$$= \Sigma_s \int e^{i(\underline{k}_\alpha-\underline{k}_\tau)\cdot\underline{b}_s + i\underline{k}_\tau\cdot\underline{r}} G_s(\tau,\alpha) d\tau/\pi \quad . \tag{39}$$

(We can sum directly over s for infinite periodic and "random" planar distributions of scatterers for which [2] G_s is essentially independent of s . Similarly for "slab region" volume distributions [7] for which G_s depends essentially only on its distance from the slab face. Then we may evaluate the complex integral by residue methods (as was done for analogous expressions for gratings by Franz, Carlson and Heins, and Millar [8]), or else change variables to $\sin\tau = t$ and treat the resulting real integrals by δ-function methods [2, 7].

Expressing ψ_i of (33) and $\mathcal{U}$ of (39) in the local coordinates of scatterer t (i.e., $\underline{r}_t = \underline{r}-\underline{b}_t$), we write the total field as a set of plane waves plus one outgoing wave U_t :

$$\Psi(\underline{b}_t+\underline{r}_t) = (\psi_i + \Sigma'_s U_s e^{i\underline{k}\cdot\underline{b}_s}) + U_t e^{i\underline{k}\cdot\underline{b}_t}$$

$$= e^{i\underline{k}\cdot\underline{b}_t}[e^{i\underline{k}\cdot\underline{r}_t} + \Sigma'_s e^{i\underline{k}\cdot(\underline{b}_s-\underline{b}_t)} \int e^{i(\underline{r}_t+\underline{b}_t-\underline{b}_s)\cdot\underline{k}_t} G_s(\tau,\alpha) d\tau/\pi + U_t] \tag{40}$$

where the prime indicates $s \neq t$. Consequently it follows from (40) and (22) that

$$U_t = u_t(\alpha) + \Sigma'_s \int e^{i(\underline{b}_t-\underline{b}_s)\cdot(\underline{k}_\tau-\underline{k})} u_t(\tau) G_s(\tau,\alpha) d\tau/\pi \,. \tag{41}$$

Similarly from (24), we obtain the "self-consistent" system of equations

$$G_t(\theta,\alpha) = g_t(\theta,\alpha) + \Sigma'_s \int e^{i(\underline{b}_t-\underline{b}_s)\cdot(\underline{k}_\tau-\underline{k})} g_t(\theta,\tau) G_s(\tau,\alpha) d\tau/\pi \ , \tag{42}$$

where we will use $(\underline{b}_t-\underline{b}_s)\cdot\underline{k}_\tau = \underline{b}_{ts}\cdot\underline{k}_\tau = kb_{ts}\cos(\tau-\beta_s)$, $\beta_{st} = \pi+\beta_{ts}$, etc. Since

$$g_t(\theta,\tau) = g_t(\pi+\tau, \pi+\theta) = \{e^{ik\rho_t\cos(\tau-\phi_t)}, u(\pi+\theta)\}$$

the integral converges if $b_{ts}\sin(\gamma-\beta_{ts}) + \rho_t \sin(\gamma-\phi_t) - \rho_s \sin(\gamma-\phi_s) < 0$ for all ρ_t and ρ_s on the appropriate scatterers' surfaces. If we take $\gamma = \beta_{ts} - \pi/2$, then we require $b_{ts} > \rho_s \cos(\beta_{ts}-\phi_s) - \rho_t \cos(\beta_{ts}-\phi_t) = \rho_s \cos(\beta_{ts}-\phi_s) + \rho_t \cos(\beta_{st}-\phi_t)$, i.e., that the separation of scatterer "centers" (b_{ts}) be greater than the sum of the scatterer's projections on $\underline{b}_{ts}$. (See also Millar [8] for analogous forms.)

4.2. <u>Algebraic equations</u>: Eq. (42) is a "self-consistent" set of integral equations for the multiple scattered amplitudes in terms of the single scattered values. The analogous self-consistent algebraic equations for the multiple scattered coefficients follow on substituting the appropriate Fourier series (12) and $G_t(\theta,\alpha) = \Sigma A_n^t(\alpha) e^{in\theta}$ in (42). Thus

$$A_n^t = a_n^t(\alpha) + \sum_s{}' \sum_m \sum_p a_{nm}^t A_p^s E(s,t;p,m) \ ,$$

$$E(s,t;p,m) \equiv e^{-ikb_{ts}\cos(\beta_{ts}-\alpha)} \int e^{ikb_{ts}\cos(\beta_{ts}-\tau)+i(p+m)\tau} d\tau/\pi$$

$$= e^{-ikb_{ts}\cos(\beta_{ts}-\alpha)} H_{p+m}(kb_{ts}) e^{i(p+m)(\beta_{ts}+\pi/2)} \ ; \tag{43}$$

writing $A_n^t(\alpha) = \Sigma A_{n\nu} e^{i\nu\alpha}$, yields

$$A_{n\nu}^t = a_{n\nu}^t + \sum_s{}' \sum_m \sum_p \sum_q a_{nm}^t A_{pq}^s H_{p+m}(kb_{ts}) e^{i(m+p+q-\nu)(\beta_{ts}+\pi/2)} J_{q-\nu}(kb_{ts}) . \tag{44}$$

Similarly we may construct mixed representations involving both amplitudes and coefficients. In particular, if we write $G = \Sigma B_n(\theta) e^{in\alpha}$, etc., we see that

$$B_n(\theta) = b_n(\theta) + \Sigma_s' \Sigma_m J_{m-n}(kb_{ts}) i^{m-n} \int e^{ikb_{ts}\cos(\beta_{ts}-\tau)} g(\theta,\tau) B_m(\tau) d\tau/\pi \tag{45}$$

where $b_n(\theta) = a_n(\pi+\theta) e^{in\pi}$, and $g(\theta,\tau)$ are presumed known.

For circular cylinders, we use (13) and $G = \Sigma A_n e^{in\theta}$ (or substitute $a_n^t(\alpha) = a_n^t e^{-in\alpha}$, $a_{nm} = a_n \delta_{n+m}$ in (43)) to obtain

$$A_n^t(\alpha) = a_n^t [e^{-in\alpha} + \sum_s{}' \sum_p A_p^s E(s,t;p,-n)] \ , \tag{46}$$

where E is defined in (43). This simpler set of equations was derived by separating variables in circular coordinates by Zaviska [9], Ignatowsky [10], Row [11], and Twersky [12]. Twersky also uses essentially the present integral equation procedure with other operators than $\Sigma'\int$ in (42) to obtain equations of the form (46) for infinite symmetrical distributions; thus the periodic planar distribution of circular cylinders is treated [13] by means of the "grating operator" of reference 2 (1956), and a planar "liquid state" distribution is treated in reference 2(1959).

Similarly for elliptic cylinders, such that all surfaces after translation are coordinate surfaces in one elliptic system, we use the form (14) and $G = \Sigma[A_{en}S_{en}(\theta) + A_{on}S_{on}(\theta)]$ to obtain

$$A^t_{i_n} = a^t_{i_n}[S_{i_n}(\alpha) + \sum_s{}' \sum_p A^s_{i_p}\mathscr{E}(s,t;i_p,i_n) + \sum_s{}' \sum_p A^s_{j_p}\mathscr{E}(s,t;j_p,i_n)] \quad (47)$$

where if i stands for e, then j stands for o, and vice versa. The functions

$$\mathscr{E}(s,t;i_p,j_n) = e^{ikb_{ts}\cos(\beta_{ts}-\alpha)}\int e^{ikb_{ts}\cos(\beta_{ts}-\tau)}S_{i_p}(\tau)S_{j_p}(\tau)\,d\tau \quad (48)$$

may be expressed as double sum of the E's defined in (43) by introducing the representations

$$S_{e_n} = \sum_{n'=0}^{\infty} D^n_{e_{n'}}\cos n'\phi\,, \quad S_{o_n} = \sum_{n'=0}^{\infty} D^n_{o_{n'}}\sin n'\phi$$ (where the D's are proportional to those given by Morse and Feshbach [14]). Suppressing s, t for brevity we obtain, for example

$$\mathscr{E}(e_p,o_n) = \sum_{p'}\sum_{n'} D^p_{e_{p'}}D^n_{e_{n'}}[E(p',n')-E(p',-n')+E(-p',n')-E(-p',n')]/4i. \quad (49)$$

Similarly $\mathscr{E}(o_p,e_n)$ involves $[E_1+E_2-E_3-E_4]$, $\mathscr{E}(e_p,e_n)$ involves $i[E_1+E_2+E_3+E_4]$, and $\mathscr{E}(o_p,o_n)$ involves $i[-E_1+E_2+E_3-E_4]$; the subscripts indicate the first, second, etc., terms inside the brackets of (49). Burke and Twersky [15] follow essentially the present procedure with the operator $\Sigma'\int$ of (42) replaced by the grating operator [2] to obtain a set of equations of the form (49) for the infinite grating of elliptic cylinders. Similar sets of equations are obtained by Saermark [16] by separating variables in elliptic coordinates, and by Millar [17] by an integral equation approach to the boundary value problem for small scatterers.

In general, for arbitrary configurations and arbitrary spacings, there is little that can be done with these systems of algebraic equations except expand them by Neumann iteration (subject to whatever restrictions on the parameters this entails) to obtain a series of "successive orders of scattering" for the coefficients. Thus the simplest set (46) yields

$$A_n^t = a_n^t e^{-in\alpha} + a_n^t \Sigma_s' \Sigma_p a_p^s e^{-ip\alpha} E(s,t;p,-n)$$
$$+ a_n^t \Sigma_s' \Sigma_p a_p^s e^{-ip\alpha} E(s,t;p,-n) \Sigma_r' \Sigma_q a_q^r e^{-iq\alpha} E(t,r;q,-p) + \cdots . \tag{50}$$

This series was also obtained using separations of variables [18]: successive applications of the boundary conditions at t determined its response to "successive orders of excitation" arriving from the other cylinders. Similarly for elliptic cylinders, iterating (47) yields

$$A_{i_n}^t = a_{i_n}^t S_{i_n}(\alpha) + a^t \Sigma_s' \Sigma_p a_{i_p}^s S_{i_p}(\alpha) \quad (s,t;i_p,i_n)$$
$$+ a_{i_n}^t \Sigma_s' \Sigma_p a_{j_p}^s S_{j_p}(\alpha)\, \mathscr{E}(s,t;j_p,j_n) + \cdots , \tag{51}$$

and analogous series may be generated directly by iterating the remaining systems of equations.

The iterated forms are particularly useful if the a's decrease rapidly with increasing index; see references 13 to 17 for discussion of the a's for circles and ellipses for the usual boundary conditions. In such cases we may also truncate the original systems of equations and seek closed forms for A in terms of a for special configurations. Such closed forms are given for infinite gratings of circles and ellipses for the usual boundary conditions in references 13 and 15, and analogous forms for two scatterers will be given in the next section.

Truncating the above iterated series corresponds to taking into account only a finite number of "orders of scattering" (primarily on the basis of the smallness of the a's). We may obtain alternative approximations of the iterated series for the range where all separations are large compared to wavelength and scatterer sizes. "Far-field multiple scattering" series may be obtained by introducing the asymptotic limit $H_n \sim i^{-n}H$ into (50) (for example). Thus [19]

$$A_n^t \sim a_n^t e^{-in\alpha} + a_n^t \Sigma_s' \Sigma_p a_p^s H(kb_{ts}) e^{-ikb_{ts}\cos(\beta_{ts}-\alpha)} e^{-ip\alpha + i(p+m)\beta_{ts}} + \cdots . \tag{52}$$

Among other applications, the series of orders for the corresponding scattering amplitude (obtained by multiplying (52) by $e^{in\theta}$ and summing over n) of two circular cylinders was summed to closed form [19]. (Such closed forms, although inconsistent in spacing parameters, are convenient to work with and take into account correctly the leading terms of all orders of scattering; see reference 19 for discussion of correction terms for sample cases.) More general asymptotic series may be obtained by using Hankel type expansions of H_n in any of the above series, etc.

4.3. Asymptotic forms: We obtain forms of (42) asymptotic in $k|\underline{b}_t - \underline{b}_s| = kb_{ts}$ by proceeding essentially as for (11). Thus applying (10) to (42) and keeping only the explicit terms to order $(kb)^{-\frac{1}{2}}$ yields

$$G_t(\theta,\alpha) \sim g_t(\theta,\alpha) + \Sigma'_s \mathscr{H}_{ts} g_t(\theta,\beta_{ts}) G_s(\beta_{ts},\alpha) \quad ,$$
$$\mathscr{H}_{ts} \equiv H(kb_{ts}) e^{-ikb_{ts}\cos(\beta_{ts}-\alpha)} \tag{53}$$

which constitutes the system of algebraic equations originally obtained by Karp [20] by regarding the asymptotic form $u_s \sim HG_s$ at $\underline{b}_t$ as a plane wave giving rise to g_t. In general, (52) may be developed as a series of orders of scattering by Neumann iteration starting with $G_s = g_s$; thus

$$G_t(\theta,\alpha) \sim g_t(\theta,\alpha) + \Sigma'_s \mathscr{H}_{ts} g_t(\theta,\beta_{ts}) g_s(\beta_{ts},\alpha)$$
$$+ \Sigma'_s \mathscr{H}_{ts} g_t(\theta,\beta_{ts}) \Sigma'_p \mathscr{H}_{sp} g_s(\beta_{ts},\beta_{sp}) g_p(\beta_{sp},\alpha) \cdots \equiv \Sigma_n F_n(t;\theta,\alpha) \tag{54}$$

(the analog of (52)). The first term is the single scattered value or first order of scattering. The next is the second order of far-field multiple scattering, etc. This series is correct to powers of $(kb)^{-1}$, i.e., only to the third order of scattering (all terms given explicitly in (54)) is the expansion consistent with the spacing parameter. The supplementary notation F_n for the n'th order of far-field multiple scattering is to facilitate subsequent reference; F_n is of order $(kb)^{(1-n)/2}$.

More generally, applying (10) to (42) yields

$$G_t(\theta,\alpha) \sim g_t(\theta,\alpha) + \sum_s{}' \mathscr{H}_{ts} \sum_m \frac{(1+4\partial^2_{ts})(9+4\partial^2_{ts})\cdots([2m-1]^2+4\partial^2_{ts})}{(i8kb_{ts})^m m!} \cdot g_t(\theta,\beta_{ts}) G_s(\beta_{ts},\alpha)$$
$$= g_t(\theta,\alpha) + \sum_s{}' \mathscr{H}_{ts}\left[1 + \frac{1+4\partial^2_{ts}}{i8kb_{ts}} - \frac{9+40\partial^2_{ts}+16\partial^2_{ts}}{128(kb_{ts})^2} + \cdots\right] g_t(\theta,\beta_{ts}) G_s(\beta_{ts},\alpha) \quad , \tag{55}$$

where the derivates are to be taken with respect to β_{ts}. Iterating (55) to order $(kb)^{-3/2}$, we supplement the explicit terms of (54), i.e.

$$F_1 + F_2 + F_3 \quad , \tag{56}$$

which are correct to order $(kb)^{-1}$, by

$$F_4(t;\theta,\alpha) + \Sigma_s \mathscr{C}_{ts} g_t(\theta,\beta_{ts}) g_s(\beta_{ts},\alpha) \; , \quad \mathscr{C}_{ts} \equiv \mathscr{H}_{ts}\left[\frac{1+4\partial^2_{ts}}{i8kb_{ts}}\right] \; , \tag{57}$$

where the fourth far-field order of scattering F_4 (whose terms are products of three $\mathscr{H}$'s and four g's) may be obtained by inspection of (53) and (54), and where the new type of term is the first "mid-field" correction to the second far-field order. The derivatives are to be taken with respect to β_{ts}, i.e.,

$$\partial^2 g_t(\theta,\beta) g_s(\beta,\alpha) = g''_t(\theta,\beta) g_s(\beta,\alpha) + 2g'_t(\theta,\beta) g'_s(\beta,\alpha) + g_t(\theta,\beta) g''_s(\beta,\alpha)$$

where the primes stand for β derivatives. The next terms in the expansion of G, the terms of order $(kb)^{-2}$, are given by

$$F_5(t;\theta,\alpha) + \Sigma'_s \begin{bmatrix}\mathscr{H}\\ \mathscr{C}\end{bmatrix}_{ts} g_t(\theta,\beta_{ts}) \Sigma' \begin{bmatrix}\mathscr{C}\\ \mathscr{H}\end{bmatrix}_{sp} g_s(\beta_{ts},\beta_{sp}) g_p(\beta_{sp},\alpha) \tag{58}$$

where F_5 (whose terms are products of $4\mathscr{H}$'s and 5 g's) is the fifth far-field order, and the new types of terms are the first corrections to the third far-field order; here the bracket notation indicates two sets of terms, either $\mathscr{H}_{ts}\mathscr{C}_{sp}$, or vice versa. (Note that no β derivatives of the exponentials $e^{-ikb_{ts}\cos(\beta_{ts}-\alpha)}$ are involved: these would introduce positive powers of kb.) The next terms in G, the terms of order $(kb)^{-5/2}$ equal

$$F_6(t;\theta,\alpha) + \Sigma'_s \mathscr{H}_{ts}\left[\frac{9+40\partial^2_{ts}+16\partial^4_{ts}}{128(kb_{ts})^2}\right] g_t(\theta,\beta_{ts}) g(\beta_{ts},\alpha)$$

$$+ \Sigma'_s \begin{bmatrix}\mathscr{C}\\ \mathscr{H}\\ \mathscr{H}\end{bmatrix}_{ts} g_t(\theta,\beta_{ts}) \Sigma'_p \begin{bmatrix}\mathscr{H}\\ \mathscr{C}\\ \mathscr{H}\end{bmatrix}_{sp} g_s(\beta_{ts},\beta_{sp}) \Sigma'_q \begin{bmatrix}\mathscr{H}\\ \mathscr{H}\\ \mathscr{C}\end{bmatrix}_{pq} g_p(\beta_{sp},P_{pq}) g_q(\beta_{pq},\alpha) \tag{59}$$

where F_6 is the sixth far-field order, the next term is the second mid-field correction to the second far-field order, and the three sets of terms $\mathscr{C}\mathscr{H}\mathscr{H}$, $\mathscr{H}\mathscr{C}\mathscr{H}$, $\mathscr{H}\mathscr{H}\mathscr{C}$ are the first corrections to the fourth far-field order. Thus we have

$$G_t(\theta,\alpha) \sim (56) + (57) + (58) + (59) + \mathscr{O}[(kb)^{-3}]. \tag{60}$$

For two cylinders, terms to order $(kb)^{-3/2}$ in (60) were derived originally by Karp and Zitron [4]. Starting with U_t correct to order $(kr)^{-3/2}$ (essentially as in (11) with g replaced by G_t), they expand in plane waves around scatterer s to order $b^{-3/2}$ and then carry out a "successive scattering" procedure. The present procedure, which provides the extension (55) of Karp's [20] "self-consistent" asymptotic form (53), is more convenient. The expansion of the field in terms of plane waves is built into our formalism essentially from the start (eq. (38)), so that we are led directly to a system of integral equations (42) for the amplitudes in terms of their single scattered values. The asymptotic system of equations (55) follows essentially from the steepest descent evaluation of the integrals, and the final form (60) is obtained by iteration.

5. TWO OBJECTS. The analogous results for two scatterers follow on specializing the above. For this elementary configuration, approximations may often be obtained in closed form (or at least in "closed operator form").

We take the primary origin ($r = 0$) as the midpoint of the line joining the scatterer origins. Thus the scatterers are located by

$$\underline{b}_1 = \underline{b}_+(b, \beta_+) = \underline{b}_+(b, \beta) \ , \quad \underline{b}_2 = \underline{b}_-(b, \beta_-) = \underline{b}_-(b, \pi+\beta) \ ,$$

and their local coordinates are $\underline{r}_1 = \underline{r}_+(r_+, \theta_+)$, $\underline{r}_2 = \underline{r}_-(r_-, \theta_-)$. We then write (34) for two scatterers as

$$\mathscr{U}(\underline{r}) = e^{i\delta} U_+(\underline{r}_+) + e^{-i\delta} U_-(\underline{r}_-) \ ;$$

$$\pm\delta \equiv \underline{k} \cdot \underline{b}_\pm = kb\cos(\alpha - \beta_\pm) = \pm kb\cos(\alpha-\beta) \ ; \ \beta_+ = \beta \ , \ \beta_- = \beta + \pi \ .$$

Similarly (37) reduces to

$$\mathscr{G}(\theta, \alpha) = e^{i(\delta - \Delta)} G_+(\theta, \alpha) + e^{-i(\delta - \Delta)} G_-(\theta, \alpha)$$

$$\pm\Delta \equiv \underline{k}_\theta \cdot \underline{b}_\pm = \pm kb\cos(\theta - \beta) \ . \tag{62}$$

The plane wave representation (38) yields

$$U_\pm = \int e^{ikr_\pm \cos(\tau - \theta_\pm)} G_\pm(\tau, \alpha) \, d\tau/\pi \ , \tag{63}$$

and similarly (42) reduces to

$$G_\pm(\theta, \alpha) = g_\pm(\theta, \alpha) + e^{-i2kb\cos(\alpha - \beta_\pm)} \int e^{i2kb\cos(\tau - \beta_\pm)} g_\pm(\theta, \tau) G_\mp(\tau, \alpha) \, d\tau/\pi . \tag{64}$$

The remaining general expressions can be simplified by comparison.

5.1. Large spacing: The far-field multiple scattering form (53) for two cylinders and $2kb \gg 1$ equals

$$G_\pm(\theta, \alpha) = g_\pm(\theta, \alpha) + \mathscr{H}_\pm g_\pm(\theta, \beta_\pm) G_\mp(\beta_\pm, \alpha) \ ,$$

$$\mathscr{H}_\pm = H(2kb) e^{-i2kb\cos(\alpha - \beta_\pm)} \ ; \tag{65}$$

we have $\mathscr{H}_{\pm} = He^{\mp i\delta}$, but choose to keep $\beta_{\pm}$ explicit for subsequent considerations. These equations were originally obtained by Karp [20] by regarding $u_{\pm} \sim \mathscr{H}_{\mp} G_{\pm}$ at $\underline{b}_{\mp}$ as a plane wave giving rise to $g_{\mp}$; he then substituted $\theta = \beta_{\mp}$ and solved for the special values

$$G_{\pm}(\beta_{\mp}, \alpha) = \frac{g_{\pm}(\beta_{\mp}, \alpha) + \mathscr{H}_{\pm} g_{\pm}(\beta_{\mp}, \beta_{\pm}) g_{\mp}(\beta_{\pm}, \alpha)}{1 - H^2 g_{+}(\beta_{-}, \beta_{+}) g_{-}(\beta_{+}, \beta_{-})}, \tag{66}$$

which reduce (65) to closed form.

We note that Zaviska [9] (who used a self-consistent procedure to treat scattering by two circular cylinders by means of separations of variables) showed that for $2kb \gg 1$, the problem reduced essentially to that of one cylinder excited by two plane waves. However, he did not exploit this to obtain closed forms. The closed far-field multiple scattering form was obtained by Twersky [19] using the asymptotic orders of scattering series for two circular cylinders given in (52).

More generally, we replace (65) by the general form of (55) for two scatterers:

$$G_{\pm}(\theta, \alpha) = g_{\pm}(\theta, \alpha) + \mathscr{F}_{\pm} g_{\pm}(\theta, \beta_{\pm}) G_{\mp}(\beta_{\pm}, \alpha),$$

$$\mathscr{F}_{\pm} = H(2kb)\, e^{-i2kb\cos(\alpha-\beta_{\pm})} \sum \frac{(1+4\partial_{\pm}^2)(9+4\partial_{\pm}^2)\cdots([2m-1]^2+4\partial_{\pm}^2)}{(i\,16kb)^m m!}$$

$$= \mathscr{H}_{\pm}\left[1 + \frac{1+4\partial_{\pm}^2}{i\,16kb} - \frac{9+40\partial_{\pm}^2+16\partial_{\pm}^4}{128(2kb)^2} + \cdots\right] \tag{67}$$

$$\equiv \mathscr{H}_{\pm}(b^{-\frac{1}{2}}) + \mathscr{C}_{\pm}(b^{-\frac{3}{2}}) + \mathscr{D}_{\pm}(b^{-\frac{5}{2}}) + \cdots,$$

where $\partial_{\pm} = \dfrac{\partial}{\partial\beta_{\pm}}$.

Since (67) has the same algebraic form as (65), we "solve" for

$$G_{\pm}(\beta_{\mp}, \alpha) = [1 - \mathscr{F}_{\pm} g_{\pm}(\beta_{\mp}, \beta_{\pm}) \mathscr{F}_{\mp} g_{\mp}(\beta_{\pm}, \beta_{\mp})]^{-1} [g_{\pm}(\beta_{\mp}, \alpha) + \mathscr{F}_{\pm} g_{\pm}(\beta_{\mp}, \beta_{\pm}) g_{\mp}(\beta_{\pm}, \alpha)] \tag{68}$$

and write (67) in the compact form

$$G_{\pm}(\theta, \alpha) = g_{\pm}(\theta, \alpha) + \mathscr{F}_{\pm} g_{\pm}(\theta, \beta_{\pm}) \left[\frac{g_{\mp}(\beta_{\pm}, \alpha) + \mathscr{F}_{\mp} g_{\mp}(\beta_{\pm}, \beta_{\mp}) g_{\pm}(\beta_{\mp}, \alpha)}{1 - \mathscr{F}_{\mp} g_{\mp}(\beta_{\pm}, \beta_{\mp}) \mathscr{F}_{\pm} g_{\pm}(\beta_{\mp}, \beta_{\pm})}\right], \tag{69}$$

where it is understood that within the brackets the expanded denominator operates on the numerator from the left, and that we work from right to left in performing the $\mathscr{F}$ operations in the generated chains $\cdots \mathscr{F}g\,\mathscr{F}g\,\mathscr{F}gg$.

Terms to order $(kb)^{-1}$ are given by

$$g_\pm(\theta,\alpha) + \mathscr{H}_\pm g_\pm(\theta,\beta_\pm)[g_\mp(\beta_\pm,\alpha) + \mathscr{H}_\mp g_\mp g_\pm(\beta_\mp,\alpha)] \qquad (56')$$

where $g_\pm \equiv g_\pm(\beta_\mp,\beta_\pm)$. The $(kb)^{-\frac{3}{2}}$ terms equal

$$\mathscr{H}_\pm g_\pm(\theta,\beta_\pm)\mathscr{H}_\mp g_\mp \mathscr{H}_\pm g_\pm g_\mp(\beta_\pm,\alpha) + \mathscr{C}_\pm g_\pm(\theta,\beta_\pm)g_\mp(\beta_\pm,\alpha) \ . \qquad (57')$$

The result $G \approx (56')+(57')$ was given originally by Karp and Zitron [4]. Similarly the terms of order $(kb)^{-2}$ are given by

$$g_\pm(\theta,\beta_\pm)H^4(g_\mp)^2 g_\pm g_\pm(\beta_\mp,\alpha) + \begin{bmatrix}\mathscr{H}\\ \mathscr{C}\end{bmatrix}_\pm g_\pm(\theta,\beta_\pm)\begin{bmatrix}\mathscr{C}\\ \mathscr{H}\end{bmatrix}_\mp g_\mp(\beta_\pm,\beta_\mp)g_\pm(\beta_\mp,\alpha), \qquad (58')$$

and the $(kb)^{-\frac{5}{2}}$ equal

$$\mathscr{H}_\pm g_\pm(\theta,\beta_\pm)H^4(g_\pm g_\mp)^2 g_\mp(\beta_\pm,\alpha) + \mathscr{D}_\pm g_\pm(\theta,\beta_\pm)g_\mp(\beta_\pm,\alpha)$$
$$+ \begin{bmatrix}\mathscr{C}\\ \mathscr{H}\\ \mathscr{H}\end{bmatrix}_\pm g_\pm(\theta,\beta_\pm)\begin{bmatrix}\mathscr{H}\\ \mathscr{C}\\ \mathscr{H}\end{bmatrix}_\mp g_\mp(\beta_\pm,\beta_\mp)\begin{bmatrix}\mathscr{H}\\ \mathscr{H}\\ \mathscr{C}\end{bmatrix}_\pm g_\pm(\beta_\mp,\beta_\pm)g_\mp(\beta_\pm,\alpha) \ . \qquad (59')$$

Thus, analogous to (60), we write

$$G_\pm(\theta,\alpha) = (56')+(57')+(58')+(59') + \mathscr{O}[(kb)^{-3}] \ , \qquad (70)$$

etc.

5.2. Small scatterers: Here we exploit the algebraic equations of Section 4.2 to obtain closed forms for cylinders "narrow" compared to wavelength.

Monopoles: Thus if the scatterers are "monopoles" (or "isotropic" scatterers) such that $G_\pm = A_0^\pm$ and $g_\pm = a_0^\pm$ are independent of angles, then in any coordinate system we obtain

$$G_\pm = g_\pm[1 + G_\mp e^{\mp i2\delta}H_0(2kb)] = g_\pm \frac{[1+g_\mp e^{\mp i2\delta}H_0]}{1-H_0^2 g_+ g_-} \ . \qquad (71)$$

(This form holds approximately, for example, if the boundary condition $\Psi=0$ applies on vanishingly small scatterers. In particular, in electromagnetics, it may be used for $\underline{E}$ parallel to the sides of fine, perfectly conducting wires of arbitrary cross section.) The special forms of (71) for $\alpha-\beta=\pi/2$ ("normal incidence" on the plane of the axis) and $\alpha-\beta=0$ ("grazing incidence") were given originally by Zaviska [9], and the general case is considered by Millar [17], Saermark [18], and Twersky [19]; see these papers, as well as other relevant ones cited in reference 1, for detailed discussions and physical applications.

This case is a convenient one to illustrate the applications of the scattering theorems for lossless objects. Using $\mathscr{G}(\theta,\alpha)$ as in (62), and applying the cross section theorem as in (15) we obtain

$$\frac{kP}{4} = -\mathrm{Re}(G_+ + G_-) = |G_+|^2 + |G_-|^2 + [G_+G_-^* e^{i2\underline{k}\cdot\underline{b}} + G_+^*G_- e^{-i2\underline{k}\cdot\underline{b}}]\,J_0(2kb), \tag{72}$$

where P is the total scattering cross section of the compound object. Substituting $G_\pm$ of (71) and using the simpler form yields

$$\frac{kP}{4} = -\mathrm{Re}\left[\frac{g_+ + g_- + g_+g_-H_0(2kb)\,2\cos(2\underline{k}\cdot\underline{b})}{1 - H_0^2 g_+g_-}\right] . \tag{73}$$

For the special symmetrical case of incidence normal to the line joining identical scatterers, (72) reduces to

$$\frac{kP}{4} = -2\mathrm{Re}G = 2|G|^2[1 + J_0(2kb)] . \tag{74}$$

Here it is simple to demonstrate that the corresponding explicit form of G obtained from (71) fulfills this relation. Thus

$$G = \frac{g}{1-gH_0(2kb)} = \frac{g(1-gH_0)^*}{|1-gH_0|^2} , \tag{75}$$

and, consequently,

$$\mathrm{Re}\,G = \frac{\mathrm{Re}\,g - |g|^2 J_0}{|1-gH_0|^2} . \tag{76}$$

Since the scattering theorem (15) for arbitrary lossless monopoles yields

$$-\mathrm{Re}\,g = |g|^2 = kp/4 , \tag{77}$$

we reduce (76) to

$$\text{Re } G = \frac{\text{Re } g(1+J_0)}{|1-gH_0|^2} = -\left|\frac{g}{1-gH_0}\right|^2 (1+J_0) = -|G|^2(1+J_0) , \tag{78}$$

where the final form followed from the identity $|G|^2 = |g/(1-gH_0)|^2$ obtained from (75). Thus the explicit form of G in terms of g given in (75) is consistent within the framework of the scattering theorems: it yields a compound amplitude $\mathscr{G}$ which, as we have in effect proved, fulfills the required scattering theorem (15).

The general theorem for $\mathscr{G}$ analogous to (16) for g yields

$$\begin{aligned} &-[G_+(\delta) + G_+^*(\Delta)]e^{i(\delta-\Delta)} - [G_-(\delta) + G_-^*(\Delta)]e^{-i(\delta-\Delta)} \\ &= 2G_+(\delta)G^*(\Delta)e^{i(\delta-\Delta)} + 2G_-(\delta)G_-^*(\Delta)e^{-i(\delta-\Delta)} \\ &+ 2J_0(2kb)[G_-(\delta)G^*(\Delta)e^{-i(\delta+\Delta)} + G_+(\delta)G_-^*(\Delta)e^{i(\delta+\Delta)}] \end{aligned} \tag{79}$$

where $G_\pm(\delta)$ is given in (71), and $G_\pm(\Delta)$ has $\delta = kb\cos(\beta-\alpha)$ replaced by $\Delta = kb\cos(\beta-\theta)$.

The symmetrical situation obtained by averaging (71) over all angles β of the "axis" b is also of interest. For this randomly oriented "dumbell" we obtain

$$\overline{\mathscr{G}}(\theta,\alpha) = \frac{(g_+ + g_-)J_0[2kb\sin(\frac{\alpha-\theta}{2})] + 2g_+g_-H_0(2kb)J_0[2kb\cos(\frac{\alpha-\theta}{2})]}{1-g_+g_-H_0^2} \tag{80}$$

which, in the forward direction, reduces to

$$\overline{\mathscr{G}}(\alpha,\alpha) = \frac{(g_+ + g_-) + 2g_+g_-H_0J_0(2kb)}{1-g_+g_-H_0^2(kb)} . \tag{81}$$

<u>Circular cylinders:</u> Using $\beta_{ts} + \frac{\pi}{2} = \beta_\pm + \frac{\pi}{2} = \beta \pm \frac{\pi}{2}$, and supressing $kb_{ts} = 2kb$ in H_n , we recast (46) in a more convenient form for two arbitrary circular cylinders:

$$B_n^\pm = b_n^\pm[e^{-in\gamma} + \Sigma_p B_p^\mp H_{\mp(p-n)}] , \tag{82}$$

where $B_n^\pm = A_n^\pm e^{\pm i\delta 2 + in(\beta-\frac{\pi}{2})}$, $b_n^\pm = a_n^\pm e^{\pm i\delta 2} = a_{-n}^\pm e^{\pm i\delta 2}$, and $\gamma = \alpha + \frac{\pi}{2} - \beta$.

For two monopoles, equivalent to (71), we obtain

$$B_0^\pm = b_0^\pm(1 + B_0^\mp H_0) = \frac{b_0^\pm(1+b_0^\mp H_0)}{1-b_0^+b_0^-H_0^2} . \tag{83}$$

For two arbitrary dipoles we keep only terms $n = \pm 1$ and $p = \pm 1$ in the above, i.e.,

$$B_1^{\pm} = b_1^{\pm}[e^{-i\gamma}+B_1^{\mp}H_0 + B_{-1}^{\mp}H_2], \quad B_{-1}^{\pm} = b_{-1}^{\pm}[e^{i\gamma}+B_1^{\mp}H_2+B_{-1}^{\mp}H_0] \ . \quad (84)$$

Adding and subtracting terms of the same scatterer, and solving the resulting equations, gives

$$\begin{aligned} B_1^{+} \pm B_{-1}^{+} &= b_1^{+}[e^{-i\gamma} \pm e^{i\gamma} + (B_1^{-} \pm B_{-1}^{-})(H_0 \pm H_2)] \\ &= \frac{b_1^{+}[e^{-i\gamma} \pm e^{i\gamma}][1+b_1^{-}(H_0 \pm H_2)]}{1 - b_1^{+}b_1^{-}(H_0 \pm H_2)^2} \ , \end{aligned} \quad (85)$$

plus a similar set with the superscripts on the coefficients interchanged. These linear combinations, $B_1^{+} \pm B_{-1}^{\pm}$, are the actual "dipole" amplitudes. (Note that $b_1^{+}b_1^{-} = a_1^{+}a_1^{-}$.) This form is convenient for present purposes. It can be reduced by using $H_0 + H_2 = H_1(2kb)/kb$, and $H_0 - H_2 = 2H_1'$. (The case of dipoles is of interest, for example, in electromagnetics for E perpendicular to fine dielectric rods. See reference 19 for special applications.)

For incidence normal to the line joining identical scatterers, we have $B_{\pm 1}^{\pm} = B_1$, $A_{\pm 1}^{\pm} = B_1 e^{\pm i(\beta-\pi/2)}$, where

$$B_1 = b_1[1 + B_1(H_0 + H_2)] = \frac{b_1}{1-b_1(H_0+H_2)} \ . \quad (86)$$

Consequently

$$\mathscr{G}(\theta', 0) = 4B_1\cos\theta'\cos\Delta' \ , \quad \theta' = \theta + \frac{\pi}{2} - \beta \ , \quad \Delta' = \Delta(\theta') \ , \quad (87)$$

where θ' is measured from the normal. For this case the scattering theorems give

$$\frac{kP}{4} = -\text{Re}\ 4B_1 = 4|B_1|^2[1+J_0(2kb)+J_2(2kb)] = 4|B_1|^2[1 + \frac{J_1(2kb)}{kb}] . \quad (88)$$

Using $-\text{Re}\ 4B_1 = \dfrac{-\text{Re}\ 4b_1[1 - b_1(H_0+H_2)]^*}{|1-b_1(H_0+H_2)|^2}$, $-\text{Re}\, b_1 = |b_1|^2$, we see, essentially as for (74), that the explicit form (86) fulfills (88).

If both monopoles and dipoles are significant, we keep all terms of index 0 and ± 1 in (82). Thus

$$
\begin{aligned}
B_0^{\pm} &= b_0^{\pm}[1 + B_0^{\mp} H_0 \mp H_1(B_1^{\mp} - B_{-1}^{\mp})] \,, \\
B_1^{\pm} &= b_1^{\pm}[e^{-i\gamma} \pm B_0^{\mp} H_1 + B_1^{\mp} H_0 + B_{-1}^{\mp} H_2] \,, \\
B_{-1}^{\pm} &= b_1^{\pm}[e^{i\gamma} \mp B_0^{\mp} H_1 + B_1^{\mp} H_2 + B_{-1}^{\mp} H_0] \,.
\end{aligned}
\tag{89}
$$

[This case corresponds to $\partial_n \Psi = 0$, e.g., $\underline{E} \perp$ to perfectly conducting wires.] Adding and subtracting the second and third lines yields

$$
\begin{aligned}
B_1^{\pm} + B_{-1}^{\pm} &= \frac{b_1^{\pm}[e^{-i\gamma} + e^{i\gamma}][1 + b_1^{\mp}(H_0 + H_2)]}{1 - b_0^{+} b_0^{-} H_0^2} \,, \\
B_1^{\pm} - B_{-1}^{\pm} &= b_1^{\pm}[e^{-i\gamma} - e^{i\gamma} \pm 2B_0^{\mp} H_1 + (B_1^{\mp} - B_{-1}^{\mp})(H_0 - H_2)] \,.
\end{aligned}
\tag{90}
$$

The second line of (90) together with the first of (89) constitute a system of four equations for the essentially four unknowns:

$$
\begin{bmatrix}
1 & -b_0^{+} H_0 & 0 & b_0^{+} H_1 \\
-b_0^{-} H_0 & 1 & -b_0^{-} H_1 & 0 \\
0 & -2b_1^{+} H_1 & 1 & -b_1^{+}(H_0 - H_2) \\
2b_1^{-} H_1 & 0 & -b_1^{-}(H_0 - H_2) & 1
\end{bmatrix}
\begin{bmatrix}
B_0^{+} \\ B_0^{-} \\ B_1^{+} - B_{-1}^{+} \\ B_1^{-} - B_{-1}^{-}
\end{bmatrix}
=
\begin{bmatrix}
b_0^{+} \\ b_0^{-} \\ -b_1^{+} 2i \sin\gamma \\ -b_1^{-} 2i \sin\gamma
\end{bmatrix} .
\tag{91}
$$

Explicitly, we have

$$
\begin{aligned}
B_0^{\pm} D &= b_0^{+}[(1 + b_0^{\mp} H_0)(1 - 4b_1^{+} b_1^{-} H_1'^2) - 2b_0^{\mp} b_1^{\pm} H_1^2 (1 + 2b_1^{\mp} H_1')] \\
&\quad + i2b_0^{\pm} H_1 \sin\gamma \, \{b_1^{\mp}(1 + 2b_1^{\pm} H_1') - b_0^{\mp} b_1^{\pm}[H_0(1 + 2b_1^{\mp} H_1') + 2b_1^{\mp} H_1^2]\} \,, \\
(B_1^{\pm} - B_{-1}) D &= -i2b_1^{\pm} \sin\gamma[(1 + 2b_1^{\mp} H_1')(1 - 2b_0^{+} b_1^{-} H_0^2) - 2b_0^{\pm} b_1^{\mp} H_1^2 (1 + b_0^{\mp} H_2)] \\
&\quad \pm 2b_1^{\pm} H_1 \, \{b_0^{\mp}(1 + b_0^{\pm} H_0) - 2b_0^{\pm} b_1^{\mp}[H_1'(1 + b_0^{\mp} H_0) + b_0^{\mp} H_1^2] \,,
\end{aligned}
\tag{92}
$$

$$
\begin{aligned}
D &= 1 - b_0^{+} b_0^{-} H_0^2 - 4b_1^{+} b_1^{-} H_1'^2 - 2(b_0^{-} b_1^{+} + b_0^{+} b_1^{-}) H_1^2 \\
&\quad + 4b_0^{+} b_0^{-} b_1^{+} b_1^{-} (H_1^{+} + H_0^2 H_1'^2 + 2H_0 H_1^2 H_1')
\end{aligned}
$$

For normal incidence and identical scatterers $(B_0^{\pm} = B_0 \,,\ B_1^{\pm} = B_{-1}^{\mp})$ (92) yields

$$B_1^{\pm}-B_{-1}^{\pm} = \frac{\pm 2b_1 H_1 B_0}{1+b_1(H_0-H_2)} \equiv \pm\epsilon B_0 , \quad B_0^{\mp} = B_0 = \frac{b_0}{1-b_0 H_0 - \epsilon b_0 H_1} . \quad (92')$$

Neglecting ϵ terms, yields $B_1^{\pm} \approx B_{-1}^{\pm} \equiv B_1$, and the above reduce to the uncoupled forms

$$B_0 = b_0(1+B_0H_0) = \frac{b_0}{1-b_0H_0} , \quad B_1 = b_1[1+B_1(H_0+H_2)] = \frac{b_1}{1-b_1(H_0+H_2)}$$

$$\mathscr{G}(\theta', 0) = 2[B_0+2B_1 \cos\theta']\cos\Delta' . \quad (93)$$

These explicit forms of B_0, B_1 fulfill the energy theorem

$$\frac{kP}{4} = -\mathrm{Re}\, 2[B_0 + 2B_1] = 2[\,|B_0|^2(1+J_0)+2|B_1|^2(1+J_0+J_2)] \quad (94)$$

For normal incidence and arbitrary identical cylinders, the symmetry requirement that the field be even in θ' gives $B_n^+ = B_{-n}^-$. Consequently

$$\mathscr{G} = e^{-i\Delta'}\Sigma B_n^+ e^{in\theta'} + e^{+in\Delta'} \Sigma B_{-n}^+ e^{in\theta'} = 2\sum_{-\infty}^{\infty} B_n^+ \cos(n\theta'-\Delta')$$

$$\frac{kP}{4} = -2\mathrm{Re}\,\Sigma B_n^+ = -2\mathrm{Re}\,\Sigma B_n^- = 2\Sigma|B_n^+|^2 + 2(\Sigma\Sigma)_e (B_n^+)^* B_m^+ J_{n+m}(2kb) \quad (95)$$

where the subscript e indicates that n and m have equal parity. Equivalently if we introduce $B_{e_0} \equiv B_0$, $B_{e_n} \equiv B_n+B_{-n}$ and $B_{o_n} \equiv B_n-B_{-n}$, then

$$\mathscr{G} = 2\sum_{n=0}^{\infty}(B_{e_n}^+ \cos n\theta'\cos\Delta' + B_{o_n}^+ \sin n\theta'\sin\Delta'), \quad \frac{kP}{4} = -2\,\mathrm{Re} \sum_0^{\infty} B_{e_n}^+ . \quad (95')$$

<u>Elliptic cylinders</u>: For two elliptic cylinders, with axes along x and y and centers at $y = \pm b$ (i.e., $\beta_{\pm} = \pm\pi/2$), we reduce (47) to

$$B_{i_n}^{\pm} = b_{i_n}^{\pm}[S_{i_n}(\alpha) + \Sigma_p B_{i_p}^{\mp}\mathscr{H}(\mp; i_p, i_n) + \Sigma_p B_{j_p}^{\mp}\mathscr{H}(\mp; j_p, i_n)] , \quad (96)$$

where $B_{i_n}^{\pm} = A_{i_n}^{\pm} e^{\pm i\delta 2}$, $b_{i_n}^{\pm} = a_{i_n}^{\pm} e^{\pm i\delta 2}$. The spacing function $\mathscr{H}$ is given by

$$\mathscr{H}(\mp; e_p, o_n) = \frac{1}{4i}\sum_q \sum_m D_{e_q}^p D_{o_m}^n [H_{\mp(q+m)} - H_{\mp(q-m)} + H_{\mp(-q+m)} - H_{\mp(-q-m)}] \quad (97)$$

plus the other three combinations specified after (49). The argument 2kb is implicit in all H's . Since p and q (and n and m) have the same parity [14], it follows that if p and n have opposite parity, all terms vanish except

$$\mathscr{H}(\mp; e_p, o_n) = \frac{\mp 1}{2i} \Sigma\, \Sigma\, D^p_{e_q} D^n_{o_m}(H_{q+m} - H_{q-m}) \equiv \mp H(e_p, o_n) ,$$
$$\mathscr{H}(\mp; o_p, e_n) = \frac{\mp 1}{2i} \Sigma\, \Sigma\, D^p_{o_q} D^n_{e_m}(H_{q+m} + H_{q-m}) \equiv \mp H(o_p, e_n) . \tag{98}$$

Similarly, if p and n have the same parity, all terms vanish except

$$\mathscr{H}(\mp; e_p, e_n) = \frac{1}{2} \Sigma\, \Sigma\, D^p_{e_q} D^n_{e_m}(H_{q+m} + H_{q-m}) \equiv H(e_p, e_n)$$
$$\mathscr{H}(\mp; o_p, o_n) = \frac{1}{2} \Sigma\, \Sigma\, D^p_{o_q} D^n_{o_m}(-H_{q+m} + H_{q-m}) \equiv H(o_p, o_n) . \tag{99}$$

Thus we may reduce (96) to

$$B^{\pm}_{i_n} = b^{\pm}_{i_n} [S_{i_n}(\alpha) + \Sigma_{p_e} B^{\mp}_{i_p} H(i_p, i_n) \mp \Sigma_{p_o} B_{j_p}^{\mp} H(j_p, i_n)] , \tag{100}$$

where the subscript e or o on p indicates that the respective sum involves only terms of p having equal or opposite parity with n . (Note that the present form (100) is quite similar to the analogous result for the infinite grating of identical cylinders [15]. There the H_n terms in $H(j_p, i_n)$, are replaced by the corresponding Schlömilch series. The present result, even for two identical cylinders, is more complicated in form; i.e., only the infinite structure has the symmetry required for the coefficients B^s, B^t to be essentially equal. The same analogy exists between (82) for two circular cylinders and the result for the infinite grating of circular cylinders [13].)

For elliptic monopoles, we keep only B_{e_0} :

$$B^{\pm}_{e_0} = b^{\pm}_{e_0} [S_{e_0} + B^{\mp}_{e_0} H(e_0, e_0)] = \frac{b^{\pm}_{e_0} S_{e_0} [1 + b^{\mp}_{e_0} H(e_0, e_0)]}{1 - b^{+}_{e_0} b^{-}_{e_0} [H(e_0, e_0)]^2} . \tag{101}$$

Similarly for dipoles,

$$B^{\pm}_{i_1} = b^{\pm}_{i_1} [S_{i_1} + B^{\mp}_{i_1} H(i_1, i_1)] = \frac{b^{\pm}_{i_1} S_{i_1} [1 + b^{\mp}_{i_1} (H(i_1, i_1)]}{1 - b^{+}_{i_1} b^{-}_{i_1} [H(i_1, i_1)]^2} . \tag{102}$$

Finally for dipoles plus monopoles

$$B^{\pm}_{e_0} = b^{\pm}_{e_0} [S_{e_0} + B^{\mp}_{e_0} H(e_0, e_0) \mp B^{\mp}_{o_1} H(o_1, e_0)] , \tag{103}$$

(103 continued)

$$B^{\pm}_{o_1} = b^{\pm}_{o_1}[S_{o_1} \mp B^{\mp}_{e_0} H(e_0, o_1) + B^{\mp}_{o_1} H(o_1, o_1)] \quad ,$$

$$B^{\pm}_{e_1} = b^{\pm}_{e_1}[S_{e_1} + B^{\mp}_{e_1} H(e_1, e_1)] \; .$$

The solutions for $B^{\pm}_{e_1}$ are given in (102). The remaining coefficients, obtained from

$$\begin{bmatrix} 1 & -b_0^+ H_{00} & 0 & b_0^+ H_{10} \\ -b_0^- H_{00} & 1 & -b_0^- H_{10} & 0 \\ 0 & b_1^+ H_{01} & 1 & -b_1^+ H_{11} \\ -b_1^- H_{01} & 0 & -b_1^- H_{11} & 1 \end{bmatrix} \begin{bmatrix} B_0^+ \\ B_0^- \\ B_1^+ \\ B_1^- \end{bmatrix} = \begin{bmatrix} b_0^+ S_{e_0} \\ b_0^- S_{e_0} \\ b_1^+ S_{o_1} \\ b_1^- S_{o_1} \end{bmatrix}, \tag{104}$$

are given explicitly by

$$\begin{aligned} B^{\pm}_{e_0} D &= b_0^{\pm} S_{e_0} [(1+b_0^{\mp} H_{00})(1-b_1^+ b_1^- H_{11}^2) + b_0^{\mp} b_1^{\pm} H_{01} H_{10} (1+b_1^{\mp} H_{11})] \\ &\quad - b_0^{\pm} H_{10} S_{o_1} \{b_1^{\mp}(1+b^{\pm} H_{11}) - b_0^{\mp} b_1^{\pm} [H_{00} (1+b_1^{\mp} H_{11}) - b_1^{\mp} H_{01} H_{10}]\} , \\ B^{\pm}_{o_1} D &= b_1^{\pm} S_{o_1} [(1+b_1^{\mp} H_{11})(1-b_0^+ b_1^- H_{00}^2) + b_0^{\pm} b_1^{\mp} H_{01} H_{10} (1+b_0^{\mp} H_{00})] \\ &\quad b_1^{\pm} H_{o_1} S_{e_0} \{b_0^{\mp}(1+b_0^{\pm} H_{00}) - b_0^{\pm} b_1^{\mp} [H_{11} (1+b_0^{\mp} H_{00}) - b_0^{\mp} H_{01} H_{10}]\}, \\ D &= 1 - b_0^+ b_0^- H_{00}^2 - b_1^+ b_1^- H_{11}^2 + (b_0^- b_1^+ + b_0^+ b_1^-) H_{01} H_{10} \\ &\quad + b_0^+ b_0^- b_1^+ b_1^- (H_{01}^2 G_{10}^2 + H_{00}^2 H_{11}^2 - 2H_{00} H_{11} H_{01} H_{10}) \quad . \end{aligned} \tag{105}$$

We supressed e and o where convenient; see first two lines of (103). The relations between the above and the symmetrized coefficients for circular cylinders are clear.

For normal incidence ($S_{o_n}(0) = 0$) and identical scatterers (104) yields

$$B^{\pm}_{o_1} = \frac{\mp b_{o_1} H_{01} B_{e_0}}{1+b_{o_1} H_{11}} = \mp \epsilon \; B_{e_0} \; , \; B_{e_0} = \frac{b_{e_0} S_{e_0}(0)}{1-b_{e_0} H_{00} + \epsilon \, b_{e_0} H_{10}} \; . \tag{106}$$

Neglecting ϵ terms, we obtain

$$\begin{aligned} B_{e_0} &= B_{e_0}[S_{e_0}(0) + B_{e_0} H(e_0, e_0)] = \frac{b_{e_0} S_{e_0}(0)}{1-b_{e_0} H(e_0, e_0)} \quad , \\ B_{e_1} &= B_{e_1}[S_{e_1}(0) + B_{e_1} H(e_1, e_1)] = \frac{b_{e_1} S_{e_1}(0)}{1-b_{e_1} H(e_1, e_1)} \quad . \end{aligned} \tag{107}$$

Note that these S's equal $(2\pi/M_{i_n})^{\frac{1}{2}}$ times those of Morse and Feshbach, where M_{i_n} is their [14] normalization coefficient. Equivalently, our functions fulfill $\int_0^{2\pi} S_{i_n}^2(\theta)\,d\theta = 2\pi$.

The corresponding compound scattering amplitude equals

$$\mathcal{G}(\theta, 0) = 2\cos\Delta G(\theta, 0) = 2\cos\Delta[B_{e_0}S_{e_0}(\theta) + B_{e_1}S_{e_1}(\theta)], \quad (108)$$

and the explicit forms of the B's fulfill the scattering theorem

$$\frac{kP}{4} = -2\mathrm{Re}[B_{e_0}S_{e_0}(0) + B_{e_1}S_{e_1}(0)] = 2|B_{e_0}|^2[1+J(e_0,e_0)] + 2|B_{e_1}|^2[1+J(e_1,e_1)], \quad (109)$$

where $J(e_n, e_n) = \mathrm{Re}\, H(e_n, e_n)$ involves an integral as in (48) over the range 2π .

For normal incidence and arbitrary identical cylinders, the symmetry requirement gives $B^+_{e_n} = B^-_{e_n}$ and $B^+_{o_n} = -B^-_{o_n}$. Consequently (cf. (95'))

$$\mathcal{G}(\theta, 0) = 2\sum_{n=0}^{\infty}[B^+_{e_n}S_{e_n}(\theta)\cos\Delta - iB^-_{o_n}S_{o_n}(\theta)\sin\Delta], \quad \frac{kP}{4} = -2\mathrm{Re}\sum_{n=0}^{\infty}B^+_{e_n}S_{e_n}(0). \quad (110)$$

Related results and computations for scattering by two elliptic cylinders are given by Millar [17], and by Saermark [16]. Computations with the present forms (based on the extended low frequency series for the b's for one elliptic cylinder derived by Burke and Twersky [21]) are in progress.

REFERENCES

1. V. Twersky, "On Multiple Scattering of Waves," J. Research NBS 64D, 715(1960).

2. V. Twersky, "On the Scattering of Waves by an Infinite Grating," IRE Trans. AP-4, 330(1956); "On Scattering and Reflection of Sound by Rough Surfaces," J. Acoust. Soc. Am. 29, 209(1957); "On Scattering by Quasi-Periodic and Quasi-Random Distributions," IRE Trans. AP-7 (special supplement) S5307(1959). See also other papers cited in reference 1.

3. A. Sommerfeld, "Partial Differential Equations in Physics," Academic Press Inc., N.Y. (1949).

4. S.N. Karp and N. Zitron, "Higher Order Approximations in Multiple Scattering," Research Report EM-126, Inst. Math. Sci. NYU (1959).

5. J. E. Burke and V. Twersky, "Circular Function Representations for Arbitrary Scatterers" (in process).

6. C. Müeller, "Radiation Patterns and Radiation Fields," J. Rat. Mech. and Anal. 4, 235(1955) uses analogous expansions for three-dimensional problems.

7. V. Twersky, "On Scattering of Waves by a Slab Region of Randomly Distributed Objects," Report EDL-E26, Sylvania Electronic Defense Labs. (1958); "On a New Scattering Formalism for the Macroscopic Electromagnetic Parameters," Report EDL-E36, Sylvania Electronic Defense Labs. (1958).

8. W. Franz, "Theorie des Trentinischen Absorptionsgitters," Z. Angew. Phys. 6, 449(1954).

J. F. Carlson and A. E. Heins, "The Reflection of Electromagnetic Waves by an Infinite Set of Plates," Part I, Quart. Appl. Math. 4, 313(1946).

A. E. Heins and J. F. Carlson, same title, Part II, 5, 82(1947).

A. E. Heins, same title, Part III, 8, 281(1950).

R. F. Millar, "Scattering by Semi-Infinite Gratings" (in process); "Plane Wave Spectra in Multiple Scattering Theory," URSI Meeting, May, 1961.

9. F. Zaviska, "Über die Beugung Elektromagnetischer Wellen an Paralleln Unendlich Langen Kreiszylindern," Ann. Phys. 40, 1023 (1913).

10. W. v. Ignatowsky, "Zur Theorie der Gitter," Ann. Phys. 44, 23, 369(1914).

11. R. V. Row, "Theoretical and Experimental Study of Electromagnetic Scattering by Two Identical Conducting Cylinders," J. Appl. Phys. 26, 666(1955).

12. V. Twersky, "Multiple Scattering of Waves by Planar Random Distributions of Parallel Cylinders and Bosses," Research Report EM-58, Inst. Math. Sci., NYU (1953).

13. V. Twersky, "On Scattering of Waves by the Infinite Grating of Circular Cylinders," Report EDL-E28, Sylvania Electronic Defense Laboratories (1958).

14. P. M. Morse and H. Feshbach, "Methods of Theoretical Physics," McGraw-Hill, N. Y. (1953).

15. J. E. Burke and V. Twersky, "On Scattering of Waves by the Grating of Elliptic Cylinders," Report EDL-E44, Sylvania Electronic Defense Laboratories (1959).

16. K. Saermark, "Scattering of a Plane Monochromatic Wave by a System of Strips," Appl. Sci. Res., Section B, 7, 417(1959); "Transmission Coefficient for a System of Parallel Slits in a Thin, Plane Screen," Appl. Sci. Res., Section B, 8(1959); "On Some Two-Dimensional Diffraction Problems," Dansk Videnskabs Forlag, København (1960).

17. R.F. Millar, "The Scattering of a Plane Wave by a Row of Small Cylinders," Can. J. Phys. 38, 272(1960); "Scattering by a Grating," I and II, Can. J. Phys. 39, 81 and 104(1961).

18. V. Twersky, "Multiple Scattering of Radiation by an Arbitrary Configuration of Parallel Cylinders," J. Acoust. Soc. Am. 24, 42(1952).

19. V. Twersky, "Multiple Scattering of Radiation by an Arbitrary Planar Configuration of Parallel Cylinders and by Two Parallel Cylinders," J. Appl. Phys. 23, 407(1952); additional results are given in Research Report EM-34, Inst. Math. Sci., NYU(1951).

20. S.N. Karp, "Diffraction by Combinations of Obstacles," Proc. McGill Symp. Microw. Opt. 198(1953) (Electronic Research Directorate, AFCRC (1959)). See also

S.N. Karp and A. Russek, "Diffraction by a Wide Slit," J. Appl. Phys. 27, 886(1956).

21. J.E. Burke and V. Twersky, "On Scattering of Waves by an Elliptical Cylinder and by a Semi-Elliptical Proturberance on a Ground Plane," Report EDL-M266, Sylvania Electronic Defense Laboratories (1960).

This work supported in part by Signal Corps Contract DA 36-039 SC-87475.

INDEX

U

V

W

Z